S0-BBA-164

Radiation Chemistry

Volume I. Aqueous Media, Biology, Dosimetry

An international conference

sponsored by

Argonne National Laboratory

Argonne, Ill.

Aug. 12-15, 1968

Edwin J. Hart

Conference Chairman

ADVANCES IN CHEMISTRY SERIES **81**

AMERICAN CHEMICAL SOCIETY

WASHINGTON, D. C. 1968

Library of Congress Catalog Card 68-55363

PRINTED IN THE UNITED STATES OF AMERICA

Advances in Chemistry Series

Robert F. Gould, *Editor*

FOREWORD

Advances in Chemistry Series was founded in 1949 by the American Chemical Society as an outlet for symposia and collections of data in special areas of topical interest that could not be accommodated in the Society's journals. It provides a medium for symposia that would otherwise be fragmented, their papers distributed among several journals or not published at all. Papers are refereed critically according to ACS editorial standards and receive the careful attention and processing characteristic of ACS publications. Papers published in Advances in Chemistry Series are original contributions not published elsewhere in whole or major part and include reports of research as well as reviews since symposia may embrace both types of presentation.

CONTENTS–I

ABSTRACTS OF ORAL PRESENTATIONS

CONTENTS–II

SOLIDS

ORGANIC LIQUIDS

ABSTRACTS OF ORAL PRESENTATIONS

Hugo Fricke

PREFACE

Exceptional strides are now being made in radiation chemistry although growth has been gradual. This long induction period dates back to the discovery of radioactivity and the development of x-ray tubes. Radium salts, the first radiation sources, were supplanted in the third and fourth decades of this century by x-rays. During this period, pioneering scientists such as Fricke, Lind, Mundt, Risse, and their collaborators laid the foundations of radiation-induced gaseous and aqueous reactions. From these modest beginnings research in this field gradually gathered momentum in the fifth decade by the use of Van de Graaff and cyclotron accelerators and in the sixth through the availability of powerful ^{60}Co γ-ray sources. Finally in the seventh decade the results of basic research exploded into prominence through the use of electron pulse accelerators. In this decade, we are reaping the benefits of these new developments by drawing attention to the applications of radiation chemistry. Since the 1930s the number of active workers in this field has multiplied a hundredfold, and research has expanded from a few universities and national laboratories to research centers the world over.

The early workers established phenomena connected with the qualitative, and later with the quantitative changes taking place during irradiation. Products and some intermediate species were identified in gases and in aqueous solutions, and work progressed in three areas: dosimetry, radical and ionic yields, and relative rate constants. From these results, speculations regarding the mechanism of energy loss, of free radical and ion pair formation and distribution, were mathematically formulated and tested by the developing specialty of diffusion kinetics.

More recently, assisted by photochemistry, spectroscopy in its varied forms, chromatography, computers, and applied electronics, radiation chemistry is assaulting many of the problems associated with the properties of transient species at an unprecedented rate. Commonplace, already, is the study of intermediates lasting only milli- and micro-seconds. A rapidly developing subdivision is on the horizon—that of nanosecond and picosecond chemistry. Knowledge of the nature and rates of these reactions has been of inestimable aid in untangling reaction mechanisms in chemistry and biology. For example, the discovery of the hydrated electron and the determination of its rate constants has aided the interpretation of reactions in aqueous media. Recent studies on solvated and trapped electrons in liquids and solids assist materially in explaining phenomena in these media. Similarly, the identification of singlet and triplet states in the radiolysis of gases and organic liquids provides data crucial for understanding these complex systems.

The papers reported in these two volumes constitute about two-thirds of those presented at the Argonne National Laboratory-sponsored International Conference on Radiation Chemistry, to which 200 prominent scientists and students from 21 countries and 81 universities and institutes were invited. This conference was in celebration of Argonne National Laboratory's participation in a decade of pulse radiolysis. All phases of radiation chemistry, from the theoretical to the fundamental changes taking place in complex molecules, were included. A special session on dosimetry was planned for Dr. Hugo Fricke on August 15, his 76th birthday, to honor him for his many contributions to radiation chemistry over the past 40 years. The conference papers are assembled in these two volumes: one, largely on aqueous solutions, consists of the survey and original papers given in the aqueous, biological, and dosimetry sessions; the other, largely organic, deals with similar groups of papers on gases, liquids, and solids. The broad scope and interest in these papers reflects the influence and applications of radiation chemistry in most branches of chemistry today.

Argonne, Ill. EDWIN J. HART
July 1968

Plenary Session

Stabilization of Electrons in Low Temperature Radiolysis of Polar Systems

B. G. ERSHOV and A. K. PIKAEV

Laboratory of Radiation Chemistry, Institute of Physical Chemistry, Academy of Sciences of the USSR, Moscow, USSR

This is a review of the results of the authors on the nature and properties of trapped electrons (e^-_{tr}) *in irradiated frozen aqueous and alcoholic systems. These species are observed not only in alkaline ices and alcoholic glasses at 77°K. but also in glassy aqueous solutions of* $NaClO_4$, $LiCl$, KF, K_2CO_3, *alcohols, HCHO, HCOONa, carbohydrates, etc. In these systems* e^-_{tr} *has narrow symmetrical singlet at g-factor* $\sim$ *2001 in EPR spectrum and wide optical absorption band in visible region. The yields of* e^-_{tr} *were measured. In aqueous glasses the* e^-_{tr} *and* $(e^-_{tr})_2$ *are mutually transformed under certain conditions. The data obtained by studying the photochemistry of* e^-_{tr} *indicate the existence of dispersion of trapping energy. The nature of electron stabilization is discussed.*

One of the greatest achievements of the radiation chemistry lies in the experimental proof of the electron solvation in various irradiated polar systems (*see—e.g., 13, 17, 36*) and its stabilization under certain conditions at low temperatures. In the latter case the process may be presented in the form of the following reactions.

The electron knocked out of polar molecule M:

$$M \rightsquigarrow M^+ + e^- \quad (1)$$

after thermalization

$$e^- \rightarrow e^-_{\text{therm}} \quad (2)$$

in the absence of the scavengers is captured by trap T:

$$e^-_{\text{therm}} + T \rightarrow e^-_{\text{tr}} \quad (3)$$

The process considered is displayed most clearly in the case of glassy polar systems and in the absence of the compounds which are reactive with the electrons.

The present paper sums up the results of the performed investigations of the nature and properties of the trapped electrons in the frozen aqueous and alcohol systems. (The trapped electron marked e^{-}_{tr} is unmobile which distinguishes it from the solvated electron.)

Experimental Technics

The investigation of the nature and properties of e^{-}_{tr} involved a wide use of the methods of the electron paramagnetic resonance (EPR) and optical spectroscopy. The EPR spectra were recorded by the RE-1301 radiospectrometer while the optical spectra were registered by the SF-4A spectrophotometer.

During measurements of the EPR spectra, the samples of about 0.05 ml. were irradiated in special ampules made of glass "Luch-2" which did not give any noticeable EPR signal at irradiation (*9*). The magnetic field was calibrated with the aid of the aqueous solution of Mn^{2+} and benzene solution of α,α'-diphenyl-β-picrylhydrazyl (DPPH). The position of the lines in the spectrum was determined by reference to the position of the lines of solid DPPH. The intensity of the signal was found by double integration with the use of a special nomogram (*62*). The concentration of the free radicals in the sample was measured by reference to the standards of ultramarine whose content of the paramagnetic particles was determined with the aid of a fresh-prepared solution of DPPH in benzene. A relative error in determination of the radical concentration amounted to $\pm$ 10%. The variation of the radiospectrometer sensitivity in the course of registration was checked by paramagnetic standard $CuCl_2 \cdot 2H_2O$ placed in the resonator of the radiospectrometer. All the EPR spectra were registered under the conditions excluding the microwave power saturation effect.

The photo-annealing of the colored samples by the visible light was effected directly in the resonator of the radiospectrometer during registration of the EPR spectrum. The tungsten lamp, which was provided with the respective light filters, was used as a light source.

The optical spectra were measured with the aid of a special quartz Dewar flask. Its construction practically precluded boiling of the liquid nitrogen in the cell in which the sample was located (*48*). This prevented accumulation of frozen water and carbon dioxide on the samples. The frozen samples were irradiated in quartz cells of 2–4 mm. in thickness.

The glassy solutions were prepared by a rapid freezing at 77°K. The transparent samples of the neutral ice were obtained from twice-distilled water subjected to a slow freezing at a temperature of 270° to 272°K. in special molds. The produced ice plates of about 5 mm. in thickness were irradiated in the sealed ampules at a temperature of 77°K. After irradiation the ampules were opened and the samples were transferred into the Dewar flask for taking optical measurements.

The experiments involved the use of γ-radiation of ^{60}Co. The dose rate was commonly equal to $\sim 10^{16}$ e.v./ml. sec. The dosimetry was made by the ferrosulfate method. The calculation of the dose was performed while taking into account the difference in electron densities of the dosimetric and investigated solutions.

Water and Aqueous Solutions of Electrolytes

Among the first investigations which showed electron stabilization in the polar "glasses" at low temperatures was the work of Ershov *et al.* (*30*). This work employed the EPR method to identify e^-_{tr} in the alkaline aqueous solutions irradiated at 77°K. Later on these conclusions were confirmed in a large number of publications (*3, 5, 6, 8, 37, 42, 54, 55*). (Earlier the optical absorption of e^-_{tr} in the irradiated alkaline glass was detected in other works (*see 41, 58*).

At the present time it is certain that stabilization of electrons is a general phenomenon. Data have been obtained on the EPR and optical spectra which testify to appearance e^-_{tr} in the neutral or weak alkaline aqueous solutions of such salts as $NaClO_4$, LiCl, KF, Na_2HPO_4, NaH_2PO_4, carbonates, bicarbonates, formates, etc. (*10, 21, 26, 27, 29, 45, 47*).

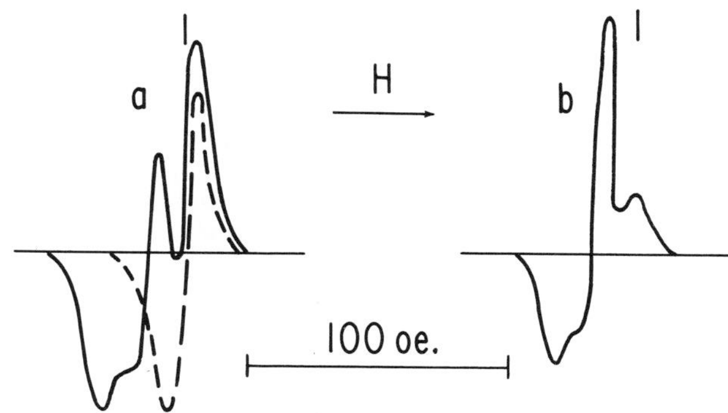

Figure 1. EPR spectrum of glassy 5M K_2CO_3 in H_2O: (a) subjected to γ-irradiation at 77° K. and (b) after illumination with visible light. Dotted line is the EPR spectrum of e^-_{tr}. On Figures 1, 2, 3, 5, 6, 7 and 10 vertical line is the position of the EPR signal of polycrystalline DPPH

The EPR spectrum of e^-_{tr} is essentially a narrow symmetrical singlet with a *g*-factor of 2.001 ± 0.001. Figures 1 and 2 show by way of example the EPR spectra of e^-_{tr} in 5*M* aqueous glasses of K_2CO_3 in H_2O and D_2O (*21*). From the analysis of the spectra it follows that the width ΔH of the line of e^-_{tr} as measured between the points of maximal slopes is reduced by two or three times when substituting D_2O for H_2O. Table I gives the ΔH values for a series of systems wherein these values have been measured accurately. The close values of ΔH for e^-_{tr} in the alkaline glasses have been obtained by other authors (*6, 8, 37, 54, 55*).

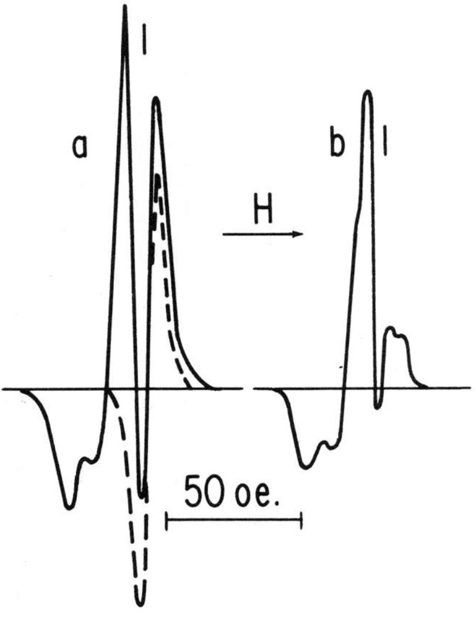

Figure 2. EPR spectrum of glassy 5M K_2CO_3 in D_2O: (a) subjected to γ-irradiation at 77°K. and (b) after illumination with visible light. Dotted line is the EPR spectrum of e^-_{tr}

Table I. Width ΔH of EPR Line of e^-_{tr} in Aqueous Glasses at 77°K.

System	ΔH, *oe*	*References*
10*M* KOH in H_2O	13.4 ± 0.2	*19, 30, 32*
10*M* KOD in D_2O	4.6 ± 0.2	*19*
10*M* NaOH in H_2O	15.1 ± 0.2	*19*
10*M* NaOD in D_2O	6.5 ± 0.2	*19*
10*M* $NaClO_4$ in H_2O	14.0 ± 2.0	*29*
10*M* $NaClO_4$ in D_2O	5.6 ± 1.0	*29*
15*M* LiCl in H_2O	18.0 ± 2.0	*29*
15*M* LiCl in D_2O	7.0 ± 1.0	*29*
5*M* K_2CO_3 in H_2O	12.0 ± 2.0	*21*
5*M* K_2CO_3 in D_2O	5.0 ± 1.0	*21*

The results given in Table I show that the water molecules are the neighbors of the electron. However, a definite contribution is made also by the interaction of the electron with the alkaline metal ions. From

Table I it is seen that ΔH increases in direction from K to Li—*i.e.*, it increases with the growth of the magnetic moments of the alkaline metal nuclei. The e^-_{tr} signal is rapidly saturated with the increase of the microwave power.

The trapped electron is optically absorbed in the visible part of the spectrum. The spectrum is asymmetric, having a more steep drop on the side of long waves. The similar shape of the absorption band is characteristic of the solvated electrons in the polar liquids. Another feature of the spectrum is large half-width $W_{1/2}$ of the band. Table II contains some characteristics of the optical absorption band of e^-_{tr} in the aqueous glasses of electrolytes at 77°K. Analogous optical bands of e^-_{tr} in the alkaline and perchlorate glasses are observed in References *6, 8, 10, 18, 41,* and *58.*

Table II. Characteristics of Optical Absorption Spectra of e^-_{tr} in Aqueous Matrixes at 77°K.

Matrix	λ_{max}, nm.	$E\lambda_{max}$, e.v.	$W_{1/2}$, e.v.	ϵ at λ_{max}, M^{-1} cm.$^{-1}$	*References*
10*M* KOH in H_2O	585	2.11	0.90	13700 (±20%)	*27, 29, 47*
10*M* KOH in D_2O	560	2.21	0.87	—	*27, 29, 47*
10*M* NaOH in H_2O	585	2.11	0.80	—	*27, 29, 47*
10*M* NaOH in D_2O	560	2.21	0.76	—	*27, 29, 47*
10*M* $NaClO_4$ in H_2O	540	2.29	0.87	—	*27, 29, 47*
10*M* $NaClO_4$ in D_2O	520	2.37	0.80	—	*27, 29, 47*
5*M* K_2CO_3 in H_2O	535	2.31	0.82	20000 (±40%)	*21, 47*
5*M* K_2CO_3 in D_2O	510	2.43	0.77	—	*21, 47*
8*M* HCOONa in H_2O	555	2.23	0.93	12000 (±40%)	*45, 47*
8*M* HCOONa in D_2O	535	2.31	0.72	—	*45, 47*

In the presence of the electron scavengers there is observed some drop in the intensities of the EPR signal of the e^-_{tr} and of the respective optical band and a new radical appears which is actually the product of reaction of the electron with the added substance. Thus, the appearance of the ion-radicals of NO_3^{2-} and NO_2^{2-} has been detected in the solutions of nitrate and nitrite (*22, 28, 31, 33, 34*), O^- in the perchlorate glasses (*29*),

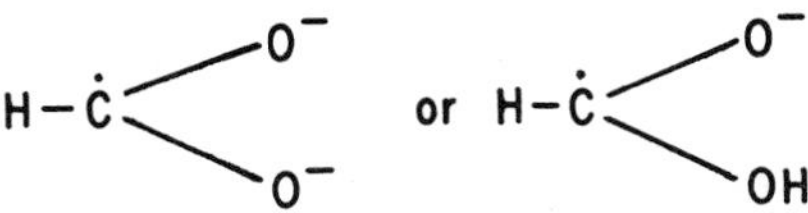

in the formate or formic acid solutions (*45, 46, 49*), etc. Shown in Figure 3 are the EPR and optical spectra of the NO_3^{2-} ion-radical (*22*).

The trapped electrons are annealed effectively by the visible light. The rate of annealing increases with the growth of the initial concentration of e^{-}_{tr} and of the other paramagnetic particles. During photo-annealing of e^{-}_{tr} in the aqueous glasses of the alkalies (*30, 32, 47*), LiCl (*29*) and carbonates (*21*) the concentration of the radicals is generally reduced which is explained by combination of the electrons released from traps with the other radicals. For instance,

$$O^{-} + e^{-} \rightarrow O^{2-} \tag{4}$$

$$Cl_2^{-} + e^{-} \rightarrow 2Cl^{-} \tag{5}$$

In the aqueous glasses of $NaClO_4$ (*29*) and HCOONa (*47*) the electrons knocked out by the light quanta partially participate in the reactions with the dissolved substances forming new radicals:

$$ClO_4^{-}(NaClO_4) + e^{-} \rightarrow ClO_3^{-}(NaClO_3) + O^{-} \tag{6}$$

$$HCOO^{-} + e^{-} \longrightarrow H-\dot{C}\begin{matrix} O^{-} \\ O^{-} \end{matrix} \tag{7}$$

Besides, the concentration of the hydrogen atoms is increased in the aqueous glasses of $NaClO_4$ (*29*) and acid phosphates (*29*) as a result of photo-annealing. Thus, the intensity of the doublet signal of H atoms increases by 10 or 20% (in H_2O) and the intensity of the triplet signal of D atoms, by 30 to 40% (in D_2O). Evidently, these results indicate the possibility of additional formation of H atoms in the following reactions in the acid phosphates:

$$H_2PO_4^{-} + e^{-} \rightarrow HPO_4^{2-} + H \tag{8}$$

$$HPO_4^{2-} + e^{-} \rightarrow PO_4^{3-} + H \tag{9}$$

It is quite possible, however, that the additional appearance of the hydrogen atoms in these systems and particularly in the perchlorate glasses is caused by the reactions of the electrons with the ions of H_3O^{+} in the spurs.

The yields of e^{-}_{tr} in the aqueous glasses depends, first, on the nature of the matrix, secondly, on the concentration of the dissolved substance, and thirdly, on the degree of crystallinity of the sample. With increase of the degree of crystallinity of the frozen solution, $G(e^{-}_{tr})$ becomes less while the rise of the concentration of the electron-inert substance increases the yield.

Most thorough measurements of the e^{-}_{tr} yields have been taken by the EPR method in the alkaline glasses. In accordance with papers *18, 28, 30, 32, 37, 42, 54,*and *55*, $G(e^{-}_{tr})$ for 10*M* glassy alkaline solution is equal to 1.5–3.0. Such scattering is caused by the errors inherent with the EPR method and by the fact that these yields have been determined at rather considerable absorbed doses when there is no linear relationship between the concentration of produced e^-_{tr} and absorbed dose. Therefore, thorough experiments have been performed in work (*47*) to determine $G(e^-_{tr})$ in the alkaline glasses both by the EPR method and by the optical spectroscopy. It has been found that in 10*M* alkaline solution the yield of the trapped electrons equals 3.0 (±20%).

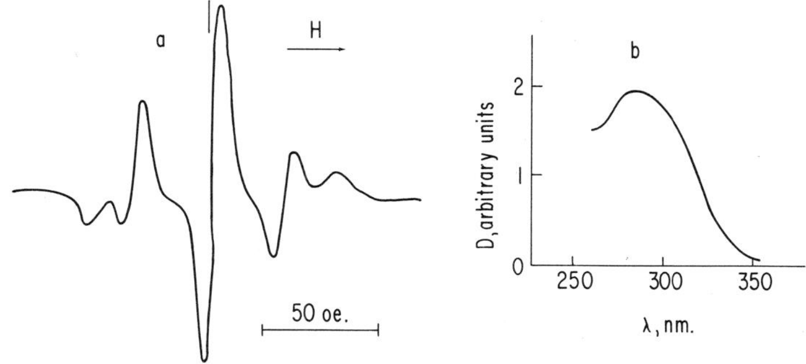

*Figure 3. EPR (a) and optical absorption (b) spectra of NO_3^{2-} ion-radical in 0.1*M *aqueous solution of $NaNO_3$ in 10*M *KOH at 77°K.*

The yield of the thermalized electrons which are produced during the radiolysis of the alkaline glass has been determined by reference to their reactions with the NO_3^- ions (*22*). The latter ions interact with the electrons to produce NO_3^{2-} ion-radicals each of which yields during defreezing 0.5 ion of NO_2^-:

$$2NO_3^{2-} + H_2O \rightarrow NO_3^- + NO_2^- + 2OH^- \quad (10)$$

Hence, when the electrons are fully scavenged (which occurs when adding 0.1*M* of NO_3^-), $G(e^-_{therm})$ should equal $2G(NO_2^-)$. It has been found that $G(e^-_{therm})$ comprises 3.0 (±10%)—*i.e.*, it equals $G(e^-_{tr})$. (The full scavenging of electrons was checked by the disappearance of e^-_{tr} color. In these conditions $G(NO_3^{2-})$ as measured by EPR method is equal to 3.0 (±30%).) Therefore, it may be concluded that in the alkaline glass all the electrons which avoided the decay in the spurs are captured by the traps after thermalization.

In case of the frozen solutions of other electrolytes the yield of e^-_{tr} are substantially less than in the alkaline glasses (*see* Table III). This is explained first of all by the differences in the behavior of the thermalized electrons. The alkali is inert relative to the electrons. In other glassy solutions the thermalized electrons partially participate in the reactions with the dissolved substances. Thus, in the case with 10*M* aqueous glass of $NaClO_4$ the electrons partially react with ClO_4^- in accordance with

Reaction 6 while for $8M$ solution of HCOONa the electrons react in accordance with Reaction 7. The competition of these reactions with Reaction 3 determines the yield of the trapped electrons.

Table III. Yields of Trapped and Thermalized Electrons from γ-Radiolysis of Aqueous Glasses at 77°K.

System	$G(e^-_{tr})$	$G(e^-_{therm})$	*References*
$10M$ KOH in H_2O	3.0 ± 0.3	3.0 ± 0.3	*22, 47*
$10M$ $NaClO_4$ in H_2O	0.5 ± 0.1	2.3 ± 0.2	*22, 47*
$15M$ LiCl in H_2O	0.6 ± 0.1	—	*29*
$5M$ K_2CO_3 in H_2O	2.0 ± 0.4	2.0	*21*
$8M$ HCOONa in H_2O	0.9 ± 0.1	2.7 ± 0.3	*45*

However, the yields of the thermalized electrons for each of the solutions under consideration are much higher than the yields of the trapped electrons (*see* Table III). Evidently, $G(e^-_{\text{therm}}) = G(e^-_{\text{tr}}) + G(R)$ where R is the radical product of reaction of the electrons with the solute.

As the glasses are made of highly concentrated solutions, it may be *a priori* assumed that some of the electrons are produced by the mechanism of the "direct action" of the radiation on the solute. For instance,

$$ClO_4^- \xrightarrow{\text{MM}} ClO_4 + e^- \qquad (11)$$

$$OH^- \xrightarrow{\text{MM}} OH + e^- \qquad (12)$$

Hence, it is essential to know the yield of the thermalized electrons directly from glassy water. Such a separate yield of e^-_{therm} has been calculated for the alkaline glasses by measuring the yield of e^-_{therm} which are fully scavenged by the NO_3^- ions in the glasses with various alkali content (*22*). It has been found that in $10M$ alkaline solution the initial yields of e^-_{therm} which appeared as a result of radiation action separately on water and alkali and avoided the decay in the spurs, equal 3.6 and 1.9, respectively. As it is known, $G_{e^-_{aq}}$ for the alkaline aqueous solutions amounts to 3.2–4.0. It should be mentioned that for $5M$ glasses of $HClO_4$ and $10M$ glasses of $NaClO_4$ at 77°K. the yield of the oxidizing component of water radiolysis (OH radicals) equals 3.0 (±30%) (*50*)—*i.e.*, it coincides with $G(e^-_{\text{therm}})$. This testifies to the fact that the form of state of the substance (liquid or solid glassy body) offers no noticeable effect on the initial yields of the radical products. This is proved also by the close values of $G(NO_2^-)$ determined in the $10M$ aqueous solution of KOH (containing $0.1M$ of NO_3^-) which has been subjected to γ-irradiation in the liquid state at room temperature and in the frozen glassy state at 77°K. (*22*). For more dilute (with respect to NO_3^-) solutions, $G(NO_2^-)$ is different in these phases. This is evidently associated with the fact that in the liquid systems the reactions of the electrons with the solutes are checked mainly by diffusion. In the glassy systems the probability of the reaction is determined by the distance passed by these primary particles from the place of their origin.

The investigation of the low temperature radiolysis of the alkaline glasses in the presence of nitrate additions (*22*) has made it possible to estimate the average and minimal distances of the electrons to the places of their trapping. These distances are equal to $\sim$ 40 and $\sim$ 15A., respectively.

Thus, the consideration of the experimental results proves the important role played by the ion processes in the low temperature radiolysis of the glassy water and aqueous solutions.

Alcohols and Water-Alcohol Mixtures

The trapped electrons appear also during irradiation of the glassy aliphatic alcohols. Similarly to the aqueous glasses, the EPR spectrum of this particle is a narrow singlet ($\Delta H = 13 - 25$ oe.) with g-factor close to the g-factor of the free electron (*7, 11, 12, 25, 53*). Figure 4 shows the EPR spectrum of ethylene glycol after γ-radiolysis at 77°K. and after bleaching with the visible light (*53*). It is clearly seen that after bleaching the EPR spectrum loses the singlet of e^-_{tr} at g-factor of the free electron.

The trapped electron in the aliphatic alcohols is characterized by optical absorption in the visible part of the spectrum. Its absorption

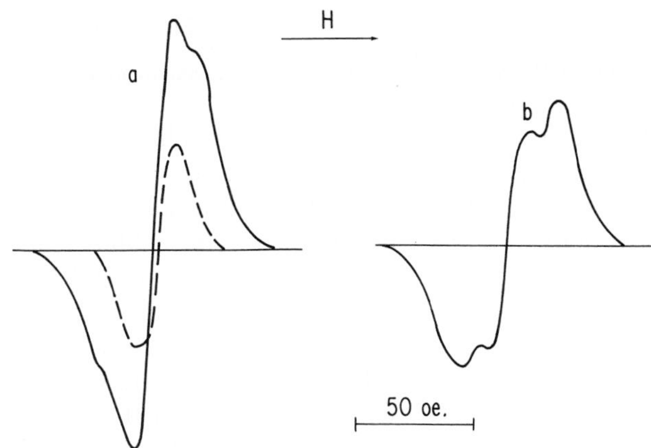

Figure 4. EPR spectrum of ethylene glycol: (a) subjected to γ-irradiation at 77°K. and (b) after illumination with visible light. Dotted line is the EPR spectrum of e^-_{tr}

band is somewhat asymmetrical and is characterized by a more steep drop on the side of long waves. Given in Table IV are some characteristics of the optical spectra of e^-_{tr} in the glassy alcohols at 77°K.

Table IV. Characteristics of Optical Spectra of e^-_{tr} in Glassy Alcohols and Water-Alcohol Mixtures at 77°K.[a]

System	λ_{max}, *nm.*	$E\lambda_{max}$, *e.v.*	$W_{1/2}$, *e.v.*	*References*
Methanol	514	2.41	0.83	*14, 15, 24*
Ethyl alcohol	530	2.34	—	*1*
Propyl alcohol	555	2.23	—	*15*
Isopropyl alcohol	613	2.02	—	*51*
n-Butyl alcohol	505	2.45	—	*1*
Ethylene glycol	502	2.48	1.63	*23, 24*
Glycerol	485	2.55	1.78	*23, 24*
90% methanol + 10% water	514	2.41	0.83	*24*
70% methanol + 30% water	526	2.35	0.79	*24*
50% methanol + 50% water	540	2.29	0.84	*24*
30% methanol + 70% water	550	2.25	0.78	*24*
90% ethylene glycol + 10% water	507	2.44	1.47	*23, 24*
80% ethylene glycol + 20% water	520	2.38	1.41	*23, 24*
60% ethylene glycol + 40% water	540	2.29	1.25	*23, 24*
40% ethylene glycol + 60% water	554	2.23	0.98	*23, 24*
20% ethylene glycol + 80% water	585	2.12	0.87	*23, 24*
80% glycerol + 20% water	505	2.45	1.48	*23, 24*
60% glycerol + 40% water	525	2.36	1.22	*23, 24*
40% glycerol + 60% water	548	2.25	0.84	*23, 24*
20% glycerol + 80% water	581	2.13	0.79	*23, 24*
10*M* HCHO in H_2O	590	2.12	0.83	*20*
4–5*M* glucose in H_2O	560	2.21	0.95	*52*

[a] The composition of the water-alcohol mixtures is given in mole percents.

Recently it has been found that the stabilization of the electrons occurs also in the glassy water-alcohol mixtures (*23, 24*), solutions of formaldehyde (*20*), and in a less degree, in the solutions of acetaldehyde (*20*) and solutions of some carbohydrates (*52*). Shown in Figure 5 is the EPR spectrum of the γ-irradiated 10*M* glass of HCHO in H_2O (a) and in D_2O (b) (*20*). In the central part of the spectra there is seen the singlet of e^-_{tr} shown in dotted lines. In case with H_2O the width of the line comprises 11 ± 1 oe. while for D_2O it is narrowed to 4.5 ± 0.5 oe. The signal is rapidly saturated with the increase of the microwave power. The characteristics of the optical absorption of e^-_{tr} in this system are given in Table IV. The illumination with the visible light results in disappearance of the EPR spectrum and optical absorption of e^-_{tr}. The stabilization of the electrons in the water-formaldehyde glasses is explained by the fact that the aqueous solution of formaldehyde is an

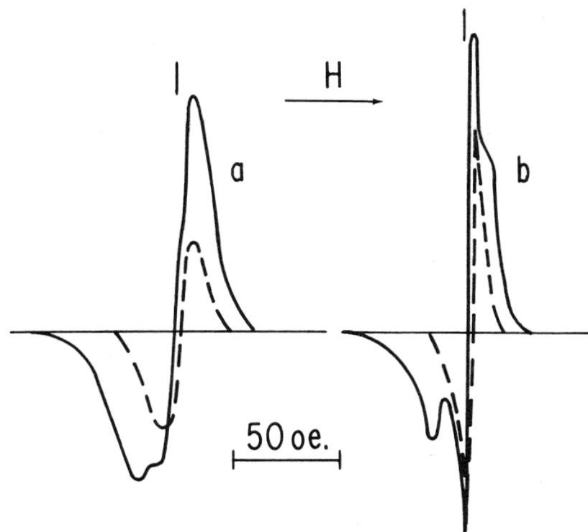

*Figure 5. EPR spectrum of 10*M *aqueous solution of HCHO in H_2O (a) and in D_2O (b) subjected to γ-irradiation at 77°K. Dotted line is the EPR spectrum of* e^-_{tr}

equilibrium mixture of monohydrate of $H_2C(OH)_2$ and low molecular polymers of the general formula $HO(CH_2O)_nH$—*i.e.*, it is essentially the aqueous solution of methylene glycol and its ethers which are low reactive in relation to the electrons. The content of non-hydrated monomer HCHO which effectively scavenges the electrons is very low in the aqueous solutions. With a transition to acetaldehyde and propionic aldehyde the concentration of the non-hydrated molecules substantially increases and hence adds to the possibility of the reaction of e^-_{therm} with formation of radicals CH_3CHO^- and $CH_3CH_2CHO^-$, respectively. Actually, if in the solutions of CH_3CHO the stabilization of the electrons is only slightly displayed, as is the case with CH_3CH_2CHO, there are no trapped electrons at all (*20*).

Similar effects take place with the glassy solutions of carbohydrates which are also characterized by the presence of the hydrated forms. The formation of e^-_{tr} has been found in the solutions of glucose, galactose, sorbose, rhamnose, maltose, and saccharose (*52*). For instance, in the case of 4–5*M* solutions of glucose the EPR spectrum of e^-_{tr} is essentially a narrow line with ΔH 10 ± 1 oe. in H_2O and 5 ± 1 oe. in D_2O (*see* Figure 6). The parameters of the optical band of e^-_{tr} in these solutions are given in Table IV. In the system under consideration $G(e^-_{tr}) = 1.5$ (±50%).

In accordance with (*23, 24*), the optical spectrum of e^-_{tr} in the water-alcohol glasses has only one maximum. With an increase in the water concentration the maximum is gradually shifted to the long wave region (*see* Table IV). In the ethylene glycol-water and glycerol-water mixtures $E\lambda_{max}$ of the trapped electron is proportional to the mole fraction of alcohol. Therefore, the extrapolation of the value of $E\lambda_{max}$ to the zero concentration of alcohol in these mixtures has made it possible to determine the position of the maximum of e^{-}_{tr} absorption in the hypothetic glassy ice (610 nm.). The values of $G(e^{-}_{tr})$ have been estimated for the mixtures of water-ethylene glycol (53). It has been found that $G(e^{-}_{tr})$ equals 1.5 (±30%) irrespective of the composition of this mixture.

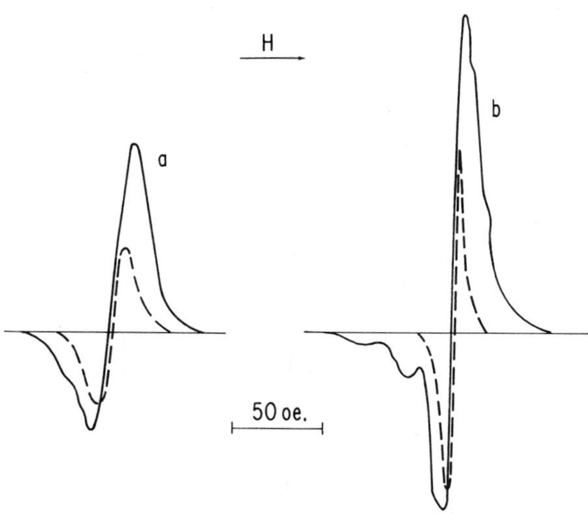

Figure 6. EPR spectrum of 4M aqueous solution of glucose in H_2O (a) and in D_2O (b) subjected to γ-irradiation at 77°K. Dotted line is the EPR spectrum of e^{-}_{tr}

In the water-alcohol mixtures e^{-}_{tr} disappears during photo-annealing but as distinguished from the aqueous glasses of the electrolytes these mixtures are characterized by the appearance of additional radicals of type RCHOH (*see 14, 15, 20, 53*) in the EPR spectra in almost equivalent concentrations. This is explained by interaction of the electrons with the positive ions produced during irradiation of alcohol. Evidently, the first stage of such processes is the neutralization of the positive ions:

$$R\text{—}CH_2 - OH_2^{+} + e^{-} \rightarrow [RCH_2OH]^{*} \rightarrow R\text{—}CH_2\text{—}OH + H \qquad (13)$$

H atoms produced participate in the dehydrogenation reaction:

$$R\text{—}CH_2\text{—}OH + H \rightarrow R\text{—}CH\text{—}OH + H_2 \qquad (14)$$

Crystalline Ice

The neutral pure ice is a crystalline formation. Khodzhaev *et al.* (*48*) have established that under long γ-irradiation stabilization of the electrons in ice will be observed. Figure 7 shows the absorption spectrum of ice subjected to γ-irradiation at 77°K. Band with $\lambda_{max} = 280$ n.m. ($\epsilon \approx 450M^{-1}$ cm.$^{-1}$) is because of the radical OH; e^-_{tr} absorbs the light in the visible part of the spectrum (λ_{max} is about 620 n.m.). The yield of e^-_{tr} in this system is very low ($\sim 10^{-3}$ electrons/100 e.v.). The concentration of the trapped electrons is very low; therefore, these electrons are not displayed in the EPR spectrum. It should be stressed that the value of λ_{max} of the trapped electron practically coincides with the value of λ_{max} for e^-_{tr} in the hypothetic glassy ice.

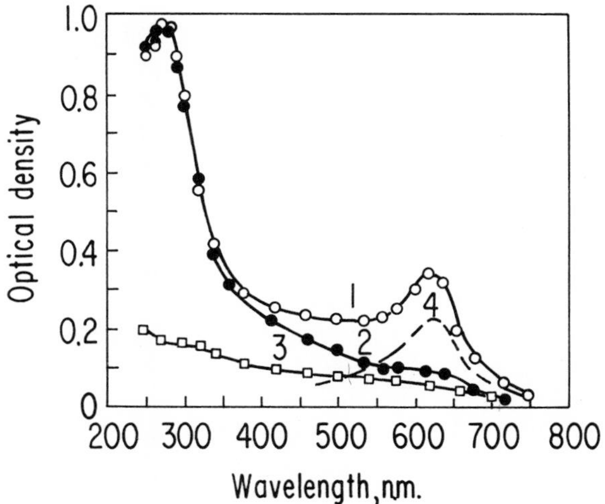

Figure 7. Optical absorption spectrum of crystalline ice: (1) subjected to γ-irradiation at 77°K.; (2) after illumination with visible light; (3) after warming to 143°K.; (4) spectrum of e^-_{tr} *obtained by difference between Curves 1 and 2*

It has been found (*56, 59, 60*) that ice irradiated by the electron pulses at 263° to 203°K. gives rather intensive short-life optical absorption with the peak in the region of 630 to 680 n.m. It has been determined (*56*) that the intensity of the absorption substantially increases with the temperature growth. The authors of the aforementioned publications explain this absorption in various ways. In accordance with Nillson *et al.* (*56*), the absorption is caused by the hydrated electron. By the opinion of Shubin *et al.* (*59, 60*) the absorption under consideration is not caused by the electron-dipole interactions but is caused by the electron interactions only—*i.e.*, by the particle of the exciton type. However, the detection of the optical band of e^-_{tr} in the crystalline ice irradiated at 77°K., in the same region of the spectrum as in ice at 263° to 203°K., speaks in favor of the first interpretation. The theoretical aspects of this process are discussed in the next section.

On Nature of Trapped Electrons

The stabilization of the electrons most probably occurs on the traps in the field of the oriented dipoles of the polar molecules. In this case the line of e^-_{tr} in the EPR spectrum is actually an envelope of the unresolved hyperfine structure brought about by the interaction of the electron with the surrounding protons. Ershov *et al.* (*19*) made an attempt to estimate, by the direct method, the region of such delocalization of the electron. The analysis of the shape of the EPR line of e^-_{tr} in the alkaline glass by the method of linear anamorphosis has shown that when the matrix is of a unique isotope composition (H or D) this line is actually a Gaussian curve. However, this shape of the line is not exactly traced in the mixtures of H_2O and D_2O. By the form of dependence of the second moment and $1/4(\Delta H)^2$ on the isotope composition it has been shown that the line of e^-_{tr} is an envelope of the hyperfine structure which is a function of the interaction of the trapped electron with 8 ± 1 protons. (Earlier the similar conclusions on the basis of several approximations have been drawn in References *54* and *55*. The same conclusion has been made by the authors of recent publication (*65*).) The similar result has been obtained in measuring the width and the number of spin-packets of the e^-_{tr} signal by the method of continuous saturation. (It has been found that the width ΔH_s of the spin-packets is equal 1.7 oe. This corresponds to the local concentration of the paramagnetic centers which exceeds by two orders the average concentration of e^-_{tr}.) For the case of the magnetic-equivalent nuclei in H_2O, it has been established that the distance between the components of the unresolved hyperfine structure comprises 5.1 oe.

The conclusion on the delocalization of e^-_{tr} on the surrounding polar molecules of the medium is evidently also true for the aqueous glasses of other electrolytes. (For most compact packing the effective radius of delocalization $r_{del} = 2r_{H_2O} + r_{cav} \approx 3.4$ A. where r_{H_2O} and r_{cav} are the radii of the water molecule and "cavity" limited by four molecules of H_2O respectively.) They also display the similar dependence of ΔH on the isotope composition of water (*see* Table I). In the case of aliphatic alcohols ΔH of the singlet of e^-_{tr} becomes less when the atoms of H in the OH groups are replaced by the D atoms (*7, 12*). However, the replacement of H by D in the alkyl group of the alcohol molecule has no noticeable effect on the amount of ΔH. This testifies to the fact that in the aliphatic alcohols the electron is stabilized in the field of the oriented hydroxyl groups.

Deigen and Pekar (*16*) have shown that in the polarons the energy correction caused by the hyperfine interaction equals zero in the first approximation. Hence, the width of the polaron line determined by the hyperfine interaction also equals zero. At the same time for the local electron centers such an interaction is actually a predominant factor which determines the width of the line. This makes it possible to distinguish by way of experiments the polarons from the local electron centers. Evidently, the solvated electrons produced during irradiation of the polar liquids are the mobile polarons. At low temperatures the polarons are stabilized in the form of local electron centers (peculiar *F*-centers) (*6, 19*). Actually, in the metal-ammonia solutions the width of the EPR line of the solvated electron comprises some hundredths of oersted; however, the freezing of the solution at 77°K. results in widening of this line up to 3.4 (*37*) or 11 (*58*) oe.

The electrons are stabilized on the structural defects in the field of definitely oriented polar molecules. If this is the fact, then the role played by the glassy state in the electron stabilization becomes clear. This state is characterized by a random arrangement of the molecules and hence by high concentration of the suitable traps. In the first approximation the number of the traps may be evaluated by reference to the maximal concentration of the trapped electrons obtained at high absorbed doses. For the alkaline glasses it equals about 10^{18} gram^{-1}. The nature of defects in which the electrons are trapped is not clear. Evidently the electrons are located in "cavities" and other defects available in the glassy structures. It is not excluded that such defects with trapped electrons are localized in the proximity of positive holes—places of radiation-induced formation of O^- (in the alkaline glasses), OH or H_3O^+ (in the neutral aqueous glasses), and ROH_2^+ (in the alcohol glasses). In the case of alkaline glasses this is proved by high local concentration of the radicals (*19*). Hence, we can consider the trapped electron in this systems as peculiar *F*-center.

Evidently, in case with the glasses, the traps will differ by the degree of direction of the molecule dipoles and sizes of "cavities." Experimentally, this will be displayed in a considerable dispersion of trapping energy.

It has been found (*24, 47*) that during a partial photo-annealing of the electrons by the filtered light the intensity of the e^-_{tr} absorption band is reduced, the maximum is shifted and $W_{1/2}$ becomes less (the limited value comprises about 0.5 to 0.6 e.v.) (*see* Figure 8). This testifies to the fact that the optical band of e^-_{tr} is an envelope of a large number of the electron absorption lines differing in electron trapping energies.

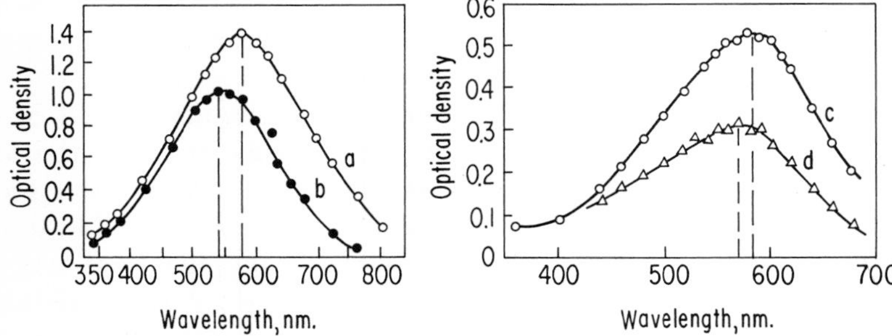

Figure 8. Optical absorption spectra of e^-_{tr} *in 10*M *solution of KOH (a, b) and in water-methanol mixture (c, d) before partial photo-annealing (a, c) and after partial photo-annealing (b, d) by monochromatic light with wavelength of 700 (b) and 650 (d) n.m.*

Thus, there exists the dispersion of the energies of electron trapping by the polar matrix, which ensures relatively large values of $W_{1/2}$ of the optical bands of e^-_{tr}. In the event of aliphatic alcohols, $W_{1/2}$ increases with the increase of the size of the medium molecules. Evidently, the greater the sizes of the solvent molecules, the broader is the energetic complex of the traps and the wider is the absorption band of e^-_{tr}. It is worth while mentioning that the value of $W_{1/2}$ increases with the growth of the value of $E\lambda_{max}$ of the trapped electron in the given system.

The theory of polarons and *F*-centers is given in detail by Pekar (*57*). Although this theory has some inexactitude (*38*), it explains principally the transformation of mobile polaron in liquids into unmobile *F*-center in frozen systems at low temperatures. Table V gives the results of the

Table V. Effective Masses of Trapped Electrons in Polar Glasses[a]

System	μ/m	$-E_{1s}$, *e.v.*	$-E_{2p}$, *e.v.*
Hypothetic glassy ice	2.5	3.74	1.71
Methanol	2.7	4.28	1.90
Ethyl alcohol	2.8	4.15	1.81
Propyl alcohol	2.3	3.41	1.44
Isopropyl alcohol	2.4	3.51	1.49
n-Butyl alcohol	2.9	4.14	1.72
Ethylene glycol	3.8	4.53	2.03
Glycerol	4.1	4.35	1.81

[a] The calculations were based on the assumption that the glasses at 77°K. have the same dielectric constants as the respective liquids at room temperature.

approximated calculations of μ/m values (μ—effective mass of the polaron, m—mass of the electron) for e^-_{tr} in some glasses. Table V also contains the computed values of E_{1s} (the energy in the ground $1s$-state) and E_{2p} (the energy in the excited $2p$-state). The effective masses obtained are relatively close to the values for the solvated electrons in the same substances in the liquid state (*24*). This agrees with the requirements of the polaron theory (*57*).

Similar calculations with the account for the electronic polarization of the dielectric have been performed by Kevan (*43*). It has been found that μ/m of the hydrated electron in the liquid water and of e^-_{tr} in the alkaline glass at 77°K. equal 1.07 and 1.27, respectively.

On the basis of a definite analogy between e^-_{tr} and F-centers we may expect the appearance under certain conditions of $(e^-_{tr})_2$- particles of the type of F'-centers. From the polaron model (*57*) it follows that the bipolaron (two electrons localized in a common polarization well) can not exist. In accordance with the work of Vinetskii and Giterman (*63*), in some cases the formation of the "bipolarons" becomes energetically possible in the result of interaction of the polarization wells of two separate polarons. However, the saving in energy for such bipolaron states is not large and hence they will not be stable in liquids under room temperature. Actually, up to the present time a series of attempts have been made to detect $(e^-_{aq})_2$ in the irradiated liquid water but these attempts were not successful. The polaron theory (*57*) predicts that F'-centers (two electrons in the anionic vacancy) may be stable. For this it is necessary that the ratio ϵ/n^2 (ϵ and n^2 are the static and optical dielectric constants, n—refraction index) should be more than 1.5. Evidently, in the glassy systems under consideration this requirement is fulfilled.

Khodzhaev *et al.* (*44, 45*) have obtained data on mutual transformation of e^-_{tr} and $(e^-_{tr})_2$. This effect has been revealed on the basis of the following conceptions. In the alkaline glass the electrons react during the photo-annealing with radicals O^- and formation of the diamagnetic particles $(e^-_{tr})_2$ is hardly probable. However, when introducing into the alkaline glass some scavengers of ions H_2O^+ which are the precursors of radicals O^- the generation of the latter is suppressed while the free-radical products produced may be less reactive in relation to the electrons so that the appearance of $(e^-_{tr})_2$ during the photo-annealing or in the course of γ-irradiation becomes quite possible.

It has been determined that formates, carbonates, and CH_3OH may be used as scavengers. The maximal effect has been observed for the glassy aqueous solution of 10M NaOH + 1M HCOONa. The blue color which appears in the result of γ-irradiation at 77°K. is caused by e^-_{tr} and is easily annealed by the visible light. If the photo-annealed

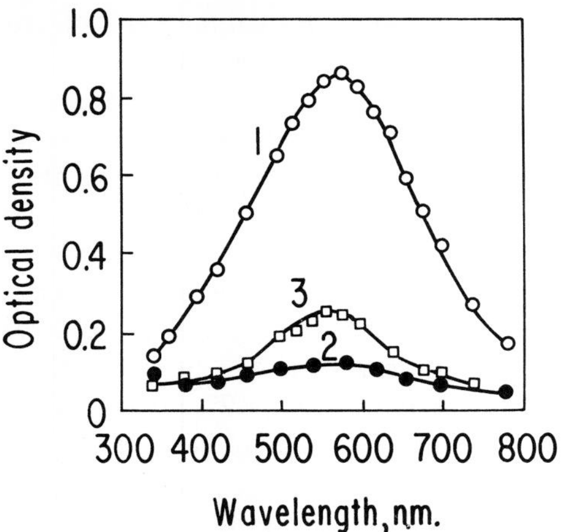

Figure 9. Optical absorption spectrum of e^-_{tr} *in aqueous glass 10*M *NaOH + 1*M *HCOONa: (1) after γ-irradiation at 77°K.; (2) after illumination with visible light; (3) after warming bleached sample to 133°K.*

sample is then heated at 130°K., about 30–40% of the original color will reappear (*see* Figure 9). Such a procedure may be performed repeatedly without a substantial change in the concentration of the e^-_{tr} which reappeared. By the EPR method it has been revealed that during the photo-annealing the singlet caused by e^-_{tr} disappears but after heating the bleached sample it is partially (approximately by 30–40%) restored (*see* Figure 10).

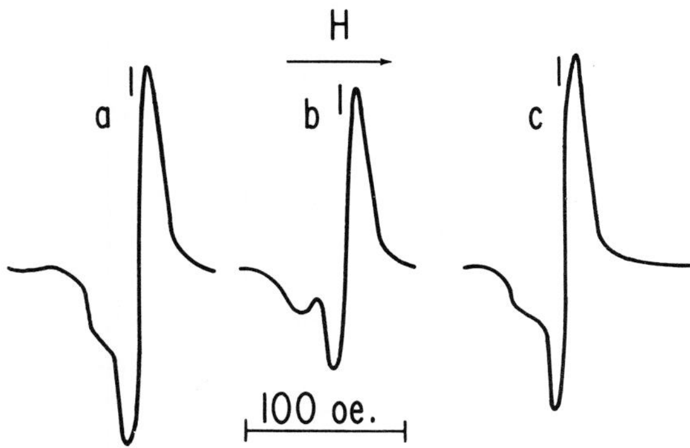

*Figure 10. EPR spectrum of aqueous glass 10*M *NaOH + 4*M *HCOONa: (a) after γ-irradiation at 77°K.; (b) after illumination with visible light; (c) after warming bleached sample to 133°K.*

Evidently, it is connected with formation of the diamagnetic bielectron center $(e^-_{tr})_2$ during the photo-annealing; during heating these particles are decomposed into e^-_{tr}. There has not been revealed any distinct optical absorption in the visible part of the spectrum belonging to $(e^-_{tr})_2$. Evidently, this is explained by the fact that the given particle has a very wide absorption band and relatively low extinction coefficient as compared with e^-_{tr}. Nevertheless, the illumination of the bleached sample by the light with the wavelengths over 700 n.m. results in a partial reappearance of e^-_{tr} color. This surely points to absorption of the light by $(e^-_{tr})_2$- centers in the given region.

The revealed effect is absent in the neutral aqueous and alcohol glasses. In these systems during photo-annealing e^-_{tr} evidently interacts with the ions of H_3O^+ or ROH_2^+. However, it may happen that $(e^-_{tr})_2$-centers formed during recombination of the electrons are generally unstable in these systems.

The formation of the bielectron centers under long γ-irradiation of the alkaline glasses at 77°K. has been recently shown by Zimbrick and Kevan (*64*).

The polaron-type model of solvated electron was properly treated in References *35, 38,* and *39.* It is assumed that the electron is located in the spherical "cavity," the potential beyond the "cavity" being continuous and the potential inside the "cavity" being constant. In this model parameter μ is replaced by some other parameter-radius r_0 of the "cavity" and the contribution of electron polarization into the depth of potential well is taken into consideration. Table VI (columns 2-8) gives the results of calculations of $E\lambda_{max}$ for e^-_{tr} at various values of r_0 (*24*). Table VI also contains the obtained values of the radii of average distribution of the electron charge in the ground (1*s*) and excited (2*p*) states.

It is known (*2, 24, 40*) that some properties of the solvated electrons are correlated with the similar properties of the halide ions in the solutions. It may be assumed that the solvated or trapped electron is essentially a hypothetic ion $(X)^-_n$ (where X is the solvent molecule or its polar part) located in the "cavity." If we then slightly modify the well-known theory (*61*) of light absorption by the halide ions in the solution to adapt it to e^-_s or e^-_{tr}, then it becomes possible on the basis of the experimental data to calculate the effective radii of the "cavity" wherein the considered particles are localized. (According to this theory, halide ion is located in the "cavity" formed by the solvent molecules.) The results of the respective calculations (*24*) for e^-_{tr} are given in the last column of Table VI. It is clear from Table VI that the values of r_{eff} determined with the help of one theory are rather close to the values of r_{1s} obtained with the use of another model.

Table VI. Calculated Values of Radii of

System	r_o, A.	$-E_{1s}$, *e.v.*	$-E_{2p}$, *e.v.*
Hypothetic	1.50	3.426	1.623
Glassy ice	1.30	3.679	1.647
Methanol	1.00	3.970	1.590
	0.95	4.051	1.593
Ethyl alcohol	1.00	3.730	1.467
	0.95	3.805	1.469
Propyl alcohol	1.00	3.560	1.383
	0.95	3.630	1.385
Isopropyl alcohol	1.20	3.264	1.350
	1.10	3.385	1.356
n-Butyl alcohol	0.75	3.721	1.299
	0.70	3.797	1.300
Ethylene	0.85	3.758	1.403
Glycol	0.80	3.897	1.404
Glycerol	0.70	3.799	1.302
	0.65	3.876	1.302

[a] *See* footnote to Table V.

Still there is no chance to find some experimental criterion for checking each of the described theories. It should be stressed that the polaron model of the "cavity" with the localized electron is definitely proved by the volume expansion of ammonia when adding the alkali metal to it (*38*). Besides, on the basis of any of the "cavity" theories it becomes comparatively easy to explain the results of investigation of e^-_{tr} photoannealing—*i.e.*, the dispersion of the trap depths, and temperature dependence of $E\lambda_{max}$ of the electrons. In this connection it is rather desirable to find some approach to determining the sizes of the "cavities" for the electrons in the irradiated polar systems, as it has been done for the metal-ammonia solutions.

The crystalline ice with its highly ordered structure has only few places with properly oriented molecules of water. This explains very low yield of e^-_{tr} in the given system. The orderliness of the structure also explains slight dispersion of the trap depths which is displayed in the relatively small $W_{1/2}$ value of the e^-_{tr} optical band ($\sim$ 0.4 e.v.) (*48*). Evidently, when such traps are absent at all, the trapped electrons are not produced. Actually, it has been found recently (*4*) that in the perfect

"Cavities" for e^-_{tr} in Polar Glasses at 77°K. (*24*) [a]

$E\lambda_{max}$, e.v.				
Cal.	*Exper.*	r_{1s}, A.	r_{2p}, A.	r_{eff}, A.
1.803		2.78	5.10	3.09
2.032	2.03	2.59	5.00	
2.380	2.41	2.34	5.03	2.77
2.458		2.30	5.02	
2.263		2.43	5.33	2.83
2.336	2.34	2.39	5.34	
2.177	2.23	2.50	5.61	2.93
2.245		2.45	5.59	
1.914		2.72	5.72	3.11
2.029	2.02	2.62	5.69	
2.422	2.45	2.34	5.87	2.75
2.497		2.29	5.86	
2.355	2.48	2.40	5.75	2.76
2.493		2.36	5.75	
2.497	2.55	2.34	6.02	2.72
2.574		2.28	6.02	

crystals of alkaline ice ($NaOH \times 3.5\ H_2O$) subjected to γ-irradiation at 77°K. $G(e^-_{tr}) = 0$.

With an increase of temperature the number of traps in the crystalline ice becomes greater because of the greater mobility of the dipoles. This, evidently, will result in the increase of the electron yield. As it has been already mentioned, in ice at 263° to 203°K. the intensity of the optical absorption in the visible part of the spectrum increases with the growth of temperature (*56, 59, 60*). As this absorption belongs most probably to the hydrated electron, this phenomenon proves the conclusion. At the temperatures under consideration the traps are not fixed. Hence, in the given case the electron is characterized by a relatively short life which is less than the time of the dielectric relaxation of the medium. It would seem that when calculating the energy of the electron self trapping it is necessary to use not D_{st} of the medium but the dielectric constant at the frequencies corresponding to the time of life of the particle under consideration (*43, 59, 60*). However, as the electrons are localized in the traps with properly oriented water molecules, evidently, D_{st} should be used in these calculations. Then the experimentally observed shift λ_{max}

of e^-_{aq} in ice to the short-wave region in comparison with liquid water may be qualitatively explained by the polaron theory (57).

Literature Cited

(1) Alger, R. S., Anderson, T. H., Webb, L. A., *J. Chem. Phys.* **30,** 695 (1959).
(2) Anbar, M., Hart, E. J., *J. Phys. Chem.* **69,** 1244 (1965).
(3) Ayscough, P. P., Collins, R. G., Dainton, F. S., *Nature* **205,** 965 (1965).
(4) Barzynski, H., Schulte-Frohlinde, D., *Z. Naturforsch.* **22a,** 2131 (1967).
(5) Blandamer, M. J., Shields, L., Symons, M. C. R., *Nature* **199,** 902 (1963).
(6) Blandamer, M. J., Shields, L., Symons, M. C. R., *J. Chem. Soc.* **1964,** 4352.
(7) *Ibid.*, **1965,** 1127.
(8) *Ibid.*, **1965,** 3759.
(9) Brekhovskikh, S. M., Vereshchinskii, I. V., Grishina, A. D., Zelentsova, S. A., Revina, A. A., Tykachinskii, I. D., "Trudy II Vsesoyuznogo soveshchaniya po radiatsionnoii khimii," p. 660, Izdatel'stvo AN SSSR, Moscow, 1962.
(10) Bugaenko, L. T., Belevskii, V. N., *Zh. Fiz. Khim.* **39,** 2958 (1965).
(11) Chachaty, C., *Compt. Rend.* **259,** 2219 (1964).
(12) Chachaty, C., Hayon, E., *J. Chim. Phys.* **61,** 1115 (1964).
(13) Compton, D. M. J., Bryant, J. F., Cesena, R. A., Gehman, B. L., "Pulse Radiolysis," M. Ebert *et al.*, ed., p. 43, Academic Press, London, 1965.
(14) Dainton, F. S., Salmon, G. A., Teply, J., *Proc. Roy. Soc.* **A286,** 27 (1965).
(15) Dainton, F. S., Salmon, G. A., Wardman, P., Zucker, U., "Proc. Second Tihany Symposium on Radiation Chemistry," p. 247, Publishing House of the Hungarian Academy of Sciences, Budapest, 1967.
(16) Deigen, M. F., Pekar, S. I., *Zh. Eksperim. i Teor. Fiz.* **34,** 684 (1958).
(17) Dorfman, L. M., ADVAN. CHEM. SER. **50,** 36 (1965).
(18) Eiben, K., Schulte-Frohlinde, D., *Z. Physik. Chem. (Neue Folge)* **45,** 20 (1965).
(19) Ershov, B. G., Grinberg, O. Ya., Lebedev, Ya. S., *Zh. Strukt. Khim.*, 1968 (in press).
(20) Ershov, B. G., Khodzhaev, O. F., Grigor'eva, L. P., Pikaev, A. K., *Khim. Vys. Energ.* **1,** 374 (1967).
(21) Ershov, B. G., Khodzhaev, O. F., Pikaev, A. K., *Khim. Vys. Energ.* **2,** 42 (1968).
(22) Ershov, B. G., Lyu, E., Pikaev, A. K., *Khim. Vys. Energ.* **1,** 554 (1967).
(23) Ershov, B. G., Makarov, I. E., Pikaev, A. K., *Khim. Vys. Energ.* **1,** 404 (1967).
(24) *Ibid.*, **1,** 472 (1967).
(25) Ershov, B. G., Moorthy, P. N., Lingam, K. V., *Indian J. Chem.* **4,** 494 (1967).
(26) Ershov, B. G., Pikaev, A. K., *Izv. Akad. Nauk. SSSR, Ser. Khim.* **1966,** 386.
(27) *Ibid.*, **1966,** 1637.
(28) Ershov, B. G., Pikaev, A. K., "Radiatsionnaya fizika. IV. Ionnye kristally," p. 39, Izdatel'stvo "Zinatne," Riga, 1966.
(29) Ershov, B. G., Pikaev, A. K., *Khim. Vys. Energ.* **1,** 29 (1967).
(30) Ershov, B. G., Pikaev, A. K., Glazunov, P. Ya., Spitsyn, V. I., *Dokl. Akad. Nauk. SSSR,* **149,** 163 (1963).
(31) *Ibid.*, **154,** 899 (1964).
(32) Ershov, B. G., Pikaev, A. K., Glazunov, P. Ya., Spitsyn, V. I., *Izv. Akad. Nauk. SSSR, Ser. Khim.* **1964,** 1755.

(33) *Ibid.*, **1965**, 1758.
(34) *Ibid.*, **1965**, 1919.
(35) Fueki, K., *J. Chem. Phys.* **44**, 3140 (1966).
(36) Hart, E. J., "Actions Chimiques et Biologiques des Radiations," X Ser., M. Haissinsky, ed., p. 1, Masson, Paris, 1966.
(37) Henriksen, T., *Radiation Res.* **23**, 63 (1964).
(38) Jortner, J., *J. Chem. Phys.* **30**, 839 (1959).
(39) Jortner, J., *Radiation Res., Suppl.* **4**, 24 (1964).
(40) Jortner, J., Noyes, R. M., *J. Phys. Chem.* **70**, 770 (1966).
(41) Jortner, J., Scharf, B., *J. Chem. Phys.* **37**, 2506 (1962).
(42) Kevan, L., *J. Phys. Chem.* **69**, 1081 (1965).
(43) Kevan, L., "Progress in Solid State Chemistry," vol. 2, H. Reiss, ed., p. 304, Pergamon Press, London, 1965.
(44) Khodzhaev, O. F., Ershov, B. G., Pikaev, A. K., *Izv. Akad. Nauk. SSSR, Ser. Khim.* **1967**, 1882.
(45) *Ibid.*, **1967**, 2253.
(46) Khodzhaev, O. F., Ershov, B. G., Pikaev, A. K., *Khim. Vys. Energ.* **1**, 161 (1967).
(47) Khodzhaev, O. F., Ershov, B. G., Pikaev, A. K., *Dokl. Akad. Nauk. SSSR,* **179**, 911 (1968).
(48) Khodzhaev, O. F., Ershov, B. G., Pikaev, A. K., *Izv. Akad. Nauk. SSSR, Ser. Khim.* **1968**, 246.
(49) Khodzhaev, O. F., Ershov, B. G., Pikaev, A. K., Spitsyn, V. I., *Dokl. Akad. Nauk. SSSR* **169**, 1379 (1966).
(50) Khodzhaev, O. F., Ershov, B. G., Pikaev, A. K., Spitsyn, V. I., *Izv. Akad. Nauk. SSSR, Ser. Khim.* **1968**, 91.
(51) Kiss, F., Bagdasaryan, Kh. S., "Proc. Second Tihany Symposium on Radiation Chemistry," p. 257, Publishing House of Hungarian Academy of Sciences, Budapest, 1967.
(52) Makarov, I. E., Ershov, B. G., Pikaev, A. K., *Izv. Akad. Nauk. SSSR, Ser. Khim.* **1968**, 447.
(53) Makarov, I. E., Ershov, B. G., Pikaev, A. K., *Khim. Vys. Energ.* (in press).
(54) Moorthy, P. N., Weiss, J. J., *Phil. Mag.* **10**, 659 (1964).
(55) Moorthy, P. N., Weiss, J. J., ADVAN. CHEM. SER. **50**, 180 (1965).
(56) Nillson, G., Christensen, H. C., Fenger, J., Pagsberg, P., Nielsen, S. O., "Summaries of Papers at VIII Intern. Symposium on Free Radicals," p. 233, Novosibirsk, 1967.
(57) Pekar, S. I., "Issledovaniya po elektronnoi teorii kristallov," Gostekhteorizdat, Moskva-Leningrad, 1951.
(58) Schulte-Frohlinde, D., Eiben, K., *Z. Naturforsch.* **17a**, 445 (1962).
(59) Shubin, V. N., Zhigunov, V. A., Zolotarevsky, V. I., Dolin, P. I., *Nature* **202**, 1002 (1966).
(60) Shubin, V. N., Zhigunov, V. A., Zolotarevsky, V. I., Dolin, P. I., *Dokl. Akad. Nauk. SSSR* **174**, 416 (1967).
(61) Stein, G., Treinin, A., *Trans. Faraday Soc.* **55**, 1086 (1959).
(62) Tolkachev, V. A., Mikhailov, A. I., *Pribory i Tekhn. Eksperim.* **1964**, 95.
(63) Vinetskii, V. L., Giterman, M. Sh., *Zh. Eksperim. i Teor. Fiz.* **33**, 730 (1957).
(64) Zimbrick, J., Kevan, L., *J. Am. Chem. Soc.* **89**, 2483 (1967).
(65) Zimbrick, J., Kevan, L., *J. Chem. Phys.* **47**, 2364 (1967).

RECEIVED January 2, 1968.

Aqueous Media

2

Theory of Radiation Chemistry. IX. Model and Structure of Heavy Particle Tracks in Water

A. MOZUMDER, A. CHATTERJEE and J. L. MAGEE

Department of Chemistry and the Radiation Laboratory, University of Notre Dame, Notre Dame, Ind. 46556

This paper describes the structure of heavy particle tracks in water with special reference to the highly charged ions of carbon through neon. Range, effective charge and contribution of charge changing processes to total energy loss have been computed as a function of particle energy and quality using a Monte Carlo procedure. Bohr's formulas have been used for electron capture and loss with slight modifications to adapt to the present case. A model of heavy particle tracks has been proposed for use in radiation chemistry. This consists of a core of high ionization density surrounded by emergent secondary electrons of lower ionization density. Extension of the present model to protons, α-particles and fission fragments is briefly considered.

Heavy positively charged particle radiations in the form of protons, deuterons and alpha-particles have been used for a long time in the radiolysis of liquids (*2, 5, 7, 9, 15, 16, 19, 20*). Fission fragments have also been used (*4*). Recently particles of higher charge and mass than protons or alpha-particles—*e.g.*, bare carbon nucleus—have become available from the heavy ion linear accelerator (HILAC) and are being used in radiolysis with interesting results (*17, 18*). Nevertheless, at the present time an adequate discussion of the structure of heavy particle tracks starting from first physical principles does not seem to exist in the literature. For a long time these tracks have been considered to have the same basic ingredients as low LET tracks. Here and in what follows LET (linear energy transfer) refers to the energy deposited in the medium by a charged particle over unit track length. Spurs, which are distantly-spaced in low LET tracks, have been thought to overlap so densely on a heavy particle track that a cylindrical column resulted (*6, 14*). Recently, a more refined model for low LET tracks in water has been proposed by the authors (*11, 12*). However, no such comparable model is available at present for heavy particle tracks. The purpose of the present paper, therefore, is to construct a reasonably physical model for heavy particle tracks with special reference to aqueous media. Hopefully a sufficiently simple description has evolved which should allow immediate application in such experimental situations as radiolysis, specific luminescence, etc.

Much of the work reported here considers the bare nuclei C^{6+}, N^{7+}, O^{8+}, F^{9+}, and Ne^{10+} as the incident radiations. However, the results so obtained can be applied to protons, deuterons, and alpha-particles on one hand and fission fragments on the other without serious difficulty—*i.e.*, with only some quantitative differences.

The interaction of a heavy positively charged particle with matter differs from that of particles of low stopping power (essentially high speed electrons in most experimental situations) in two essential aspects, *viz.* (1) charge exchange with the medium molecules and (2) production of secondary electrons. Charge exchange—*i.e.*, the capture and loss of electrons by the incident positive particle—provides additional mechanisms of energy loss and at the same time extends the range of the incident particle because the effective charge decreases gradually as the particle penetrates farther into the medium. It will be seen that in the energy range of interest the actual energy loss owing to charge exchange is quite small whereas the range extension is substantial. The secondary electrons for a heavy particle radiation are frequently ejected almost perpendicularly to the track axis. Their maximum velocity may approach twice that of the incident particle; but even at that they share only a small fraction of the incident energy in a given single encounter. In many cases of interest, secondary electrons generate tracks that have lower stopping-power compared with that of the main track. We, therefore, have a picture of a core of high LET shrouded by an envelope of lower LET. In the subsequent sections we will attempt to develop this picture quantitatively with special emphasis on energy partition between the core and the outside.

Cross-Section for Electron Capture and Loss: Energy Loss in Charge Exchange Processes

When a bare nucleus is injected into a medium it eventually captures an electron while being slowed down by the creation of ionizations and excitations in the medium. If the incident particle velocity is in excess of the 1*s*-orbital velocity of an electron around the ion then the first capture will take place in the *K*-shell. However, the captured electron will soon be lost in forthcoming collisions. Another electron will be captured in the *K*-shell and subsequently lost as well. The interplay between capture and loss continues till the particle velocity has become so small that further loss of the captured electron is energetically impossible; an electron is now permanently bound to the incident particle. The probability that a second electron will be captured by the incident particle now becomes significant. The cycle of events follows essentially the same course as in the capture of the first electron—*i.e.*, after an initial sequence of capture and loss the second electron is also permanently bound when its loss becomes energetically forbidden. The incident particle is thus gradually neutralized and subsequently thermalized. For high speed particles of interest in radiation chemistry, the incident particles retain a substantial amount of their initial charge during most of their range. However, even a single capture or loss at a time alters the local stopping power drastically; in the final result the range is extended, sometimes by a considerable amount. We are, therefore, interested in the cross sections of electron capture and loss by positive ions. These cross sections determine the equilibrium charge distribution of an ion as a function of its velocity.

There is no rigorous theory of charge exchange between an ion and the molecules of a medium into which it penetrates. Here we shall follow the classical treatment of Bohr (*3*) with indicated modifications to suit the present case. According to this treatment, electron capture is envisaged as a succession of two processes: first, ionization of the medium molecules with the ejected electron having at least the speed (v) of the incident ion, and secondly, capture of the ejected electron into an orbital of the ion. Thus, the cross section for capture is given by

$$\sigma_c = \sigma_i(v)\nu p(v) \tag{1}$$

where $\sigma_i(v)$ is the cross section of ionization with a minimum speed v of the ejected electron; ν is the number of ionizable electrons in the molecule and $p(v)$ is the probability that an ejected electron of appropriate speed will actually be captured by the ion. Using the Rutherford cross-section for ionization by collision, ignoring the small binding energy of the electron in the molecule compared with the large kinetic energy imparted to it and recognizing that the maximum velocity that can be transferred to an electron by a heavy ion is $2v$, we obtain the following equation for $\sigma_i(v)$

$$\sigma_i(v) = 3\pi Z_1^2 a_0^2 (v_0/v)^4 \tag{2a}$$

where Z_1 is the ionic charge in units of e, the magnitude of the electronic charge a_0, is the Bohr radius and v_0 is the velocity of an electron in a 1s-orbital of an H-atom. For a medium having atoms of high atomic number, Bohr derives ν from the Thomas-Fermi model. In our case dealing mostly with aqueous media, this procedure is quite unacceptable since by this one gets a value of ν greater than Z_2, the total number electrons in the water molecule for high speeds of the incident ion. For our purpose, therefore, we take $\nu = Z_2$ which has the value 10 for water. According to Bohr, $p(v)$ is given by the ratio of volumes of momentum spaces occupied by the electron in the captured and free states. Hence, if the capture takes place in an orbital with principal quantum number n, then

$$p(v) = (Z_1 v_0/nv)^3 \tag{2b}$$

Inserting Reactions 2a and 2b into Reaction 1, we get

$$\sigma_c = 3\pi Z_2 a_0^2 Z_1^5 (v_0/v)^7/n^3. \tag{3}$$

At first $n = 1$. When the K-shell is filled, we must use $n = 2$ for further captures in the L-shell.

The phenomenon of electron loss is best described as an ionization of the incident ion when looked at in its own reference frame. In this description the electron bound in the ion is being bombarded by electrons as well as nuclei of the medium. As may be expected, nuclear bombardment is more effective than electronic in ionization of the ion. A minimum energy I_s, equal to the binding energy of the electron in the ion, is required for ionization to occur. The maximum energy that can be imparted, considering nuclear collisions, is $2mv^2$, m being the electronic mass. For electronic collisions, the maximum energy transfer is $(1/4)\ mv^2$ but this difference will be ignored. The error introduced is negligible in view of the smallness of the contribution of electronic collision to this particular process. Using Rutherford's classical collision description again, the cross-section for electron loss for each electron bound with an energy I_s to the ion is given by

$$\sigma_l = \frac{2\pi e^4 (Z_2^2 + Z_2)}{mv^2} (1/I_s - 1/2mv^2).$$

Utilizing the relation $e^2/a_0 = mv_0^2$ and defining Z_{eff} through the equation $I_s = \frac{1}{2} m v_0^2 Z_{eff}^2$, we get the following equation for the electron loss cross-section per bound electron.

$$\sigma_l = 2\pi a_0^2 (Z_2^2 + Z_2)(v_0/v)^2 (2/Z_{eff}^2 - (v_0/v)^2/2) \tag{4}$$

The quantity Z_{eff} is related to the principal quantum number n and Z^*, the charge seen by the least bound electron in the ion, through the equation $Z_{eff} = Z^*/n$. In turn, Z^* is given by the following expressions as appropriately applicable:

(1) Z, the nuclear charge of the ion, when the *K*-shell has one electron,

(2) Z − 0.3 when *K*-shell is completely filled, and

(3) 0.65 (Z − 1) + 0.35 Z_1 when *K*-shell is filled completely but *L*-shell only partially.

In the above, cases (1) and (2) imply $Z_1 > Z - 2$ and case (3) implies $Z_1 \leqslant Z - 2$. In special situations, for example when an electron is bound in a higher orbital leaving the *K*-shell empty owing to small velocity of the incident ion, appropriate value of Z^* may be obtained by considering the ionic charge and Slater's screening constants.

In Figure 1 cross sections for electron capture and loss by a carbon ion in aqueous media are given. Curve A represents the case of the loss of a single electron bound in the *K*-shell of the carbon ion for which $Z_{\text{eff}} = Z = 6$. This cross section has a maximum of 0.56 A^2 at $v/v_0 = Z/\sqrt{2} = 4.24$ and it falls to zero at $v/v_0 = Z/2 = 3$; both of these conclusions may be seen by examining Equation 4. For $v < Zv_0/2$, loss of the single electron bounded in the *K*-shell of the ion is energetically impossible; however, if a second electron is captured, then one of these electrons may be lost with a cross section which is again given by Equation 4 with the new appropriate value of Z_{eff}. Curve B shows the case of electron capture by a bare carbon ion into its *K*-shell. This curve is computed from Equation 3 which is strictly valid for very high incident velocities. Actually the relevant cross section must be zero at $v/v_0 = Z = 6$ since for smaller velocities capture in the *K*-shell is energetically impossible; hence we place a vertical cut-off on Curve B at the appropriate place, *viz.* at $v/v_0 = Z$. For $v < ZV_0$, electron capture is permissible by a bare nucleus in the *L*-shell; this cross section is given by Equation 3 with $n = 2$ and shown by Curve C which has the same shape as that of B with a cut-off at $v/v_0 = Z/2 = 3$.

Other special cases (such as capture and loss of electrons by ions which have already one or more electrons permanently bound to them) may be treated by consideration of Equations 3 and 4 with appropriate values of Z_1 and Z_{eff}. However, these have not been shown in Figure 1.

Both electron capture and loss represent special cases of energy loss of the incident particle. In the case of electron capture, an electron must be ionized from the water molecule and it must be given a minimum speed v. The energy to effect this process must come from the particle. The energy requirement is somewhat reduced because of the binding of the electron in the ion. Hence, the energy loss in the electron capture process is given approximately by

$$E_C = I_p + \tfrac{1}{2}m(v^2 - Z_{\text{eff}}^2 v_0^2) \qquad (5)$$

where I_p is the mean ionization potential for an electron in the water molecule and Z_{eff} must be calculated considering the ionic charge Z_1 after the capture has taken place. Ignoring the small contribution owing to K-ionization and using a logarithmic average, we obtain $I_p = 17$ e.v. Usually in Equation 5 other terms are small compared with $\frac{1}{2}mv^2$. In electron loss the ejected electron has a speed of approximately v in the laboratory frame and hence the energy loss in this process is simply given by

$$E_L = I_s + \tfrac{1}{2}mv^2 = \tfrac{1}{2}m(v^2 + Z_{eff}{}^2 v_0{}^2). \quad (6)$$

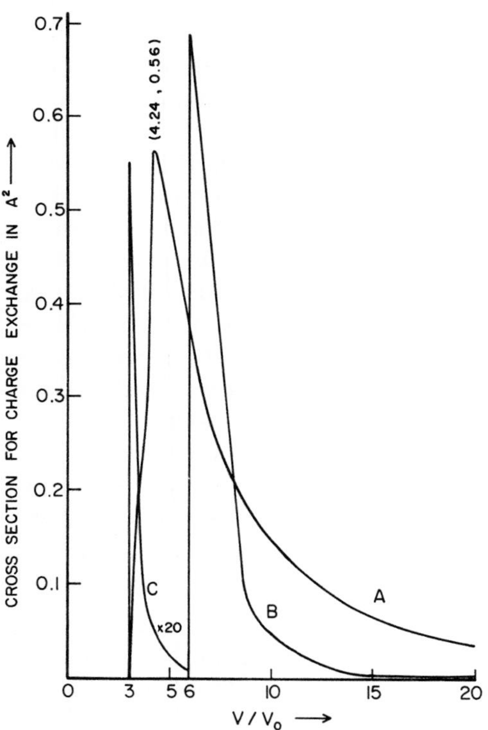

Figure 1. Graphs of cross sections of electron capture (B and C) and loss (A) by carbon ions in water as a function of velocity. For capture, a bare nucleus is considered whereas for loss the ion considered has one electron bound to it in the K-shell before the occurrence of the process. Bohr's formulas are used with some modifications (see *text*). *Notice that when the velocity is less than the K-orbital velocity, capture may only take place at higher orbitals*

Range-Energy Relation: Extension of Range Owing to Charge Exchange

For the purpose of the present work, range is defined as the distance the particle travels before its energy is reduced to 0.25 Mev./n. We use a Monte Carlo procedure in conjunction with Bethe's stopping power to calculate the range. This is described as follows.

On entering the medium, the first charge exchange process experienced by a bare nucleus is an electron capture. The distance that the particle moves before this happens is given in a Monte Carlo scheme by

$$l_1 = (1/N\sigma_c)\ln(1/X_1) \tag{7}$$

where N = number of molecules in the medium per unit volume, σ_c is an appropriate capture cross section and X_1 is a uniformly distributed random number between 0 and 1. After this, the next charge exchange process is either the loss of the captured electron or a further capture with cross section denoted by σ_1 and $\sigma_{c'}$ respectively. Accordingly, another random number X_2 is selected and the decision is for an electron loss if $X_2 \leqslant \sigma_1/(\sigma_{c'} + \sigma_1)$; otherwise, it is for a further capture. In either case the distance travelled by the incident particle in the meantime is given by the same basic Formula 7 with σ_1 or $\sigma_{c'}$ replacing σ_c as the case may be and X_1 standing for a new random number. The energy loss of the incident particle is given by the sum of energy losses owing to (1) charge exchange which is given by Equation 5 or 6 as applicable and (2) ordinary stopping by creation of excitation and ionizations in the medium which is given by Bethe's formula:

$$-dE/dx = (4\pi Z_1^2 e^4/mv^2)NZ_2\ln(2mv^2/I), \tag{8}$$

where I is the "mean excitation potential" having the value of 65 e.v. for water.

In using Equation 8 above, one takes a value of Z_1 that is appropriate between successive charge changing collisions and one integrates the stopping power along the free length for charge exchange if velocity varies significantly over it. In the very last charge changing free path an adjustment of path length is necessary to bring the energy down to the desired value. The sum of the free paths now is the range in a given trial.

Machine calculations have been made in which the computer does the bookkeeping with regard to range, energy losses caused by electron capture and loss, total energy loss, etc. in a large number of trials and then finally averages these quantities and finds their r.m.s. dispersion. The entire set of calculations have been done for incident bare nuclei of C through Ne and for each particle with incident energies starting from 10 Mev./n down to 1 Mev./n in steps of 1 Mev./n. Results of range calculations are shown in Figure 2 as a function of initial energy and

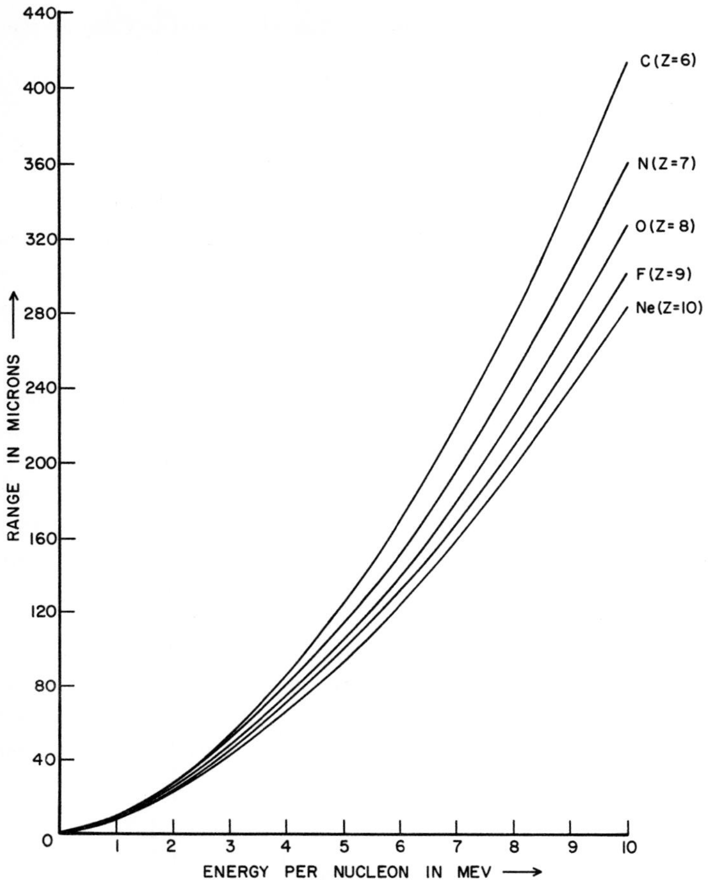

Figure 2. Range-energy plot of heavy positively charged ions in water according to the Monte Carlo method. All ions enter the medium as bare nuclei. At high velocities a square law is expected whereas at low velocities range is quite well described by a combination of a linear and a quadratic term

particle quality. A comparison with Northcliffe's (*13*) computed ranges for the same particles in Al shows qualitative similarity. Within the scope of initial energies studied in the present case, range-energy relation can be accurately described by a fifth-order polynomial as given below

$$R = \sum_{i=1}^{5} a_i E^i. \tag{9}$$

The values of the coefficients a_i for various particle qualities are shown in Table I; in this it is understood that R is expressed in microns and E in Mev./n.

Table I. Coefficients in the Range-Energy Relation in Water Expressed as a Fifth-Order Polynomial

Particle	a_1	a_2	$a_3 \times 10$	$a_4 \times 10^2$	$a_5 \times 10^5$
C	5.341	4.635	−1.770	.738	−1.297
N	4.675	4.844	−3.216	1.539	−1.956
O	4.091	4.693	−3.396	1.574	−1.353
F	2.853	4.871	−3.743	1.569	2.511
Ne	3.803	3.914	−2.365	.895	− .165

A hypothetical heavy particle of mass M and charge Z penetrating a medium without any charge exchange has a range given to a good approximation by

$$R_0 = R_p(v)M/Z^2 \tag{10}$$

where nuclear elastic collisions have been neglected and $R_p(v)$ denotes the range of a proton in the same medium having a starting velocity v equal to that of the heavy particle. From Equations 9 and 10 we may now define the extension of range caused by progressive lowering of charge as the heavy particle penetrates the medium as follows:

$$R_{\text{ext}} = R - R_0$$

As expected, for a given particle, the fractional range extension is more at smaller incident velocities and for a given velocity it is more for a particle of higher Z. It is customary (*10*) to display range extension as a

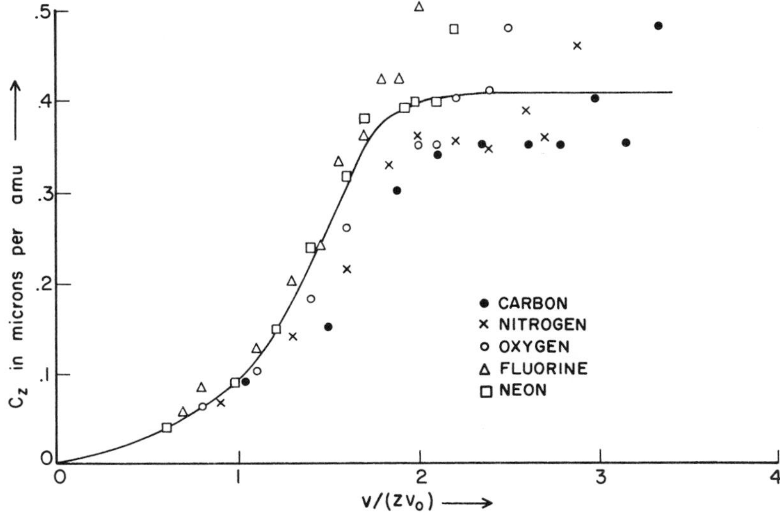

Figure 3. Plot of C_z = *Rext.* $Z^{2/3}/M$ *as a function of* $v/(Zv_0)$. *The approximate universal curve is indicated by the full line*

plot of $C_Z = R_{ext}Z^{2/3}/M$ against v/Zv_0; this is shown in Figure 3. To evaluate R_0, we have used the proton ranges in water given by Barkas and Berger (*1*) with appropriate correction for the residual range at 0.25 Mev./n. If the Fermi-Thomas model happens to be a good approximation in a given case, one expects a universal curve (*1*). Experimental verification of this expectation is available for emulsions (*8*). In our case we get a universal curve for $v/v_0 < 2Z$; above this velocity there is considerable scatter. However, it is possible to indicate a mean curve which is shown by the full line. Of course we do not expect the consequences of Fermi-Thomas model to hold to great accuracy in the case of an aqueous medium.

Figure 4 shows, as a function of particle quality and initial energy, a plot of the percentage of total energy that is spent in charge exchange processes. In this, entire slowing down of the particle has been con-

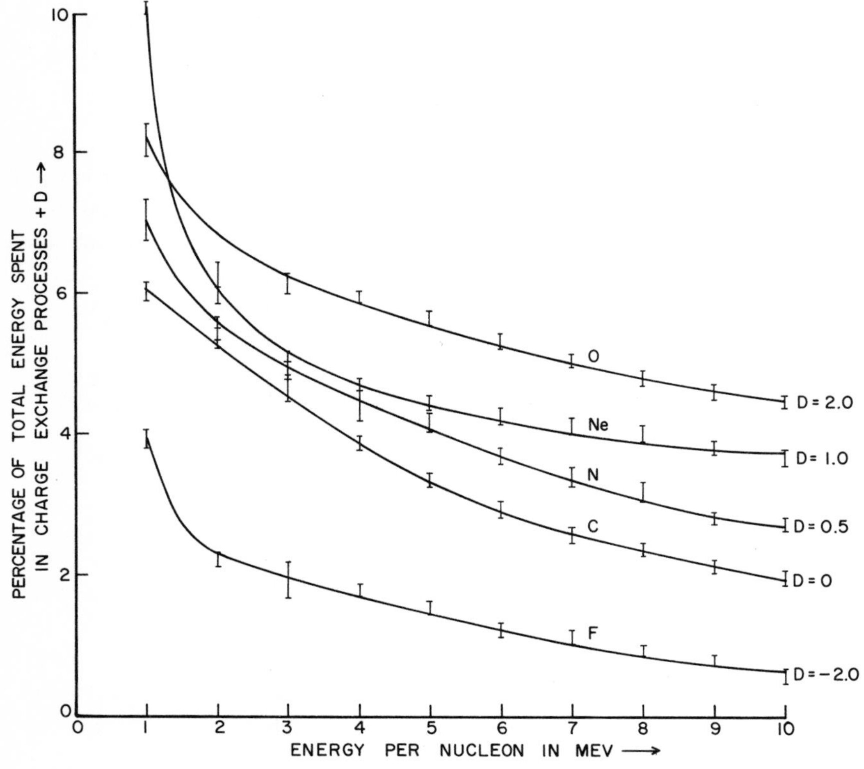

Figure 4. Graph of percentage contribution of charge exchange processes to energy loss as a function of particle energy and quality according to the Monte Carlo method. To avoid overlap of curves, the quantity plotted is the percentage + D, *where* D *has values for particles as specified*

sidered. This percentage, as expected, behaves in the same fashion as range extension, that is it is more for a particle of higher charge and lower velocity.

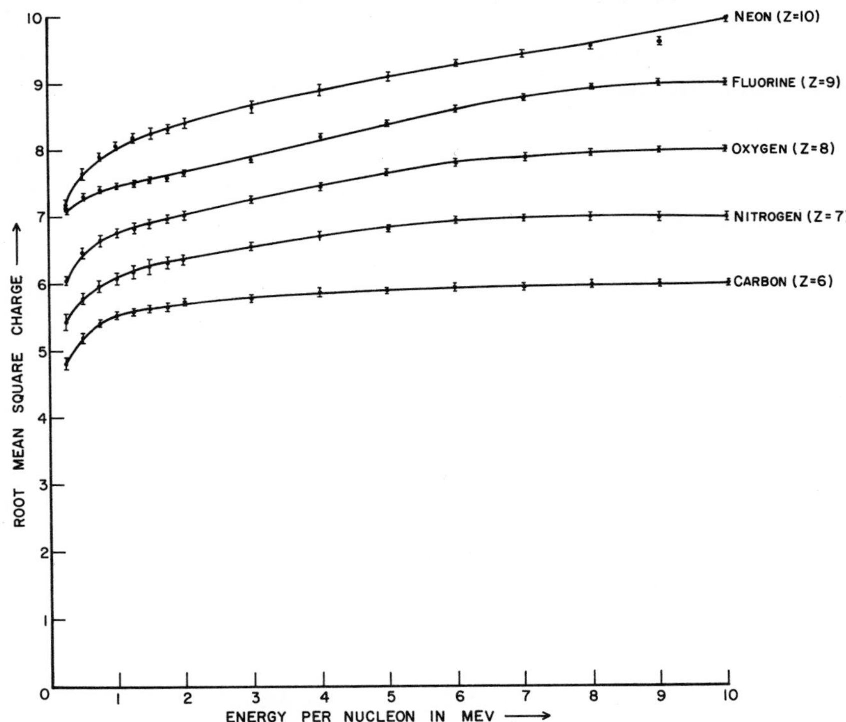

Figure 5. Root mean square charge of positive ions in water as a function of their energy per nucleon according to the Monte Carlo method. Ion charge approaches bare nucleus value at high energies. Generally speaking substantial changes start to occur at around K-orbital velocities

Variation of Effective Charge with Energy

Because of the statistical nature of electron capture and loss phenomena, positive ions having the same velocity in a medium do not exactly have the same charge but they exhibit a distribution in charge states. The most important moment of this distribution in stopping power theory is the mean square charge $<Z^2>$. At a given velocity v this can be related to the slope of the range-energy curve as follows.

$$<Z^2>_v = mv^2/4\pi e^4 N Z_2 \ln(2mv^2/I)\,(dR/dE)_v, \qquad (11)$$

where $(dR/dE)_v$ is given from Equation 9 by $\Sigma i a_i E^{i-1}$. Figure 5 shows a plot of $<Z^2>_v^{1/2}$ as a function of particle quality and energy. If the particle energy is high, the bare nucleus contributes more to the charge distribution whereas for much lower particle energy, states with one or two captured electrons contribute more to the charge distribution. An alternative procedure to arrive at the charge state statistics is to work in a Monte Carlo scheme and classify the charge states of particles acquiring a given velocity in a large number of sample runs. Spot checks done with a few particles at selected energies show agreement between this and the method used here.

Track Model: Energy Partition Between Core and the Emergent Secondary Electrons

It is well known that heavy particles, having non-relativistic velocities, lose approximately equal amounts of energy in glancing and knock-on collisions. Glancing collisions involve small energy transfer and result in the formation of spurs. Knock-on collisions, on the other hand, generate energetic secondary electrons. A secondary electron of energy ϵ is ejected at angle θ to the track axis given by $\cos^{-1}(\epsilon/\epsilon_{max})^{1/2}$ where $\epsilon_{max} = 2\,mv^2$ is the maximum energy that the ejected electron may have. Secondary electrons with energies in the interval 100–5000 e.v. are stopped within a short distance, generating what are called blobs and short tracks (*11, 12*).

Heavy particles usually have such high stopping power that the spurs on the track overlap very densely creating an approximately cylindrical column which we call the "core." For high speed incident particles the radius of the "core" is given by the maximum impact parameter that can excite an electronic state. Based on the impulse principle introduced by Bohr, this is given by $hv/2E_1$ where h = Planck's constant/2π and E_1 is the lowest electronic transition energy. Taking $E_1 = 5$ e.v., the core radius turns out to be $\sim$30 A. when the energy of the incident particle is 10 Mev./n. For much lower incident energies the core radius, given by the above formula, is not meaningful because the ionized electrons generated by glancing collisions penetrate farther than the calculated radius. In water, it is usual to recognize the demarcation between glancing and knock-on collisions at an energy transfer of $\sim$ 100 e.v. The estimated range of a 100 e.v. electron in water is $\sim$ 15 A. (*11, 12*). The particle velocity for which the calculated core radius is equal to 15 A. is $u = 2.28 \times 10^9$ cm./sec. For our purpose we take the core radius Y as $hv/2E_1$ for $v \geqslant u$ and as 15 A. for $v \leqslant u$. The resultant picture of the core is shown in Figure 6a.

The stopping-power of heavy particles in the range of energies 1–10 Mev./n is quite high. For example, if the incident particle is C^{6+}, a typical value is $\sim$ 20 e.v./A. The emergent secondary electrons have stopping-power which are about an order of magnitude less. Therefore, the model of heavy particle tracks presented here may be described as a core of high-LET surrounded by a region traversed by comparatively low-LET secondary electrons. These electrons emerge at various angles to the track (depending upon their energies). However, their directions in the plane perpendicular to the track axis are random.

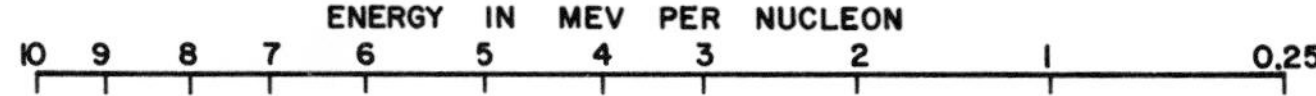

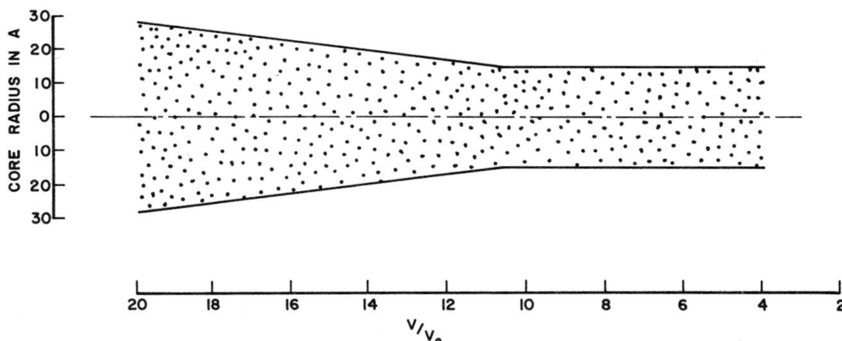

Figure 6(a). Diagram of core as a function of velocity. The critical velocity separating the conical and cylindrical regions is 2.28 × 10^9 cm./sec. At this velocity the core radius computed from Bohr's criterion for maximum impact parameter is equal to our estimated range of 100 e.v. electrons in water

If the incident particle is a fission fragment, the outcoming secondary electrons overlap with each other so densely that they lose their independent identity and merge into a cylindrical sheath. For other incident particles the emergent secondary electrons do not overlap significantly. Figures 6b, c, and d show schematically the emergent secondary electron geometry over small sections of track for the proton, O^{8+}, and fission fragment respectively.

After an approximate separation of the track into its high and low LET regions, we want to know about the energy partition between these two regions. The energy loss in the electron capture process is confined to the core by virtue of the fact that a capture may only occur in a close collision. In the electron loss process the lost electron is likely to be ejected with a small angle in the center of mass reference frame which happens to be the laboratory frame since collisions between the electron in the ion and the nuclei of the medium contribute most significantly to

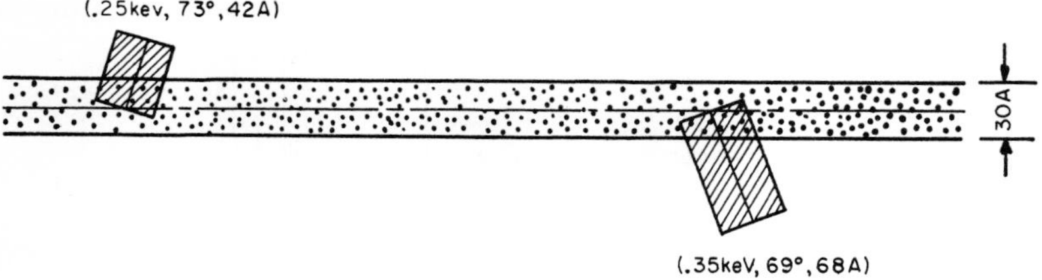

Figure 6(b). Section of a typical track due to protons in water having energy ~ 1 − 2 Mev./n. The secondary electrons have roughly the same LET as in the core; they are spaced by ~ 300 A. on the track axis. Figures in parentheses denote respectively energy of ejected electron (ϵ), its direction of ejection (θ) with respect to track axis and its range in water. The angle θ is given by $\cos^{-1} (\epsilon/\epsilon_{max})^{1/2}$ where ϵ_{max} is the maximum energy that the ejected electron may have

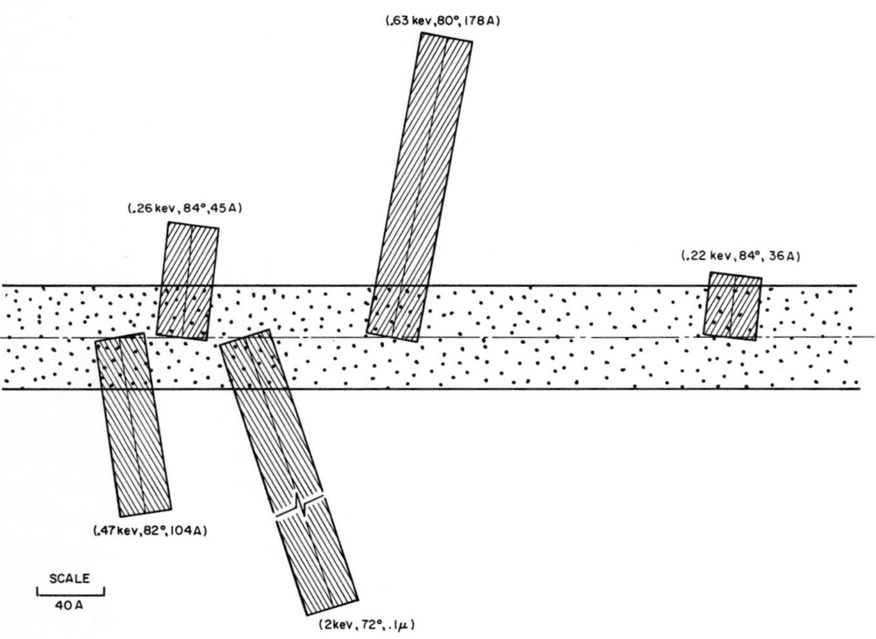

Figure 6(c). Schematic view of a track of an O^{8+} ion in water projected in a plane through the track axis. Secondary electron tracks are shown shaded in the diagram. Figures in parenthesis denote respectively energy of ejected electron (ϵ), its direction of ejection (θ) with respect to track axis and its range in water. The angle θ is given by $\cos^{-1} (\epsilon/\epsilon_{max})^{1/2}$ where ϵ_{max} is the maximum energy that the ejected electron may have

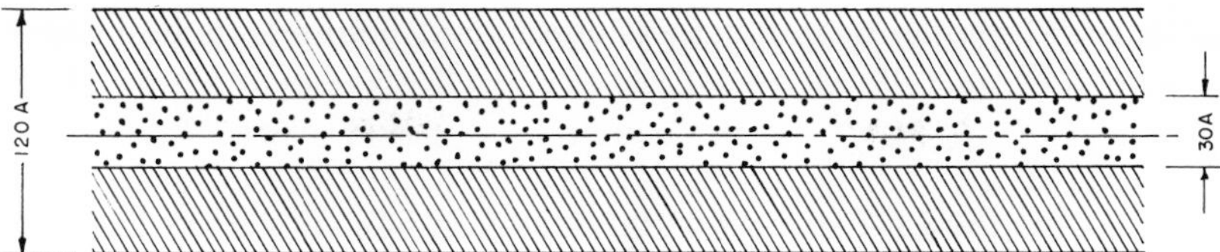

Figure 6(d). Typical fission fragment track in water. Secondary electrons densely overlap to form the "sheath." Their LET is about two orders of magnitude smaller than that of the core

this process. Hence, the energy loss in the electron loss process is also confined to the core.

The remaining factor to be determined is the energy deposition by the secondary electrons into the core as they penetrate through it. Consider a section of the track over which the incident particle loses an amount of energy dE. For the discussion of energy loss of secondary electrons such a section may be taken as cylindrical. Using the Rutherford cross section, the number of secondary electrons created with energies between ϵ and $\epsilon + d\epsilon$ is given by $(F/\epsilon^2)d\epsilon$ where F is a certain constant. The total energy carried by all the secondary electrons is then $F \ln 2mv^2/\epsilon_o$ where ϵ_o is the minimum energy of the secondary electrons taken here as 100 e.v. By the equipartition principle between glancing and knock-on processes, the same amount of energy loss must equal $dE/2$. Hence, $F = dE/2 \ln 2mv^2/\epsilon_o$. Now the secondary electrons which are stopped in the core have energies much smaller than ϵ_{max} so that they are ejected almost normally to the track. Therefore, their contribution to energy deposited in the core over the differential track length may be written as

$$d\xi = (1/2)dE\ln\{\rho(Y)/\epsilon_o\}/(\ln 4E/\mu\epsilon_o) \tag{12}$$

where $\rho(Y)$ is the energy of a secondary electron having a range equal to the local core radius Y and μ is the ratio of proton to electron mass. The energy deposited over the entire track by secondary electrons which are stopped within the core is now given from Equation 12 as

$$\xi = (1/2)\int_{E_u}^{E_i} dE\ln\{\rho(Y)/\epsilon_o\}/(\ln 4E/\mu\epsilon_o) \tag{13}$$

where E_i is the starting energy per nucleon of the incident particle and E_u (2.715 Mev./n) corresponds to the particle energy at velocity u. Obviously $\xi = 0$ for $E_i \leqslant E_u$.

An energetic secondary electron is ejected at angle θ to the track axis. Its path length within the core is Y cosec θ. Therefore, the energy deposited by the secondary electrons that are incompletely stopped over the same differential track length as considered before is given by

$$d\eta = (1/2)\ \{dE\, Y/(\ln 4E/\mu\epsilon_o)\} \int_{\rho(Y)}^{4E/\mu} S(\epsilon)\ \mathrm{cosec}\ \theta\ d\epsilon/\epsilon^2$$

where $S(\epsilon)$ is the LET of a secondary electron having a starting energy ϵ, averaged over an initial path length confined within the core. Integrating the above expression we get

$$\eta = (1/2) \int_{E_f}^{E_i} dE\{Y/(\ln 4E/\mu\epsilon_o)\} \int_{\rho(Y)}^{4E/\mu} S(\epsilon)\ \mathrm{cosec}\ \theta\ d\epsilon/\epsilon^2 \qquad (14)$$

where E_f is the final energy at which the incident particle is assumed to be stopped. We have used E_f = 0.25 Mev./n. In numerical evaluation of ρ and S, we use the range-energy relation for electrons in water given in References 11 and 12. The quantity $S(\epsilon)$ has a mild dependence on Y which has been neglected in the present work. For ϵ between 100 and 500 e.v., $S(\epsilon)$ is taken to be ϵ divided by the electron range in water at energy ϵ. It is tabulated as a function of ϵ at intervals of 50 e.v. in Table II. For $\epsilon > 500$ e.v., one can write a range-energy relation for electrons in water as $R(\epsilon) = \lambda\epsilon^n$ so that $S(\epsilon) = 1/(dR/d\epsilon) = 1/(n\lambda\epsilon^{n-1})$. Following Mozumder and Magee (*11, 12*), we use $n = 1.75$ for 500 e.v. $\leqslant \epsilon \leqslant 5$ Kev. and $n = 2$ for $\epsilon > 5$ Kev. The constant λ has been obtained from the range-energy relation of low energy electrons given in References 11 and 12.

Table II. Average Stopping Power of Low Energy Electrons

Electron Energy ϵ (e.v.)	*Average Stopping Power, $S(\epsilon)$ (e.v./A)*
100	6.667
150	6.818
200	6.250
250	5.952
300	5.576
350	5.170
400	4.878
450	4.615
500	4.386

Energy partition between the core and the emergent secondary electrons may now be given by considering Figure 4, Equations 13 and 14 and using a basic equipartition between glancing and knock-on collisions. The results are summarized in Figure 7 which demonstrates a more or less universal curve. The slight difference between the various particles at the same energy is caused by charge exchange. At high incident energies there is an expansion of the core because of Bohr's impulse principle which gives the core radius as proportional to the incident velocity. Hence, more energy is deposited in the core at high incident energies. At low incident energies, on the other hand, the secondary electrons produced are also lower in energy and cannot penetrate the core effectively. Therefore, the percentage energy deposited in the core increases again at low incident energies. We expect then, that the percentage energy deposited in the core will show a minimum at an intermediate energy. Our computations reveal a minimum of about 68.5% at around 2.5 Mev./n incident energy.

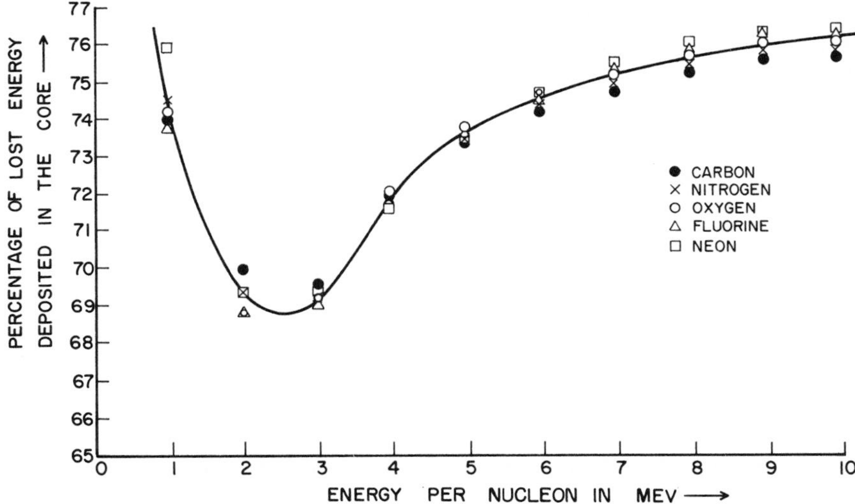

Figure 7. Partition of energy loss between the core and emergent secondary electrons plotted as a function of incident energy. At a given incident energy variation with respect to particle quality is small

Cases of Protons, α-Particles, and Fission Fragments

In some cases of radiolysis using protons and α-particles, typical incident energies lie in the interval 1 to 2 Mev./n. The core of the track is then well represented by a cylindrical column (*see* Figure 6b); expansion of the core caused by high incident speed is not a relevant consideration here. Maximum energy of the ejected secondary electrons lie in the interval 2 to 4 Kev. and the average energy is around 350 e.v. Hence, in these cases, the secondary electrons and the incident particle have about the same stopping-power. The secondary electrons are separated on the track axis by several hundred A. and there is practically no interaction between them. The ion charge is small and effects of charge changing on energy loss and range becomes significant only when the energy drops below $\sim$ 100 Kev./n; therefore, in most cases they are negligible. For protons, deuterons, and α-particles of higher energy per nucleon, one must consider core enlargement owing to high velocity. In this case the stopping-power is lower but the ejected secondary electrons have higher energy and penetrate further. Hence, the secondary electron tracks are even more widely separated. A simple track model thus emerges for heavy particles of low charge.

Treatment of the stopping of fission fragments in a condensed medium and the description of resultant tracks along the lines of the present discussion are available in the literature only in fragmentary form. High values of charge, stopping power and cross section for electron capture, and loss complicate a detailed description for any particular ion. Moreover, in radiation chemistry, there are two other uncertainties regarding fission fragments. One arises from the statistical nature of the fission process. Fission fragment radiation is not at all homogeneous but consists of ions of widely differing charge and mass states. The other uncertainty relates to thermal effects. For all other radiations, thermal effects may be largely discounted. In the case of fission fragments the situation is not clear, but thermal effects are probably important. Here we shall discuss fission fragment tracks only qualitatively, deferring a somewhat detailed analysis for later report.

Massive fragments born out of ^{235}U fission have (1) masses $\sim$ 140 and 95 times the proton mass, (2) typical velocities $\approx 4\ v_0$ to $6\ v_0$, and (3) typical initial charges $\approx 15e$ to $20e$. Such ions, on entering an aqueous medium have starting LET around 600 e.v./A. This, however, falls quickly as a result of progressive electron capture. The velocities of these particles are low enough and their charges are high enough so that in the beginning electron loss is energetically forbidden. After a reasonable amount of electron capture and resultant slowing down, however, charge equilibrium may be established through electron capture and loss of comparable cross sections (*3*). Using Bohr's formula (*3*) for electron capture by fission fragments, *viz.* $\sigma_c = 4\pi a_0{}^2 Z_1{}^{1/3} Z_2{}^5 (v_0/v)^6$ and taking appropriate values of the physical parameters, we calculate that in the beginning $\sigma_c \sim 10^3$ A.^{2} which means that in water the mean free path for electron capture is only 0.03 A. However, very little energy is lost in these captures since the energy spent in ionization of water molecule and in imparting the ionized electron sufficient speed is almost entirely recovered by binding the electron to the fission fragment. Therefore, we derive qualitatively the same conclusion as in the cases of heavy particles of lower charge, *viz.* that charge pick up contributes little to energy loss but extends range significantly.

Geometry of secondary electrons, on the other hand, shows a dramatic change because of excessive overlap. With approximately 300 e.v./A. going into secondary electrons having an average energy $\approx$ 300 e.v., the mean distance between secondary electron tracks turns out to be $\sim$ 1 A. Even with a 2π angular distribution, the overlap is sufficiently great to obliterate the individuality of the secondary electron tracks. The result is that the track model caused by a fission fragment is more realistically described by a cylindrical core of very high ionization density surrounded by a sheath of lower ionization density (*see* Figure 6d). This particular feature does not seem to have appeared in the literature before.

Discussion

In this paper an attempt has been made to describe models of tracks of heavy charged particles in water starting from elementary physical considerations. Three slightly different models have been proposed for (1) α-particles and protons, (2) bare nucleii of relatively small A and Z, and (3) fission fragments (*see* Figures 6b, c, and d). These differ among themselves in details of core geometry and disposition of secondary electrons. Rigor and completeness have not been sought in this work; it would be difficult to do so since charge exchange cross sections are not known accurately. Nevertheless, it is hoped that the proposed models will find applications in radiolysis with heavy charged particles; in particular they should prove to be more useful that the current simple cylindrical model in the discussion of variation of yields with particle quality and dose-rate.

The relationships of the present models to results of radiation chemistry will not be discussed in this paper. However, it may be pointed out that the rise of the Fe^{3+} yield in the Fricke dosimeter for C^{6+} radiations of energies 6.7 and 4.5 Mev./n (LET of 20 and 25 e.v./A.) over the yield owing to B^{10} (n, α) $L_i{}^7$ radiations of comparable LET finds a natural explanation because of the effect of secondary electrons (*17, 18*). Two heavy particles having the same ratio of Z/v also have approximately the same stopping power. But the heavier of them has higher Z and therefore higher v as well. As a result the heavier particle (C^{6+}) ejects more energetic secondary electrons which penetrate the core more effectively. The net yield is therefore a combination of yields because of the core and the emergent secondary electrons. Since the LET is high, the core yield may be approximated to 3.6 which is expected for radiations of infinite LET (*16*). The yield caused by secondary electrons are not known accurately and hence a quantitative calculation for the total yield is not feasible at present. However, we know that this yield is greater than 3.6 and that it increases with increasing electron energy. Considering $B^{10}(n, \alpha)$ $L_i{}^7$ radiations, we estimate that the ionizing particles have a starting energy of $\sim$ 0.3 Mev./n. The average energy of the secondary electrons is $\sim$ 200 e.v. With this we calculate that the energy partition between the core and the emergent electrons is roughly as 80:20. So we expect that $G(Fe^{3+})$ in this case will only be slightly greater than 3.6. The observed value is 4.2. The small excess is seen to be caused by the minor contribution of the emergent secondary electrons. On the other hand if we take C^{6+} ions at energies of 8.5, 6.7 and 4.5 Mev./n we find that in our model the average energy of the emergent secondary electrons are about 1200, 1000, and 800 e.v. respectively. The estimated stopping-power of these electrons are 3.5, 3.7, and 4.4 e.v./A. respectively. Using the relationship between G and stopping-power as given by Schuler and Allen (*16*) and ignoring the difference between light and heavy particles (which is strictly not permissible in our model) we get the $G(Fe^{3+})$ yields caused by these electrons as 8.3, 8.1, and 7.7 respectively. We use these values and a value of 3.6 for the core. We also use the energy partition ratio between the core and emergent secondary electrons obtained from Figure 7. It is roughly 75:25 for 8.5 and 6.7 Mev./n and 73:27 for 4.5 Mev./n. Combining these data we obtain the overall yield $G(Fe^{3+})$ at these energies as 4.8, 4.7, and 4.6 respectively. These should be compared with the experimental values of 4.9, 4.6, and 4.1 respectively (*17, 18*). The calculations presented here are rough especially in view of the use of yields for electrons which are taken as the same as that caused by deuterons at equal stopping-power. Nevertheless, the qualitative agreement is significant. Similar difference regarding heavy particles was known before between protons and helium ions (*16*).

It may be argued that a number of physical factors are independent of the mass of the incident particle. They are (1) core radius, (2) stopping power, (3) energy loss in charge exchange processes, and (4) energy partition between the core and the emergent secondary electrons. Of these (3) is a small effect and (1) is exactly and (4) is approximately independent of charge also. Core radius is proportional to velocity for high velocities; at low velocities it is rather well given by the range of 100 e.v. electrons. Frequently protons, α-particles, etc. used in radiolysis lie in the low velocity region; hence, the core of their tracks may be taken as cylindrical.

In computing the energy deposited in the core by the emergent secondary electrons, we used their stopping power $S(\epsilon)$ averaged over an initial path-length in the core appropriate to the specific part of the track. This simplifies the computation a great deal and hopefully has not introduced serious errors. Actually for low energy electrons (100–500 e.v.), which should be affected most by this approximation shows only a mild variation of $S(\epsilon)$ with ϵ (*see* Table II). Hence, we feel that the approximation used is not of a drastic nature.

The present paper lays emphasis on energy deposition in two qualitatively different regions, namely the core and the sheath. At first sight this seems unnecessary; all that one needs is the distribution of energy loss in the vertical direction. However, this is not easily given even though there are reasons to believe that the distribution is probably a monotonically decreasing function of distance. High energy losses producing energetic δ-electrons obey the law of inverse impact parameter. However, these losses are strictly not restricted in time scales $\gtrsim 10^{-15}$ secs. On the other hand small energy losses like those produced in a glancing encounter do not have a well-defined law of vertical distribution. In the opinion of the authors the separation of core and sheath is an essential feature of heavy particle tracks.

Further developments using track models presented here will be reported later. We propose to include: (1) diffusion kinetic studies based on present track models, (2) discussion of thermalization lengths of electrons generated in these tracks, and (3) detailed description of fission fragment tracks.

Acknowledgment

This paper is dedicated to Dr. Hugo Fricke on the occasion of his seventy-sixth birthday.

Literature Cited

(1) Barkas, W. H., Berger, M. J., *Natl. Acad. Sci.-Natl. Res. Council, Publ.* **1133,** contribution **No. 7,** p. 103 (1964).
(2) Barr, N. F., Schuler, R. H., *J. Phys. Chem.* **63,** 808 (1959).
(3) Bohr, N., *Kgl. Danske Videnskab, Selskab. Mat.-Fys. Medd.* **18** (8) (1948).
(4) Boyle, J. W., Hochanadel, C. J., Sworski, T. J., Ghormley, J. A., Kiefer, W. F., *Proc. 1st Int. Conf. Peaceful Uses of At. Energy, Geneva,* **7,** 576 (1955).
(5) Burton, M., Kurien, K. C., *J. Phys. Chem.* **63,** 899 (1959).
(6) Ganguly, A. K., Magee, J. L., *J. Chem. Phys.* **25,** 129 (1956).
(7) Hart, E. J., Ramler, W. J., Rocklin, S. R., *Radiation Res.* **4,** 378 (1956).
(8) Heckman, H. H., Perkins, B. L., Simon, W. C., Smith, F. M., Barkas, W. H., *Phys. Rev.* **117,** 544 (1960).
(9) Lefort, M., *J. Chim. Phys.* **51,** 351 (1954).
(10) Lou, A., Sandes, L. R., Prowse, D. J., *Nuovo Cimento* **45,** 214 (1966).
(11) Mozumder, A., Magee, J. L., *Radiation Res.* **20,** 203 (1966).
(12) Mozumder, A., Magee, J. L., *J. Chem. Phys.* **45,** 3332 (1966).
(13) Northcliffe, L. C., *Ann. Rev. Nucl. Science* **13,** 67 (1963).
(14) Samuel, A. H., Magee, J. L., *J. Chem. Phys.* **21,** 1080 (1953).
(15) Schuler, R. H., Allen, A. O., *J. Am. Chem. Soc.* **77,** 507 (1955).
(16) *Ibid.,* **79,** 1565 (1957).
(17) Schuler, R. H., *J. Phys. Chem.* **71,** 3712 (1967).
(18) Schuler, R. H., *Mellon Inst. R.R.L. Report* **No. 207** (1967).

(19) Schwarz, H. A., Caffrey, J. M., Scholes, G., *J. Am. Chem. Soc.* **81**, 1801 (1959).

(20) Voltz, R., DaSilva, J. L., Laustriat, G., Coche, A., *J. Chem. Phys.* **45**, 3306 (1966).

RECEIVED January 26, 1968. The Radiation Laboratory of the University of Notre Dame is operated under contract with the U. S. Atomic Energy Commission. This is AEC document number COO-38-574.

Previous paper of series: Mozumder, A., Magee, J. L., *J. Chem. Phys.* **47**, 939 (1967).

3

Hydrated Electrons in Chemistry

DAVID C. WALKER

University of British Columbia, Vancouver, Canada

Following the discovery of the hydrated electron in radiation chemistry, the reexamination of some fields of aqueous chemistry gave rise to a new concept of primary reduction processes. This paper surveys aspects of these investigations in which it appears that e^-_{aq}*, as opposed to its conjugate acid (H atom), is invariably the precursor to* H_2 *when water is reduced. Evidence is reviewed for the production of* e^-_{aq} *(a) photochemically, (b) by chemical reduction of water, (c) electrolytically, (d) by photo-induced electron emission from metals, (e) from stable solvated electrons, and (f) from H atoms. The basis of standard electrode potentials and various aspects of hydrated electron chemistry are discussed briefly.*

A review, correlation, and discussion of hydrated electron chemistry is justified in its inclusion in a radiation chemistry conference because of the impact upon aqueous chemistry that has resulted directly from the discovery of hydrated electrons.

It would be superfluous to review here the story of e^-_{aq} in the radiation chemistry of aqueous solutions. High energy radiations cause ionizations and the free electrons so generated dissipate their excess energy and are eventually trapped in solvation shells. The discovery of hydrated electrons showed that electrons in water were chemical entities (as distinct from possessing purely physical characteristics) in having diffusion properties, size and sphere of influence, associated ion atmosphere, and reaction rate parameters all of which are comparable to normal chemical reagents.

A symposium on solvated electrons (*41*) and a number of recent reviews (*15, 42, 57, 58, 73*) have highlighted the discovery of hydrated electrons (e^-_{aq}), their chemical reactivity and correlations to other solvated electrons. Some of the physical properties of hydrated electrons,

most of which have been reviewed several times previously, are included in Table I.

Table I. Properties of Hydrated Electrons Determined Experimentally

Optical Absorption Band:	
Wavelength of maximum absorption	7200A. (1.72 e.v.) (*55*)
Extinction coefficient at 7200A.	15,800 (*55*); 18,500 M^{-1} sec.$^{-1}$ (*33*)
Width at half-height	~0.9 e.v. (*55*)
Oscillator strength	~0.8 (*55*)
Diffusion Constant	4.7×10^{-5} cm.^{2} sec.$^{-1}$ (*66*)
Equivalent Conductance	177 ohm^{-1} cm.^{2} (*66*)
Effective Collision Radius	~2.5 to 3.0A. (*36*)
Ion Atmosphere Relaxation Time at $\mu = 0.24M$	3×10^{-9} sec. (*21*)
Partial Molal Volume	−5.5 to −1.1 cc. mole^{-1} (*45*)
Standard Free Energy of Solvation	−39.4 kcal. mole^{-1} (*50*)
$G(e^-_{aq})$, γ-Radiation Yield	2.5 moles per 100 e.v.
Lifetime with respect to H_3O^+ at pH 7	230 μsec. (*37*)
Lifetime with respect to H_2O	≥800 μsec. (*44*)

Whereas the detailed nature of electron binding is still unsettled a great deal is known about the chemical reactivity of e^-_{aq} towards a wide range of substrates, principally through use of its intense absorption band in pulse radiolysis studies (*1, 42*). e^-_{aq} must rank as the most intensively and probably the most extensively studied reactive chemical reagent. In an analysis of the kinetic parameters of e^-_{aq} reactions Anbar *et al.* (*2*) concluded that the energy of diffusion alone constitutes the activation energy (except where acid-base or hydrolysis pre-equilibria exist) and that differences in reaction rate constants of several orders of magnitude can be attributed to pre-exponential factors which reflect the probability of finding an electron vacancy on the substrate molecule. Perhaps the latter also reflects the probability of finding the right solvation shell on the reaction product. Thus, one returns to Platzman's paradox which led to his prediction for the existence of e^-_{aq} (*64*), namely, because of the Franck-Condon restriction on electron transfer processes the same solvation shell is appropriate to reactants and products.

If the Franck-Condon restriction applies to reactions producing e^-_{aq}, then, for those processes discussed later which require the solvation energy of e^-_{aq} to be available, either the electron binding of e^-_{aq} must be principally by electronic rather than electron-dipole interaction or the electron is rapidly caught in a pre-existing polarized site in the solvent. In any event, there is not time for electron-induced orientational polarization. The measured mobility and diffusion constant of e^-_{aq} is also consistent with this view because during the relaxation time of the water dipoles e^-_{aq} has diffused a mean distance of $\sim$3A., (though of course its diffusion could possibly involve infrequent but long jumps).

Most of the rate data on e^-_{aq} reactions is concerned with the rate of disappearance of e^-_{aq} and very little on the rate of formation of products. Thus, for Reaction 1

$$e^-_{aq} + e^-_{aq} \rightarrow [(e_2^{2-})_{aq}] \rightarrow H_2 + 2OH^-_{aq} \quad (1)$$

the rate of formation of H_2 has not been measured and consequently the lifetime of the intermediate is unknown. It should be noted that Dorfman and Taub (*30*) have shown unambiguously that the combination of two hydrated electrons gives rise to H_2 as given by Reaction 1 without involving H atoms as intermediates. In some of the work reviewed here, such as the alkali metal and electrolysis experiments, the possible existence of a comparatively long-lived e_2 species should be seriously considered.

H and e^-_{aq} *as Conjugate Acid-Base Pair*

From the known rate constants for Reactions 2 and 3 it is apparent that interconversion of H and e^-_{aq}

$$H + OH^-_{aq} \rightarrow e^-_{aq} + H_2O, \; k_2 = 2 \times 10^7 \, M^{-1} \, \text{sec.}^{-1} \; (59) \quad (2)$$

$$e^-_{aq} + H^+_{aq} \rightarrow H, \qquad k_3 = 2.3 \times 10^{10} \, M^{-1} \, \text{sec.}^{-1} \; (36) \quad (3)$$

cannot occur within $\sim 10^{-7}$ sec. within the range $3 < pH < 14$. Furthermore, interconversion by the reverse processes, Reactions –2 and –3, are clearly unimportant at neutral pH since $k_{-2} \leqslant 16 \; M^{-1}$ sec.$^{-1}$ (*43*) and k_{-3} has been estimated to be $\sim$4 sec.$^{-1}$ (*50*). Combining k_2 and k_{-2} one finds $\Delta G_2° \leqslant -8.3$ kcal. mole^{-1} at 25°C. and hence that $\Delta G_2 \leqslant 3.7$ for an equimolar mixture of H and e^-_{aq} at pH 7. This spontaneous tendency for the H/e^-_{aq} ratio to approach $\geqslant 500$ at natural pH is, however, seldom realized in practice and e^-_{aq} cannot be regarded as a precursor of H-atoms unless the lifetime of e^-_{aq} exceeds 10^{-3} sec. Another way of expressing the above is to say that $pK_a \leqslant 9.6$ for the H-atom. Thus, H and e^-_{aq} constitute a conjugate acid-base pair given by Equilibrium 4.

$$e^-_{aq} \overset{H^+}{\rightleftharpoons} H \quad (4)$$

Schwarz (*67*) has pointed out that, because of the high reactivity of both e^-_{aq} and H in most systems, this equilibrium is seldom, if ever, established.

The species which reacts in a given system is consequently normally the species formed initially. This paper is concerned with a discussion of the species produced in systems formerly regarded as producing "nascent hydrogen" in aqueous solution at pH $\sim$ 7. It is apparent that e^-_{aq} is better understood than its elusive partner the hydrated H-atom. The exact nature of H when it is produced by Reaction 3 remains uncertain because it depends on the structure of H^{+}_{aq} (be it H_3O^+, $H_9O_4^+$, or larger), on whether Reaction 3 is an electron transfer or proton transfer process, and on the lifetime of H_3O or H_9O_4—*i.e.*, whether they have a chemical significance.

Methods of Producing e^{-}_{aq}

Photochemically. One might anticipate free electrons, and then hydrated electrons, to be formed when photoionization occurs in aqueous solutions. In order to photoionize water itself a high photon energy is required. Gutman and Lyons (*40*) have drawn attention to the fact that many simple molecules have substantially lower ionization potentials in the condensed phases compared with the isolated molecules in the vapor. This is not surprising when one considers, for instance, the spreading and overlap of electron orbitals in the enormous "molecules" in liquid water (or crystalline ice). Quoting Dorsey's data (*30*) on water Gutmann and Lyons infer that the ionization potential of liquid water may be only 7 e.v., but despite this Sokolov and Stein (*69*) found no evidence for e^{-}_{aq} when water was illuminated with 1470A. light.

Figure 1 shows an experimental arrangement used by this writer to try to detect spectrophotometrically e^{-}_{aq} produced by the photolysis of pure water by light $<$ 1000A.—*i.e.*, at a photon energy greater than the ionization potential of H_2O molecules. A low pressure He flash photolysis lamp was used in conjunction with a windowless reaction vessel, the fast flow of He onto the surface of the water preventing water vapor absorbing the light. All the radiation below 1000A. should be absorbed by the very thin layer of pure deaerated water at the surface of the liquid at which point the white analyzing light was focussed. The light baffles and reflectors were designed to permit only the analyzing light to reach the photomultiplier after dispersion by the monochromator. Unfortunately any absorption, even at 7000A., was swamped by scattered light from the photolysis flash in these experiments. Perhaps if laser light sources were used as analyzing light this problem could be alleviated.

The photoionization of pure water would be a valuable source of e^{-}_{aq} in that, for those electrons which escape immediate geminate recombination, it would provide a uniformly dispersed distribution over a small volume. For most of the other methods described such a goal is virtually impossible.

An alternative is to photoionize a solute in water at wavelengths where water transmits—*i.e.*, $\lambda >$ 2000A.—or illuminate a substrate at wavelengths within a suitable charge-transfer-to-solvent absorption band.

In recent years this approach has been extensively employed and there is substantial evidence for the production of e^-_{aq}. When steady state ultraviolet light sources were used, hydrated electrons were detected by competitive scavenging techniques (*9, 21, 22, 51, 63, 71*). When flash photolysis techniques were employed, e^-_{aq} was identified by its absorption spectrum and its reactivity followed spectrophotometrically (*28, 38, 60*).

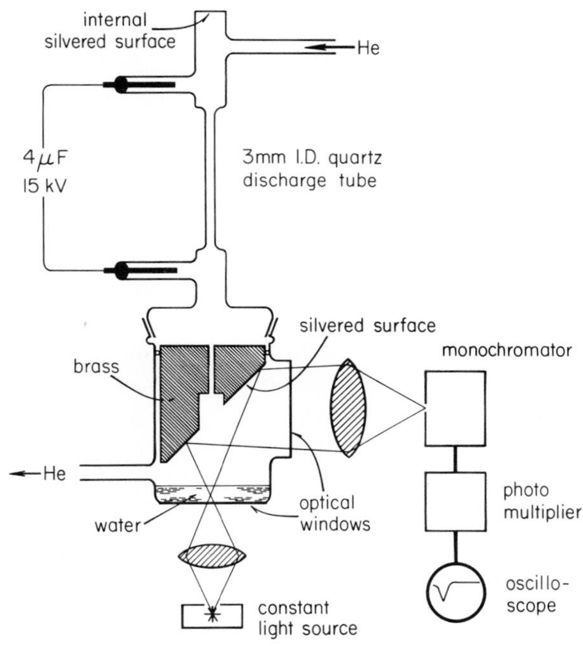

Figure 1. Apparatus for the flash photoionization of pure liquid water

Both reducing ions and molecules, organic and inorganic, have been so studied and the overall reactions may be exemplified by Reactions 5, 6, and 7. There is some disagreement concerning the extent to which the

$$I^-_{aq} + h\nu \rightarrow I_{aq} + e^-_{aq} \quad (5)$$

$$Fe^{2+}_{aq} + h\nu \rightarrow Fe^{3+}_{aq} + e^-_{aq} \quad (6)$$

$$C_6H_5NH_2 + h\nu \rightarrow C_6H_5NH_2^+ + e^-_{aq} \quad (7)$$

electron escapes the influence of the concomitant ion or radical (*21, 72, 78*) as evidenced by the fact that the quantum yield is in general temperature dependent and always much less than unity (*57*). Grossweiner (*39*) recently reviewed the photogeneration of e^-_{aq} from organic compounds in aqueous solution and pointed out the importance of this in biological systems.

It is interesting to compare these results with a proposal by Franck and Scheibe in 1938 (*35*) (who suggested that aquated electrons may be responsible for the common absorption band found in many transition metal ion solutions) and with the theoretical analysis of charge-transfer-to-solvent spectra by Platzman and Franck (*65*). Also, Dainton and James (*23*) found a linear relationship between the energy of the long wavelength limit of the absorption band of many bivalent transition metal ions and the redox potential of the M^{2+}/M^{3+} couple, and in particular that the photon energy (3.55 e.v.) corresponding to a redox potential of zero is the same photon limit noted by Heyrovsky (*46*) for the photo-induced discharge of an illuminated Hg surface held at zero potential (both potentials being based on the Standard Hydrogen Electrode (S.H.E.)).

Finally, it should be noted that Dainton *et al.* (*24*) have obtained, by the matrix isolation technique, a very small quantum efficiency of 0.07 for the photobleaching of electrons trapped in methanol glasses, which they interpet to mean that photoreleased electrons are rapidly retrapped.

Chemical Reduction of Water. METALS. It is well known that metals with high reduction potentials, such as the alkali and most of the alkaline earths, reduce water to H_2. Hughes and Roach (*48*) and Shaede and Walker (*68, 74*) have reported experiments designed to identify the precursors of molecular hydrogen by competitive scavenging techniques. Both studies used sodium metal "diluted" with Hg to enable the scavengers to compete successfully with the bimolecular reaction occurring on the metal surface to form H_2 (a 10 ml. sample of 1% Na amalgam takes several hours to react completely). Hughes and Roach followed the H_2 production when Na–Hg reacted with acidified water containing a variety of additives —*i.e.*, Cu^{2+}, Zn^{2+}, Co^{2+}, $Co(NH_3)_6{}^{3+}$, and $Fe(CN)_6{}^{3-}$, and found the relative decrease in hydrogen production was consistent with the ratio of rate constants for the reaction of these additives with e^-_{aq}, as determined by pulse radiolysis, and not related to their rates of reaction with H-atoms. Shaede and Walker studied the competition between N_2O and methanol (and isopropyl alcohol) for the species produced by Na–Hg in water at pH 1, 7, and 13. They followed the N_2 and H_2 production and from the known relative rate constants for N_2O and CH_3OH with e^-_{aq} and H concluded that hydrated electrons were produced at pH 7 and 13; but that N_2O could not significantly inhibit H_2 formation at pH 1, doubtless because of Reaction 3.

Apparently then Na reacts with water (even in fairly strongly acidic solution) according to Reaction 8

$$Na + nH_2O \rightarrow Na^+_{aq} + e^-_{aq} \quad (8)$$

rather than Reaction 9 as formerly supposed, and that combination of two

$$Na + H_2O \rightarrow Na^+_{aq} + OH^-_{aq} + H \quad (9)$$

e^-_{aq} leads to H_2. These observations are not particularly surprising when one considers the analogous reaction in liquid ammonia, various amines and ethers, and doubtless any polar liquid (even the aprotic solvent hexamethylphosphoramide gives a stable blue solution when it reacts with Na (*34*)). It is pertinent to consider the relative stabilities of solutions of metal ions and solvated electrons in water, alcohol, and ammonia (particularly when one notes that irradiated NH_3 does not produce a permanent blue solution—because e^-_{am} reacts with the concomitant positive ion). Shaede and Walker (*68, 73*) thus suggested that perhaps Equilibrium 10 exists in polar solvents, including water,

$$e^-_s + e^-_s \rightleftharpoons (e_2^{2-})_s \quad (10)$$

and that the rate at which the e_2 species is protonated by the solvent to give H_2 determines the lifetime of solvated electrons in metal solutions and hence the stability of the metal solutions.

It is often mentioned that films of alkali metals in contact with water appear blue just prior to their disappearance, and Jortner and Stein (*52*) reported measuring an absorption spectrum. One must be cautious about ascribing this coloration to e^-_{aq} because very thin mirrors of vaporized alkali metals are notorious in producing strange interference and other purely optical effects; but Bennett, Mile, and Thomas find similar colorations when alkali metals are deposited in a low temperature ice matrix (*13, 14*). Although the structure and hence facility for solvating or trapping electrons is very different in water and ice, the ESR studies of Bennett *et al.* certainly add credence to the notion that when Na is placed in water, even ice, an electron is released into the solvent. Their hyperfine tensor data shows clearly that H_2O^- is not formed in ice but rather that the trapped electron interacts weakly with six equivalent protons. $H_2O^-_{aq}$ has normally been disregarded in discussion on the nature of e^-_{aq} (*53*) on both theoretical grounds and on the failure to find H_2O^- mass spectrometrically; but just as the ionization potential decreases on going to the liquid phase so the electron affinity increases and in addition $H_2O^-_{aq}$ will have a large solvation energy.

We have made a study of the reaction of aluminum in alkaline water (*37*), where again H_2 is produced. When N_2O-methanol scavenging competition is applied, N_2 is generated and the indications are that the precursor of H_2 is again e^-_{aq}. In this system the results were irreproducible from one experiment to the next mainly because of the difficulty in obtaining the same surface area of contact between metal and solution.

Other Reducing Agents. Cations having reduction potentials greater than 0.41 volts, the potential necessary to reduce water at natural pH, spontaneously generate H_2 from water. Since the standard potential for U^{3+}/U^{4+} and Eu^{2+}/Eu^{3+} are 0.61 and 0.43 volts, respectively, we have examined the intermediates in the reaction of crystalline UCl_3 and $EuCl_2$ with water using the N_2O/methanol competition. For the case of U^{3+} there is evidence that H-atoms are not produced and the data is consistent with e^-_{aq} being formed by Reaction 11 (*74*)

$$U^{3+} \xrightarrow{H_2O} U^{4+}_{aq} + e^-_{aq} \tag{11}$$

Meyerstein (*61*) has reported the difficulty of scavenging the hydride ion, even with molar concentration of solute, when LiH is dissolved in water. We used the N_2O/methanol competition scavenging technique on the reaction between KBH_4 and water, because the latter is believed to yield a hydride ion slowly and, in part, we wanted to test the N_2O–CH_3OH competition with H^-. However, so much H_2 was produced from the additional decomposition of BH_3 that our test was insensitive and inconclusive (*75*). One might also wonder about the reaction of $Ni(CN)_4^{4-}$, AsH_3, and TeH_2 with water, or even reductions involving H_2 gas on a catalyst—particularly in alkaline solution.

Perhaps, in general, hydrated electrons are the reaction intermediates whenever water is reduced to H_2.

Electrochemically. The hydrogen electrode reaction, which is the basis of the standard electrode potential scale, is given by the overall Reaction 12. After more than fifty years of intensive and sophisticated

$$H^+_{aq} + e^-(\text{cathode}) \rightarrow 1/2\, H_2(g) \tag{12}$$

examination the detailed mechanism of this reaction remains unresolved (*16, 79*). Three mechanisms are currently favored but none is universally acceptable. They are (1) the "slow discharge," (2) the "catalytic," and (3) the "electrochemical" mechanisms. The first two involve adsorbed H atoms the last involves an H_2^+ adsorbed on the electrode surface. Whenever aqueous solutions of electrolytes consisting of "non-reducible" cations are electrolyzed, H_2 is evolved at the cathode and the decomposition is attributed to Reaction 12.

Again, when considering water, a comparison with the analogous process occurring in liquid ammonia is a natural one to make. For instance, tetrabutylammonium iodide in liquid ammonia when electrolyzed between mercury electrodes produces a vivid blue coloration at the cathode which has been described by Laitinen and Nyman (*56*) as "the electron electrode."

As part of our study of H_2 production from water we investigated the cathodic decomposition of aqueous solutions of Na_2SO_4 at a smooth Pt electrode (*74*). The competitive scavenging by N_2O and CH_3OH showed that free H-atoms were not produced and that the pH dependence was entirely consistent with e^-_{aq} being the precursor of H_2. We examined N_2O solutions polarographically (*68*) but found no half-wave potential corresponding to the direct reduction of N_2O (although this was at a dropping mercury electrode). However, there did remain the possibility that the relative reactivity of adsorbed H-atoms and e^-_{aq} towards N_2O and CH_3OH were very smiliar. Thus, we looked for absorption of red light along a cathode surface as this might corroborate the formation of e^-_{aq}. In these experiments (*76*) the 6328A. light from a He–Ne laser was directed tangentially onto a highly polished cylindrical silver cathode surface in such a way that it made innumerable minute specular reflections and thus swept out a long optical path. High sensitivity was achieved by modulating the electrode potential at a frequency to which the detector's amplifier had been tuned. A diminution in the light transmitted was observed only when the silver surface was the cathode of the cell. Analysis of the equivalent optical cell (*77*) revealed that the data was consistent with absorption by e^-_{aq} and that, if e^-_{aq} was formed, it existed within 1.7×10^{-4} cm. of the surface at a mean (but rather inhomogeneous) concentration of $8 \times 10^{-7}M$.

The conclusion drawn from this work is that Process 13 rather than 14 represents the net formation of the H_2 precursor

$$e^-(\text{cathode}) \rightarrow e^-_{aq} \tag{13}$$

$$e^-(\text{cathode}) \rightarrow OH^- + H(\text{adsorbed or free}) \tag{14}$$

and that H_2 is formed by combination of two e^-_{aq}. At least three possible mechanisms for the overall Process 13 may be envisaged. It may be (1) a direct transfer of an electron from metal to water, or (2) liberated from the diffuse electrical double-layer, or (3) generated from a Na atom (or whatever non-reducible cation was used) by Reaction 15 followed by Reaction 8

$$Na^+_{aq} + e^-(\text{cathode}) \rightarrow Na \tag{15}$$

$$Na + nH_2O \rightarrow Na^+_{aq} + e^-_{aq} \tag{8}$$

In any event the detailed mechanism must adequately explain the 1/2 in the slope of the Tafel plot and the effect of the electrode material on the overvoltage. In strongly acidic solution, even if Reaction 13 was the primary step, hydrated electrons would be rapidly transformed to H-atoms by Reaction 3 prior to the generation of H_2.

Hills and Kinnibrugh (*47*) have reported some work which is on a sound electrochemical basis, but the evidence for e^-_{aq} is much less direct.

By studying the pressure dependence of the hydrogen evolution reaction on Hg at pH 1 they obtained a negative volume of activation (-3.4 ml. mole^{-1}), which, they argued, was not in accord with any H-atom process but could result from the "emission and hydration of metallic electrons" as the rate-determining step. This interpretation thus invokes the formation of e^-_{aq} even at pH 1. (This value of -3.4 agrees well with the partial molal volume of e^-_{aq} (-5.5 to -1.1 mole^{-1}) obtained indirectly in a radiation chemical system (*45*). It is interesting to note the difference in $\overline{V}$ for e^-_{aq} and $e^-_{(ammonia)}$, where the value is $\sim$60 ml. mole^{-1} (*49*)).

In 1907, Cameron and Ramsay suggested the analogy between the action of high energy radiations and electrolysis but did not formulate this as a generalization when they failed to deposit Cu from $CuSO_4$ solution using Rn α particles (*70*)! One advantage of electrolysis over radiolysis for studying primary species is that the oxidizing and reducing species can be produced in separate compartments and each studied independently of the other.

Photoinduced Electron Emission from Metals. In 1931 Bowden (*17*) reported an increased current density at a Hg cathode in contact with *N*/5 aqueous H_2SO_4 when it was illuminated with light of photon energy $\sim$3 e.v. He suggested that the light provided an activation energy to the oriented dipoles at the cathode surface which thus altered the interfacial potential and reduced the overvoltage. Very recently this effect has been studied in greater detail by Barker, Gardner, and Sammon (*8*), by Delahay and Srinivasan (*25*), and by Heyrovsky (*46*).

In some most elegant experiments Barker *et al.* (*8*) studied the photocurrents, produced by light of various wavelengths directed onto a dropping Hg electrode, as a function of the electrode potential and the concentration of various scavengers added to the electrolyte. They used advanced polarographic equipment capable of measuring minute photocurrents and illuminated the cathode with constant, frequency-controlled-intermittent and flash light sources. When N_2O, H_3O^+, or NO_3^- was present as a scavenger the photocurrent increased for a given light energy and cathode potential, and in addition the effect of neutral salts indicated that the photocurrent was caused by diffusing negatively charged species. These authors interpret their results in the following way: electron emission from the Hg is induced by photolysis; the photo-ejected electron travels about 10–100A. from the surface—*i.e.*, beyond the electrical double-layer—before becoming thermalized and hydrated; the electrode potential and presence of scavengers which react with e^-_{aq} determine the magnitude of the photocurrent by controlling the lifetime of charged species in the solution.

Delahay and Srinivasan (*25*) have performed similar experiments using polychromatic light from conventional flash photolysis equipment directed at mercury and thallium amalgam electrodes polarized by a potential below the faradic process level. They found that the charge produced depended on the concentration of H^+ in the solution and the polarizing potential and interpreted their findings in terms of e^-_{aq}. Heyrovsky (*46*), as previously mentioned, studied the variation of threshold potential with photon energy for discharge at a Hg cathode, but attributed the process to reduction of H_2O to give H and OH^-.

In all these experiments photo-induced electron emission is produced by photon energies substantially smaller than the work function of the metal.

Again it is demonstrated that when electrons are injected into liquid water hydrated electrons are formed and do not convert rapidly to hydrogen atoms. Local concentrations of e^-_{aq} up to about $10^{-8}M$ are estimated in the experiments of Barker *et al.* (*8*).

Reaction of Stable Solvated Electrons with Water. One of the most promising ways of generating a homogeneous solution of hydrated electrons has been pursued by Dewald, Dye, Eigen, and DeMaeyer (*26*), who mixed a solution of electrons solvated in ethylenediamine with water. These authors took a solution of Cs in ethylenediamine, a solvent in which solvated electrons are stable, and combined it in a fast-flow mixing cell with a solution of water in ethylenediamine. They then followed the rate of decay of the near infrared absorption band of $e^-_{e.d}$ as a function of water concentration. More recently other active metals have been used and the kinetics fully analyzed (*32*). The second-order rate constant ($20M^{-1}$ sec.$^{-1}$) obtained is attributed to Reaction 16 and compared with

$$e^- + H_2O \rightarrow H + OH^- \qquad (16)$$

k_{-2}. It has been pointed out (*73*) that it may be invalid to draw any conclusions about the close correspondence of k_{16} and k_{-2} because the rate of decay of $e^-_{e.d}$ was being followed, and one needs to be sure that the conversion $e^-_{e.d.} \rightarrow e_{aq}^-$, if it occurred, was not rate controlling.

This is a fascinating approach to the study of solvated electrons and has been extended by Dewald and Tsina (*27*) to the reaction of water with the electron in liquid ammonia. For the mixture water-Na-liquid NH_3 these authors find a very slow reaction and conclude that $k_{17} < 5 \times 10^{-3}M^{-1}$ sec.$^{-1}$ at $-34°$C.

$$e^-_{am} + H_2O \rightarrow H + OH^- \qquad (17)$$

Perhaps alkali halide crystals containing stable F-centers could be dissolved or dispersed in water sufficiently rapidly to be able to detect e^-_{aq}.

By the Ionic Dissociation of H Atoms. If all the preceding discussion is correct it is evident that hydrated hydrogen atoms are seldom formed.

One method which seems to produce them is to bubble H_2 gas, which has been partially dissociated by passage through an electrodeless discharge, into water. Czapski and Stein (*19, 20*) developed this technique and studied the reactive species produced by competitive scavenging kinetics. In this way Jortner and Rabani (*54*) demonstrated the very striking and complete transformation from H to e^-_{aq} for solutions at pH $\geqslant$ 12 given by Reaction 2.

$$H + OH^-_{aq} \rightarrow e^-_{aq} \quad (2)$$

Bases other than OH^-_{aq} could conceivably induce the ionization of the H atom but Anbar and Neta (*3*) have found HPO_4^{2-} and $B_4O_7^{2-}$ ineffective in this regard. They did, however, find a conversion H to e^-_{aq} caused by the weak base F^- according to the slow Reaction 18, but believe

$$H + F^-_{aq} \rightarrow HF + e^-_{aq} \quad (18)$$

this to be an addition reaction rather than an acid-base transfer. These authors generated the H atoms for their study by ultrasonic excitation of water in a hydrogen atmosphere (*4*).

Perhaps H atoms produced by the catalytic cracking of H_2 can be converted at high pH to e^-_{aq}, because colloidal iridium has been shown to possess a high activity for hydrogenation of aromatic compounds in strongly alkaline solution (*31*).

Absolute Scale of Standard Potentials

Noyes (*62*) has drawn attention to our inability to assign an absolute potential to the standard hydrogen electrode, Reaction 19, and thus to

$$H^+_{aq} + e^-_{(Pt)} \rightarrow 1/2\ H_{2(g)} \quad (19)$$

other half-cell reactions, because of the unknown thermodynamic state of $e^-_{(Pt)}$. The convention of arbitrarily assigning $E^\circ_{19} = 0$ is consistent with choosing the standard free energy of formation to be zero for an electron in the highest energy level normally occupied in platinum black metal, since $\Delta G^\circ_f(H^+_{aq})$ is also arbitrarily chosen to be zero. The standard potential for Reaction 20 is thus directly related to the difference in

$$M^{n+}_{aq} + e^- \rightarrow M^{(n-1)+}_{aq} \quad (20)$$

ΔG° for Reactions 19 and 20 and this implies that e^- in Reaction 20, although its state is not specified, must also have $\Delta G^\circ_f = 0$. Even using an absolute value for ΔG° for $H^+_{(g)} \rightarrow H^+_{aq}$ one cannot obtain an absolute value for ΔG°_{19} from the cycle

$$\begin{array}{ccccc} & & (19) & & \\ H^+_{aq} + e^-_{(Pt)} & & \rightarrow & & 1/2\ H_{2(g)} \\ \downarrow \quad\quad \downarrow & & & & \uparrow \\ H^+_{(g)} + e^-_{(g)} & & \rightarrow & & H_{(g)} \end{array}$$

because the possibility is remote of getting a good value for $e^-_{(Pt)} \rightarrow e^-_{(g)}$, since work functions depend critically on surface state, interfacial potential, and method of measurement.

Baxendale (*10*) proposed that a different and "absolute" scale of potentials could be established by defining potentials with respect to real reactions such as Reaction 21, in which the state of the electron, e^-_{aq}, is

$$M^{n+}_{aq} + e^-_{aq} \rightarrow M^{(n-1)+}_{aq} \quad (21)$$

clearly specified. Now, since $E°_{22}$ = 2.6 volts (Reference *10,* corrected for best value of k_{-2}—*see* Reference *43*) [2.6 volts is the upper limit for two reasons; (1) $k_{-2} = 16M^{-1}$ sec.$^{-1}$ is probably only an upper limit to the rate of Reaction −2 (*73*); (2) The standard free energy of hydration of the odd electron species, the H atom, may be substantially greater than for H_2 and He.] for Reaction 22, on Baxendale's scale potentials for all

$$H^+_{aq} + e^-_{aq} \rightarrow 1/2\ H_{2(g)} \quad (22)$$

oxidation-reduction couples, as given for instance by Reaction 21, would be 2.6 volts more negative than on the present conventional scale. [In a review article (*73*) this writer incorrectly interpreted Baxendale's suggestion and wrongly stated that potentials so defined differ from the S.H.E. scale by at least the free energy of hydration of e^-_{aq}.]

If the discharge step in the hydrogen electrode reaction, as discussed earlier, really is Reaction 13 then for platinum black electrode this would represent the step $e^-_{(Pt)} \rightarrow e^-_{aq}$. The following cycle is thus worth considering

$$\begin{array}{ccc} & (19) & \\ H^+_{aq} + e^-_{(Pt)} & \rightarrow & 1/2\ H_{2(g)} \\ \downarrow(13) & \nearrow & \\ H^+_{aq} + e^-_{aq} & & (22) \end{array}$$

Only if $E°_{19} = 0$—*i.e.*, if the standard hydrogen electrode is zero on an absolute scale—can one deduce from Baxendale's considerations that the potential neecssary to produce e^-_{aq} in its standard state from a platinum black electrode is −2.6 volts. In fact in our work we used total potential differences across the cell much less than 2.6 volts. (One can of course make $E°_{19} = 0$ on an absolute basis simply by selecting the appropriate standard state of $e^-_{(Pt)}$ for this to be so, even if it turns out to be 10^{40}. However, if one arbitrarily takes some reasonable standard state for $e^-_{(Pt)}$ then $E°_{19} \neq 0$ on an absolute basis).

On the other hand if $E°_{13}$ could be measured directly one could combine this with Baxendale's $E°_{22}$ to put the S.H.E. on an absolute basis. Perhaps $E°_{13}$ could be obtained by pursuing the method of Barker *et al.* (*8*), by measuring the wavelength limit for photocurrent production at a platinum black electrode with zero potential difference between electrode and solution. (It would of course be necessary to understand the mechanism fully, to know if the solvation energy of e^-_{aq} should be included, to measure the concentration of e^-_{aq} in equilibrium with the illuminated electrode and make the appropriate correction to ideal 1 molal concentration).

Conclusions

Hydrated electron chemistry is doubtless still in its infancy, but some of its impact has already been felt in various branches of chemistry. (1) What was loosely referred to as "nascent hydrogen" appears to be e^-_{aq} rather than its conjugate acid—the hydrogen atom. (2) It is quite a powerful and a highly selective reducing agent which should be useful in synthetic and preparative chemistry. As Anbar and Hart have shown (*5, 6*) it is the ideal nucleophile and its reactivity with an enormous array of chemicals is known (*7*). (3) As a sensitive analytical reagent e^-_{aq} has great possibilities (*44*). (4) Many new chemical species, such as the unusual valence states of transition metals, have been discovered and their behavior and structure examined (*11, 12, 18*). (5) Absolute rate constants for elementary reactions involving e^-_{aq} are easily measured and this could lead to profound development in reaction rate theories and provide thermodynamic data. (6) Its structure, stability, and mobility provides data on the structure of water and polar liquids in general. (7) The photochemical generation of e^-_{aq} from inorganic and organic substrates in aqueous media has important implications in photosynthesis and biology in general. (8) If e^-_{aq} (or O_2^- formed from $e^-_{aq} + O_2$) is responsible for cell death during mitosis when exposed to ionizing radiations then electrolysis, for instance, might be as effective in this regard.

Literature Cited

(1) Anbar, M., Advan. Chem. Ser. **50,** 55 (1965).
(2) Anbar, M., Alfassi, Z. B., Bregman-Reislar, H., *J. Am. Chem. Soc.* **89,** 1263 (1967).
(3) Anbar, M., Neta, P., *Trans. Faraday Soc.* **63,** 141 (1967).
(4) Anbar, M., Pecht, I., *J. Phys. Chem.* **68,** 352 (1964).
(5) Anbar, M., Hart, E. J., *J. Phys. Chem.* **69,** 271 (1965).
(6) Anbar, M., Hart, E. J., *J. Am. Chem. Soc.* **86,** 5633 (1964).
(7) Anbar, M., Neta, P., *Intern. J. Appl. Radiation Isotopes* **18,** 493 (1967).
(8) Barker, G. S., Gardner, A. W., Sammon, D. C., *J. Electrochem. Soc.* **113,** 1183 (1966).
(9) Barrett, J., Fox, M. F., Mansell, A. L., *J. Chem. Soc.* **1967,** 483.
(10) Baxendale, J. H., *Radiation Res. Suppl.* **4,** 139 (1964).
(11) Baxendale, J. H., Fielden, E. M., Keene, J. P., *Proc. Roy. Soc.* **A286,** 320 (1965).

(12) Baxendale, J. J., Keene, J. P., Stott, D. A., *Chem. Comm.* **1966,** 715.
(13) Bennett, J. E., Mile, B., Thomas, A., *Nature* **201,** 919 (1964).
(14) Bennett, J. E., Mile, B., Thomas, A., *J. Chem. Soc.* **A 1967,** 1393.
(15) Boag, J. W., *Am. J. Roent, Radiation & Nucl. Med.* **15,** 896 (1963).
(16) Bockris, J. O. M., "Electrochemistry," Friend, Gutman, eds., Pergamon, London, England, 1965.
(17) Bowden, F. P., *Trans. Faraday Soc.* **28,** 505 (1931).
(18) Brown, D. M., Dainton, F. S., *Trans. Faraday Soc.* **62,** 1139 (1966).
(19) Czapski, G., Stein, G., *J. Phys. Chem.* **63,** 850 (1959).
(20) Czapski, G., Jortner, J., Stein, G., *J. Phys. Chem.* **65,** 956 (1961).
(21) Dainton, F. S., Logan, S. R., *Proc. Roy. Soc.* **A287,** 281 (1965).
(22) Dainton, F. S., Fowles, P., *Proc. Roy. Soc.* **A287,** 312 (1965).
(23) Dainton, F. S., James, D. G. L., *Trans. Faraday Soc.* **54,** 649 (1958).
(24) Dainton, F. S., Keene, J. P., Kemp, T. J., Salmon, G. A., Teply, J., *Proc. Chem. Soc.* **1964,** 265.
(25) Delahay, P., Srinivasan, V. S., *J. Phys. Chem.* **70,** 420 (1966).
(26) Dewald, R. R., Dye, J. L., Eigen, M., Demaeyer, L., *J. Chem. Phys.* **39,** 2388 (1963).
(27) Dewald, R. R., Tsina, R. V., *Chem. Comm.* **1967,** 647.
(28) Dobson, G., Grossweiner, L. I., *Radiation Res.* **23,** 290 (1964).
(29) Dorfman, L. M., Taub, I. A., *J. Am. Chem Soc.* **85,** 2370 (1963).
(30) Dorsey, N. E., "Water-Substance," Reinhold, New York, 1940.
(31) Dunworth, W. P., Nord, F. F., *J. Am. Chem. Soc.* **72,** 4199 (1950).
(32) Feldman, L. H., Dewald, R. R., Dye, J. L., ADVAN. CHEM. SER. **50,** 163 (1965).
(33) Fielden, E. M., Hart, E. J., *Trans. Faraday Soc.* **63,** 2975 (1967).
(34) Fraenkel, G., Ellis, S. H., Dix, D. T., *J. Am. Chem. Soc.* **87,** 1406 (1965).
(35) Franck, J., Scheibe, G., *Z. Phys. Chem.* **A139,** 22 (1938).
(36) Gordon, S., Hart, E. J., Matheson, M. S., Rabani, J., Thomas, J. K., *Discussions Faraday Soc.* **36,** 193 (1963).
(37) Green, J. D., Walker, D. C. (unpublished work).
(38) Grossweiner, L. I., Swenson, G. W., Zwicker, E. F., *Science* **141,** 805 (1963).
(39) Grossweiner, L. I., *Advan. Radiation Biol.* **2,** 83 (1966).
(40) Gutmann, F., Lyons, L., "Organic Semiconductors," Wiley, New York, N. Y., 1967.
(41) Hart, E. J., Symp. Chairman, ADVAN. CHEM. SER. **50** (1965).
(42) Hart, E. J. in "Actions Chimiques et Biologiques des Radiations," Ed. Haissinsky, Vol. 10 (1966).
(43) Hart, E. J., Gordon, S., Fielden, E. M., *J. Phys. Chem.* **70,** 150 (1966).
(44) Hart, E. J., Fielden, E. M., ADVAN. CHEM. SER. **50,** 253 (1965).
(45) Hentz, R. R. Farhataziz, Milner, D. J., Burton, M., *J. Chem. Phys.* **47,** 374 (1967).
(46) Heyrovsky, M., *Nature* **206,** 1356 (1965).
(47) Hills, G. J., Kinnibrugh, D. R., *J. Electrochem. Soc.* **113,** 1111 (1966).
(48) Hughes, G., Roach, R. J., *Chem. Comm.* **1965,** 600.
(49) Jolly, W. L., "Progress in Inorganic Chemistry," Vol. I, Interscience, New York, N. Y., 1959.
(50) Jortner, J., Noyes, R. M., *J. Phys. Chem.* **70,** 770 (1966).
(51) Jortner, J., Ottolenghi, M., Stein, G., *J. Phys. Chem.* **66,** 2029 (1962).
(52) Jortner, J., Stein, G., *Nature* **175,** 893 (1955).
(53) Jortner, J., *Radiation Res. Suppl.* **4,** 24 (1964).
(54) Jortner, J., Rabani, J., *J. Phys. Chem.* **66,** 2081 (1962).
(55) Keene, J. P., *Radiation Res.* **22,** 1 (1964).
(56) Laitinen, H. A., Nyman, C. J., *J. Am. Chem. Soc.* **70,** 3002 (1948).
(57) Logan, S. R., *J. Chem. Educ.* **44,** 345 (1967).

(58) Matheson, M. S., ADVAN. CHEM. SER. **50,** 45 (1965).
(59) Matheson, M. S., Rabani, J., *J. Phys. Chem.* **69,** 1324 (1965).
(60) Matheson, M. S., Mulac, W. A., Rabani, J., *J. Phys. Chem.* **67,** 2613 (1963).
(61) Meyerstein, D., *Proc. 5th Informal Conf. Notre Dame,* p. 75 (1966).
(62) Noyes, R. M., *J. Chem. Educ.* **40,** 2 (1963).
(63) Ohno, S., Tsuchihashi, G., *Bull. Chem. Soc. Japan* **38,** 1052 (1965).
(64) Platzman, R. L., *Natl. Acad. Sci.—Natl. Res. Council Rept.* **305,** 22 (1953).
(65) Platzman, R. L., Franck, J., *Z. Physik.* **138,** 411 (1954).
(66) Schmidt, K. H., Buck, W. L., *Science* **151,** 70 (1966).
(67) Schwarz, H. A., *Ann. Rev. Phys. Chem.* **16,** 347 (1965).
(68) Shaede, E. A., Walker, D. C., *Chem. Soc. Spec. Publ.* **22,** 277 (1967).
(69) Sokolov, U., Stein, G., *J. Chem. Phys.* **44,** 2189 (1966).
(70) Spinks, J. W. T., Woods, R. J., "An Introduction to Radiation Chemistry," p. 3, Wiley, New York, N. Y., 1964.
(71) Stein, G., ADVAN. CHEM. SER. **50,** 230 (1965).
(72) Stein, G., "Chemistry of Ionization and Excitation," p. 25, Johnson, Scholes, eds., Taylor and Francis, London, 1967.
(73) Walker, D. C., *Quart. Rev.* **21,** 79 (1967).
(74) Walker, D. C., *Can. J. Chem.* **44,** 2226 (1966).
(75) Walker, D. C., Wallace, S. C. (unpublished work).
(76) Walker, D. C., *Can. J. Chem.* **45,** 807 (1967).
(77) Walker, D. C., *Anal. Chem.* **39,** 896 (1967).
(78) Weiss, J. J., "Chemistry of Ionization and Excitation," p. 17, Johnson, Scholes, eds., Taylor and Francis, London, 1967.
(79) Yamazaki, T., Kita, H., *J. Res. Inst. Catalysis,* Hokkaido Univ., **13, 77** (1965).

RECEIVED December 26, 1967.

4

Further Predictions of Thermodynamic Properties of the Hydrated Electron

RICHARD M. NOYES

University of Oregon, Eugene, Ore. 97403

The free energy, enthalpy, entropy, and volume of the hydrated electron are measurable in principle from the temperature and pressure dependencies of the forward and reverse rates of the unimolecular reaction of this species with water to form hydrogen atom and hydroxide ion. Data presently available determine values only for free energies of activation in both directions and for enthalpy and entropy of activation in one direction. Values for the other properties can be predicted if it is assumed that the enthalpy, entropy, and volume of the hydrated electron can be calculated by extrapolating measurements on halide ions to the radius (2.98 A.) necessary to fit the free energy data. The predictions for enthalpy and entropy are thought to be reasonably accurate, but the value for volume change is less reliable.

It is desirable to know the changes in thermodynamic properties associated with hydration of the electron, but true equilibrium cannot be established because e^-_{aq} is unstable with respect to reduction of solvent. It is also impossible to establish an equilibrium for the reaction with a weak oxidizing agent like Na^+_{aq} because the product of the reaction would also reduce solvent virtually irreversibly.

The only method by which useful data can be obtained is to identify a reversible reaction involving some transient metastable species whose thermodynamic properties can be estimated separately. If rates in forward and reverse directions are measurable, changes in thermodynamic properties can be determined.

The reaction

$$H_2O(l) + e^-_{aq} \rightleftarrows H_{aq} + OH^-_{aq} \qquad (1)$$

appears to be almost uniquely suited for such measurements. Rate constants at 25°C. in the forward (*3*) and reverse (*5*) directions permit the equilibrium constant and standard free energy change for the reaction to be calculated.

Since the free energies of formation of the other species in Equation 1 are known, the free energy of hydration of the electron is also calculable (*1, 4*).

The free energy change for hydration of a free electron is much less than that for hydration of free halide ions. Jortner and Noyes (*4*) extrapolated the data for halide ions by means of a formula developed previously (*7*) and showed that the free energy of hydration of the electron is equal to that to be expected for a halide ion of radius 2.98 A.

Although the measurements presently completed at 25°C. and 1 atm. permit only the free energy change to be calculated for Equation 1, temperature and pressure derivatives of the rates could be used in the same way to determine changes in other properties such as enthalpy, entropy, and volume. Such measurements will undoubtedly be made in the near future, and it is interesting to discover how well the values for these thermodynamic properties can be predicted by extrapolating halide data to the same radius of 2.98 A.

Properties of Individual Species

Table I presents the measured or predicted thermodynamic properties for the various chemical species of concern for this discussion. The entries are based on the following considerations:

Table I. Thermodynamic Properties of Individual Species

	$\Delta G_f°$, *kcal./mole*	$\Delta H_f°$, *kcal./mole*	$\bar{S}°$, *cal./mole deg.*	$\bar{V}°$, *ml./mole*
$H_2O(l)$	−56.69	−68.32	16.72	18.0
H_{aq}	53.03	51.09	9.08	2.5
OH^-_{aq}	−141.41	−153.79	−1.35	−3.8
H^+_{aq}	103.81	98.83	−1.17	−1.5
e^-_{aq}	−37.54	(−36.61) [a]	(3.13) [a]	(99.3) [a]

[a] Values in parentheses are predicted.

The standard state of H_2O is the pure liquid at 25°C. and 1 atm. The standard states of the other species are ideal one molal solution.

The quantities $\Delta G_f°$ and $\Delta H_f°$ refer to free energies and enthalpies of formation from the elements with consumption or production of gaseous electrons if necessary. Standard states of elementary hydrogen and oxygen are one atmosphere fugacity. The standard state of the gaseous electron is zero enthalpy, entropy, and free energy and at the same bulk electrostatic potential as the interior of a body of water.

The quantity $\overline{S}°$ is the standard partial molal entropy based on the usual third law convention, and the quantity $\overline{V}°$ is the partial molal volume.

Entries for H_2O (l) are available from any tabulation of thermodynamic properties.

The first three entries for H_{aq} are derived from the properties of gaseous hydrogen atoms with the assumption that for solution of such atoms $\Delta G° = 4.5$ kcal./mole and $\Delta H° = -1.0$ kcal./mole. These values are based on the solvation properties of He and H_2 and have been discussed previously (*4*).

Of course the partial molal volume of H_{aq} is not directly measurable. This parameter could be measured for the solutes H_2 and He by determining densities of solutions, but no record of such observations has been found. The entry for $\overline{V}°$ of H_{aq} in Table I is simply the volume of a sphere of radius 1.0 A. (the volume containing 99% of the electronic charge distribution). The ideas of Némethy and Scheraga (*6*) on hydrophobic bonding suggest that even this small estimate may be somewhat too large.

The entries for H^+_{aq} are based on a procedure that extrapolates thermodynamic properties of alkali and halide ions as functions of reciprocal radius with limiting slopes determined by the known properties of macroscopic conducting spheres. The procedures are discussed in detail elsewhere (*7*). If any of these entries for H^+_{aq} is in error by an amount Z, the entries for the same property of OH^-_{aq} and e^-_{aq} are in error by $-Z$, but the values of kinetic and equilibrium property changes for Reaction 1 are unaffected.

Most tables of thermodynamic properties for OH^-_{aq} use the convention that values for H^+_{aq} are identically zero. Values from such tables were modified in obvious ways to obtain the entries for OH^-_{aq} in Table I.

The entry for $\Delta G_f°$ of e^-_{aq} was calculated by Jortner and Noyes (*4*) from the kinetic data discussed in the introduction. Values of $\Delta H_f°$ and of $S°$ were also calculated in the previous paper (*4*) by assuming that changes in these properties during solvation of a gaseous electron were the same as those during solvation of a gaseous halide ion of radius 2.98 A. The entry for $\overline{V}°$ is derived from the previous conclusion (*7*) that the partial molal volume (in ml./mole) of a singly charged spherically symmetrical anion of radius r (in A.) is given by

$$\overline{V}° = 2.523r^3 + 4.09r^2 - 4.175/r - 21.30/r^2 \qquad (2)$$

Note that the value for $\Delta G_f°$ of e^-_{aq} is based on experimental observations while the values for the other three properties of this species are placed in parentheses and are based on the assumption that all such properties can be estimated by extrapolating values for halide ions to the radius that fits the free energy data. These predicted values are potentially subject to experimental test.

All entries in Table I are presented to at least one more significant figure than could possibly be justified by the applications of this paper.

Measured and Predicted Changes in Properties

Table II presents changes in thermodynamic properties associated with Reaction 1. In this Table, X is an extensive thermodynamic property, $\Delta X_f^{\neq}$ and $\Delta X_r^{\neq}$ are the activation changes in X for the forward and reverse steps of Reaction 1, respectively, and ΔX° is the standard change in X for that reaction. Experimental values are entered directly, and predicted values are given in parentheses.

Table II. Measured and Predicted Changes in Thermodynamic Properties

	$\Delta X_f^{\neq}$	$\Delta X_r^{\neq}$	ΔX°
G, kcal./mole	13.4	7.5	5.9
H, kcal./mole	6.1	(3.9) [a]	(2.2) [a]
S, cal./mole deg.	−24.4	(−12.3) [a]	(−12.1) [a]
V, ml./mole	(negative)	(positive)	(−119)

[a] Values in parentheses are predicted.

The free energy values are taken directly from the paper by Jortner and Noyes (*4*).

The temperature dependence of the forward rate for Reaction 1 has now been measured directly by Fielden and Hart (*2*). The value of 6.1 kcal./mole for $\Delta H_f^{\neq}$ is based on the observed Arrhenius activation energy of 6.7 kcal./mole. The reported values for $\Delta H_f^{\neq}$ and $\Delta S_f^{\neq}$ lie well within the rather wide range predicted by Jortner and Noyes (*4*). Since predicted values of ΔH° and ΔS° can be calculated from the entries in Table I, the measurements of Fielden and Hart (*2*) also permit $\Delta H_r^{\neq}$ and $\Delta S_r^{\neq}$ to be predicted.

The entries in Table I also permit ΔV° to be predicted. Volumes of activation do not lend themselves to the same type of treatment, but the probable charge distributions in the initial, final, and transition states for Reaction 1 support the signs for $\Delta V_f^{\neq}$ and $\Delta V_r^{\neq}$ predicted in Table II.

If pK_c is the equilibrium quotient for Reaction 1 based on molalities in dilute solution, $(\partial pK_c/\partial P)_T = \Delta V^\circ/2.303RT = -0.00211$ atm.$^{-1}$.

Aqueous hydrogen atom can also be regarded as a weak acid ionizing with a pK of 9.7 according to the equation

$$H_{aq} \rightleftarrows H^{+}_{aq} + e^{-}_{aq} \qquad (3)$$

The entries in Table I predict that for Reaction 3, $\Delta V° = 95.3$ ml./mole and $(\partial pK_c/\partial P)_T = 0.00169$ atm.$^{-1}$. If these predictions are even approximately correct, Equilibria 1 and 3 should be quite sensitive to changes in pressure, and 200 atm. should shift the molality equilibrium quotients by more than a factor of two.

Probable Validity of Predictions

The enthalpy and entropy entries in parentheses in Table II represent predictions that will be tested whenever the temperature dependence of the rate of reaction of hydrogen atoms with hydroxide ions is known. Pressure dependence measurements must be made on rates in both directions before the prediction for $\Delta V°$ can be tested.

Until such experimental data are available, the predictions in Tables I and II may be used cautiously in appropriate calculations. Probable errors are rather difficult to assess, but certain considerations suggest that the enthalpy and entropy estimates can not be seriously in error:

The rate constant for the reverse of Reaction 1 is 1.8×10^7 liter/mole sec. (5). This value is somewhat less than would be expected for a diffusion controlled reaction. If the pre-exponential factor is near the 10^{10} liter/mole sec. considered "normal" for an activation-controlled reaction of an ion with a neutral molecule, the Arrhenius energy of activation would be about 3.8 kcal./mole in reasonable agreement with the value of 4.5 kcal./mole based on the $\Delta H_r^{\neq}$ entry in Table II. Since the transition state for Reaction 1 almost certainly has negative charge more dispersed than in the neighborhood of an hydroxide ion, the pre-exponential term for the reverse reaction may even be somewhat more positive than the "normal" 10^{10} liter/mole sec., and the enthalpy of activation would then be larger also. Even if the correct enthalpy of activation is less than the value quoted in Table II, the difference could hardly be more than 2 kcal./mole.

The upper limit for the enthalpy of activation is somewhat harder to set. An attempt can be made by noting that the partial molal entropy of e^{-}_{aq} is estimated to be positive. It is unprecedented for solution of a charged species to cause an increase in entropy of the surrounding medium, and the effect, if real, must be associated with the very dispersed charge of the hydrated electron. If the enthalpy of activation for the reverse of Reaction 1 is greater than the value estimated in Table II, then the partial molal entropy of the hydrated electron in Table I must be still more positive. This argument makes it appear very doubtful that the enthalpy of activation is more than about 2 kcal./mole greater than the value quoted in Table II.

These arguments lend some support to the claim that enthalpy estimates are correct to within 2 kcal./mole and entropy estimates are correct to within 6 cal./mole deg. In fact, even deviations of these magnitudes appear to be unlikely.

The volume estimates are made with much less confidence. The value of ΔV° in Table II appears somewhat excessive in magnitude. The volume decrease associated with Reaction 1 may well turn out to be considerably less than is predicted, but the signs of the volumes of activation for the two directions are probably predicted correctly.

Only in rather unusual circumstances can parameters for chemical reactions be predicted in advance within limits as narrow as has been done here for the enthalpy and entropy terms. It will be very interesting to see the extent to which these predictions are indeed validated.

Acknowledgment

This work was supported in part by the U.S. Atomic Energy Commission under Contract AT(45-1)-1310. E. M. Fielden and E. J. Hart kindly made experimental results available in advance of publication.

Literature Cited

(1) Baxendale, J. H., *Radiation Res. Suppl.* **4,** 139 (1964).
(2) Fielden, E. M., Hart, E. J., *Trans. Faraday Soc.* **63,** 2975 (1967).
(3) Hart, E. J., Gordon, S., Fielden, E. M., *J. Phys. Chem.* **70,** 150 (1966).
(4) Jortner, J., Noyes, R. M., *J. Phys. Chem.* **70,** 770 (1966).
(5) Matheson, M. S., Rabani, J., *J. Phys. Chem.* **69,** 1324 (1965).
(6) Némethy, G., Scheraga, H. A., *J. Chem. Phys.* **36,** 3401 (1962).
(7) Noyes, R. M., *J. Am. Chem. Soc.* **86,** 971 (1964).

RECEIVED December 18, 1967.

5

Pulse Radiolysis of Ice and Frozen HF Solutions

G. NILSSON and H. C. CHRISTENSEN

AB Atomenergi, Studsvik, Sweden

J. FENGER, P. PAGSBERG, and S. O. NIELSEN

Danish AEC Research Establishment, Risö, Denmark

A transient species, supposed to be a trapped electron, has been observed in pure ice and in frozen 3×10^{-5}M *HF solution by means of the pulse radiolysis technique. The maximum of the absorption band of the transient is located at about 680 n.m. in pure ice at −10°, −31°, and −50°C. The half-width of the band is considerably smaller than that of the solvated electron in liquid water. The* G*-values for the transient are estimated to be 0.3, 0.07, and 0.02 at −10°, −31°, and −50°C. respectively and to be 0.1 in the frozen HF solution at −10°C. The decay of the transient is complex in pure ice but first order in the frozen HF solution.*

It is now a well established fact that electrons produced by ionizing radiation in liquid water can exist in the water as solvated electrons for several hundred μsec. (*9*). They have a high extinction coefficient for light absorption and the absorption spectrum is a broad band with a maximum at 720 n.m. (*11*). The trap for the electron is supposed to be a potential well formed by polarization of the water by the electron itself (*16*).

Electrons are also trapped at 77°K. in irradiated alkaline glassy ice (*8, 22, 23, 25*), in glassy ice containing $NaClO_4$, LiCl, and KF (*6, 7*) and in frozen sugar solutions (*5*). Electrons trapped in glassy ice at this temperature are stabilized and can therefore be studied by ESR or optical spectroscopy a long time after irradiation. The electrons trapped in alkaline ice are characterized by an ESR singlet at $g = 2.001$ and an absorption band with a maximum at 585 n.m. (*22, 23*). The trap is supposed to be a hydroxide anion vacancy formed during irradiation (*25*) or a defect present in the ice lattice before irradiation (*2*).

Trapped electrons are furthermore formed by the deposition of alkali-metal atoms on pure ice at 77°K. (*3*). The ice samples were microcrystalline or amorphous and from the ESR spectrum which exhibited hyperfine structure one could draw the conclusion that the electron was located in a well defined trap in which it was surrounded by six protons. The optical absorption band had a broad plateau ranging from about 600 to 680 n.m.

Until recently no ESR signals or optical absorption caused by electrons were detected when pure crystalline ice was examined after irradiation at 77°K. This result had been expected since the self-trapping mechanism will probably give very shallow traps in crystalline ice. The reason is that the dielectric relaxation time even at the melting point of ice is roughly six orders of magnitude longer than for water, and it has therefore been assumed that the dipole orientation will not contribute to the energy. The concentration of lattice defects which can act as traps is also smaller in pure crystalline ice than in glassy ice. The most likely result would therefore be that the electrons are rapidly recaptured by their parent ions (*15, 17, 18, 19*).

A year ago Shubin, Zhigunov, Zolotarevsky, and Dolin used the pulse radiolysis technique and discovered a transient species in pure crystalline ice and in frozen crystalline solutions of $LiClO_4$ and KOH which had an absorption band in the same spectral range as the solvated electron in liquid water (*20, 21*). Similar experiments were independently started at Risö and spectra of the same shape as those reported by Shubin *et al.* were recorded when pure crystalline ice and crystalline ice containing HF was irradiated.

In a quite recent report Eiben and Taub have demonstrated that electrons are stabilized also in pure crystalline ice at 77°K. (*4*). The maximum of the absorption band appeared at 640 n.m. The *G*-value was only 2×10^{-4} and the yield increased with dose up to about 5 Mrad and then approached a constant value.

Experimental

The pure ice crystals were prepared in a quartz tube from triply distilled water which was degassed by shaking and evacuation. This procedure included saturation of the water twice at a pressure of 1 atm. with hydrogen gas that had passed a liquid nitrogen cooled trap. The freezing was then performed under a hydrogen pressure of 1 atm. In order to get sufficiently transparent crystals a method for single crystal preparation (*10*) was adopted and the water samples were frozen slowly from the surface by putting the quartz tube in a thermally controlled jacket. The transparency of the ice samples obtained in this way was satisfactory. Examination of the samples with polarized light showed that they generally consisted of a few large crystals oriented in different directions.

When the HF crystals were prepared the quartz tube was protected by a thin layer of paraffin wax. Triply distilled water was degassed by shaking and evacuation to remove most of the O_2 and CO_2 and then some tenth of a ml. of a 0.5*M* HF solution was added. The solution was saturated with H_2, degassed, resaturated, and degassed again. Finally the solution was saturated with H_2 and frozen in the same way as the pure water samples. A piece of the top and the bottom of the crystal was cut away, and the concentration of HF in the two samples was determined spectrophotometrically by the zirconium-alizarin method (*14*). The crystal was discarded if a concentration gradient was detected. The concentration of HF in the irradiated part of the crystal was also determined.

A schematic drawing of the irradiation setup is shown in Figure 1. The ice samples, about 30 mm. long and 25 mm. in diameter, are placed in a tube of stainless steel which has a mirror in one end and a Suprasil window in the other. Methanol cooled with dry ice is pumped through a jacket surrounding the tube and the temperature of the ice crystal is measured with a small thermocouple in direct contact with the crystal surface. Light from an Osram xenon lamp passes twice through the crystal which was irradiated from the mirror end of the Cryostat with single 0.4–3.6 μsec. electron pulses with a current of about 300 mA. The electron energy was about 11 Mev. and the dose in the order of 10^4 rad. The experiments were performed at the linear electron accelerator at Risö and the transient spectra were recorded by means of a fast photoelectric

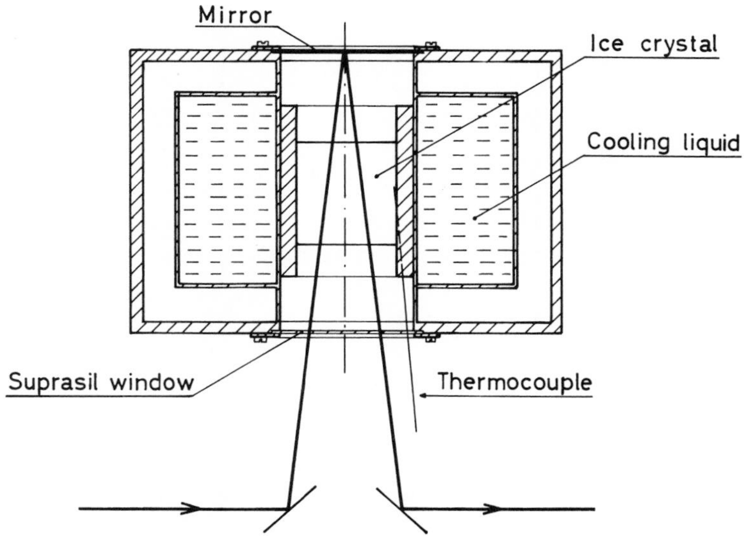

Figure 1. Schematic drawing of the irradiation setup

system developed for pulse radiolysis studies. The dose was measured by replacing the ice crystal with a polystyrene cell with thin polystyrene windows which was filled with N_2O saturated, 1 mM hexacyanoferrate(II) solution and subsequently recording the concentration of the hexacyanoferrate(III) ions produced by the electron pulse.

Results and Discussion

The absorption spectra of pure ice irradiated at −10°, −31°, and −50°C. are shown in Figure 2 and the absorption spectra of pure ice and frozen $3 \times 10^{-5}M$ HF solution irradiated at −10°C. are shown in Figure 3. The points refer to minimum light transmission as read from the oscilloscope traces and to a crystal length of 30 mm. and a dose of 10^4 rad.

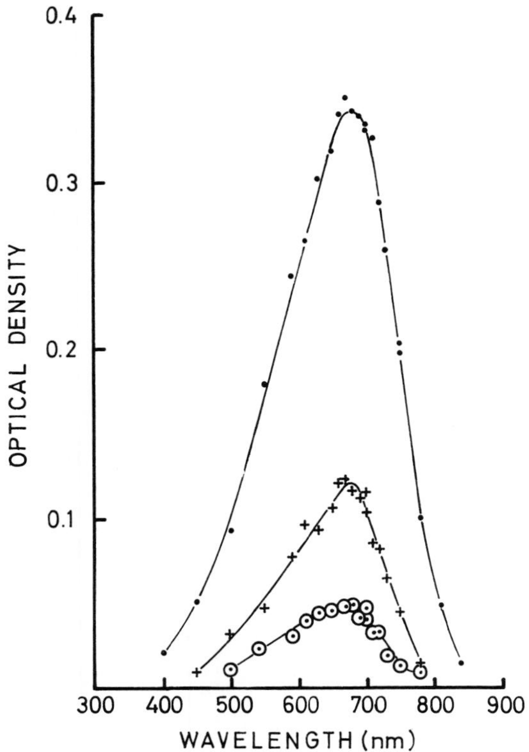

Figure 2. The absorption spectra of pure ice irradiated at −10° (●), −31° (+) and −50°C.(⊙)

The figures show that the transient species has a broad absorption band with maximum absorption in the same spectral range as the solvated electron in liquid water. The peak height decreases with decreasing temperature and for the HF crystal the yield is about one third of that in pure ice. The shape and position of the spectrum indicates that the observed species is a trapped electron.

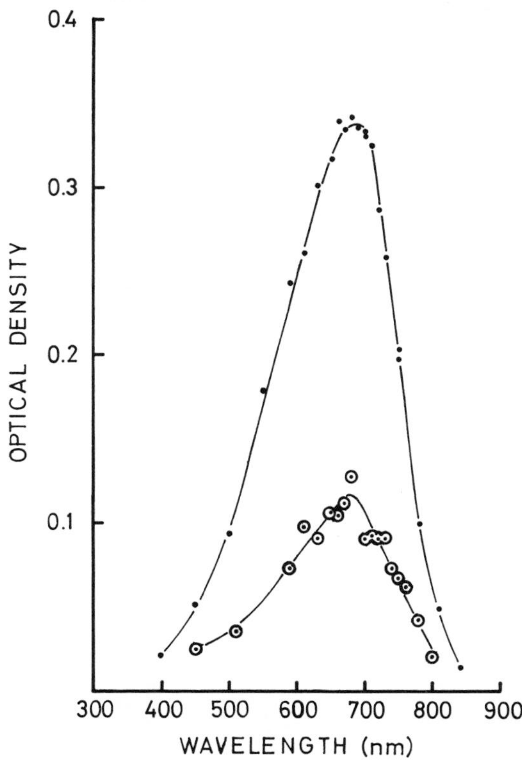

Figure 3. The absorption spectra at −10°C. of irradiated pure ice (●) and frozen 3 × 10⁻⁵M HF solution (⊙)

The nature of the electron trap is not known. If the electron is trapped by the same mechanism as in liquid water its energy in e.v. may be given by (*12*)

$$E = \mu/m[4.41(\epsilon_{op}^{-1} - \epsilon_s^{-1})^2 + 1.37(\epsilon_{op}^{-1} - \epsilon_s^{-1})(1 - \epsilon_{op}^{-1})] \quad (1)$$

where ϵ_{op} is the optical and ϵ_s the static dielectric constant and m and μ are the mass and effective mass of the electron respectively. In this formula both orientation and electronic polarization is included. If the data for water at 20°C. ($E = 1.72$ e.v. (*11*), $\epsilon_s = 80.2$ (*24*), and $\epsilon_{op} = 1.78$) are substituted in Equation 1, then $\mu/m = 1.03$. The value of μ/m would probably be about the same in ice at −10°C. The dielectric relaxation time at this temperature is, however, about 60 μsec. (*1*), which means that the dipole orientation would not contribute to the energy of the trapped electron. Then ϵ_s should be replaced by the high frequency value ϵ_∞ = 3.15 in Equation 1 and the absorption peak would have been found at about 2600 n.m. Instead the position of the peak is at 680 n.m.—*i.e.*, the trapping energy is larger than in water. This result indicates that it is likely that the dipole orientation contributes to the energy whatever the details of the trapping mechanism are. There was, however, no displacement of the absorption peak during the lifetime of the transient—*i.e.*, the full trapping energy was developed within 0.4 μsec., which is much shorter than the dielectric relaxation time. The explanation may be that the electrons are trapped at positions in the ice lattice where the dipole relaxation time is not given by the dielectric relaxation time but is considerably shorter. The existence of electron traps in pure ice has been

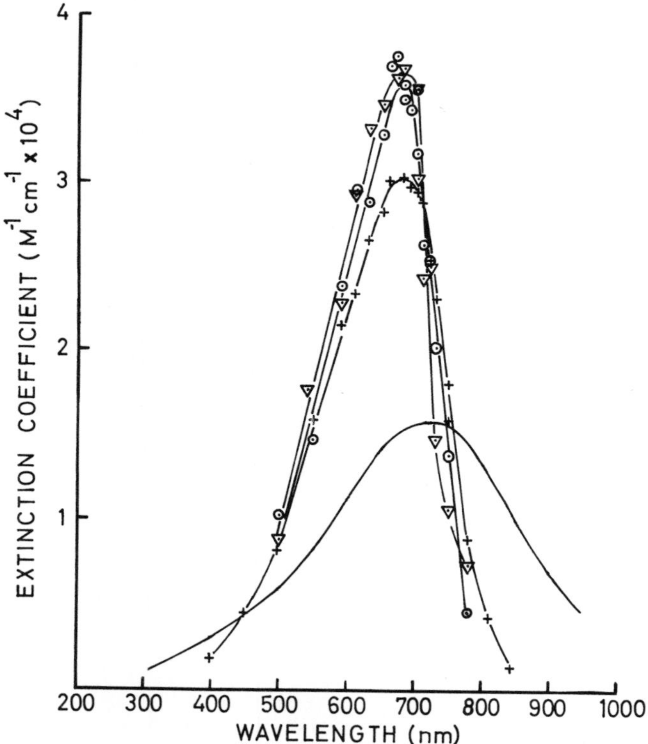

Figure 4. The absorption spectra of the electron trapped in ice at −10° (+), −31° (⊙) and −50°C. (△) and the absorption spectrum of the solvated electron in water at 20°C. (solid line). The spectra for the electron in ice are calculated using an oscillator strength = 0.65

demonstrated by Bennett *et al.* (*3*) and by Eiben and Taub (*4*). If the traps are dislocations it seems reasonable to assume that the relaxation time for dipole orientation is decreased in this perturbated part of the ice lattice. The relaxation time may be so short that it takes less than 0.4 μsec. for the electron to polarize the lattice and create a trap of full depth. These regions need not be large since the potential energy of the trapped electron is proportional to $\int_R^\infty \frac{dr}{r^2}$ where R is the cage radius, and integration to 10R will give 90% of the energy. The trapping energy may then be given by Equation 1. The value of ϵ_{op} for ice is 1.71 and ϵ_s is equal to 94.2 at −10°C. (*1*). If these values and μ/m = 1.03 are substituted in Equation 1 we find that the absorption maximum is located at 679 nm.

If this trapping mechanism is correct a reasonable assumption would be that the oscillator strength has the same value in ice and water. This assumption has been made and the result is shown in Figure 4. The spectra are calculated for f = 0.65 (*13*) and the absorption spectrum of the solvated electron is shown for comparison. As seen from the figure the maximum of the absorption band is displaced to a shorter wavelength in ice and the half width of the peak is smaller in ice than in water.

The *G*-values, collected in Table I, have been calculated from the optical densities by using the extinction coefficients in Figure 4. The values have been corrected with respect to the decay of the transient during the electron pulse.

Table I.

Sample	°C.	D_o	ϵ	G
Pure ice	−10	0.358	30200	0.3
	−31	~0.134	35800	~0.07
	−50	~0.054	36500	~0.02
Frozen 3 × $10^{-5}M$ HF sol.	−10	~0.086	30200	~0.1

The yield of the transient was not changed even after 100 electron pulses had been given to the same ice crystal. We do not know if there is a sufficient number of traps in the ice crystal to account for this.

The decay of the transient in ice containing 3 × $10^{-5}M$ HF is first order with a half-life of 0.5 μsec. The decay of the transient in pure ice is, however, complex and we have therefore used a computer to evaluate the data. A large number of kinetic models have been investigated and we have found that the decay contains a second order reaction with a rate constant of about $10^{11}M^{-1}$ sec.$^{-1}$. The value of the constant is very little temperature dependent and may therefore represent tunneling of the protons to the trapping site. It seems likely that a fraction of the electrons decay according to first order kinetics.

Literature Cited

(1) Auty, R. P., Cole, R. H., *J. Chem. Phys.* **20,** 1309 (1952).
(2) Barzynski, H., Schulte-Frohlinde, D., Z. *Naturforsch.* **22a,** 2131 (1967).
(3) Bennett, J. E., Mile, B., Thomas, A., *J. Chem. Soc.* **1967,** 1393.
(4) Eiben, K., Taub, I. A., *Nature* **216,** 782 (1967).
(5) Elliott, W. R., *Science* **157,** 558 (1967).
(6) Ershov, B. G., Pikaev, A. K., *Izv. Akad. Nauk. SSSR Ser. Khim* **9,** 1637 (1966).
(7) Ershov, B. G., Pikaev, A. K., *High Energy Chem.* **1,** 25 (1967).
(8) Ershov, B. G., Pikaev, A. K., Glazunov, P. J., Spitsyn, V. I., *Dokl. Akad. Nauk SSSR* **149,** 363 (1963).
(9) Hart, E. J., Gordon, S., Fielden, E. M., *J. Phys. Chem.* **70,** 150 (1966).
(10) Jona, F., Scherrer, P., *Helv. Phys. Acta* **25,** 35 (1952).
(11) Keene, J. P., *Discussions Faraday Soc.* **36,** 304 (1963).
(12) Kevan, L., *Progr. Solid State Chem.* **2,** 304 (1965).
(13) Matheson, M. S., Advan. Chem. Ser. **50,** 45 (1965).
(14) Megregian, S., Maier, F. J., *J. Am. Water Works Assoc.* **44,** 239 (1952).
(15) Moorthy, P. N., Weiss, J. J., Advan. Chem. Ser. **50,** 180 (1965).
(16) Platzman, R. L., *U. S. Natl. Acad. Sci. Pub.* **No. 305,** 34 (1953).
(17) Schiller, R., *J. Chem. Phys.* **43,** 2760 (1965).
(18) *Ibid.*, **47,** 2278 (1967).
(19) *Ibid.*, **47,** 2281 (1967).
(20) Shubin, V. N., Zhigunov, V. I., Zolotarevsky, V. I., Dolin, P. I., *Nature* **212,** 1002 (1966).
(21) Shubin, V. N., Zhigunov, V. I., Zolotarevsky, V. I., Dolin, P. I., *Dokl. Akad. Nauk. SSSR* **174,** 416 (1967).
(22) Schulte-Frohlinde, D., Eiben, K., Z. *Naturforsch.* **17a,** 445 (1962).
(23) *Ibid.*, **18a,** 199 (1963).
(24) Vidulich, G. A., Evans, D. F., Kay, R. L., *J. Phys. Chem.* **71,** 656 (1967).
(25) Zimbrick, J., Kevan, L., *J. Chem. Phys.* **47,** 2364 (1967).

Received January 5, 1968.

6

On the Reactivity of Hydrated Electrons Toward Inorganic Compounds

MICHAEL ANBAR[1] and EDWIN J. HART

Chemistry Division, Argonne National Laboratory, Argonne, Ill. 60439

The rates of reaction of a number of inorganic complex ions and oxy-anions with hydrated electrons have been measured and the parameters which determine the rate of their diffusion-controlled reactions have been evaluated and discussed. Ligands modify the reactivity of ions by their effect on the configuration and stability of the lower state of oxidation, on the electronic distribution of the central atom, and on their capacity of acting as electron transfer bridges. Each of these factors contributes to the reactivity of inorganic complexes. The reaction cross section of certain highly reactive oxidants is significantly larger than their crystallographic dimensions, suggesting long range electron tunneling. General trends in the reactivity of the hydrated electron with inorganic compounds are discussed.

Since the discovery of its absorption spectrum, the rate of reaction of the hydrated electron with inorganic cations, anions, and complex ions has been extensively studied (*2, 7, 12, 13, 14, 18, 23, 29, 36, 39*) and several attempts have been made to deduce some generalizations on the mechanism of e^-_{aq} reactions with inorganic compounds. Substantial differences in reactivity exist, however, between "similar" inorganic compounds, and the interpretation of their kinetic behavior is therefore much less successful than that for organic systems (*1, 5, 6*). Our understanding of the reactivity of inorganic compounds is limited at best, to the qualitative level. In some early studies salt effects were not critically considered; consequently, some erroneous conclusions were drawn. We further evaluate these data and provide new rate constant data on some inorganic ions not heretofore studied.

[1] Weizmann Institute of Science, Rehovoth, Israel.

Table I. The Reactivity of Hydrated

	Compound	Supplier	pH	$\mu \times 10^5$M	k_{obs} $\times 10^{-10}$ M^{-1} sec.$^{-1}$	k_{corr}
1.1	$[Co(NH_3)_6](ClO_4)_3$	[a]	6.7	6	8.15	8.2
1.2	$[Co(NH_3)_5H_2O](ClO_4)_3$	[a]	4.9	6	8.1	8.2
1.3	$[Co(NH_3)_5CN](ClO_4)_2$	[a]	6.1	4	6.3	6.3
1.4	$[Co(NH_3)_5Cl](ClO_4)_2$	[a]	7.3	4	6.1	6.1
1.5	$[Co(NH_3)_5Br](ClO_4)_2$	[a]	7.7	4	6.2	6.2
1.6	$[Co(NH_3)_5N_3]ClO_4)_2$	[a]	6.3	4	6.3	6.3
1.7	$[Co(NH_3)_5(CN)H_2O](ClO_4)_2$	[a]	6.1	4	5.6	5.6
1.8	$[Co(en)_2CO_3]ClO_4$	[a]	7.2	2	4.9	4.9
1.9	$[en_2CoO_2(NH_2)Coen_2]Br_4$	[g]	6.2	10	9.6	9.7
1.10	$[(NH_3)_5CoO_2Co(NH_3)_5]Br_5$	[g]	5.9	5	8.2	8.3
1.11	$[(CN)_5CoO_2Co(CN)_5]K_5$	[g]	7.0	10	2.9	2.8

[a] Obtained from the group of H. Taube, Stanford University.
[b] Calculated from the ionic mobility of $Co(NH_3)^{3+} = 1.02 \times 10^{-3}$ cm.^{2}/volts sec. (*16*).
[c] Estimated.
[d] Estimated from Co–NH_3 bond length (*37, 38*) in Co(III) amino complexes.

Many of the reactions of inorganic compounds with hydrated electrons are extremely rapid, their reactions being essentially diffusion controlled. A detailed analysis of these reactions reveals new information on the mode of interaction of hydrated electrons with reactive inorganic solutes.

Experimental

The preparation of solutions, irradiation of the samples, and analysis of decay curves by "Chloe" follow our previously described techniques (*24*). Hydrated electron scavengers were removed from the hydrogen-saturated matrix by its pre-irradiation before injection of the solute in cases where concentrations of the order of $10\mu M$ solute were tested. The sources of supply of the chemicals used appear in Tables I and II.

Results

A number of inorganic compounds have been investigated for their rates of reaction with hydrated electrons. For purposes of later discussions, we divide them into two groups: compounds which approach the diffusion controlled rate and compounds which react much slower. The data of the first group are presented in Table I which includes a number of cobalt complexes, and in Table II which contains the remaining fast reacting compounds. Here they are presented in the order of increasing atomic number of their central atom. In addition to the experimental conditions and the observed specific rate constants (k_{obs}), these tables

Electrons with Cobaltic Complexes

$D \times 10^5$ $cm.^2$ $sec.^{-1}$	$r \times 10^8$ cm.	$k_{diff} \times 10^{-10}$ M^{-1} $sec.^{-1}$	$\alpha = \frac{k_{corr}}{k_{diff}}$
0.9	2.6	9.2	0.89
0.8 [b]	2.6 [d]	9.0	0.91
0.7 [c]	2.8	6.3	1.00
0.7 [c]	2.6 [e]	6.2	0.98
0.7 [c]	2.7 [f]	6.2	1.00
0.7 [c]	2.8 [c]	6.3	1.00
0.7 [c]	2.7 [c]	6.2	0.91
0.7 [c]	3.7 [c]	4.4	1.11
0.6 [c]	4.5 [c]	11.6	0.84
0.6 [c]	4.0 [c]	14.3	0.58
0.6 [c]	5.0 [c]	0.12	23.3

[e] Estimated from (37, 38) for $[Co(NH_3)_3Cl_2H_2O]^+$.
[f] Estimated from $[Pt(NH_3)_2Br_4]^{2-}$ and $[Co(en)_2Br_2]^+$.
[g] Obtained from J. A. Weil, Argonne National Laboratory.

contain the specific rate constant corrected for the salt effect (k_{corr}), according to (*28*)

$$\log \frac{k_{corr}}{k_{obs}} = 1.02\ Z \frac{\mu^{1/2}}{1 + a\mu^{1/2}}.$$

Z is the charge of the substrate ion, μ is the ionic strength of the solution, $\mu = 1/2\ \Sigma_i Z_i^2 c_i$, and $a = r/3$, where r = the sum of radii of the two reactants in A. In these tables, k_{diff} is the diffusion limited bimolecular specific rate constant calculated from the Debye equation (*20*) from the sums of the diffusion coefficients ($D_{e^-} + D_x$) and radii of e^-_{aq} and the substrate ion ($r_{e^-} + r_x$) (*22*).

$$k_{diff} = 4\pi N(D_{e^-} + D_x)(r_{e^-} + r_x)Q/(e^Q - 1)$$

where $Q = -Z_x e^2/\epsilon k T(r_{e^-} + r_x)$; ϵ = the macroscopic dielectric constant of water; 78.6 at 25°C.; N = Avogadro's number, 6.025×10^{23} molecules/mole; k = Bolzmann's Constant, 1.38×10^{-16} erg/degree; Z_x = charge on substrate ion; $D_{e^-} = 4.7 \times 10^{-5}$ sq. cm. sec.$^{-1}$ (*33*). The diffusion coefficients of the substrate ions were taken or estimated from the values of published ionic mobilities (*16, 25*). We used 2.5 A. as the radius of e^-_{aq}; that of the substrate ion was calculated or estimated from known bond lengths (*37, 38*).

Specific rate constants for less reactive compounds are presented in Table III in the order of increasing atomic number of the central atom. The implications of these results are discussed below.

Table II. Reactions of Hydrated Electrons

	Compound	*Supplier*	*pH*	μ $\times$ *10*^{5}M	k_{obs} $\times$ *10*$^{-9}$M^{-1} *sec.*$^{-1}$	k_{corr}
2.1	NaOCl	–	10.2	10^2	7.2	7.0
2.2	Na_2TiF_6	a	6.6	10^4	5.8	3.5
2.3	NH_4VO_3	d	11.0	10	4.9	4.9
2.4	$[Cr(NH_3)_5Cl]Cl_2$	g	6.7	10	62.	62.
2.5	$K_4Cr(CN)_6$	i	10.0	5×10^3	14.	3.3
2.6	$Na_2[Fe(CN)_5NO]$	j	10.5	10	23.5	23.5
2.7	K_3FeF_6	i	6.6	10^4	10.5	2.2
2.8	$Ni(en)_2SO_4$	i	11.0	100	7.5	8.0
2.9	$K_2Ni(CN)_4$	i	11.0	5×10^2	5.5	4.1
2.10	$KNiF(H_2O)_3$	j	8.5	10^4	7.2	12.0
2.11	Na_2SeO_4	d	11.0	10^2	1.1	1.0
2.12	$K_2Pd(CN)_4$	i	10.6	10^3	2.8	1.9
2.13	$K_4Mn(CN)_6$	j	9.0	5×10^3	25.	5.9
2.14	K_2SnF_6	n	6.5	10^3	4.1	2.9
2.15	$KSbO_3$	p	11.0	10^2	13.	12.
2.16	Na_2TeO_3	a	10.9	10^2	1.1	1.0
2.17	Na_2TeO_4	a	11.0	10^2	16.	15.
2.18	$K_2Pt(CN)_4$	j	10.6	10^3	3.9	2.9
2.19	K_2PtCl_6	j	10.0	10^3	2.0	1.4
2.20	Tl_2SO_4	j	8.5	10^2	37.	40.
2.21	$KAu(CN)_2$	j	10.6	10^3	4.2	3.5
2.22	K_2IrCl_6	i	10.2	5×10^3	20.	9.3
2.23	K_3IrCl_6	i	10.6	5×10^3	9.4	3.0

[a] BDH Lab Reagent, purified.
[b] Estimated by analogy with SO_4^{2-} and $Fe(CN)_6^{3-}$.
[c] Calculated from experimental data (*37, 38*).
[d] BDH Analar.
[e] Estimated by analogy with ClO_3^- and BrO_3^-.
[f] Estimate based on planar configuration.
[g] Obtained from H. Taube's group, Stanford University.
[h] Estimated from (*37, 38*) $Cr(CNS)_4(NH_3)_2^-$.

The effect of ionic environment on the rate of diffusion controlled e^-_{aq} reactions is revealed when one compares the experimental rate constants with the calculated values. In Table I the highly charged bis-pentacyano cobaltic peroxide (I) is much more reactive than expected for a pentavalent anion (1.11). It has been claimed (*19*) that polyvalent anions exhibit a lower effective charge in their kinetic behavior than expected from their structural formulae. We have checked the salt effect on the reaction of I + e^-_{aq} and compared it with the NO_3^- + e^-_{aq} reaction. The results presented in Table IV and Figure 1 show that nitrate ions possess a normal salt effect, a result previously obtained by competition kinetics (*15, 17*). On the other hand, the salt effect of the I + e^-_{aq} reaction shows that this bis-pentacyano cobaltic peroxide ion has an

with Various Reactive Inorganic Compounds

$D_x \times 10^5$ *cm.² sec.⁻¹*	$r_x \times 10^8$ *cm.*	$k_{diff} \times 10^{-9}$ M^{-1} *sec.⁻¹*	$\alpha = \frac{k_{corr}}{k_{diff}}$
2.2	1.1	5.9	1.2
1.1 [b]	2.6 [c]	4.1	0.85
1.5 [e]	2.3 [f]	9.8	0.50
1.2	2.6	68.	0.96
0.8 [k]	3.0	0.66	5.0
0.8	3.0	4.8	4.9
1.0	2.6 [l]	1.4	1.6
0.9	3.5	64.	0.13
1.2	2.8 [f]	4.6	0.89
1.2	2.5	42.	0.29
1.0 [m]	2.2	3.1	0.29
1.2	2.8	4.6	0.41
0.8	3.0	0.68	8.7
1.0	2.7	4.2	0.69
1.3	2.5	10.2	1.08
0.9	2.0 [f]	2.6	0.36
1.1	2.4	3.6	4.2
1.2	3.0	5.1	0.77
0.9	3.2	5.4	2.6
1.9	2.2	46.	0.87
1.5	2.0	8.6	0.41
1.0	3.2	5.5	1.7
0.8	3.2	2.1	1.5

[i] Alfa Inorganic Inc.
[j] Fluka puriss.
[k] Estimated by analogy with $Fe(CN)_6^{3-}$ which has been determined (*37, 38*).
[l] Estimated on basis (*37, 38*) of FeF_3.
[m] Estimated by analogy with SO_4^{2-}.
[n] Williams and Hopkins Reagent.
[p] Baker Analyzed.

effective charge close to unity and is far from behaving kinetically as a pentavalent anion.

Discussion

Diffusion Controlled Reactions. Many reactions of hydrated electrons approach the diffusion controlled limit. This has been pointed out in previous reviews (*1, 28, 34*), but there has not been an extensive evaluation of a large number of these reactions. In the present study we evaluate quantitatively the parameters of diffusion controlled reactions and compare the calculated results with experimental data.

The measured rates of reaction of Co(III) complexes clearly approach the diffusion controlled limit. A comparison between the diffusion

Table III. Some Slower Reactions of e^-_{aq} with Inorganic Compounds

	Compounds	*Supplier*	*pH*	μ	M^{-1} *sec.*$^{-1}$ k_{obs}	M^{-1} *sec.*$^{-1}$ k_{corr}
3.1	$NaBF_4$	[a]	5.8	0.2	4.0×10^5	$<2.3 \times 10^5$
3.2	Li_2SiF_6	[b]	5.9	0.15	1.5×10^6	$<5.5 \times 10^5$
3.3	KH_2PO_4	[a]	7.1	0.1	7.7×10^6	$<5.5 \times 10^5$
3.4	KH_2PO_3	[c]	6.7	0.02	7.2×10^6	5.5×10^6
3.5	NaH_2PO_2	[a]	6.8	0.01	1.1×10^5	1.0×10^5
3.6	$NaSO_3NH_2$	[d]	11.7	0.02	$<1.7 \times 10^6$	$<1.3 \times 10^6$
3.7	Na_2SO_3	[c]	10.0	0.001	$<1.3 \times 10^6$	$<1.3 \times 10^6$
3.8	$Na_3Fe(CN)_5NH_3$	[d]	8.6	0.005	$<1.0 \times 10^7$	$<1.0 \times 10^7$
3.9	$NaAsO_2$	[c]	10.6	0.0075	5.9×10^8	5.5×10^8
3.10	NaH_2AsO_4	[c]	11.0	0.001	2.0×10^8	1.9×10^8
3.11	Na_2SeO_3	[d]	10.8	0.25	1.2×10^7	2.3×10^6
3.12	$K_4Ru(CN)_6$	[d]	10.6	0.01	$<1.0 \times 10^6$	$<1.0 \times 10^6$
3.13	Na_2SnO_3	[c]	11.0	0.001	6.3×10^8	5.9×10^8
3.14	$K_4Os(CN)_6$	[d]	10.5	0.001	$<1.0 \times 10^6$	$<1.0 \times 10^6$

[a] BDH Analar.
[b] Prepared from Fluka analytical reagents.
[c] Baker Analyzed.
[d] Fluka puriss.

Table IV. The Kinetic Salt Effect on the Reactions $e^-_{aq} + NO_3^-$ and $e^-_{aq} + [(CN)_5CoO_2Co(CN)_5]^{5-}$

μ	k M^{-1} *sec.*$^{-1}$ $\times 10^{-9}$	*log* k/k_o	$\dfrac{\mu^{1/2}}{1 + 1.33\mu^{1/2}}$
	A. NO_3^-		
0 (extrap)	8.5	0	0
0.000036	8.8	0.012	0.006
0.0013	9.0	0.022	0.035
0.0015	9.6	0.050	0.037
0.0024	10.0	0.067	0.071
0.0100	11.1	0.116	0.089
0.0126	10.3	0.082	0.098
0.0185	11.2	0.118	0.116
0.0247	11.0	0.110	0.130
0.0373	11.9	0.114	0.154
	B. $[(CN)_5CoO_2Co(CN)_5]^{5-}$		
0	2.80	0	0
0.00075	2.91	0.016	0.025[a]
0.0146	3.40	0.084	0.093[a]
0.027	3.53	0.100	0.116[a]
0.052	3.78	0.130	0.141[a]

[a] $\mu^{1/2}/(1 + 2.5\mu^{1/2})$.

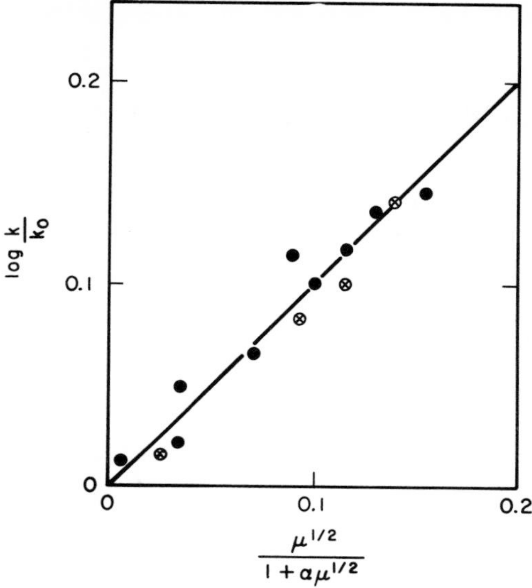

Figure 1. The effect of ionic strength on the reactivities of NO_3^- and $[Co(CN)_5O_2Co(CN)_5]^{5-}$

● NO_3^-, $\alpha = 1.33$
⊕ $[Co(CN)_5O_2Co(CN)_5]^{5-}$, $\alpha = 2.5$

controlled rates for these ions calculated according to Debye's formula (*20*) with the experimental data (Table I) shows excellent agreement for a series of tri and divalent cations (1.1–1.9). The lower value for $k_{corr}/k_{diff} = \alpha$ for pentavalent $(NH_3)_5CoO_2Co(NH_3)_5^{5+}$ (1.10) is easily explained if one assumes that one or two of the positive charges are permanently neutralized by gegen anions in the outer sphere (*26*). If two of the charges are neutralized, α equals unity within experimental error. The very large α for the pentavalent anion $(CN)_5CoO_2Co(CN)_5^{5-}$ (1.11) is most probably caused by the same effect, as has been demonstrated by its behavior in the presence of inert electrolytes (Figure 1) where a kinetically apparent charge of unity has been found. In fact, when one calculates k_{diff} for $[(CN)_5CoO_2Co(CN)_5K_4]^-$, α is equal to unity within experimental error. Another series of fifteen highly reactive cations and cationic complexes of various metals is presented in Table V. With the exception of $Cd(NH_3)_4^{2+}$ and $Ni(H_2O)_4^{2+}$ each of these complexes reacts with e^-_{aq} at a rate which is within 25% of the calculated diffusion controlled rate. In view of the uncertainties involved in the parameters which determine k_{corr} and k_{diff}, the results indicate that the calculated k_{diff} is a fairly good estimate of the diffusion controlled limit of e^-_{aq} reactions. This conclusion implies that the experimental value of $D(e^-_{aq}) = 4.7 \times 10^{-5}$ cm.^{2} sec.$^{-1}$ is reliable. We now consider the question as to whether or not $r_{e^-_{aq}} \simeq 2.5$ A. provides a reasonable encounter radius to describe the behavior of anionic and neutral reactants.

Table V. A Comparison Between k_{corr} and k_{diff} of Highly Reactive Cations and Cationic Complexes

	Compounds	$k_{corr} \times 10^{-10}$ M^{-1} sec.$^{-1}$	D_x 10^5 cm.^{2} sec.$^{-1}$	$r \times 10^8$ cm.	$k_{diff} \times 10^{-10}$ M^{-1} sec.$^{-1}$	$\alpha = \frac{k_{corr}}{k_{diff}}$	Ref.
5.1	$Cr(H_2O)_6^{+2}$	6.2	1.3	2.4	6.9	0.90	7
5.2	$Cr(H_2O)_5OH^{2+}$	6.3	1.0	2.4	6.5	0.97	7
5.3	$Cr(NH_3)_5Cl^{2+}$	6.2	0.8	2.8	6.4	0.96	This work
5.4	$Cr(en)_3^{3+}$	7.8	0.8	3.5	9.2	0.87	13
5.5	$Cr(en)_2(NCS)_2^+$	4.2	1.0	3.5	4.4	0.96	36
5.6	Cd_{aq}^{2+}	4.9	1.0	2.2	6.5	0.76	7
5.7	$Cd(NH_3)_4^{2+}$	3.1	0.9	2.6	6.4	0.49	7
5.8	Ag^+_{aq}	3.2	1.6	1.8	4.2	0.76	29
5.9	$Os(NH_3)^{3+}$	7.2	0.7	3.0	8.9	0.87	11
5.10	$Rh(NH_3)^{3+}$	7.9	0.7	3.0	8.9	0.89	11
5.11	Tl_{aq}^+	4.0	1.9	2.2	4.6	0.87	This work
5.12	UO_2^{2+}	7.4	1.6	2.6	7.2	1.03	13
5.13	$CuOH^+_{aq}$	3.3	1.3	2.0	4.1	0.81	7
5.14	$Ni(H_2O)_4^{2+}$	2.9	1.2	2.0	6.7	0.43	11
5.15	$Pb(OH)_{aq}^+$	3.9	1.3	2.7	4.3	0.91	7

An analogous comparison of the reactivity of anions and anionic complexes of Table VI reveals several interesting facts. In this table there are 40 compounds which react with e^-_{aq} at a rate which is more than 70% of the calculated diffusion controlled rate (11 of these compounds have been measured in the present study for the first time). However, only 18 compounds have α values between 0.7 and 1.5 and we consider them to agree reasonably well with the calculated ones. In some cases, the high α values may be because of the fact that they were calculated from the experimental rate constants without correcting for salt effects. These include the following compounds: $Cr(EDTA)^-$, (6.9); $Cr(OX)_3^{3-}$, (6.10); $Co(CN)_6^{3-}$, (6.20); $Co(CN)_5Cl^{3-}$, (6.21); $Co(CN)_5NO_2^{3-}$, (6.22); $Co(NO_2)_6^{3-}$, (6.23); and $Co(EDTA)^-$, (6.24).

Another group with α values higher than 1.5 may be explained by a lower effective negative charge. Figure 1 shows that the highly charged anion, bis-cobalti-cyano-peroxide (6.25), possesses an effective charge of −1. In this case, when one computes k_{diff} for a monovalent anion, α is reduced from 23.3 to 1.3. A lower effective charge could also account for the high values of the following: $Cr(CN)_6^{3-}$, (6.7); $Cr(CN)_6^{4-}$, (6.8); CrF_6^{3-}, (6.12); and FeF_6^{3-}, (6.18); and possibly $Mn(CN)_6^{4-}$.

Even after these corrections we are left with nine compounds which react with e^-_{aq} significantly faster than the calculated diffusion controlled rates. These compounds include O^- ($\alpha = 2.5$), CrO_4^{2-} ($\alpha = 3.0$), $Cr_2O_7^{2-}$ ($\alpha = 6.2$), MnO_4^- ($\alpha = 2.1$), $Fe(CN)_5NO^{2-}$ ($\alpha = 4.8$), $PdCl_4^{2-}$ ($\alpha = 1.6$), TeO_4^{2-} ($\alpha = 4.2$), $IrCl_6^{2-}$ ($\alpha = 1.7$), $PtCl_6^{2-}$ ($\alpha = 2.6$) and perhaps some of those mentioned above.

These high α values may be explained by assuming that the Debye formula does not apply to hydrated electron reactions with negatively charged ions. This suggestion does not seem plausible for two reasons: First, there are too many compounds including negatively charged ones, which do react at a rate surprisingly close to the calculated one to make this agreement fortuitous. Second, it can be shown that a number of neutral substrates also exhibit α values larger than 1.5. These include CCl_4, $CHCl_3$, $C(NO_2)_4$, and OH, each of which is an efficient oxidizing agent. One could argue that the estimated value of $r_{e^-_{aq}} = 2.5$ A. is too low and that $r_{e^-_{aq}}$ is of the order of 5.0 A. This suggestion does not conflict with the experimental behavior of the cations, especially the di- and tri-positively charged reactants, but it does imply that none of the monovalent anion reduction reactions is diffusion controlled. Furthermore, there are a number of neutral reactants, including *inter alia* hydrogen atoms, oxygen molecules, methyl iodide, methyl mercaptan, cyanobenzene, nitrotoluene, tetracyanoethylene, and cysteamine which have α values close to unity when calculated with $r_{e^-_{aq}} = 2.5$ A. Therefore, we conclude that 2.5 A. is a good approximation of the reaction radius of e^-_{aq} in most of its reactions.

Tunneling is another explanation for the abnormally high α's since the effective cross section of certain e^-_{aq} reactions is larger than that calculated from the sum of the radii. In order to apply Debye's formula, we must assign an effective radius, $r_{e^-} + r_X$, of 9 to 12 A. for these reactions instead of the "geometrical" sum of 4–6 A. Distances as long as 9–12 A. are unlikely to facilitate electron transfer by orbital overlap but electron tunneling through a free-energy barrier is expected if the energy level of the accommodated electron in the acceptor molecule matches that of its initial state in water. When the gain in free energy is large enough one can envisage many available electronic states thereby enhancing the probability for tunneling in spite of the high potential barrier. Alternatively, the overall rate of the reaction may depend not only on the initial tunneling step leading to an excited state but on the electron transition from this state to a more stable one. This transition is favored by an increase in the energy difference between these states.

Table VI. A Comparison Between k_{corr} and k_{diff} of

	Compound	$k_{corr} \times 10^{-9}$ M^{-1} *sec.*$^{-1}$	D_x 10^5 *cm.*^{2} *sec.*$^{-1}$
6.1	O^-	22.0	6.0
6.2	NO^{2-}	4.6	1.4
6.3	NO_3^-	8.5	1.8
6.4	$S_2O_8^{2-}$	10.6	0.9
6.5	ClO^-	7.0	2.2
6.6	VO_3^-	4.9	1.5
6.7	$Cr(CN)_6^{3-}$	4.0	0.9
6.8	$Cr(CN)_6^{4-}$	3.3	0.8
6.9	$Cr(EDTA)^-$	26.0[a]	0.9
6.10	$Cr(OX)_3^{3-}$	18.0[a]	0.9
6.11	CrO_4^{2-}	10.0	1.0
6.12	CrF_6^{3-}	2.7	1.0
6.13	$Cr_2O_7^{2-}$	33.0	0.8
6.14	MnO_4^-	22.0	1.5
6.15	$Mn(CN)_6^{4-}$	5.4	0.9
6.16	$Fe(CN)_6^{3-}$	3.0	0.9
6.17	$Fe(CN)_5NO^{2-}$	24.0	1.0
6.18	FeF_6^{3-}	2.7	1.0
6.19	$Fe(EDTA)OH^{2-}$	7.1	0.9
6.20	$Co(CN)_6^{3-}$	3.6[a]	0.9
6.21	$Co(CN)_5Cl^{3-}$	18.0[a]	0.9
6.22	$Co(CN)_5NO_2^{3-}$	8.0[a]	0.9
6.23	$Co(NO_2^-)_6^{3-}$	12.5[a]	0.8
6.24	$Co(EDTA)^-$	29.0[a]	0.9
6.25	$(CN)_5CoO_2Co(CN)_5^{5-}$	28.0	0.6
6.26	$Ni(EDTA)^-$	0.1[a]	0.9
6.27	$Ni(CN)_4^{2-}$	2.7	1.2
6.28	AsF_6^-	9.0	1.3
6.29	Br_2^-	13.0	1.8
6.30	$Pd(CN)_6^{2-}$	1.9	1.1
6.31	$PdCl_4^{2-}$	7.7	0.9
6.32	$Ag(EDTA)_3^-$	1.6[a]	0.7
6.33	$Ag(CN)_2^-$	1.5	1.3
6.34	$Cd(EDTA)^{2-}$	0.39[a]	0.9
6.35	SnO_2^{2-}	3.2	1.0
6.36	$Sn(EDTA)^{2-}$	0.7	0.9
6.37	SbO_3^-	12.0	1.3

Highly Reactive Anions and Anionic Complexes

$r \times 10^8$ *cm.*	$k_{diff} \times 10^{-9}$ M^{-1} *sec.*$^{-1}$	$\alpha = \frac{k_{corr}}{k_{diff}}$	*Ref.*
1.0	8.6	2.5	*30*
1.1	5.2	0.88	*39*
1.4	6.7	1.3	This work
5.0	10.6	1.00	*39*
1.1	5.9	1.2	This work
2.3	9.8	0.5	This work
3.0	1.9	2.1	*7*
3.0	0.66	5.0	This work
3.2	12.0	2.2	*36*
3.4	2.5	7.2	*36*
2.3	3.3	3.0	*13*
2.2	1.0	2.7	*7*
3.2	5.3	6.2	*39*
2.2	9.4	2.1	*39*
3.0	0.68	7.9	*2*
3.0	1.9	1.5	*23*
3.0	5.0	4.8	This work
2.6	1.4	1.9	This work
3.2	5.5	1.3	*9*
3.0	1.9	1.9	*7*
3.0	1.9	9.5	*13*
3.2	2.2	3.6	*13*
3.6	2.7	4.6	*13*
3.2	12.0	2.4	*13*
5.0	1.2 (21.0)[b]	23.3 (1.3)[b]	This work
3.2	5.5	0.018	*9*
2.8	4.6	0.59	This work
2.3	9.4	0.96	*7*
2.3	10.2	1.3	*29*
3.0	5.1	0.37	This work
3.0	4.9	1.6	*7*
3.0	1.8	0.9	*9*
2.1	8.7	0.17	*7*
3.2	5.5	0.07	*9*
2.3	3.3	0.97	*7*
3.2	5.5	0.13	*9*
2.5	10.0	1.2	This work

Table VI. A Comparison Between k_{corr} and k_{diff} of Highly

	Compound	$k_{corr} \times 10^{-9}$ M^{-1} sec.$^{-1}$	D_x 10^5 cm.^{2} sec.$^{-1}$
6.38	TeO_4^{2-}	15.0	0.9
6.39	I^-_3	20.0	1.5
6.40	IO_3^-	7.7	1.4
6.41	IO_4^-	11.0	1.4
6.42	$IrCl_6^{2-}$	9.3	1.0
6.43	$IrCl_6^{3-}$	3.0	0.8
6.44	$PtCl_6^{2-}$	14.0	0.9
6.45	Hg(EDTA)$^{2-}$	5.1[a]	0.9
6.46	Pb(EDTA)$^{2-}$	3.8[a]	0.9
6.47	PbO_2^{2-}	3.5	0.8

[a] k_{obs}.

In the latter case we expect a correlation between the rate of the reaction and the overall gain in free energy.

In a second type of reaction electron transfer takes place at a slow rate, not because of an appreciable energy of activation, but because the formation of a chemical bond between the reactants is not feasible even in the transition state, thus no classical transition state can ever be formed. Still, if electron transfer is energetically feasible, electron tunneling may take place between two adjacent reactants without the formation of any "classical" transition state. Such tunneling may have a transmission coefficient much lower than unity. The energy level of the accommodated electron should be low enough to allow electron transfer even before any atomic rearrangement takes place. Since it is expected that an increase in temperature will facilitate the formation of a chemical bond between e^-_{aq} and the reactant in the transition state, the constancy of the activation energy of many e^-_{aq} reactions (*4, 8*), including the slower ones, strongly suggests a process such as electron tunneling.

The Effect of Ligands on the Reactivity of Metal Ions. We pointed out before (*7*) that ligands affect electron transfer to the central atom. Besides, they alter the electron affinity of the central atom by affecting its electronic configuration (*1, 2*). These conclusions are supported by the experimental findings of this paper. In addition, one must consider that in reactions with a large ΔF, electron tunneling may exist. In this case, electron transfer takes place instantaneously irrespective of the electron transfer capacity of the ligands.

Reactive Anions and Anionic Complexes (Continued)

$r \times 10^8$ *cm.*	$k_{diff} \times 10^{-9}$ M^{-1} *sec.*$^{-1}$	$\alpha = \frac{k_{corr}}{k_{diff}}$	*Ref.*
2.4	3.6	4.2	This work
5.0	21.0	0.95	*10*
2.2	9.2	0.83	*7*
2.4	10.0	1.1	*7*
3.0	5.0	1.7	This work
3.0	1.9	1.4	This work
3.2	5.4	2.6	This work
3.3	5.6	0.9	9
3.3	5.6	0.74	9
2.5	3.6	1.0	*7*

[b] *see* text.

The effect of cyanide on the reactivity of its complexes is primarily due to its ligand field, which in the case of d^4 and d^5 ions stabilizes the vacant d orbitals and thus by increasing the electron affinity it increases the reactivity of its complexes. This is observed for the cyano complexes of Cr(II)(2.5), Mn(II)(2.13), and Fe(III)(2.6). Because of destabilization of the vacant orbital, the reactivity of cyano complexes of d^6 ions is dramatically decreased. This effect is illustrated by Fe(II)(3.8), Ru(II)(3.12), and Os(II)(3.14) cyano complexes, in addition to the previously measured (*2*) extremely low reactivity of $Fe(CN)_6^{4-}$. The cyanide ligand seems to inhibit the reactivity of complexes even in cases where its effect on the d electron distribution cannot be exhibited as can be seen by comparing Zn_{aq}(II) and $Zn(CN)_4^{2-}$, Cd_{aq}(II) and $Cd(CN)_4^{2-}$. This effect which has been attributed to a limited conductivity of electrons through cyanide (*7*), could as well be attributed to a hindrance of approach of e^-_{aq} and the central atom thus increasing the thickness of the potential barrier and thereby diminishing the probability of tunneling. In the case of d^8 complexes there may be a diminution of the ligand field effect, which tends to increase the reactivity, by the inhibitory effect of the cyanide ligand as electron conductor. Thus, one finds in the case of Ni(II) an increase in reactivity (2.9, 2.10) whereas $Pd(CN)_4^{2-}$ (2.12) and $Pt(CN)_4^{2-}$ (2.18) seem to be somewhat less reactive than their chloro complexes (*7, 13*).

Ethylenediamine as well as EDTA are poorer electron conductors than H_2O. This can be seen from the reactivity of the corresponding Ni(II) complexes (2.8, 6.26) and $Ni(en_3)^{2+}$ ($k = 2 \times 10^7 M^{-1}$ sec.$^{-1}$)

(*31*) compared with Ni^{2+}_{aq}, as well as Cd(II) EDTA complex (6.34)(*9*) and $Cd(en)_3^{2+}$ ($k = 3 \times 10^7 M^{-1}$ sec.$^{-1}$) (*31*) compared with $Cd(II)_{aq}$ (*7, 13*). Meyerstein's data (*31*) shows that ethylenediamine is a poorer electron conductor than EDTA but this effect is not fully exhibited as long as some coordination sites remain unsubstituted by ethylenediamine. In other words, the presence of one or more water molecules on a given complex facilitates the incorporation of an electron even in the presence of other non-conducting ligands. The role of the ligand as electron conductor has been further elaborated in the case of the EDTA complexes of the rare earths and other trivalent cations (*9*). In these ions the reactivity increases with increasing stability of the complex—*i.e.*, with increasing overlap of the metal-ligand orbitals (*9*).

The oxide ion, O^{2-}, is an extremely poor electron conductor probably because of lack of orbital overlap with the hydrated electron in solution. Thus, the high reactivity of SnF_6^{2-} (2.14) compared with SnO_3^{2-} (3.13), that of TiF_6^{2-} (2.2) compared with TiO_3^{2-} ($k < 10^6 M^{-1}$ sec.$^{-1}$) (*35*) or that of AsF_6^- (6.28) (*3*) compared with $H_2AsO_4^-$ (3.10). In these fluoride complexes there is room for orbital overlap of e^-_{aq} and the central atom. In the case of oxy complexes with a higher coordination number than 4—*e.g.*, SeO_4^{2-} (2.11) or TeO_4^{2-} (2.17) or IO_4^- (7)—one observes, as expected from the ΔF–ΔF^* relationship, that reactivity increases with increasing oxidation state of the central atom.

In spite of the above discussed effects of ligands on the reactivity of complexes, d^3 $Cr(CN)_6^{3-}$ (6.7), d^6 $Co(CN)_6^{3-}$ (6.20), $Cr(EDTA)^-$ (6.9), $Co(EDTA)^-$ (6.24), $Hg(EDTA)^{2-}$ (6.95), and $Pb(EDTA)^{2-}$ (6.46), as well as CrO_4^{2-} (6.11), MnO_4^- (6.14), and TeO_4^{2-} (6.38), react at diffusion controlled rates, some of them with abnormally high cross sections. These high ΔF reactions may involve electron tunneling which proceeds regardless of the electron conducting capacity of the ligands.

Non-metallic Compounds. Certain generalizations may be reached by considering the reactivity of non-metallic elements throughout the periodic table. Phosphorus oxy-anions are non-reactive toward e^-_{aq}. The comparable reactivities of $H_2PO_3^-$ and $H_2PO_4^-$ (Table III) are probably because of their behavior as general protonic acids (*32*), as their pK's are comparable. $H_2PO_2^-$, the anion of monobasic H_3PO_2, is non-reactive towards e^-_{aq}. It should be noted, however, that the Brönsted relation between the pK values of protonic acids and their rates of reaction with e^-_{aq} does not necessarily imply a proton transfer in the rate determining step (*10*). The observed Brönsted relation suggests that the same parameters which facilitate proton transfer to water by electron withdrawal from the hydrogen atom, $XH \rightarrow X^- + H_3O^+$, enhance the incorporation of an additional electron into the vacant orbital of this atom without a simultaneous cleavage of the X–H bond. The non-reactivity of SiF_6^{2-}, $H_2PO_4^-$, $H_2PO_3^-$, $H_2PO_2^-$, SO_3^{2-}, and SO_4^{2-} toward e^-_{aq} (Table III) may be correlated with the instability of the intermediate valencies of Si(III), P(IV), P(II), S(V), and S(III).

In a given subgroup of the periodic table, e^-_{aq} reactivity increases with increasing atomic number. This general trend, which has been previously pointed out (*1, 7*), is confirmed by the behavior of homologous compounds of the elements in the fifth and sixth groups, P $<$ As $<$ Sb; S $<$ Se $<$ Te.

Concluding Remarks. It has recently been shown that the activation energy of many e^-_{aq}-solute reactions is 3.4 $\pm$ 0.6 kcal./mole (*4, 8*). From this result we have reasoned that the rates of many of the "slow" reactions are determined principally by their entropies of activation. These findings do not conflict with the mechanisms discussed above. If electron tunneling is a major contributing factor in these electron transfer reactions, the slower rates may be attributed to transmission coefficients smaller than unity. The factors which partially inhibit an electron transfer may thus be considered "geometrical" in nature, demonstrable by the entropy term of the free energy of activation, or by a decrease in the transmission coefficient as a result of an increase in the width of the potential barrier.

The nature of the primary product of the $e^-_{aq} + X \rightarrow X^-$ reaction remains an unsolved problem. It is probably produced in a vibrationally or even electronically excited state (*9*). (The de-excitation of this excited intermediate is still an open question (*27, 35*). In the absence of reliable experimental evidence on the immediate product of the rate determining step of the e^-_{aq} reactions, it is not practical to describe a detailed mechanism of the interaction of e^-_{aq} with a given compound.

In conclusion, we admit that our knowledge of inorganic compounds and their reactions with e^-_{aq} is far from being complete. Thus, the reactivity of these compounds towards e^-_{aq} is less predictable than for organic compounds. However, we hope that the rate constant information supplied by the e^-_{aq} reactions will lead to a better understanding of inorganic chemistry, and that out of the information and ideas presented in this paper some general principles will develop.

Literature Cited

(1) Anbar, M., ADVAN. CHEM. SER. **50,** 55 (1965).
(2) Anbar, M., *Chem. Commun.* **1966,** 416.
(3) Anbar, M. (unpublished).
(4) Anbar, M., Alfasi, Z., Reisler, H., *J. Am. Chem. Soc.* **89,** 1263 (1967).
(5) Anbar, M., Hart, E. J., *J. Am. Chem. Soc.* **86,** 5633 (1964).
(6) Anbar, M., Hart, E. J., *J. Phys. Chem.* **69,** 271 (1965).
(7) *Ibid.,* **69,** 973 (1965).
(8) *Ibid.,* **71,** 3700 (1967).

(9) Anbar, H., Meyerstein, D., *J. Phys. Chem.* (submitted).
(10) Anbar, M., Neta, P., *Trans. Faraday Soc.* **63,** 141 (1967).
(11) Anbar, M., Neta, P., *Intern. J. Appl. Radiation Isotopes* **18,** 493 (1967).
(12) Baxendale, J. H., Fielden, E. M., Capellos, C., Francis, J. M., Davies, J. V., Ebert, M., Gilbert, C. W., Keene, J. P., Land, E. J., Swallow, A. J., Nosworthy, J. M., *Nature* **201,** 468 (1964).
(13) Baxendale, J. H., Fielden, E. M., Keene, J. P., *Proc. Roy. Soc.* **286A,** 320 (1965).
(14) Brown, D. M., Dainton, F. S., Keene, J. P., Walker, D. C., *Proc. Chem. Soc.* **1964,** 266.
(15) Collinson, E., Dainton, F. S., Smith, D. R., Tazuke, S., *Proc. Chem. Soc.* **1962,** 140.
(16) Conway, B. E., "Electrochemical Data," p. 145, Elsevier, Amsterdam, 1952.
(17) Czapski, G., Schwarz, H. A., *J. Phys. Chem.* **66,** 471 (1962).
(18) Dainton, F. S., Rumfelt, R., *Proc. Roy. Soc.* **287A,** 444 (1965).
(19) Dainton, F. S., Watt, W. S., *Proc. Roy. Soc.* **A275,** 447 (1963).
(20) Debye, P., *Trans. Electrochem. Soc.* **82,** 265 (1942).
(21) Dorfman, L. M., Matheson, M. S., "Progress in Reaction Kinetics," G. Porter, ed., Vol. III, p. 237, Pergamon Press, London, England, 1965.
(22) Eigen, M., Kruse, W., Maass, H., DeMayer, L., "Progress in Reaction Kinetics," G. Porter, ed., Vol. II, p. 287, Pergamon Press, London, England, 1964.
(23) Gordon, S., Hart, E. J., Matheson, M. S., Rabani, J., Thomas, J. K., *J. Am. Chem. Soc.* **85,** 1375 (1963).
(24) Hart, E. J., Fielden, E. M., Anbar, M., *J. Phys. Chem.* **71,** 3993 (1967).
(25) Kortum, G., "Treatise on Electrochemistry," p. 248, Elsevier, Amsterdam, 1965.
(26) *Ibid.*, p. 235.
(27) Marcus, R. A., ADVAN. CHEM. SER. **50,** 138 (1965).
(28) Matheson, M. S., ADVAN. CHEM. SER. **50,** 45 (1965).
(29) Matheson, M. S., Mulac, W. A., Weeks, J. L., Rabani, J., *J. Phys. Chem.* **70,** 2092 (1966).
(30) Matheson, M. S., Rabani, J., *J. Phys. Chem.* **69,** 1324 (1965).
(31) Meyerstein, D., Mulac, W. A. (to be published).
(32) Rabani, J., ADVAN. CHEM. SER. **50,** 292 (1965).
(33) Schmidt, K. H., Buck, W. L., *Science* **151,** 70 (1966).
(34) Schwarz, H. A., *Radiation Res. Suppl.* **4,** 89 (1965).
(35) Sutin, N., "Exchange Reaction," p. 7, IAEA, Vienna, 1965.
(36) Szutka, A., Thomas, J. K., Gordon, S., Hart, E. J., *J. Phys. Chem.* **69,** 289 (1965).
(37) "Tables of Interatomic Distances," *Chem. Soc. (London) Spec. Publ.* **11,** 1958.
(38) *Ibid.*, **18,** 1965.
(39) Thomas, J. K., Gordon, S., Hart, E. J., *J. Phys. Chem.* **68,** 1524 (1964).

RECEIVED December 27, 1967. This work was performed under the auspices of the U. S. Atomic Energy Commission.

7

Concentration Influence of Different Acceptors in Pulse Radiolysis of Aqueous and Ammonium Solutions

V. N. SHUBIN, V. A. ZHIGUNOV, G. I. KHAIKIN, L. P. BERUCHASHVILI, and P. I. DOLIN

Institute of Electrochemistry, Academy of Sciences of the USSR, Moscow, USSR

Pulse radiolysis of some scavenger solutions in water, intermediates spectra, and kinetics of their decay in liquid ammonia are investigated. Rate constant and activation energy are calculated for the latter. The dependence of the disappearance of intermediates on concentration is analyzed. It is shown that rate constant of reactions of pseudo-first order is not proportional to acceptors concentration. One of the possible reasons is that first order reaction was not taken into consideration. On this basis, rate constants of reactions with acceptors and these of monomolecular decay are calculated. It is revealed the decay of intermediates in 10^{-5}–10^{-3}M *perchloric acid solutions does not depend upon* H_3O^+ *ion concentration. This fact is contrary to the present day theories about the nature of intermediates.*

Recently many works devoted to the determination of the kinetic characteristics of the solvated electron have been carried out. However, the high reaction activity of the solvated electron has forced scientists to use a rather narrow concentration region. As it was shown in one of our previous papers (*1*), only by studying the concentration dependence in a wide region of concentrations is it possible to get more complete information and to define the true value of the rate constant of reaction with the acceptor. In this paper the results of further investigations along the same line, which were performed in aqueous and ammonium solutions, are described.

Experimental

All aqueous solutions were prepared with twice-distilled water. Hydrogen peroxide and perchloric acid were distilled twice, and the cuprum perchloride was recrystallized three times. Aqueous solutions in special silica cells were saturated with hydrogen or nitrogen and then irradiated.

In order to prepare ammonium salt solutions of "chemical purity," the salts were refined by recrystallizing three times. Ammonia, which had been dried over metallic sodium for ten hours, was recondensed three times. After recondensation, frozen ammonia was evaculated to deep vacuum (10^{-6} mm. Hg).

Silica cells, which gave the possibility of working up to 25°C., were used in experiments with liquid ammonia and ammonium solutions. A thermostated jacket for investigating shortlived intermediates by pulse radiolysis with fast spectrophotometric recording is shown in Figure 1.

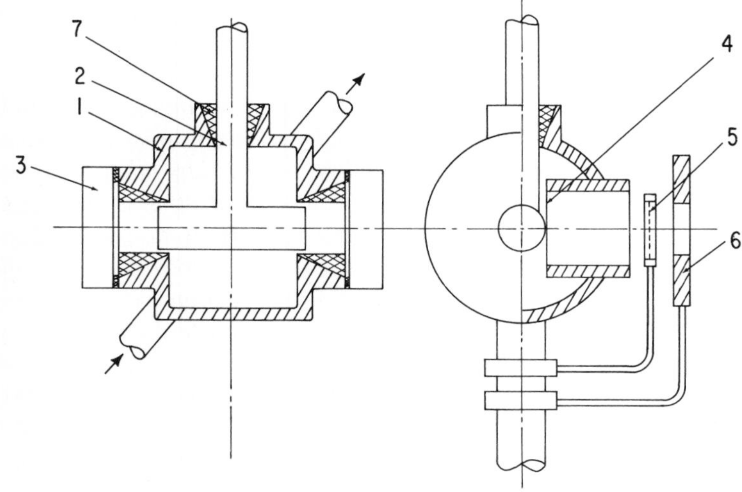

Figure 1. Thermostated jacket. (1)—metallic thermo-isolated vessel; (2)—silica cell with a sample; (3)—evacuated silica windows; (4)—aluminum film (0.1 mm.); (5)—wire-net electrode for dose control in electron pulse; (6)—diaphragm; (7)—rubber clout

A linear electron accelerator A-12 was used as a source of radiation. Energy of accelerated electrons was up to 5 Mev., the current in impulse up to 80 ma, and duration of impulse 1:8 μsec. The dose in the cell was about 10^{17} e.v./cc. Photomultipliers PEM-46a, PEM-28, and fast photodiod 9E-111 enabled us to carry out experiments within the range of 240 to 1700 n.m. The change in sample absorption which arose as a result of appearance of shortlived absorbing intermediates under the influence of electron pulse was registered. All the kinetic measurements in the aqueous solutions were carried out at the wavelength 700 n.m.

The installation made it possible to study the change of light flow coming through the cell to within 2% at the process duration from 1 to 1000 μsec. and ratio signal-noise 10:1. Thus, we were able to get spectral data of shortlived intermediates as well as kinetics of their decay process with an accuracy about 20%. In order to examine the operation rapidity of the electronics, the light pulse from the flask discharger (time of discharge—10^{-8} sec.) was directed on the photocathode PM and the relaxation time was controlled at the oscilloscope.

Aqueous Solutions

Hydrogen peroxide, cuprum perchloride, and perchloric acid were used as acceptors in aqueous solutions. The experimentally observed process of hydrated electron decay in solutions of these three substances obeyed the first-order reaction law. Kinetic characteristics of observed processes were calculated by the method of the least squares using 15–20 photo-oscillograms. Values of rate constants of corresponding pseudo-first order reactions are shown in Table I. There one can see also values of bimolecular rate constants calculated on the basis of above data. The rate constant does not vary occasionally within some limits but it changes monotonously with the variation of concentration. This may mean that some process of the decay of the intermediates was not taken into consideration. It was shown in earlier work (*1*), that we had satisfactory agreement with the experiment supposing that the process was the monomolecular intermediates decay.

Then rate constant observed will be:

$$K_{\text{obs.}} = K_{\text{m}} + K_{\text{s}}(\text{S}) \tag{1}$$

Table I. Rate Constants of Pseudo-first Order Reactions and Bimolecular Rate Constants

Scavenger	*Solute Concentration, Moles/liter*	K_{obs}, *sec.*$^{-1}$	K_{bim}, M^{-1} *sec.*$^{-1}$
	5×10^{-5}	5.2×10^{5}	10^{10}
H_2O_2	1×10^{-4}	6.0×10^{5}	6×10^{9}
	3×10^{-4}	7.4×10^{5}	2.7×10^{9}
	6×10^{-4}	9.6×10^{5}	1.6×10^{9}
	6×10^{-5}	0.6×10^{6}	1×10^{10}
$Cu(ClO_4)_2$	1×10^{-4}		
	3×10^{-4}	1.0×10^{6}	3.3×10^{9}
	6×10^{-4}	1.4×10^{6}	2.3×10^{9}
	1×10^{-5}	6.0×10^{5}	6×10^{10}
$HClO_4$	3×10^{-5}	5.4×10^{5}	1.8×10^{10}
	1×10^{-4}	6.45×10^{5}	6.45×10^{9}
	1×10^{-3}	5.75×10^{5}	5.75×10^{8}

A graphic solution of Equation 1 in coordinates K_{obs} — (S) produces a straight line with the slope equal to K_s. Figure 2 shows the results of the treatment according to Table I. In all three cases the value of the decay constant K_m is approximately the same. While the experiments are carried out with different systems but under reproduced conditions, K_m is stable in above mentioned limits (±20%) and the value of K_s is steady too.

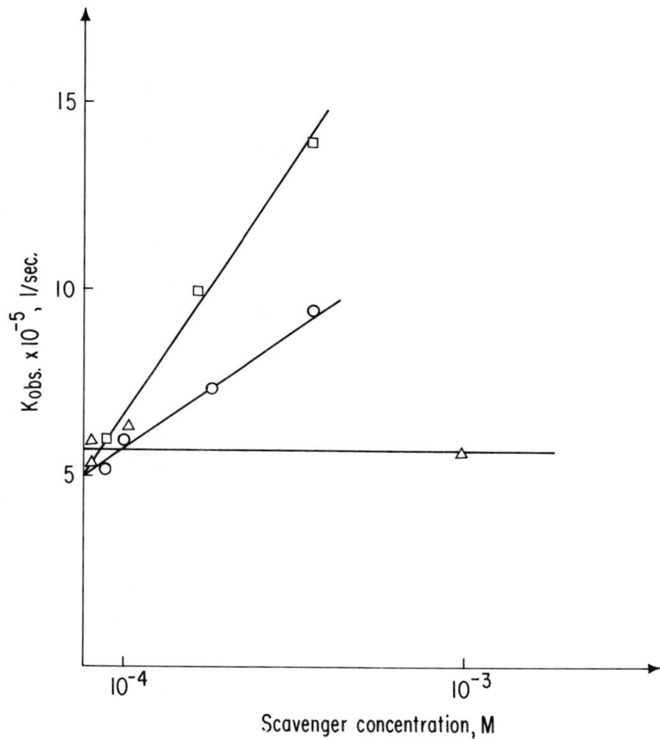

Figure 2. Graphic solution of Equation 1 from data of Table I. ○—H_2O_2; △—$HClO_4$; □—$Cu(ClO_4)_2$

Special consideration should be given to the results in perchloric acid solutions. These were chosen because ClO_4^- anions do not chemically interact with molecular and radical products of water radiolysis (2). It excluded accessory effects and let us investigate reaction kinetics with the H_3O^+ ion. The results which were obtained were unexpected. As shown in Table I, the value of observed rate constant is constant and independent of hydronium ion concentration over two orders of magnitude.

To make the role of the recombination processes clear, this influence of dose rate was analyzed. The kinetics of the observed process did not change essentially while the dose rate had been changed five to six times. Since the rate of reaction between radical products of radiolysis under these conditions must change 30 times, it indicated their role in defining the decay kinetics of optically absorbing intermediates.

Thus, the results from perchloric acid solutions show that the kinetics do not change when the concentration of $HClO_4$ varies. The rate of the spectral decay obeys the first-order reaction law. Calculated rate constants coincide when perchloric acid solutions and pure water are used. It can likely be explained that the intermediates which arose under irradiation do not interact with hydronium ions. Obviously, it is rather difficult to understand the results in view of the accepted theory of the hydrated electron.

Some other scientists (*5*) have already noted the phenomenon of the changes of optical density with changes of pH in solutions under steady dose. One needs to note that in Reference 3 the increase in optical density in H_2 saturated solutions irradiated under constant dose conditions was explained by e^-_{aq} formation *via*

$$OH + H_2 \rightarrow H_2O + H$$

$$H + OH^- \rightarrow e^-_{aq} + H_2O$$

According to the theory it can be explained by changes of extinction coefficient of optically active formation as the latter formations were taken into traps different by their nature. As the result of this, the change of the wave functions of the electron in main and excited states takes place. The first results involve the changing of the probability of its transformation from main to excited state as well as changes in the molecular absorption coefficient. The absorption spectrum became wider under these conditions and that is why its corresponding change can not be fixed.

Liquid Ammonia

It is known that the first idea of solvated electrons appeared to explain the properties of alkaline metal solutions in liquid ammonia. In this connection the pulse radiolysis of liquid ammonia is of special interest because it is possible to compare properties of intermediates formed by different methods.

The spectral chracteristics of intermediates formed by irradiation of liquid ammonia probably do not differ greatly from those in metal-ammonium solutions (*4*) (Figure 3). In Figure 3, one sees the optical spectra of an intermediate which appears in the pulse radiolysis of liquid

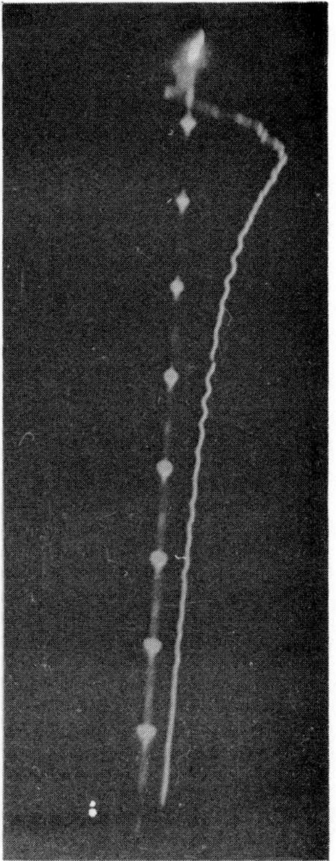

Figure 3. Optical absorption dependence on time for pure liquid ammonia (time scale 5 μsec.)

ammonia. The observed spectra differs from published results (*3*). This can be because of the difficulties of measuring in the infrared region of the spectrum.

Unlike water and aqueous solutions, this intermediate's decay is slower (*see* Figure 4) and follows a second-order reaction law (Figure 5) with a rate constant of (1.1 ± 0.2). $10^{10}M^{-1}$ sec.$^{-1}$. Analysis of temperature dependence of rate constant gives the activation energy of observed reaction as 2 ± 0.5 kcal./mole.

It is known that the decay of solvated electron in alkaline metals solutions even at lower concentrations than $10^{-3}M$, corresponds to a first order process. Moreover, the process is very slow. That is why solvated electrons formed in radiolysis do not disappear according to the reaction:

$$e^-_s + e^-_s \rightarrow \text{products} \qquad (2)$$

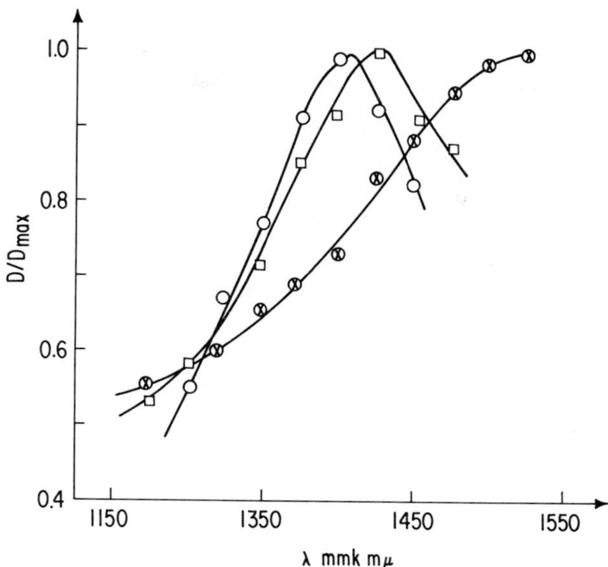

Figure 4. Optical absorption spectrum of primary intermediates in liquid ammonia at different temperatures: ○—225 ± 2°K.; □—257 ± 0.2°K.; ⊗—293 ± 0.2°K.

but as a result of interaction with some other active particles, which are formed simultaneously with the intermediates, perhaps, hydrogen ions:

$$e^-_s + H^{+\prime} \rightarrow \text{products} \tag{3}$$

In order to clarify this process, Reaction 3 was studied in acid solutions. We carried out some experiments on the radiolysis of ammonium solutions (NH_4Cl) and other acceptors. The results obtained in solutions of NH_4Cl, $NaNO_3$, and NaCl are shown in Table II.

The addition of acceptors changes the observed kinetics, the disappearance of intermediates now obeys a first-order reaction law (Figures 6 and 7). However, as in the case of aqueous solutions, we do not find a proportionality between the value of pseudo-first order rate constant and the concentration of acceptor (Table II). The rate constant of Reaction 3 is calculated from data of the concentration dependence in NH_4Cl solutions as $3 \times 10^9 M^{-1}$ sec.$^{-1}$. This means that the decay of solvated electrons by Reaction 3 proceeds slower than the experimentally observed process—*i.e.*, if Reaction 3 really takes place—one more decay process precedes it.

It is very interesting that such a chemically inert additive as NaCl influences the kinetics of the process. Its rate obeys a first-order reaction law and does not change when NaCl concentration varies from $10^{-3}M$ to

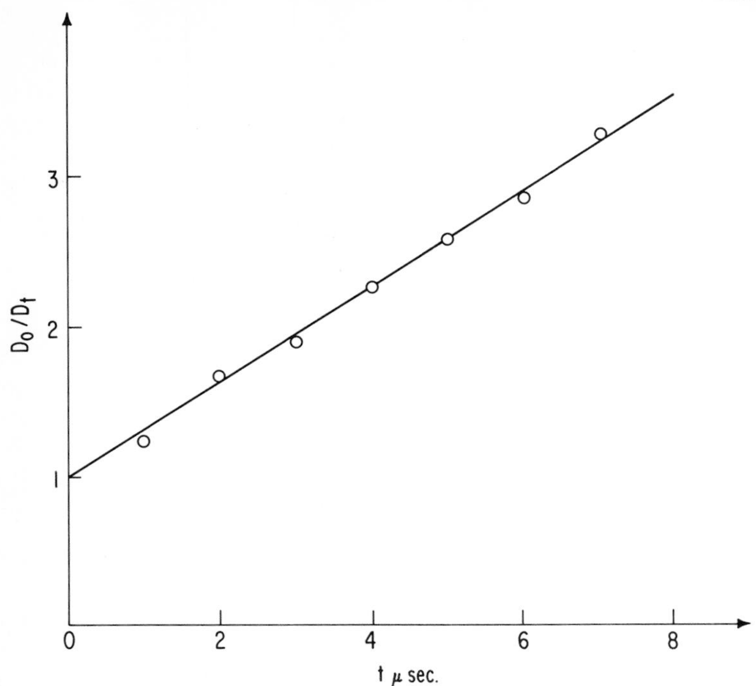

Figure 5. Dependence of ratio D_0/D_t *on time for pure liquid ammonia*

0.45*M*. This shows that the decay of trapped intermediates takes place in a manner which is similar to the case of the pulse radiolysis of frozen alkaline and $LiClO_4$ solutions, observed earlier (*7, 8*). It is significant that in this case, the absorption spectrum of the intermediates does not differ significantly from that in pure ammonia and NaCl solutions.

Data given in this work show that it is necessary to carry out a detailed analysis of the concentration dependence to define the correct values of the rate constants of intermediates' interaction with acceptors.

The experimental results in aqueous and ammonium solutions show that the process of intermediates' decay in the presence of acceptors follows a first-order law. However, a proportionality between the calculated rate constant of the pseudo-first order reaction and the concentration is not observed. Under these conditions no influence of dose rate on the kinetics of intermediates' decay is found, so recombination interactions play a rather small role. By kinetic treatment of the results, satisfactory agreement with experimental data can be obtained by supposing that the intermediates disappear in a monomolecular decay which simultaneously proceeds with scavenger reactions.

All we have mentioned above combined with the fact that intermediates do not interact (or interact at a very low rate) with hydronium ion is in contradiction with generally accepted view on the nature of these intermediates.

Table II. Radiolysis of Ammonium Solutions (NH_4Cl) and Other Acceptors

System	*Solute Concentration, Moles/liter*	*T °C.*	K_{obs}, *sec.*$^{-1}$	K_{bim}, M^{-1} *sec.*$^{-1}$
NH_3		293		1.10×10^{10}
		257		0.76×10^{10}
		225		0.58×10^{10}
$NH_3 + NaNO_3$	2.5×10^{-5}	293	0.91×10^{6}	3.62×10^{10}
	1×10^{-4}	293	1.69×10^{6}	1.63×10^{10}
$NH_3 + NH_4Cl$	5×10^{-5}	293	0.56×10^{6}	1.06×10^{10}
	10^{-4}	293	0.71×10^{6}	0.71×10^{10}
$NH_3 + NaCl$	1×10^{-3}	293	1.61×10^{5}	1.61×10^{8}
	4.5×10^{-1}	293	1.42×10^{5}	3.15×10^{5}

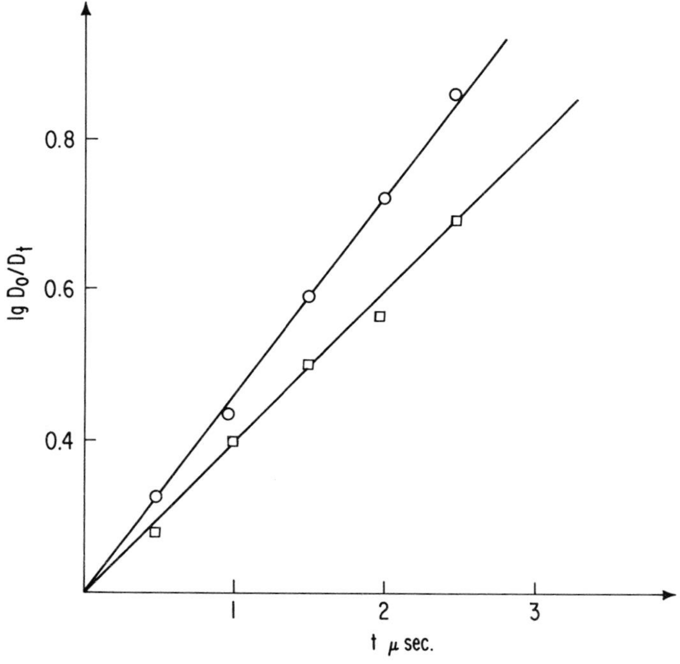

Figure 6. Dependence of lg D_o/D_t *on time for* $NaNO_3$ *ammonium solution.* □—2.5×10^{-5}M; ○—1×10^{-4}M

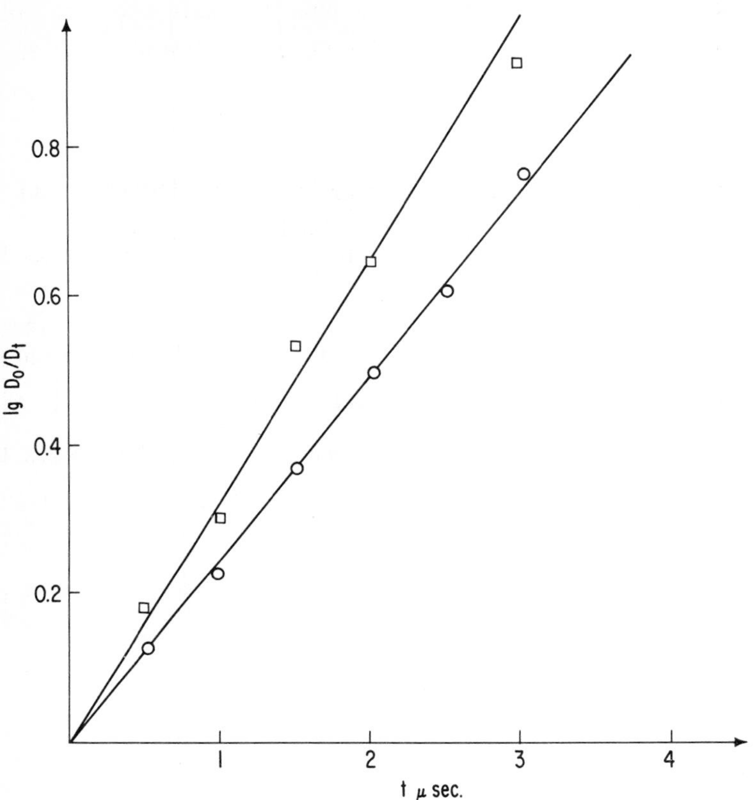

Figure 7. Dependence of lg D_o/D_t *on time for* NH_4Cl *ammonium solution.* ○—*5* × *10*$^{-5}$M; □—*1* × *10*$^{-4}$M

Because of earlier data concerning the pulse radiolysis of crystalline ice, we came to the conclusion that the existence and physical properties of observed transients are concerned with purely electronic rather than electron-dipole interactions (*7, 8*). This idea recalls the assumption of a number of scientists concerning the possible participation in radiation-induced processes of intermediates which are radical (H–OH) or ionic (H_2O–e^-_{aq}, H_3O–e^-_{aq}) pairs correlated in their motion.

Another possible change of the above idea is possible. In a number of our papers which were concerned with the oxygen solution radiolysis, we already assumed the exicton-like nature of the primary species. The excellent results of our theory were demonstrated during the establishment of the radiolysis mechanism (*6, 9*). Recently the similar supposition was presented by Weiss (*10*), who bases his theory on the data obtained in frozen systems.

Undoubtedly further examinations must be made since none of the evidence presented at the present time could be used as the basis of a definite conclusion.

Literature Cited

(1) Beruchashvili, L. P., Shubin, V. N., Dolin, P. I., Zolotarevsky, V. I., *Dokl. Acad. Nauk. SSSR* **174,** 1115 (1967.
(2) Bugaenko, L. T., *Vestn. Moscow University* **N3,** 21 (1961).
(3) Compton, D. M., Bryant, Cesena, R. A., Gehman, B. L., "Pulse Radiolysis," p. 43, M. Ebert *et al.*, eds., Academic Press, New York, 1965.
(4) Douthit, R. C., Dye, J. L., *J. Am. Chem. Soc.* **82,** 4472 (1960).
(5) Hart, E. J., Gordon, S., Fielden, E. M., *J. Phys. Chem.* **70,** 150 (1966).
(6) Kabakchi, S. A., Shubin, V. N., Dolin, P. I., *Chim. Visokich Energii* **2,** 40 (1968).
(7) Shubin, V. N., Zhigunov, V. A., Zolotarevsky, V. I., Dolin, P. I., *Nature* **212,** 1002 (1966).
(8) Shubin, V. N., Zhigunov, V. A., Zolotarevsky, V. I., Dolin, P. I., *Dokl. Acad. SSSR* **174,** 416 (1967).
(9) Shubin, V. N., Kabakchi, S. A., *Chim. Visokich Energii* **1,** 142 (1967).
(10) Weiss, J. J., *Nature* **215,** 150 (1967).

RECEIVED January 5, 1968.

8

Radical Yields as a Function of pH and Scavenger Concentration

GIDEON CZAPSKI

Department of Physical Chemistry, Hebrew University, Jerusalem, Israel

G values of radicals and molecular products have been measured and have appeared in numerous publications. It has been generally assumed that at extreme acidity, alkalinity, or at high concentrations of radical scavengers, the radical yields effectively increase. This behavior was summarized in a recent review by Hayon, who generalized by assuming G radicals to depend solely on the product of $k_{R+S} \cdot [S]$. *This approach is criticized on theoretical (the different models proposed) as well as experimental grounds. In many cases, where G values of radicals seem to depend on pH or scavenger concentrations, the effect observed was really an artifact caused by neglecting the effect of back reactions.*

Numerous determinations of product yields have been measured in irradiated aqueous systems. The assumption of a mechanism and the measuring of product yields in such systems led to the conclusion that several species are produced in the radiolytic decomposition of water. [Systems of this kind, up to 1960, have been summarized by Allen (*7*).]

These studies showed that water decomposes, yielding radicals (*69*) and molecular entities (*5*). Later studies have shown that the two molecular products, H_2 and H_2O_2, are formed with different yields (*30*), $G_{H_2} < G_{H_2O_2}$. The radical products were assumed to be H and OH radicals (*69*). Later, it was shown that the reducing radical may exist in two forms (*12*), one being a H atom (*20*) and the other a hydrated electron (*19, 24*). It was also shown that an e_{aq} reacts with H^+ to yield a H atom (*23, 43*), while the opposite reaction—the conversion of H atoms by OH^- into e_{aq}—has been demonstrated as well (*50*).

Allan and Scholes have proved that in neutral solutions both H and e_{aq} are formed as products of the radiolysis of water (*3, 57*).

These investigations may be summarized by the following equation:

$$H_2O \rightarrow H,\ e_{aq},\ OH,\ H_3O^+,\ H_2,\ \text{and}\ H_2O_2$$

The primary yields of these species have been determined in many systems. G_{H_2} and $G_{H_2O_2}$ are lower in systems where high concentrations of e_{aq} or OH scavengers are added (*7*).

Recently, it has also been shown that G_H is decreased by both electron and H_3O^+ scavengers (*9, 38*). The radical yields are increased by e_{aq} and OH scavengers as well as by increased acidity or alkalinity. These results were summarized in a recent review by Hayon (*47*).

The diffusion model drawn up by Samuel and Magee (*59*) and later modified in the light of the knowledge that the reducing radical is a hydrated electron rather than a H atom, tried to explain the yield of all entities in the following manner (*53, 54, 55, 63*).

The basic assumption is that water is decomposed by radiation into e_{aq}, OH, and H_3O^+, which are formed inhomogeneously in spurs. In these spurs, which are spherical, with a diameter of 10–40 A., several pairs of these radicals are initially formed where their initial concentration is very high (0.1–1*M*). The distance between spurs depends on the LET of the radiation. For γ-, x-rays, or fast electrons most of the spurs are isolated, and only a small fraction overlaps and forms blobs or short tracks (*56*). At high LET radiation, the overlapping of the spurs produces cylindrical tracks.

This model assumes that after the spur is formed, two simultaneous processes occur: diffusion of the radicals from the spur into the bulk, and during this process, several reactions between the radicals take place. These latter reactions are responsible for the H_2, H_2O_2, and H formed.

The success of this model is quite impressive as its calculations succeed in predicting quantitatively many effects found experimentally (*53, 54, 55, 56, 63*), namely:

(1) The absolute value of G_{H_2}, $G_{H_2O_2}$, G_H, $G_{e_{aq}}$, and G_{OH} for γ-rays.

(2) The dependence of the molecular and radical yields on the LET.

(3) The effect of scavengers on the radical and molecular yields.

(4) The increase of G_{HO_2} from almost zero (0.02) (*42*), for γ-rays, to 0.25 (*36*) for α-rays (owing to the reaction of OH with H_2O_2 in the tracks).

Little has been done in calculating the pH effect on yields according to the diffusion model.

As mentioned above, the dependence of the molecular and radical yields on pH and scavenger concentration have been studied for γ-rays in many systems. There is some general agreement concerning this dependence for molecular yields. However, the dependence of the reducing radical yield on the pH and scavenger concentrations have given rise to much controversy in the literature.

Several theories explain the pH or scavenger effect on the *G* value. Hayon (*47*), in a recent review, advanced a unique theory covering these effects and reviewed many publications connected with this hypothesis.

In this paper, my aim is to review and discuss mainly two points:

(1) The actual dependence of *G* values on pH and scavenger concentrations.

(2) The various theories concerning the dependence of the yield on the pH and scavenger concentrations.

The discussion will be limited almost entirely to the dependence of the radical yield rather than that of the molecular yields; regarding the latter, theory and experiment agree reasonably well.

Possible Errors in Determining G *Values*

G values are generally determined from experimental yields of products in an irradiated system. To obtain, from the actual *G*(product), the *G* values of the radicals, knowledge of the reaction mechanism is necessary.

The value of *G*(product) is derived as the slope of a straight line when plotting the product concentration *vs.* dose. Possible errors in evaluating G_{radicals} may be caused either by misinterpreting the reaction mechanism or by incorrect slopes of the product dose plots. To avoid ambiguity, we will define the different symbols of *G* being used. All these *G* values are in units of number of x molecules or radicals per 100 e.v. absorbed.

The symbol *G*(x) is used generally as the measured yield of an entity x in a given system. G_x is used as primary yields of x, where x is one of the radical or molecular primary products, as H_2, H_2O_2, H, OH, and e_{aq}.

To estimate errors in *G* values, let us take as an example the determination of $G_{e_{aq}}$ and see how this value has been measured in numerous systems.

The reactions which may occur and which may affect the measured $G_{e_{aq}}$ are:

$$e_{aq} + S_1 \xrightarrow{k_1} P_1$$

$$OH + S_2 \xrightarrow{k_2} P_2$$

$$\mathrm{H} + \mathrm{S}_3 \xrightarrow{k_3} \mathrm{P}_3$$

$$e_{\mathrm{aq}} + \mathrm{P}_1 \xrightarrow{k_4} \mathrm{P}_4$$

$$e_{\mathrm{aq}} + \mathrm{P}_2 \xrightarrow{k_5} \mathrm{P}_5$$

$$e_{\mathrm{aq}} + \mathrm{H}_2\mathrm{O}_2 \xrightarrow{k_6} \mathrm{OH}^- + \mathrm{OH}$$

$$\mathrm{H} + \mathrm{P}_1 \xrightarrow{k_7} \mathrm{P}_6$$

$$\mathrm{H} + \mathrm{OH}^- \xrightarrow{k_8} e_{\mathrm{aq}}$$

$G_{e_{\mathrm{aq}}}$ is determined from the initial yield of P_1. (We deal only with systems where e_{aq} reacts with one solute rather than competing for two or more solutes.)

Let us divide these systems into the following groups.

(I) The e_{aq} competition with S_1, P_2, and H_2O_2; the yield in this system is given by Equation I:

$$\frac{d[\mathrm{P}_1]}{d\,\mathrm{dose}} = \frac{G_{e_{\mathrm{aq}}}}{1 + \frac{k_5[\mathrm{P}_2]}{k_1[\mathrm{S}_1]} + \frac{k_6[\mathrm{H}_2\mathrm{O}_2]}{k_1[\mathrm{S}_1]}} = G_{e_{\mathrm{aq}}} \cdot \alpha \tag{I}$$

(II) The electron competing in reaction with S_1, P_1, or H_2O_2; the yield will be given by Equation II:

$$\frac{d[\mathrm{P}_1]}{d\,\mathrm{dose}} = G_{e_{\mathrm{aq}}} \frac{1 - \frac{k_4[\mathrm{P}_1]}{k_1[\mathrm{S}_1]}}{1 + \frac{k_4[\mathrm{P}_1]}{k_1[\mathrm{S}_1]} + \frac{k_6[\mathrm{H}_2\mathrm{O}_2]}{k_1[\mathrm{S}_1]}} = G_{e_{\mathrm{aq}}} \cdot \beta \tag{II}$$

(III) Should the competition be that of H for C_3 and P_1, the yield will be given by Equation III:

$$\frac{d[\mathrm{P}_1]}{d\,\mathrm{dose}} = G_{e_{\mathrm{aq}}} - \frac{G_{\mathrm{H}}}{1 + \frac{k_3[\mathrm{S}_3]}{k_7[\mathrm{P}_1]}} = G_{e_{\mathrm{aq}}} - G_{\mathrm{H}} \cdot \gamma \tag{III}$$

(IV) Should the atom be partially converted to an electron, the yield will be given by:

$$\frac{d[\mathrm{P}_1]}{d\,\mathrm{dose}} = G_{e_{\mathrm{aq}}} + G_{\mathrm{H}} \cdot \frac{1 - \frac{k_7[\mathrm{P}_1]}{k_8[\mathrm{OH}^-]}}{1 + \frac{k_3[\mathrm{S}_3]}{k_8[\mathrm{OH}^-]} + \frac{k_7[\mathrm{P}_1]}{k_8[\mathrm{OH}^-]}} = G_{e_{\mathrm{aq}}} + G_{\mathrm{H}} \cdot \delta \tag{IV}$$

In Equations I–IV, as long as the terms of P_1 and H_2O_2 can be set aside when comparing the other terms and provided the scavenger concentration does not change, the yield of P_1 will be linear with dose, and $(G_{e_{aq}})_{observed}$ can be obtained from the slopes of the line of P_1 *vs.* dose plots. (In Equation IV, the slope would yield: $G_{e_{aq}} + \dfrac{G_H}{1 + \dfrac{k_3[S_3]}{k_8[OH^-]}}$.) The situation will be different if this assumption is not valid; then, Equations 1–IV would have to be used without cancelling out the terms competing with the reactions of the e_{aq} with S_1, or H with P_1. In these cases, P_1 is not really linear with dose, and the curve bends over.

In Tables I–IV, the ratio of the observed $G_{e_{aq}}$ to the real $G_{e_{aq}}$ was calculated. $(G_{e_{aq}})_{observed}$ is obtained from the slope of the best straight line of P_1 *vs.* dose dependence by the least-mean square method. (P_1 *vs.* dose values were calculated by a computer, using Equations I–IV).

The value of $\dfrac{(G_{e_{aq}})_{observed}}{(G_{e_{aq}})_{real}}$ depends on the relative rate constants, concentration, and total dose or, more explicitly, on the value of the denominator in Equations I and III or the fraction in Equations II and IV at the maximum dose used in the P_1 *vs.* dose plot.

Values in Tables I–IV are given for Equations I–IV, with either of the two following assumptions:

(a) P_1 *vs.* dose yields a straight line with zero intercept,

(b) P_1 *vs.* dose yields a straight line with non-zero intercept.

These tables are calculated assuming:

$\dfrac{k_6[H_2O_2]}{k_1[S_1]}$ need not be considered. It is assumed also that the concentrations of S_1, S_2, S_3 are not depleted during irradiation, while P_1, P_2, and P_3 are computed by solving the differential Equations I–IV, taking $G_{e_{aq}} =$ 2.8, $G_H = 0.6$, $G_{OH} = 2.8$. The values of α, β, γ, and δ are thus functions of $\dfrac{k_4}{k_1[S_1]}$, $\dfrac{k_5}{k_1[S_1]}$, $\dfrac{k_3[S_3]}{k_7}$, $\dfrac{k_3[S_3]}{k_8[OH^-]}$, $\dfrac{k_7}{k_8[OH^-]}$, and the dose. (Should an observable depletion in S_1, S_2, or S_3 occur during irradiation, the correction is even larger.)

Tables I–IV can be used to estimate the error in different determinations of $G_{e_{aq}}$, where the experimental details given in the published paper are sufficient to calculate the value of α, β, γ, or δ (as defined in Equations I–IV) at the highest dose used. The fact that in most of the publications from which *G* values were calculated the plot of product *vs.* dose yielded straight lines, does not in itself constitute proof that the slope is really the initial slope.

Table I.[a]

$\frac{k_5[P_2]_{max}}{k_1[S_1]}$	α	$\frac{(G_{e_{aq}})_{observed}}{(G_{e_{aq}})_{real}}$ Zero Intercept	$\frac{(G_{e_{aq}})_{observed}}{(G_{e_{aq}})_{real}}$ Non-Zero Intercept	$\frac{(P_1)_{max}}{Intercept}$
0.02	0.98	0.993	0.991	640
0.049	0.95	0.982	0.976	260
0.095	0.91	0.965	0.954	136
0.18	0.84	0.934	0.916	72
0.29	0.78	0.899	0.871	46
0.41	0.71	0.861	0.825	34
0.73	0.58	0.777	0.725	20

[a] It is assumed that $\frac{k_6[H_2O_2]}{k_1[S_1]} << \frac{k_5[P_1]}{k_1[S_1]}$.

Table II.[a]

$\frac{k_4[P_1]_{max}}{k_1[S_1]}$	β	$\frac{(G_{e_{aq}})_{observed}}{(G_{e_{aq}})_{real}}$ Zero Intercept	$\frac{(G_{e_{aq}})_{observed}}{(G_{e_{aq}})_{real}}$ Non-Zero Intercept	$\frac{(P_1)_{max}}{Intercept}$
0.0196	0.96	0.985	0.981	320
0.0476	0.91	0.964	0.953	130
0.091	0.83	0.931	0.911	67
0.168	0.71	0.874	0.839	35
0.255	0.59	0.811	0.760	22
0.345	0.48	0.745	0.681	16

[a] It is assumed that $\frac{k_6[H_2O_2]}{k_1[S_1]} << \frac{k_4[P_1]}{k_1[S_1]}$.

Table III.

$\frac{k_3[S_3]}{k_7[P_1]_{max}}$	γ	$\frac{(G_{e_{aq}})_{observed}}{(G_{e_{aq}})_{real}}$ Zero Intercept	$\frac{(G_{e_{aq}})_{observed}}{(G_{e_{aq}})_{real}}$ Non-Zero Intercept	$\frac{(P_1)_{max}}{Intercept}$
0.55	0.645	0.917	0.902	100
1.0	0.5	0.944	0.934	130
1.59	0.381	0.957	0.949	180
2.55	0.282	0.971	0.966	300
5.10	0.164	0.982	0.981	900

Table IV.[a]

$\frac{k_7[P_1]_{max}}{k_8[OH^-]}$	δ	$\frac{(G_{e_{aq}})_{observed}}{(G_{e_{aq}})_{real}}$ Zero Intercept	Non-Zero Intercept	$\frac{(P_1)_{max}}{Intercept}$
0.925	0.039	1.097	1.07	52
0.56	0.282	1.14	1.12	86
0.383	0.446	1.16	1.14	115
0.234	0.62	1.18	1.17	175
0.119	0.787	1.196	1.19	322
0.06	0.888	1.205	1.20	610

$\frac{k_3[S_3]}{k_8[OH^-]}$ can be neglected in comparison with $\frac{k_7[P_1]}{k_8[OH^-]}$.

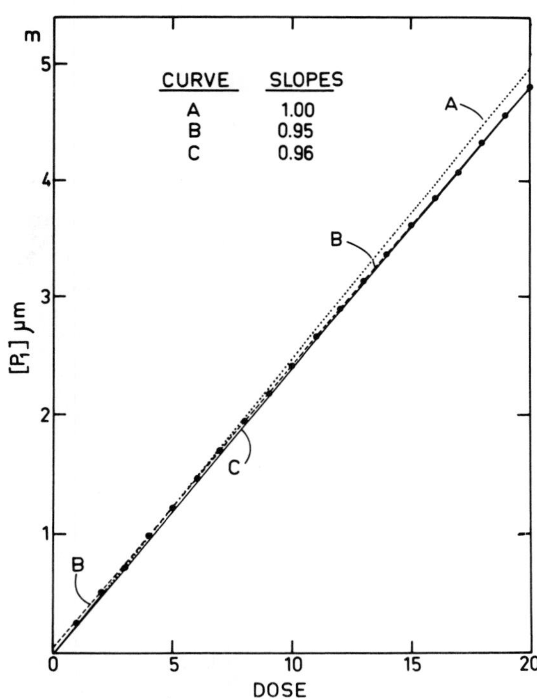

Figure 1. P_1 as function of dose calculated from Equation II with k_4/k_1. $[S_1] = 10^4$ up to a maximum dose where $P_{1\,max} = 4.8 \times 10^{-6}$

——— *Initial slope*
– – – – – *Calculated by least mean squares*
. . . . *Calculated by least mean squares assuming zero intercept*

Figures 1 and 2 show a computed plot of yield *vs.* dose according to Equation II (taking $\frac{k_6[H_2O_2]}{k_1[S_1]} = 0$, and $\frac{k_4[P_1]}{k_1[S_1]}$ reaching 0.048 and 0.168 at the maximum dose.) The straight lines are calculated using the least-mean square method, having a slope which is lower by 5 or 13–16%, respectively, than the initial one. (Such a difference may lower $G_{e_{aq}}$ from an initial value of 2.8 to an "observed" value of 2.4.)

As will be shown, many determined *G* values were too low since the slopes measured were not the initial ones.

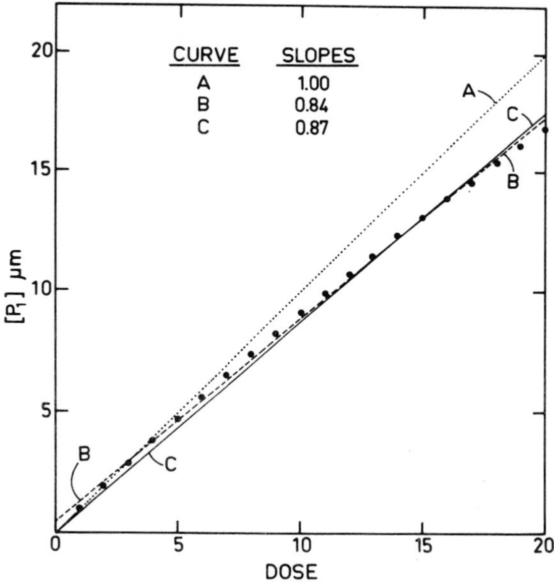

Figure 2. P_1 as function of dose calculated from Equation II with k_4/k_1. $S_1 = 10^4$ up to a maximum dose where $P_{1\,max} = 1.68 \times 10^{-5}$

——— *Initial slope*
– – – – – *Calculated by least mean squares*
. . . . *Calculated by least mean squares, assuming zero intercept*

Dependence of $G_{radicals}$ *On pH*

Numerous determinations of G_R have been undertaken with various chemical systems, and a wide spectrum for the observed *G* values has resulted. The value of $G_{reducing}$ lies generally in the range of 2.8–3.5, where G_H is about 0.6, the balance being $G_{e_{aq}}$.

In a recent review, Hayon (*47*) endeavored to show general dependence of G_R on pH and on radical scavenger concentration. He asserted that G_R is a function of $k_{R+S}[S]$ and the difference of G_R, when measured in the different systems, and he attributed this to dissimilar values of $k_{R+S_1}[S_1]$ in these systems.

Before analyzing the different theories concerning the dependence of G_R on pH and electron scavengers, I shall review and analyze different systems, to determine and verify whether there is an actual dependence of G_R on pH and scavenger concentrations.

pH Dependence of G_R. The hydrated electron may react in the spur with H^+ to form H atoms, while OH radicals may yield O^- in the spur in high alkaline solutions. Thus, it is clear that extreme pH values will change the relative abundance of H compared with e_{aq} and of OH compared with O^- in the spurs.

Since these radicals to some extent have different rate constants in their recombination reactions, the pH may affect the $G(H_2)$, $G(H_2O_2)$, G(Radicals), and $G(-H_2O)$. The extent of this effect is not known, and so far, its calculation has not been attempted.

Acid Solutions. There are relatively few systems in which the G values of radicals have been measured as functions of acidity. The principal systems where this has been done are Fe^{2+}–O_2 (*6*), Fe^{2+}–N_2O (*31*), CO–O_2 (*11*), ethyl alcohol–O_2 (*45*), formic acid–O_2 (*39, 40, 41*), and Br^-–O_2 (*17, 67*) systems. All these systems revealed that the yield of the radicals increased with acidity, whereas G_{red} increases by about 0.9 units from pH 7 to 0.3.

Schwarz (*61*) was able to show that in the Fe^{2+}–O_2 (*6*) system, most of the pH dependence may be attributed to the competition of e_{aq} with O_2 and Fe^{3+} formed during radiation. His calculations led him to conclude that at lower pH all e_{aq} are converted into H atoms which react preferentially with O_2. Hence, the change G_{red} undergoes from pH 2.1 to more acid solutions is really slight.

Dainton and Peterson (*31*), in studying the Fe^{2+}–N_2O system observed that $G(Fe^{3+})$ decreases when the pH increases from 0.3–3.0. The decrease also depends on the initial Fe^{2+} concentration. Again, some reactions with Fe^{3+} may occur in this system. The H atoms compete for Fe^{2+} and Fe^{3+}, and the higher the pH, the faster Fe^{3+} reacts with the H atoms (*6, 22*). This fact alone accounts for the pH dependence in the system, and it is consistent with the smaller pH effect observed at higher initial Fe^{2+} concentration.

The CO–O_2 (*11*) solutions are another system, where $G(H_2)$, $G(-O_2)$, $G(CO_2)$, $G(H_2O_2)$, and $G(-CO)$ were measured at pH 0.45–12.1. The yields change appreciably between pH 0.45 and 6.9, the entire change occurring between pH 1.4 and 2.2. Up to pH 2.2, practically all e_{aq} react with H^+ rather than with O_2, H_2O_2, CO, or CO_2. Perhaps the pH dependence is caused by the different reactivities of COOH and HCO compared with the dissociated radical CO_2^- and CO^-. In this system, we cannot explain the pH dependence which may be a genuine effect; it is, however, very steep, and the inflection is at a higher pH than that observed elsewhere (*6, 16, 31*).

Hart (*39*) more than a decade ago, determined in formate solutions G_{red} and G_{OH} from pH 0.32–11.58. He found $G(-H_2O)$ almost constant over this range. G_{red} remained constant at $2.7 < pH < 12$, while an increase of 15–20% occurred at lower pH. The total dose is not given in this work (*39*), but some of the earlier plots (*40*), show that H_2O_2 reaches values of up to 1 m*M* where $[O_2]_{final} < [H_2O_2]_{final}$, while in another work (*41*) Hart mentions that at low oxygen concentration the peroxide is not linear with dose.

In the systems where $[O_2]_{initial} \leqslant 50\ \mu M$, products have been measured at concentrations of 5–50 μM (once more, under these conditions the final concentrations of O_2 and H_2O_2 are comparable). It may be possible that in this system and at $pH > 2$, not all the solvated electrons react with O_2, leaving some to react with H_2O_2. This possibility, however, disappears at $pH < 2$, when all electrons are converted into H atoms which react only with oxygen.

Unfortunately, we do not possess enough experimental data on this system to be able to assess the error caused by possible back reactions, but it does seem that *G* values above pH 2 may be too low, owing to reactions of electrons with peroxide. When $G(-O_2)$ was measured, obviously a substantial fraction of O_2 disappeared, and hence H_2O_2 concentration would not be negligible compared with the O_2 concentration. It seems that this system also cannot be used as evidence for a pH dependence of G_{red}.

However, there are two determinations (*17, 67*) using the pulse radiolysis of Br^- in the pH range 0–6, where the radical yield was found to be pH independent. The ethyl alcohol–oxygen system (*45*) shows that $G(H_2O_2)$ decreases by 0.8 units between pH 0.5–6.0. At least part of this decrease should be caused by the reaction of e_{aq} with H_2O_2 and aldehyde rather than with O_2, when the acidity is low.

Another system was studied with x-rays, which should give results similar to when γ-rays are used. In the acetone–isopropyl alcohol system Rabani and Stein (*57*) reported $G(H_2)$ as function of pH, acetone, and isopropyl alcohol concentrations. They report $G_H = 0.55$ and $G_{e_{aq}} = 2.65$ at pH 2–4.

To summarize the effect of acidity on $G_{radicals}$, it would seem that in the Fe^{2+}–O_2, Fe^{2+}–N_2O systems, most—if not all—of the pH effect is caused by reactions of radicals with products, and quite possibly the same may be valid for the O_2–C_2H_5OH and formate–O_2 systems; in the CO–O_2 system the pH effect is probably not caused by reactions of the radicals with products, but the increase is sharp at low pH (1.4–2.2) and does not rise above pH 1.4. In pulse radiolysis studies of Br^- solutions and in the acetone–isopropyl alcohol system, no pH dependence was observed. These results seem to indicate that there is no real evidence in favor of an appreciable increase in G_R with acidity, as there seemed to be and as was summarized by Hayon (*47*).

ALKALINE SOLUTIONS. Several systems have been irradiated in alkaline solutions in recent years. In most of these systems G_R increases with pH. However, although most determinations do agree on the trend of increase of G_R, the measured G values differed extensively. Hayon (*47*) reviewed the difficulties, pitfalls, and some of the possible reasons as to why G values disagree.

The radiation chemistry of alkaline solutions is fraught with many complications. For instance, in oxygenated solutions O_3^- is formed from $O^- + O_2$, and the product of the reaction of $e_{aq} + O_2$ has a lifetime of up to several minutes (*25*). Such facts as these are liable to render more intricate the reaction mechanism on which the evaluation of G values depends. In strong alkaline solutions at pH > 13 there exists the danger of impurities. (In 1M NaOH, 0.01% of an impurity in the reagent may yield up to $10^{-4}M$ impurities in the solutions.)

Another difficulty lies in determining $G_{H_2O_2}$ or $G(H_2O_2)$ since H_2O_2 is unstable in alkaline solutions. In alkaline solutions both H and OH react with OH^- to yield e_{aq} and O^- respectively; hence, one should account for the different reactivities of the neutral and alkaline forms of the radicals with various scavengers.

In a number of instances G_{red} increased between pH 10 and 14, but the mechanisms assumed the existence of only one reducing radical—the solvated electron. It is now known that both e_{aq} and H atoms are formed by irradiation. We should consider that in these systems the H atom is converted, in alkaline solution, into e_{aq}, and that the reaction mechanism involving H and e_{aq} are responsible for the apparent increase of G_{red}. This would mean that what was really measured in many of these determinations was $G(e_{aq})$, which at low pH equals $G_{e_{aq}}$ but increases, in strong alkaline solutions, up to the value of $G_{e_{aq}} + G_H$. Most irradiated systems containing N_2O belong to this group.

The reactivity of e_{aq} towards N_2O is assumed to be 2×10^4-fold faster than that of H atoms.

$$N_2O + e_{aq} \rightarrow N_2 + O^-$$

$$N_2O + H \rightarrow N_2 + OH$$

k_1 is about $5.6 \times 10^9 M^{-1}$ sec.$^{-1}$, while k_2 is much lower. [The value of $2 \times 10^5 M^{-1}$ sec.$^{-1}$ has been estimated (*21*), but recent measurements indicate the value to be about one order of magnitude higher (*29, 40*).]

The first and simplest systems to be irradiated were solutions of N_2O over the entire pH range (*31*). In this system, $G(N_2)$ increased between pH 11–13, by about one unit, while $G(O_2)$ increased by only 0.35 units. In this same system, the net effect of radiation is that N_2O decomposes into $O_2 + N_2$, as H_2 and H_2O_2 descend to very low steady states owing to their decomposition by OH radicals which have no solute to react with. Thus, one expects $G(N_2) = 2G(O_2)$.

The experimental value of $\frac{G(N_2)}{G(O_2)}$ is 2.5 below pH 11 and about 2.85 at pH 14, but neither of these values provides a material balance. Although quantitatively this system is open to question, the observed increase of $G(N_2)$ and of $G(O_2)$ is expected and should be equal to G_H and to $\frac{1}{2}G_H$, respectively. The average value of G_H owing to the increase in $G(N_2)$ and $G(O_2)$ coincides with the known value of $G_H = 0.6$. ($\Delta G(N_2) = 0.95$, $\Delta G(O_2) = 0.2$.)

Another system that has been studied is the ferri–ferrocyanide–N_2O system (*32*). Here, G_{red} increases from 2.75 to 3.85 between pH 6.5 and 13.5. This increase is attributed to H_2O^* or (H . . . OH) which are scavenged by OH^-. It was assumed in the analysis that only e_{aq} was formed. At low pH, the H atoms with $G_H \sim 0.6$ are more likely to reduce ferricyanide than to react with N_2O, while at a higher pH, the H atoms can be converted into e_{aq} which reacts with N_2O.

Thus, $G(N_2)$ should increase by 0.6 units between pH 9 to 14, and $G(Fe^{III})$ will increase in the same range by about 1.2 units. The experimental results are in semiquantitative agreement with this prediction and mechanism. It has been shown recently (*29*) that $G(N_2)$ in this system is not pH dependent, but depends only on the ratio $\frac{[OH^-]}{[Fe^{III}]}$. This indicates that the increase in $G(N_2)$ is caused by competition of H atoms in the reactions:

$$H + OH^- \rightarrow e_{aq} \text{ (followed by } e_{aq} + N_2O \rightarrow N_2 + OH \text{ and } OH + Fe^{II} \rightarrow OH^- + Fe^{III})$$

$$H + Fe^{III} \rightarrow H^+ + Fe^{II}$$

Buxton and Dainton have investigated the N_2O–I^- system (*16*). Here $G(N_2)$ increases by about 0.7 units between pH 11 and 14; in this same pH range, $G(I_2)$ increases by about 1.4 units. This increase may again be caused by the competition of I_2 reduction by H atoms or by the conversion of the H into e_{aq} which oxidizes iodide.

The reactions are:

$$H + OH^- \rightarrow e_{aq}\ (e_{aq} + N_2O \rightarrow N_2 + O^-,$$
$$OH + I^- \rightarrow OH^- + I) \qquad (I)$$
$$H + I_2 \rightarrow HI + I$$

The average I_2 concentration during radiation amounted to 50 μM. At pH 13 when $[I_2] = 50\ \mu M$, Reactions I and II have comparable rates, so we expect $G(I_2)$ and $G(N_2)$ to increase by 0.7 or 0.35 units, respectively, over their value at low pH.

This prediction is in full agreement with experimental evidence. It follows that this increase can be attributed to G_H and Reactions I and II. Buxton and Dainton (*16*) discussed this possibility but discarded it since they assumed $G(N_2)$ reached too high a value for $G_{e_{aq}} + G_H$, which they assumed was about 2.9.

To summarize this system, the increase of $G(N_2)$ and $G(I_2)$ with pH is in good agreement with the accepted value of G_H. The value this system gives for $G_{e_{aq}}$ is 3.2, which is higher than that usually assumed.

Other systems studied and showing G_R to increase between pH 10 and 14 were: the N_2O–Tellurite (*34*), Pt^{II}–N_2O (*35*), and Ir^{III}–N_2O (*35*) solutions. The behavior in these systems is identical to that in the I^-–N_2O system. The increase of $G(H_2) + G(N_2)$ from 3.38 to 4.28 between pH 10.5 and pH 13.8 in the tellurite solutions can be accounted for by the competition of H atoms with OH^- and tellurite. The similar behavior in the Ir and Pt solutions can be caused by the reduction of Pt^{IV} or Ir^{IV} by H atoms. It is not yet possible to check these observations quantitatively because the rate constants of the reactions of H atoms with tellurite, Pt^{IV}, and Ir^{IV} are unknown.

In the two systems ferricyanide–formate–O_2 and ferricyanide–ethanol–O_2, Hayon (*46*) has shown that G_{red} increases from 2.85 to about 3.45 at pH 11.5–14.

In the ferricyanide–formate–O_2 solutions and ferricyanide–ethyl alcohol–O_2 systems, G_{red} is derived by assuming that all the OH radicals react with the organic solute and that none react with the ferrocyanide. These systems are further complicated by the fact that OH radicals can convert into O^- radicals, whose rate constants with the solutes are not known.

In these systems the initial ferricyanide was 800 μM, and the concentration of ferrocyanide at the end of irradiation reached a concentration of 300 μM.

At the end of radiation the following ratios would be obtained:

$$\frac{k_{\mathrm{OH+formate}}[\text{formate}]}{k_{\mathrm{OH+ferrocyanide}}[\text{ferricyanide}]} = 4.2$$

$$\frac{k_{\mathrm{OH+ethyl\ alcohol}}[\text{ethyl alcohol}]}{k_{\mathrm{OH+ferrocyanide}}[\text{ferrocyanide}]} = 3.3$$

Thus, in the formate or ethyl alcohol cases (*46*), 10–15% of OH (not O^-) would react with ferrocyanide formed. The increase with pH may be attributed to OH and O^- reacting differently with the solutes. At any rate, the G_{red} yields calculated by Hayon at pH < 11 appear to be too low by 10–15%.

Another determination (*15*) of *G* values in the formate–ferri–ferrocyanide system yielded results which suffer the same criticism. The values of $\frac{k_{\mathrm{OH+formate}}[\text{formate}]}{k_{\mathrm{OH+ferrocyanide}}[\mathrm{Fe^{II}}]}$ at maximum doses, were as low as 6, which cannot vindicate the assumption that OH reacts with formate only.

No pH dependence was reported in several systems studied in alkaline solution. The BrO^- (*18*) was studied by Cheek and Linnenbom who found that G_{red} was 2.85 for NaOH 0.01–1.0*M*. Julien and Pucheault (*45*) arrived at a similar conclusion when studying the irradiation of hypochlorite. Haissinsky (*38*) demonstrated two features in the nitrate–phosphate system: $G_{e_{aq}}$ increases and G_H decreases in the pH range 8.2–13.9, but G_{red} has the value of 3.2–3.3 in this range.

Two determinations of $G_{e_{aq}}$ as function of pH have been made using pulse radiolysis. Brown *et al.* (*14*) found that $G_{e_{aq}}$ increased by 50% from pH 9 to 13. (This increase includes the partial contribution of H atoms converted into solvated electrons.) Fielden and Hart (*37*) also observed an increase in $G_{e_{aq}}$ at pH 10–13. They found that all the increase is between pH 9 and 12, while at pH > 12, in contrast to other determinations (*34*) no further increase was observed.

Fielden and Hart (*37*) determined $G(e_{aq})$ in this pH range in three solutions: (a) $7 \times 10^{-4}M$ H_2, (b) $7 \times 10^{4}M$ H_2 + 1–2 $\times 10^{-3}M$ ethyl alcohol, (c) 1*M* ethyl alcohol. They compared the value at pH 13 with $G(e_{aq})$ in neutral solution and reported the ratios 2.42, 1.35, and 1.15 for solutions a, b, and c, respectively.

They assumed that at pH 13 in $7 \times 10^{-4}M$ H_2 $G(e_{aq}) = G_{e_{aq}} + G_H + G_{OH}$, in 1*M* ethyl alcohol $G(e_{aq}) = G_{e_{aq}}$ and in $7 \times 10^{-4}M$ H_2 + 1–2 $\times$ $10^{-3}M$ ethyl alcohol $G(e_{aq}) = G_{e_{aq}} + G_H$. With this assumption and the measured yield of $G_{e_{aq}}$ in neutral solution having the value of 2.7, they found at pH 13: $G_{e_{aq}} = 3.10$, $G_{OH} = 2.87$, and $G_H = 0.54$. The authors suggest that G_H should fall at pH 13 compared with neutral solution but failed to get such an effect. At pH ~ 13 in $7 \times 10^{-4}M$ H_2 + 1–2 $\times 10^{-3}$ ethyl alcohol solutions, OH is converted by OH^- into O^- before reacting with either H_2 or ethyl alcohol, as $k_{OH^- + OH}[OH^-] > k_{OH + H_2}[H_2]$ (*8*) or $k_{OH + C_2H_5OH}[C_2H_5OH]$. However, O^- can compete in the solution for H_2 and C_2H_5OH. The rate of O^- with ethyl alcohol is not known, but since it does not react faster than the rate of OH with C_2H_5OH (*58*), up to 10% of O^- would react with H_2, yielding H atoms which are converted into electrons. On this assumption, the following *G* values are recalculated:

$$G_{e_{aq}} = 3.10 \qquad G_{OH} = 3.2 \qquad G_H = 0.21$$

These values are only approximate since $k_{O^- + C_2H_5OH}$ is not known accurately. The interesting point is that G_{red} is about 3.4, almost unchanged from the value in neutral solution, while G_H is lower in the alkaline solutions as Fielden and Hart expected (*37*). The second feature is the high value of G_{OH} which might exceed $G_{e_{aq}}$. Similar behavior was observed in alkaline oxygenated ferrocyanide solutions (*44*), where $G_{e_{aq}} \sim 3.16$ and $G_{OH} = 3.2$. In the pulse radiolysis of ferrocyanide it was shown (*2*) that G_{OH} is pH independent over the range 4.4–13. The last point worth mentioning in Fielden and Hart's (*37*) study, is the pH independence of the yield in the range 12–13.

Two main questions exist concerning the pH dependence of G_R: is there a pH dependence, and what are the radical yields?

The increase observed for G_R when passing from neutral to either acid or alkaline soltuions is, in most systems, an artifact resulting from several causes.

In both acid and alkaline solutions, the two reducing entities, e_{aq} and H atoms, can be converted into each other in reactions:

$$e_{aq} + H^+ \rightarrow H$$

$$H + OH^- \rightarrow e_{aq}$$

Since these two species have different reactivities towards various solutes and radiation product, they must be taken into account.

The oxidizing OH radical exists in two forms in alkaline solutions, and these radicals may react in different ways with solutes or with radiation products.

Some of the radicals react with radiation products; therefore back reactions must also be considered. The relative contribution of these back reactions may also be pH dependent, either in their reaction with a solute, as in the $H + Fe^{3+}$ reaction in acid solutions, or because of the competition of an intermediate radical with a solute or radiation product, and the conversion of this radical into its other form.

In my opinion, in most of the cases where pH dependence was observed, it is caused by neglect of the above-mentioned points. When proper consideration is given to these effects, little or no pH effect on the yield is observed.

As for the value of G_R, different systems lead to different values. This inconsistency will be discussed below.

Dependence of $G_{e_{aq}}$ on Electron Scavenger Concentration

Numerous determinations of $G_{e_{aq}}$ in many chemical systems resulted in a wide range of values—namely, 2.3–2.9.

Hayon endeavored to prove that $G_{e_{aq}}$ is equal to 2.3 at low concentrations of electron scavenger, where $k_{e_{aq}+s}[S] < 10^7$, and at higher concentrations follows $G(e_{aq}) = 2.3 + f(k_{e_{aq}+s}[S])$. The function $(f(k_{e_{aq}+s}[S]))$ is given as an experimental curve (*47*). Hayon believes that the observed spread in $G_{e_{aq}}$ is caused only by the different values of $k_{e_{aq}+s}[S]$ in the systems which were studied and proposes a theory (*45*). However, on checking his data, it can be shown that in these systems, an appreciable—if not the entire—effect of the decrease in $G_{e_{aq}}$ as the concentration of S decreases, is caused by e_{aq} competition with the irradiation products formed.

In the NO_3^-–O_2–C_2H_5OH system, he states that yields are linear up to 1.5×10^{18} e.v./ml. However, upon calculating his observed G values, at the maximum dose applied, in this solution the peroxide concentration reaches 60–80μM. Since the e_{aq} reacts 1.3 times faster with peroxide than with nitrate (*8*), an appreciable fraction of e_{aq} does not react with nitrate at low nitrate concentrations. This would explain the lower G_{red} found by Hayon at nitrate concentration below 2 mM.

In the N_2O–I^- system (*45*), the dependence of $G_{e_{aq}}$ on N_2O concentration was studied in the range 0.53–16 mM N_2O. Iodine concentration, at maximum dose, is 20–30μM, but since e_{aq} reacts about 9 times faster with I_2 than with N_2O in this system (*8*), at low N_2O concentrations, up to 20% of e_{aq} competes for I_2 and N_2O.

In the Tl^+–N_2O system, the results are even stranger since the reaction of e_{aq} with Tl^+ is overlooked even though under Hayon's experimental conditions a large fraction of e_{aq} should react with Tl^+ rather than with N_2O (30–99%). (The results hint at a possible decomposition of N_2O by Tl^0.)

In the ferricyanide–ferrocyanide–N_2O and O_2–H^+–C_2H_5OH system (*45*), maximum doses are missing, but in the latter system, the pH effect can be attributed to the competition of electrons on the O_2 and aldehyde formed, while at low pH, H atoms would probably react with O_2 only.

Neutral Saturated N_2O Solutions. Several determinations of $G(N_2)$ were made in neutral solutions of N_2O (*26, 31, 33, 48, 60*), according to which $G(N_2)$ depends on N_2O concentration. In an earlier determination (*31*) it was found that in neutral solution $G(N_2) = 3.1$, $G(O_2) = 1.23$, $G(H_2) = 0.2$, $G(H_2O_2) = 0.5$. Since there are no OH scavengers in this system, H_2 and H_2O_2 are attacked by OH and should reach low steady-state values.

Taking into account all possible reactions with their known rate constants and assuming the accepted G values of e_{aq}, H, OH, H_2O_2, and H_2, we were able to solve all the differential equations for the radicals and molecular products N_2 and O_2 for the various dose rates used by using a computer. The results (*26*) showed that H_2 and H_2O_2 reach steady-state concentrations of the order of $10^{-7}M$ or less when nitrogen is formed at a concentration of about $10^{-5}M$ or even less. These results contradict the experimental observations and suggest that the higher yields of H_2 and H_2O_2 (*31*) are caused by impurities which react with OH radicals.

Dainton and Walker (*33*) observed that $G(H_2)$ and $G(H_2O_2)$ depend on dose and reach a steady state at a dose of 3×10^{21} and 3×10^{20} e.v./liter, respectively. These authors observed that $G(N_2)$ decreases at lower N_2O concentrations and higher total dose. The dose dependence is obvious as almost total decomposition of N_2O occurred at the higher doses used. Therefore, the oxygen produced competes with the N_2O for e_{aq}. Again, the increase of $G(N_2)$ with N_2O concentration is consistent with the competition of e_{aq} for O_2 and N_2O as, under the doses used, O_2 reached concentrations comparable with and even larger than the N_2O present.

Head and Walker (*48*) restudied this N_2O system recently at pH 7 in 10^{-5}–$2.5 \times 10^{-2}M$ N_2O solutions. They report that in $2.5 \times 10^{-2}M$ N_2O solutions, $G(O_2) = 0.65$, $G(H_2) = 0.1$, and $G(N_2) = 3.2$. These values are dose dependent. The authors explained the low O_2 yield by the fact that H_2O_2 had not yet reached a steady state. Their reasoning is not immediately obvious since H_2O_2 should reach a steady state of about $10^{-7}M$ at doses of less than 1% of the applied. This would seem to imply the presence of impurities; hence, the dependence of $G(N_2)$ on N_2O concentration may well be caused by competition with these impurities. Furthermore, at the dose used, O_2 reaches a concentration of $7 \times 10^{-6}M$; thus, in solutions of $2.5 \times 10^{-4}M$ N_2O, 10% of the electrons will react with O_2.

Scholes and Simic studied the system (*60*) and observed that the N_2 and O_2 yields had negative intercepts. In $1.6 \times 10^{-2}M$ N_2O at pH 6, $G(N_2) = 3.2 \pm 0.1$ and $G(O_2) = 1.68 \pm 0.05$, while H_2 and H_2O_2 reached steady-state values below $10^{-6}M$. In $2.10^{-3}M$ N_2O these authors found G values lower by about 30%, but in this solution, their plot extrapolates to very large negative intercepts which are nonlinear.

The N_2O system, in the absence of OH scavengers, seems very sensitive to impurities and therefore vulnerable to misinterpretations. The relatively high $G(H_2)$ and $G(H_2O_2)$ values required that this system be treated with caution, especially since computer calculations show that these products should reach values lower by more than one order of magnitude.

ISOPROPYL ALCOHOL–N_2O. Allan and Beck (*4*) measured $G(N_2)$ and $G(H_2)$ in $10^{-2}M$ isopropyl alcohol at pH 5.90 as a function of N_2O in the range 3–22 $\times$ $10^{-3}M$. $G(N_2)$ increased and $G(H_2)$ decreased at higher N_2O concentrations. They observed $\Delta G(N_2) \sim 2\Delta G(H_2)$, a result which they attributed to competition of N_2O in the spurs with the recombination of e_{aq} in the spur.

SOLUTIONS CONTAINING TNM. Henglein (*49*) introduced tetranitromethane (TNM) as a scavenger in radiation chemistry of aqueous systems and was able to show that both the reducing radical and the hydroperoxy radical react with TNM to yield NF^-, $(C(NO_2)_3^-)$, and NO_2. The OH radical is unreactive towards TNM. In the presence of an organic solute, such as alcohol, the OH reacts with the organic solute and yields a radical R, which reacts with TNM as does the reducing radical (*49*). This system is thus suitable for measuring G_{red} and $G_{red} + G_{ox}$.

In their study of G_{red} in the TNM system, Asmus and Henglein (*10*) showed that G_{red} increases with increased TNM concentration. The G_{red} for 1.3 $\times$ 10^{-4} and 6.4 $\times$ $10^{-4}M$ TNM is 3.05 and 3.3, respectively.

As NO_2^-, NO_3^-, and NF^- all react with e_{aq} and H with comparable rate constants and as the G values were derived from initial slopes where $(NF^-) > 1.5 \times 10^{-5}M$, it can be expected that at a low TNM concentration such as $(1.3 \times 10^{-4}M)$, up to 10% of the electrons will be reacting with NF^-, NO_2^-, or NO_3^-, and lower G_{red} values would be obtained.

Bielski and Allen (*13*) restudied this system in presence of air. At neutral pH, they found $G_{red} = 3.37 \pm 0.15$, with TNM concentration ranging from 2.1 $\times$ 10^{-5} to 3.82 $\times$ $10^{-3}M$. They also showed that NF^- reacts with O_2^- or e_{aq}. They were able to measure initial yields, in solutions where $(NF^-) < 2 \times 10^{-6}M$. Under these conditions, back reactions could be ignored at TNM concentrations above 4 $\times$ $10^{-5}M$.

This seems to be one of the most successfully studied systems since true initial yields were measured, and an exact material balance of products was achieved.

Pulse Radiolysis Studies. The effect of scavengers on G_R was also studied using the pulse radiolysis technique. In oxygenated bromide solutions in neutral pH $G(Br_2^-)$ is constant for 2 $\times$ 10^{-3} to $1M$ Br^- (*67*). Similar behavior was observed wtih thiocyanate, where in 10^{-3} to $0.1M$ CNS^- $G(CNS)$ was constant (*1*).

To summarize the effect of scavengers on the radical yields: in the majority of cases reviewed most, if not all, of the observed increase of radical yield at high alkalinity, acidity or, radical scavenger concentration is an artifact. There is no real experimental evidence in *most* systems studied, that G_R is affected to a large extent by adding high concentrations of solutes, although in a *few* systems the yield does increase with solute concentration.

The Diffusion Model

The diffusion model used in recent calculations accounted well for yields observed in γ-radiolysis (*53, 54, 55, 63*). However, recent computations (*55, 63*) assumed that some of the G_H was formed in an independent reaction and not by $H^+ + e_{aq} \rightarrow H$. The calculations enabled other effects to be explained, such as the decrease of molecular yield with scavenger concentrations. As to the effect of electron and OH scavengers on radical yields, both calculations agree that the increase in $G_{e_{aq}}$ is about eight times higher than the decrease of G_{H_2} when e_{aq} scavengers are added (*55, 63*).

Kuppermann has given plots of all the predicted yields (*55*): $G_{e_{aq}}$, G_H, G_{OH}, G_{H_2}, and $G_{H_2O_2}$ as a function of electron and OH scavengers. Schwarz (*63*) noted that NO_2^- and I^- should have, and do have, different effects on $G_{H_2O_2}$ since the NO_2^- reacts with either e_{aq} or OH efficiently, while the I^- reacts with OH only. Thus, in the first case, H_2O_2 is protected against e_{aq} by NO_2^-.

Accordingly, Kuppermann's curves of $G_{e_{aq}}$, G_H, and G_{OH} as functions of electron or OH scavengers, respectively, are not always justified. He reports the yield only as a function $k_{R+S}[S]$. Let us take a simple case where S reacts with only one of the radicals, as in the iodide case.

The calculations assumed that Reactions 1 to 12 occur in the spur while reactions of iodine atoms (Reactions 13 to 19) are neglected.

$$e_{aq} + e_{aq} \rightarrow H_2 \quad (1)$$

$$e_{aq} + H \rightarrow H_2 \quad (2)$$

$$e_{aq} + OH \rightarrow OH^- \quad (3)$$

$$e_{aq} + H^+ \rightarrow H \quad (4)$$

$$H + H \rightarrow H_2 \quad (5)$$

$$H + OH \rightarrow H_2O \quad (6)$$

$$OH + OH \rightarrow H_2O_2 \quad (7)$$

$$OH + H_2 \rightarrow H + H_2O \quad (8)$$

$$OH + H_2O_2 \rightarrow HO_2 + H_2O \quad (9)$$

$$e_{aq} + H_2O_2 \rightarrow OH + OH^- \quad (10)$$

$$H + H_2O_2 \rightarrow H_2O + OH \quad (11)$$

$$OH + I^- \rightarrow OH^- + I \quad (12)$$

$$I + I \rightarrow I_2 \quad (13)$$

$$I + e_{aq} \rightarrow I^- \quad (14)$$

$$I + H \rightarrow I^- + H^+ \quad (15)$$

$$I_2 + e_{aq} \rightarrow I_2^- \quad (16)$$

$$I_2 + H \rightarrow I_2^- + H^+ \quad (17)$$

$$I + H_2O_2 \rightarrow HO_2 + H^+ + I^- \quad (18)$$

$$I + OH \rightarrow HIO \quad (19)$$

If $k_{13} \sim k_7 \sim k_{19}$, $k_{14} \sim k_3$, $k_{15} \sim k_6$, $k_{16} \sim k_{10}$, $k_{17} \sim k_{11}$ and $k_{18} \sim k_9$ and some of these equivalencies are valid, these reactions should then be included in the calculations, and their omission will lead to grave errors.

The result of a calculation in which all reactions would be included would be that $G_{e_{aq}}$, and G_{H_2} do not depend at all on I^- concentration, and only I_2 and I would replace some of the H_2O_2 and OH, while the sum of $G(I_2 + H_2O_2)$ and $G(I + OH)$ remains constant.

Generally speaking, scavengers are liable to react with several of the e_{aq}, H, and OH radicals, and any calculation of yields should also take into account all possible reactions of the products of the scavenger radical reactions.

Thus, the yields of radicals do not depend only on the concentration of scavengers and their rate constant with the radicals but also on the product of this reaction. Then one should take into consideration the possible secondary reactions and the rates of these products with every entity which could be present in the spur. Therefore, there should be no general dependence of G_R on $k_{R+S}[S]$ since it also depends on the reactivity of the product P, of the reactions $S + R \rightarrow P$ in its reaction with radicals in the spur.

As to the effect of pH on the yields, one must consider this effect on the spur. In varying the pH from 0–14 the relative abundance of e_{aq} and H or of OH and O^- may change. Since the neutral and alkaline form of the radicals may have different diffusion constants and rate constants, they may affect the molecular and radical yields as well as $G(-H_2O)$.

At present no calculation of the pH effect using the diffusion model has been reported. Without such a calculation it is difficult to estimate the pH effect on G_R, $G_{H_2O_2}$, and G_{H_2}, although one would expect G_{H_2} to increase at high acidity. This is not observed.

Other Theories

There are other theories explaining the dependence of radical yields on pH and scavenger concentration. Dainton and Watt (*39*) postulate excited water $-H_2O^*$ in addition to the radicals formed. In the absence of suitable scavengers H_2O^* is quenched, and no net chemical change occurs, owing to the reaction

$$H_2O^* \rightarrow H_2O$$

In the presence of H^+, OH^-, or suitable scavenger, the following reactions with H_2O^* are suggested:

$$H_2O^* + H^+ \rightarrow H + OH + H^+ \text{ or } OH + H_2^+$$

$$H_2O^* + OH^- \rightarrow H + OH + OH^- \text{ or } OH + e_{aq}$$

$$H_2O^* + S \rightarrow \text{Intermediate and free radicals}$$

The lifetime of this H_2O^* must be longer than 10^{-8} sec. to account for the observed increase of yields.

Evidence for the existence of any excited water molecule with such a long lifetime is lacking since little if any fluorescence from T_2O solutions was observed (*27*). The very low *G* value for fluorescence observed could not be quenched by 1*M* acid, base, and other solutes (*27*). These results rule out an excited singlet of H_2O and make an excited triplet very unprobable, or if it exists, its *G* value would be below 0.1. (There are indications that the water triplet is a repulsive state, hence of no chemical importance (*51*).

The alternative theory suggests pairs or cages of H and OH radicals (H . . . OH) rather than H_2O^* (*3, 32, 44*). In this case the reactions would be similar to those of H_2O^*, namely:

$$(H \ldots OH) \rightarrow H + OH \quad \text{(I)}$$

$$(H \ldots OH) \rightarrow H_2O \quad \text{(II)}$$

$$(H \ldots OH) + H^+ \rightarrow H + OH + H^+ \text{ or } H_2^+ + OH \quad \text{(III)}$$

$$(H \ldots OH) + OH^- \rightarrow H + OH + OH^- \text{ or } e_{aq} + OH \quad \text{(IV)}$$

$$(H \ldots OH) + S \rightarrow \text{intermediates and radicals} \quad \text{(V)}$$

This hypothesis requires that in the absence of scavengers (Reactions III–V) Reaction II predominates over I since otherwise most of the pairs would form H and OH in the bulk by escaping out of this cage. This requirement limits the lifetime of this pair. One would require much higher concentrations of H^+, OH^-, or S in order to compete in Reactions III–V with II than is experimentally observed (*62*).

Similar behavior is observed in the photochemistry of water at 1849 A., where water yields H and OH radicals (*65*). The dependence of the quantum yield on scavenger concentration agrees well with the model of geminate recombination of the radicals.

Stein (*66*) criticized this treatment and reports that although formally the system follows the geminate recombination model, unreasonable parameters are obtained since too-low concentrations of scavengers bring the quantum yield to its limiting value.

It seems to me that Stein's self-criticism of this model rules out the model, and an alternative explanation to geminate recombination should be sought. A possible explanation is that in the photochemical studies, where geminate recombination was postulated, the lower quantum yields observed at low scavenger concentrations is caused by back reactions with products. In many of these systems, yields were not linear with dose at low scavenger concentrations, and possibly the initial yield was not obtained by the extrapolation used. [Czapski and Ottolenghi have shown recently that in these systems the cage effect is non-existent, and the back reactions can account for the system's behavior (*28*).]

Hayon's theory (*47*) explains the dependence of G_R on scavenger concentration. He assumes the diffusion model and explains the *G* dependence by reactions of solutes with the radicals in the spurs.

The observed *G* values satisfactorily fix a general curve with only one parameter, k_{R+S}[scavenger] (*47*). My criticism of the theory is identical with that of the diffusion model. I do not expect a general behavior of e_{aq} scavengers on the yield. The product of the reaction of the different scavengers with the electrons yield products which are not identical and thus have different reactivities with other radicals in the spur. Furthermore, it was demonstrated earlier that in many cases the observed yields at low scavenger concentrations are incorrect since initial yields were not always measured.

G Values According to Theory and Experiment

It is beyond the scope of this paper to analyze all determinations of G_R as functions of pH and scavenger concentrations. The systems reviewed are examples given to show that many of the pH and scavenger concentration effects are at least partially caused by indirect reasons—mainly by back reactions or competitions which were neglected. As to theories concerning the prediction of the pH and scavenger concentration effects, no general behavior is expected. No adequate calculation of the diffusion model was carried out to study the pH effect. As to the radical scavengers concentration effect on radical yields, the calculations made with the diffusion model suffer from the assumed simplifications which neglected secondary spur reactions of radicals with products of radical–solute scavenging reactions.

This simplification would indicate a general behavior, while one would expect each system to behave quantitatively different. There may be e_{aq} scavengers which increase, decrease, or do not change the radical yields. (In the iodide system, as discussed earlier, no change is expected—a fact experimentally verified (*67*). However, in oxygenated solution G_R is expected to increase, as was indeed observed, owing to the replacement of e_{aq} by O_2^- or HO_2—the latter radicals reacting slower than e_{aq} with other radicals in the spur.)

Although in many systems the dependence of G_R on pH or scavengers, for a given system, is mainly an artifact, the G values in some of the systems vary immensely.

Most observations seem to lead to the value 3.4 to 3.6 for G_{red}. Nevertheless, there are some systems where the yield is lower by about 0.6 units (*18, 52, 64*). Similar results are obtained for G_{OH}.

Inconsistencies in G values still exist, and while many are artifacts, others cannot be explained by any present theory.

Acknowledgment

The author thanks E. J. Hart, D. Mayerstein, J. Rabani, G. Stein, and E. Peled for reading and discussing the manuscript.

Literature Cited

(1) Adams, G. E., Boag, J. W., Currant, J., Michael, B. D., "Pulse Radiolysis," p. 117, Academic Press, New York, 1965.
(2) Adams, G. E., Boag, J. W., Michael, B. D., *Trans. Faraday Soc.* **61,** 492 (1965).
(3) Allan, J. T., Scholes, G., *Nature* **187,** 218 (1960).
(4) Allan, J. T., Beck, C. M., *J. Am. Chem. Soc.* **86,** 1483 (1964).
(5) Allen, A. O., *J. Phys. Chem.* **52,** 479 (1948).
(6) Allen, A. O., Rothschild, W. G., *Radiation Res.* **8,** 101 (1958).
(7) Allen, A. O., "The Radiation Chemistry of Water and Aqueous Solutions," Van Nostrand, New York, 1961.
(8) Anbar, M., Neta, P., *Intern. J. Appl. Radiation Isotopes* **18,** 493 (1967).
(9) Appleby, A., "The Chemistry of Ionization and Excitation," p. 269, Taylor & Francis, London, 1967.
(10) Asmus, K. D., Henglein, A., *Ber. Bunsen Ges. Phys. Chem.* **68,** 348 (1967).
(11) Balkas, T., Dainton, F. S., Dishman, J. K., Smithies, D., *Trans. Faraday Soc.* **62,** 81 (1966).
(12) Barr, N. F., Allen, A. O., *J. Phys. Chem.* **63,** 928 (1959).
(13) Bielski, B. H. J., Allen, H. O., *J. Phys. Chem.*, in press.
(14) Brown, D. M., Dainton, F. S., Keene, J. P., Walker, D. C., *Proc. Chem. Soc. (London)* **1964,** 266.
(15) Burchill, G. E., Dainton, F. S., Smithies, D., *Trans. Faraday Soc.* **63,** 432 (1967).
(16) Buxton, G. V., Dainton, F. S., *Proc. Roy. Soc.* **A287,** 427 (1965).

(17) Cercek, B., Ebert, M., Gilbert, C. W., Swallow, A. J., "Pulse Radiolysis," p. 83, Academic Press, New York, 1965.
(18) Cheek, C. H., Linnenbom, U. J., *J. Phys. Chem.* **67,** 1956 (1963).
(19) Collinson, E., Dainton, F. S., Smith, D. R., Tazuke, S., *Proc. Chem. Soc. (London)* **1962,** 140.
(20) Czapski, G., Ph.D. Thesis, Hebrew University, Jerusalem, Israel.
(21) Czapski, G., Jortner, J., *Nature* **188,** 50 (1960).
(22) Czapski, G., Stein, G., *J. Phys. Chem.* **63,** 850 (1959).
(23) Czapski, G., Allen, A. O., *J. Phys. Chem.* **66,** 262 (1962).
(24) Czapski, G., Schwarz, H. A., *J. Phys. Chem.* **66,** 471 (1962).
(25) Czapski, G., Dorfman, L. M., *J. Phys. Chem.* **68,** 1169 (1964).
(26) Czapski, G., *Israel J. Chem.*, in press.
(27) Czapski, G., Katakis, D., *J. Phys. Chem.* **70,** 637 (1966).
(28) Czapski, G., Ottolenghi, M., *Israel J. Chem.*, in press.
(29) Czapski, G., Peled, E., *Israel J. Chem.*, in press.
(30) Dainton, F. S., Sutton, H. C., *Discussions Faraday Soc.* **12,** 121 (1952).
(31) Dainton, F. S., Peterson, D. B., *Proc. Roy. Soc.* **A267,** 443 (1962).
(32) Dainton, F. S., Watt, W. S., *Proc. Roy. Soc.* **A275,** 447 (1963).
(33) Dainton, F. S., Walker, D. C., *Proc. Roy. Soc.* **A285,** 339 (1965).
(34) Dainton, F. S., Rumfeldt, R., *Proc. Roy. Soc.* **A287,** 444 (1965).
(35) *Ibid.*, **A298,** 239 (1967).
(36) Donaldson, D. M., Miller, N., *Trans. Faraday Soc.* **52,** 652 (1956).
(37) Fielden, E. M., Hart, E. J., in press.
(38) Haissinsky, M., *J. Chim. Phys.* **62,** 1141, 1149 (1965).
(39) Hart, E. J., *J. Am. Chem. Soc.* **76,** 4198 (1954).
(40) Hart, E. J., *J. Chem. Phys.* **56,** 594 (1952).
(41) Hart, E. J., *J. Am. Chem. Soc.* **76,** 4312 (1954).
(42) Hart, E. J., *Radiation Res.* **2,** 33 (1955).
(43) Hayon, E., Weiss, J., *Proc. Intern. Conf. Peaceful Uses Atomic Energy, 2nd, Geneva, 1958,* **29,** 80.
(44) Hayon, E., *Trans. Faraday Soc.* **60,** 1059 (1964).
(45) *Ibid.*, **61,** 723 (1965).
(46) *Ibid.*, p. 734.
(47) Hayon, E., Farkas Symposium, Jerusalem, 1967.
(48) Head, D. A., Walker, D. C., *Can. J. Chem.* **45,** 2051 (1967).
(49) Henglein, A., Jaspert, J., *Z. Physik Chem.* **12,** 324 (1957).
(50) Jortner, J., Rabani, J., *J. Am. Chem. Soc.* **83,** 4868 (1961).
(51) Jortner, J., private communication.
(52) Julien, R., Pucheault, J., *J. Chim. Phys.* **64,** 725 (1967).
(53) Kuppermann, A., *Radiation Res. Suppl.* **4,** 69 (1964).
(54) Kuppermann, A., *Radiation Res.* **25,** 101 (1965).
(55) Kuppermann, A., "Radiation Research," p. 212, North Holland Publishing Co., Amsterdam, 1967.
(56) Mozumder, A., Magee, J. L., *Radiation Res.* **28,** 215 (1966).
(57) Rabani, J., Stein, G., *J. Chem. Phys.* **37,** 1865 (1962).
(58) Rabani, J., Farkas Symposium, Jerusalem, 1967.
(59) Samuel, A. H., Magee, J. L., *J. Chem. Phys.* **21,** 1080 (1953).
(60) Scholes, G., Simic, M., *J. Phys. Chem.* **68,** 1731 (1964).
(61) Schwarz, H. A., *Radiation Res. Suppl.* **4,** 137 (1964).
(62) Schwarz, H. A., *Ann. Rev. Phys. Chem.* **16,** 347 (1965).
(63) Schwarz, H. A., *Proc. Informal Conf. Hc Radiation Chem. Water, 5th, Notre Dame, Ind., 1966,* p. 51.
(64) Seddon, W. A., Allen, A. O., *J. Phys. Chem.* **71,** 1914 (1967).
(65) Sokolov, U., Stein, G., *J. Chem. Phys.* **44,** 2189, 3329 (1966).
(66) Stein, G., "The Chemistry of Ionization and Excitation," p. 25, Taylor & Francis, London, 1967.

(67) Sutton, H. C., Adams, G. E., Boag, J. W., Michael, B. D., "Pulse Radiolysis," p. 61, Academic Press, New York, 1965.
(68) Weiss, J., *Nature* **153,** 748 (1944).

RECEIVED January 12, 1968. Work partially supported by AEC contract AT(30-1)-3753.

9

Pulse Radiolysis of Alkaline Solutions

JOSEPH RABANI

Department of Physical Chemistry, The Hebrew University, Jerusalem, Israel

The absorption spectrum of O^-, with a peak at 2400A. ($\epsilon = 240M^{-1}$ cm.$^{-1}$) is reported. Extinction coefficients at 2600A. of intermediates produced in alkaline solutions are reported. $\epsilon_{O^-}^{2600} = 200$, $\epsilon_{O_2^-}^{2600} = 1000$ at neutral pH, 1100 in alkaline solutions containing both N_2O and H_2O_2, and 1900 and 1600 in aerated and oxygenated solutions respectively (all at pH = 13, in units of M^{-1} cm.$^{-1}$). The possible formation of species equivalent to O_2^- and having different absorptions is discussed. The effect of pH on the apparent reaction rate constant of hydroxyl radicals with hydrogen peroxide was studied. We find: $k_{(O^- + HO_2^-)} = 2.74 \times 10^8 M^{-1}$ sec.$^{-1}$ for zero ionic strength, and $(k_{(O^- + H_2O_2)} + 1.42\, k_{(OH + HO_2^-)}) = 1.18 \times 10^{10} M^{-1}$ sec.$^{-1}$. The error in the above rate constants and extinction coefficients is 10–15%.

Pulse radiolysis of N_2O alkaline solutions has not yet been interpreted. Rabani and Matheson (*33*) reported an optical absorption at 2600A. in N_2O aqueous solutions at both neutral and alkaline pH's. They suggested that this absorption might be caused by OH in neutral and O^- in alkaline solutions. In neutral solutions, the absorption decayed away and the rate could be accounted for by reactions between the products listed on the right hand side of Equation 1 and Reaction 2.

$$H_2O \xrightarrow{\sim\sim} H,\ e^-_{aq},\ OH,\ H_3O^+,\ OH^-,\ H_2O_2,\ H_2 \qquad (1)$$

$$e^-_{aq} + N_2O \xrightarrow{H_2O} N_2 + OH + OH^- \qquad (2)$$

The absorption at pH = 13 lasted several seconds, and four formation and decay steps could be separated. Demonstration of the observations at pH = 13, at both 2600 and 4300A. has been presented in a previous paper (*30*).

The present work has been carried out with the aim of obtaining more data on possible intermediates in pulsed alkaline solutions. Data concerning optical absorptions and reactivities of these intermediates is essential for the future interpretation of irradiated alkaline N_2O aqueous solutions.

Experimental

The pulse radiolysis apparatus (*15, 17, 27*) and syringe technique (*17, 20, 39*) for cell filling has been previously described. A 450-w Osram xenon lamp used to produce the analyzing light beam (*18*). Irradiation temperature was 24°C. A four-cm. cell with an 8 cm. light path was used, instead of the multiple reflection cell (*35*). This was done to avoid interference from transients formed in the cell house water. This is important when relatively small optical absorptions are investigated, especially below 3000A. Below 2800A., scattered light passed through the monochromator and was collected by the photomultiplier. The amount of scattered light depended on the wavelength and on the optical alignment. Thus, at 2600A. it was usually between 3–6%, rising to about 8% at 2500A., 10–15% at 2400A., 20–25% at 2300A., and 50% at 2220A. The scattered light was checked using a Corning glass filter which is supposed to cut all the light below the wavelength region, which is just higher than the wavelength used. Alkaline solutions, carbonate free, have been prepared using either $Ba(OH)_2$-NaOH mixtures, or from 20*M* NaOH stock solutions in which carbonate is relatively unsoluble. Unless otherwise stated, $[Ba(OH)_2]/[NaOH] = 0.038$. N_2O has been purified as described before (*34*). For the spectrum of O^- the light beam was split into two, each beam passed through a Baush and Lomb monochromator. One of the monochromators has been set on 2600A. and used as a monitor for the electron beam intensity, while the other was used to obtain the absorption of the pulsed solution at various wavelengths (*41*).

The stock alkali solutions have been stored in borosilicate glass bottles as long as seven days. The stock ferrocyanide solutions were stocked in the dark for as long as 30 hours in a refrigerator and as long as 12 hours at room temperature before use. Hydrogen peroxide was unstable in our alkaline solutions, the decomposition was enhanced by alkali up to the highest alkali concentrations used (0.3*M*). The rate of decomposition was not reproducible. Therefore, a neutral stock solution of H_2O_2 was prepared ($\sim 1 \times 10^{-2}M$). Measurements showed that only 3% of the stock H_2O_2 decomposed during the 4–5 hours of storage of this solution. The microsyringe injection technique (*20*) was used to obtain alkaline solutions with the desired H_2O_2 concentrations immediately before pulsing. Analysis of the H_2O_2 concentrations was carried out immediately before and after pulse, for each sample. Neutral H_2O_2 solutions were analyzed by mixing with $3 \times 10^{-3}M$ $FeSO_4$ in 0.8*N* H_2SO_4. The Fe^{3+} formed by the oxidation of Fe^{2+} was determined spectrophotometrically. Alkaline solutions were made acid by mixing with 0.8*N* H_2SO_4 and then transferred to a volumetric flask containing $3 \times 10^{-3}M$ $FeSO_4$ in 0.8*N* H_2SO_4. Since all the alkaline solutions used for the investigations of H_2O_2 contained Ba^{2+} ions, $BaSO_4$ precipitated. After several hours (usually overnight) the solution could be separated from $BaSO_4$ by decantation. The H_2O_2 concentrations were calculated from the ferric sulfate absorption at 3040A., taking $\epsilon = 2190$ at 24°C. (*36*).

An electron pulse of 1 μsec. duration was used in all the experiments. In the following, time zero will always be chosen at the beginning of the electron pulse, unless otherwise stated.

The Absorption Spectrum of O^-

Presentation of Data. In Figures 1a and 1b, we present the optical absorption spectrum obtained in pulsed 0.105*M* NaOH solutions in the presence of 0.05 atmospheres N_2O. Experiments in a solution of both NaOH and $Ba(OH)_2$, $[Ba(OH)_2]/[NaOH] = 0.035$, but with the same $[OH^-]$ gave similar results. During the electron pulse, optical absorption is formed in the region 2200–2800A. Within the first 100 μsec. after the pulse the optical density increases (half-life ~25 μsec. under the conditions of Figure 1) by 25% or less. Then, part of the optical density decays away within ~2 msec. Finally, the major part of the optical absorption decays away with a half-life of several seconds. Because of the instability of the xenon lamp we were not able to obtain a reliable spectrum of the products after 30 seconds, and the lifetime of these products is also unknown. Typical oscilloscope traces showing the changes of the optical density with time at 2600A. and 4300A. have been published (*32*).

Although the pulse duration was only 1 μsec., the electronic "noise" lasted longer, and its duration depended on the wavelength—*e.g.*, at 2600A. it lasted 1.5 μsec. after the end of the pulse. At shorter wave lengths, where the xenon lamp was less intense and the "noise" to signal ratios were greater, more and longer "noise" was observed during and after the pulse. However, 5 μsec. after the pulse ($t = o$ is the beginning of the pulse.) "noise" could be neglected at all wavelengths. In Figure 1 we present both the spectrum after 5 μsec. (Figure 1a) and the extrapolated spectrum (to the middle of the electron pulse) (Figure 1a). This extrapolated spectrum represents the "initial" spectrum, after correcting for changes of absorption with time caused by chemical reactions during the pulse and the following "noise." Using $5 \times 10^{-4}M$ $K_4Fe(CN)_6$ under the same conditions, produced optical absorption at 4200A. corresponding to $1.96 \times 10^{-5}M$ ferricyanide. (Extinction coefficient of ferricyanide taken as $1000M^{-1}$ cm.$^{-1}$). Under such conditions, practically all OH and O^- oxidize ferrocyanide (*34*), hence, G (ferricyanide) $= G$ (OH) $+$ $G(O^-)$. The absorption obtained at 4300A. after 100 μsec. is almost certainly because of O_3^- and will be discussed later. The absorption at 6000A. has been obtained in Ba^{2+} free NaOH. It is caused by traces of

CO_3^{2-} ions which are known to react with OH radicals to form CO_3^- (*2, 41*). Using an extinction coefficient of about $2000M^{-1}$ cm.$^{-1}$ for CO_3^- at 6000A., [CO_3^-] can be calculated as 0.6 μM (maximum concentration). This corresponds to 3% of the initially formed OH and O^- radicals. The formation of CO_3^- may have a very small effect on the absorption in the ultraviolet light (*41*), but will not affect the initial absorption since no CO_3^- was formed during the pulse or shortly after.

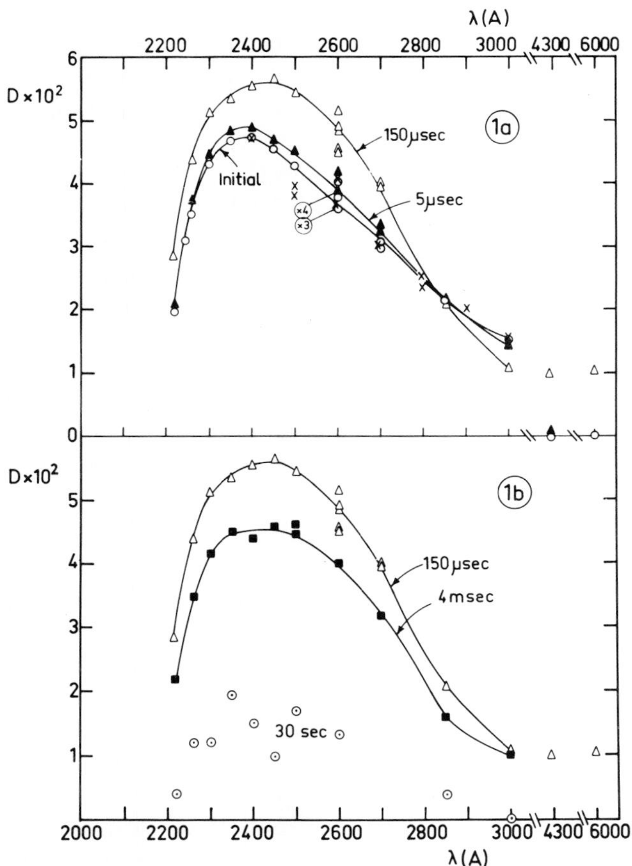

Figure 1a and 1b. Absorption spectra in solutions containing 0.05 atm. N_2O at pH = 13

Spectra taken in Ba^{2+} free solutions. ○—optical densities extrapolated to the middle of the 1 μsec. electron pulse from figures such as 3c. ▲—after 5 μsec., △—150 μsec., ■—4 msec., and ⊙—30 sec. ×—Spectrum in a solution containing [$Ba(OH)_2$]/[NaOH] = 0.035, normalyzed to the absorption at 2600A. in Ba^{2+} free solutions, obtained by extrapolation of the optical density to the middle of the pulse

Calculation of the O^- Spectrum. OH and H_2O_2 p*K*'s are 11.85 (*1, 34, 41*) and 11.7 (*23*) respectively. H atoms are converted into e^-_{aq} according to Reaction 3 (*22, 29*), $k_3 = 2.2 \times 10^7 M^{-1}$ sec.$^{-1}$ (*31*).

$$H + OH^- \rightarrow e^-_{aq} \quad (3)$$

When N_2O is present, the hydrated electrons formed by Equation 1 and Reaction 3 are converted into (*13, 24*) OH or O^-, k_4 (*14, 17, 25*) $= 8.6 \times 10^9 M^{-1}$ sec.$^{-1}$.

$$e^-_{aq} + N_2O \rightarrow N_2 + O^- \quad (4)$$

$$O^- + H_2O \rightleftharpoons OH + OH^- \quad (5)$$

Thus, in 0.05 atms. N_2O, at pH = 13, only OH, O^-, and HO_2^- contribute significantly to the optical absorption below 3000A. The absorption spectrum of H_2O_2 (*23*), HO_2^- (*23*), and OH (*30, 40*), have been studied previously. In Figure 2, we present the optical absorptions of hydrogen peroxide (HO_2^- in equilibrium with H_2O_2), OH and O^-, the sum of which equals the absorption spectrum of Figure 1 Curve a. The absorption attributed to hydrogen peroxide was calculated from the spectrum taken with a Cary spectrophotometer in a solution containing 0.105*M* NaOH and $1.34 \times 10^{-3}M$ hydrogen peroxide. Our results were in agreement with those obtained by Jortner and Stein (*23*). The total concentration of hydrogen peroxide (H_2O_2 and HO_2^-) in the pulse irradiated solutions was calculated to be $2.36 \times 10^{-6}M$, based on *G* (hydrogen peroxide total) = 0.7.

The optical density attributed to OH radicals (Figure 2) was calculated from the previous work (*40*). Above 2400A., the results obtained in H_2O_2, N_2O, or acid solutions were consistent (*30, 40*). Below 2400A. the results obtained in H_2O_2 and N_2O differed from those obtained in $HClO_4$ (*24, 25*). The spectrum obtained in N_2O and H_2O_2 represents the absorption of OH radicals (*25*). The absorption of OH in Figure 2 was obtained from these results, after correcting for H_2O_2 formation or destruction in the N_2O and H_2O_2 solutions respectively. (This correction is quite small and was neglected previously).

$(G(OH) + G(O^-)) = G_{OH} + G_e + G_H = 5.8$ and $G_{H_2O_2} = 0.7$ were used for the calculation of Figure 2, together with our values for the extinction coefficient of OH, $\epsilon_{OH} = 410M^{-1}$ cm.$^{-1}$ and $\epsilon_{\text{hydrogen peroxide}} = 177$ (pH = 13). The pulsed solutions used to obtain Figures 1 and 2, contained $1.96 \times 10^{-5}M$ ($OH + O^-$) and $2.36 \times 10^{-6}M$ hydrogen peroxide. Of the oxidizing radicals, $1.29 \times 10^{-6}M$ were OH, and $1.83 \times 10^{-5}M$ were O^- radical ions. The optical density scale in Figure 2 can be easily converted to an extinction coefficient scale for O^-, using $\epsilon_{O^-} = 200M^{-1}$ cm.$^{-1}$ at 2600A. Later we shall provide the data used for the evaluation of ϵ_{O^-} at 2600A.

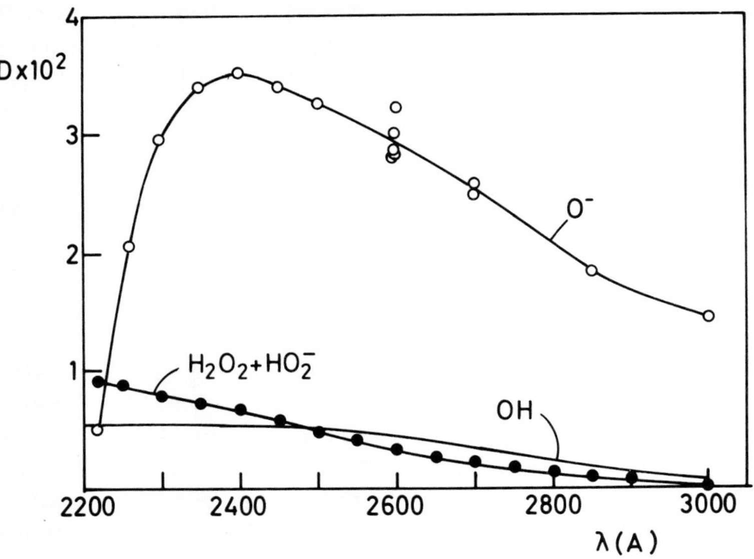

Figure 2. The absorption spectra of O^-, hydrogen peroxide, and OH radicals at pH = 13

The absorption of O^- differs considerably from that of OH. A peak at 2400A. is obtained for O^-, with $\epsilon_{O^-} = 240M^{-1}$ cm.$^{-1}$. As to OH, no peak is observed down to 2100A. (*30, 40*), although a broad peak between 2100 and 2400A. cannot be excluded. The difference in absorption at 2600A. between OH and O^- has been used for the evaluation of pK_{OH} (*32*).

Evidence for the Identification of the Spectrum as Owing to O^-. Figure 2 shows that OH, HO_2^-, and H_2O_2 cannot account for the entire optical absorption formed in the ultraviolet in pulsed alkaline solutions containing N_2O. Of the species on the right hand side of Equation 1, H_3O^+, OH^-, and H_2 are ruled out because their optical absorptions are known to be negligible in the range used in Figures 1 and 2, H atoms have a life time of about 0.35 μsec. at pH = 13, and hydrated electrons are converted into OH and O^- according to Equation 2 in less than a microsecond. Thus, of the species on the right hand side of Equation 1 (including their alkaline forms), only O^- remains as qualified to account for the major part of the absorption.

The change of initial optical density with pH, in pulsed aqueous N_2O solutions, agrees with the conversion of OH into O^- in alkaline solutions (*32*).

The formation of absorption during the electron pulse shows that the absorption is caused by a primary product or a product formed from N_2O. The possibility of reaction with impurities is unlikely to produce absorption within the 1 μsec. pulse. Only O^- and N_2O^- (or N_2OH) remain as qualified species. There is strong evidence against N_2O^- (or N_2OH), and those have been summarized in previous publications (*32, 34, 41*). We do not have an alternative satisfactory interpretation for each of the previous studies which suggested N_2O^- (or N_2OH) being relatively stable intermediates in N_2O irradiated solutions (*5, 6, 7*). However, in our opinion, the evidence against a long life time of N_2O^- (or N_2OH) in both neutral and alkaline solutions is very strong, and it is highly unlikely that N_2OH or N_2O^- will live more than 1 μsec.

It can be argued that the decay of the optical absorption in alkaline solutions does not agree with the expected rate of O^- decay. Indeed, as seen from Figure 1, there is only a partial decay within the first 4 msec., and the time dependency of the optical density is not in agreement with the assumption that O^- absorbs initially and then decays to form non-absorbing products. The complexity of the kinetics was demonstrated in a previous publication (*32*) (*see* Figure 2). As will be discussed later, the mechanism for O^- decay involves several possible intermediates, some of which are known to have optical absorptions in the ultraviolet. Thus, the long life time of the absorption may be caused by the conversion of O^- into other, more stable, absorbing species.

In a solution containing $0.1M$ CO_3^{2-} and 5×10^{-2} atm. N_2O at pH $= 13$, the initial optical density after a 1 μsec. electron pulse was 0.035. This is about 15 per cent higher than the absorption obtained with a similar solution containing no carbonate. However, in the carbonate solution, at least 85 per cent of the absorption decayed away within 100 msec., and assuming the reaction was second order, $2k = 5 \times 10^{-7} M^{-1}$ sec.$^{-1}$ has been obtained, in agreement with previous results (*2, 41*). The small change in initial optical density, when $0.1M$ CO_3^{2-} is added to the alkaline solution, shows that CO_3^- and O^- have comparable absorptions at 2600A. Since carbonate ions react as specific scavengers for OH radicals (*2, 41*) and adding the carbonate eliminated the complicated kinetic sequence which was found in carbonate free solutions, we conclude that OH (or O^-) are the precursors of the above long living species. Therefore, the absence of a fast decay of the optical density corresponding to $k_{(O^- + O^-)} = 10^9 M^{-1}$ sec.$^{-1}$ (*34*) is not evidence against the assignment of the major part of the initial absorption in pulse irradiated N_2O alkaline solutions because of O^- radical ions.

In Figure 3, we present oscilloscope traces obtained in the presence (Figures 3c and 3d) and absence (Figures 3a and 3b) of N_2O. These traces were photographed on Polaroid pictures, and then projected and plotted on optical density paper which enables the direct reading of optical densities. The electron beam intensity was the same for Figures 3a and 3b and Figures 3c and 3d. The initial (extrapolated to the middle of the electron pulse) optical density in the N_2O solutions is one half of that obtained in N_2O free solutions under the same conditions. This is owing to the hydrated electrons ($\epsilon = 600M^{-1}$ cm.$^{-1}$ at 2600A.) (*19*).

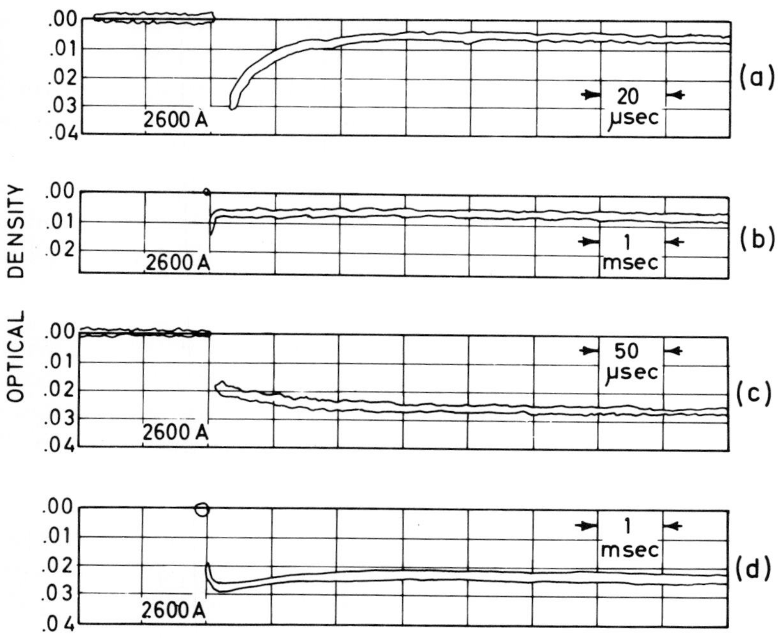

Figure 3. Oscilloscope traces plotted on O.D. paper at pH = 13, (a) and (b)—N_2O free solutions. (c) and (d)—0.05 atmosphere N_2O present

Elimination of the major fraction (about 75%) of the long lasting absorption occurs when N_2O is absent. The long lasting absorption in the absence of N_2O is too great to be accounted for by the molecular hydrogen peroxide alone. Figure 3 shows that N_2O is not essential for forming the long lasting absorption, although the presence of N_2O increases this absorption. These observations can be explained if O^- is assumed to be the precursor of the long living optical absorption in both N_2O and N_2O-free solutions. The effect of N_2O is then interpreted as caused by both increasing the available O^-, *via* Reaction 2, as well as preventing the combination of e^-_{aq} with O^-. In the N_2O free solutions, the combination of e^-_{aq} with O^-, in competition with other e^-_{aq} and O^- reactions, determines the concentrations of the long living species.

It might be argued that the reaction $N_2O + O^- \rightarrow N_2 + O_2^-$ takes place in N_2O alkaline solutions, and the absorption assigned by us to O^- is caused by O_2^-. The initial optical density in alkaline N_2O solutions gives $\epsilon = 200$ at 2600A. for species which are formed with $G = 5.8$. Therefore, it is apparent that only a fraction of the O^- could have been converted during the pulse to O_2^-. Otherwise, a much higher absorption would have been observed initially. If only part of O^- were converted to O_2^- during the electron pulse, we should have observed changes in optical density after the pulse, corresponding to the conversion of O^- into O_2^-. This process should be first order in N_2O. However, we varied the pressure of N_2O from 0.03 to 1 atm. and did not observe any significant effect on the time dependency of the optical density. Therefore, we conclude that N_2O does not react with O^- under our conditions.

Effect of pH on the Reaction of Hydroxyl Radicals with Hydrogen Peroxide in 0.05 Atmosphere N_2O Solutions

OH radicals react with hydrogen peroxide in neutral solutions according to Equation 6. The reaction rate constant, $k_6 = 4.5 \times 10^7 M^{-1}$

$$OH + H_2O_2 \rightarrow O_2^- + H_2O + H^+ \quad (6)$$

sec.$^{-1}$ has been reported (*38*). In alkaline solutions, the apparent reactivity of hydroxyl radicals with hydrogen peroxide is enhanced. This has been previously suggested (*29*) on the basis of photochemical experiments (*21*). A rate constant for Reaction 7, $k_7 = (7 \pm 3) \times 10^8 M^{1-}$ sec.$^{-1}$ has been reported by Felix, Gall, and Dorfman (*16*) for pH = 13, and $k_7 = 5 \times 10^8 M^{-1}$ sec.$^{-1}$ by Czapski and Behar (*12*) for pH = 13–13.7.

$$O^- + HO_2^- \rightarrow OH^- + O_2^- \quad (7)$$

The results of Felix *et al.* are based on competition between Reaction 7 and the reaction of O^- with O_2, taking (*3, 16*) $k_{(O^- + O_2)} = 2.5 \times 10^9 M^{-1}$ sec.$^{-1}$. The study of the reaction between hydroxyl radicals and hydrogen peroxide is important for the understanding of irradiated alkaline solutions, since both species are formed primarily. Besides, OH and O^- may form hydrogen peroxide by their recombination reactions. We used a direct method to measure the reactivity of hydroxyl radicals with hydrogen peroxide as a function of pH. In addition to Reactions 6 and 7, Reactions 8 and 9 have been considered.

$$OH + HO_2^- \rightarrow O_2^- + H_2O \quad (8)$$

$$O^- + H_2O_2 \rightarrow O_2^- + H_2O \quad (9)$$

When a sufficient concentration of hydrogen peroxide is initially present, Reactions 6 to 9 are the only important reactions taking place in the microsecond range. Reactions such as 10, 11, and 12 have only a small contribution to the overall rate of hydroxyl radicals decay.

$$OH + OH \rightarrow H_2O_2 \quad (10)$$

$$OH + O^- \rightarrow HO_2^- \quad (11)$$

$$O^- + O^- \xrightarrow{H_2O} HO_2^- \text{ or } O_2^{2-} \quad (12)$$

The apparent rate of reaction of hydroxyl radicals with hydrogen peroxide can be obtained from the increase of optical density with time at 2600A. because of the formation of O_2^- by Reactions 6 to 9. The absorption of O_2^- in the ultraviolet light has been reported by Czapski and Dorfman (*11*). Typical oscilloscope traces, projected and replotted on O.D. paper and a plot of $D_{plateau} - D_t$ *vs. t,* using a semilogarithmic scale are shown in Figures 4 and 5 respectively. ($D_{plateau}$ — the optical density obtained, after all the OH and O^- have reacted with the hydrogen peroxide, D_t-optical density at time t). The straight line in Figure 5 is typical of a first order reaction, and when the slope is divided by $([H_2O_2] + [HO_2^-])$, the apparent rate constant of the reaction between hydroxyl radicals and hydrogen peroxide is obtained.

Corrections which were made to Obtain a Precise Rate Constant for the Reaction of Hydroxyl Radicals and Hydrogen Peroxide. (1) Reactions such as 10, 11, 12, 13, and 14 compete with Reactions 6, 7, 8, and 9.

$$OH + O_2^- \rightarrow O_2 + OH^- \quad (13)$$

$$O^- + O_2^- \rightarrow O_2 + 2OH^- \quad (14)$$

$$\text{or } O_3^{2-}$$

$$\text{or } HO_3^- + OH^-$$

The nature and the reactivity of some of the intermediates towards hydroxyl radicals and radical ions are not known. However, the effective overall rate constants for OH (and O^-) reactions in a similar system containing ferrocyanide ions instead of hydrogen peroxide have been investigated (*34*). Using the results of the ferrocyanide work (*34*), we corrected the apparent rate constants for the reaction of hydroxyl radicals with hydrogen peroxide by adding the calculated first half-life of hydroxyl radical's decay in the absence of added hydrogen peroxide, to that measured in our hydrogen peroxide solutions.

(2) A correction was made to account for the decomposition of H_2O_2 before pulsing the alkaline solutions. We assumed that over the short time periods in which hydrogen peroxide was kept alkaline (usually less than 15 minutes), the decomposition was linear with time. In most cases, the differences between the concentrations of hydrogen peroxide found by analysis and those calculated from the concentrations of the

neutral stock solutions, did not exceed 10%. In all cases it was less than 20%. Thus, the concentration of hydrogen peroxide was chosen as the average between the values obtained by analysis before and after the electron pulse, after correcting for the change in hydrogen peroxide concentration by the pulse.

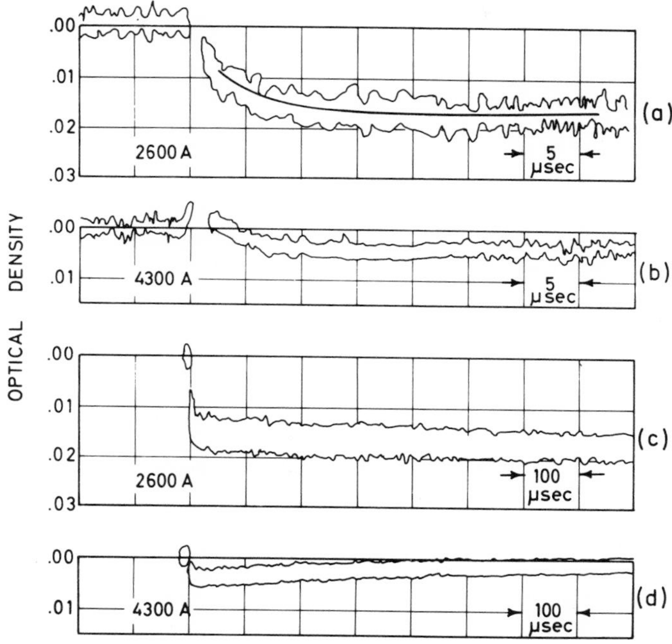

Figure 4. Oscilloscope traces, plotted on O.D. paper, taken at pH = 13, in hydrogen peroxide solutions containing 0.05 atmospheres N_2O. The solid line in (a) represents the average change of the measured optical density with time.

(3) O_2, which may be formed in the solution as a result of the decomposition of hydrogen peroxide, is an efficient scavenger for O^- (*11*). O_3^-, the product of Reaction 15 has optical absorption with a maximum at 4300A. (*11*). Values of k_{15}

$$O^- + O_2 \rightarrow O_3^- \tag{15}$$

ranging between 2.5×10^9 and $3.6 \times 10^9 M^{-1}$ sec.$^{-1}$ have been reported (*32*). Corrections owing to Reaction 15 were made using three different methods; all gave identical results within experimental error. The first method is based on the comparison between the maximum O_3^- absorption at 4300A. and the absorption of O_2^- at 2600A. obtained after all the OH radicals have reacted (obtained in the same pulsed solution). The maximum absorption at 4300A. is used to calculate the fraction of O^- which reacted with O_2 in competition with Reactions 6 to 9. For these calculations we used $\epsilon_{O_2^-}^{2600} = 1000$ and $\epsilon_{O_3^-}^{4300} = 2000M^{-1}$ cm.$^{-1}$ (*4*).

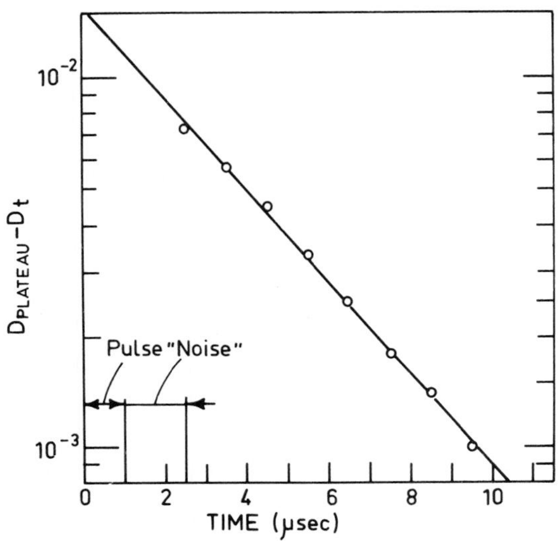

Figure 5. The pseudo first order plot obtained using Figure 4 (a)

The second method is based on the comparison between the optical densities obtained at 4300A. in the H_2O_2 solutions and in solutions containing 0.9 atm. N_2O and 0.1 atm. O_2 but without hydrogen peroxide. (All other conditions were the same). From such comparisons the fraction of O^- which formed O_3^- in the H_2O_2 solutions could be calculated, and appropriate corrections could be made.

The third method is based on the reaction of O_3^- with hydrogen peroxide which follows the oxidation of hydrogen peroxide by the hydroxyl radicals. Evidence of such a reaction can be seen from the simultaneous decay of absorption at 4300A. and the formation of absorption at 2600A. (Figures 4c and 4d). We assume that O_3^- only reacts with hydrogen peroxide, under our experimental conditions.

Other experiments carried out in the presence of 10^{-5} to $10^{-3}M$ O_2 show: (1) Reaction 16 or 16′ can be followed at both 2600A. and 4300A.; (2) the same rate constants are obtained at both wavelengths; and (3) the increase in absorption at 2600A. is about one half of the decrease in 4300A. within any time interval. This shows that the product of Reaction 16 or 16′ has an extinction coefficient of about 1000 at 2600A. Thus, the fraction of O^- which reacted with O_2 can be obtained as approximately equal to 1-$D^{2600}_{plateau}/D^{2600}_{\infty}$, where $D^{2600}_{plateau}$ is the optical density obtained after all the hydroxyl radicals have reacted, and D^{2600}_{∞} is the optical density obtained after the O_3^- radical ions also reacted with hydrogen peroxide

$$O_3^- + H_2O_2 \rightarrow O_2 + O_2^- + H_2O \quad (16)$$

$$O_3^- + HO_2^- \rightarrow O_2 + O_2^- + OH^- \quad (16')$$

The corrections for Reaction 15 were less than 5% for the experiments carried out at pH $\leqslant$ 12, and 8–15% for pH = 12.3–13.5. In general the correction was greater at higher pH's.

(4) Finally, a correction had to be made because of Reaction 3, which, being followed by Reaction 4, supplies additional hydroxyl radicals. If $k_3 \times [OH^-]$ is either much greater or much smaller than "$k_{(OH+H_2O_2)}$" $\times$ $[H_2O_2]_T$ at the given pH, the effect of Reaction 3 can be neglected. "$k_{(OH+H_2O_2)}$" is the apparent rate constant of the reaction between hydroxyl radicals and hydrogen peroxide. $[H_2O_2]_T$ is the sum ($[H_2O_2]$ + $[HO_2^-]$). In these cases, Reaction 3 affects only the total number of available hydroxyl radicals but not their apparent rate constant with hydrogen peroxide. When necessary computer calculations using the program made by Schmidt (*37*) were made to correct for Reaction 3, we found that no correction was necessary for pH > 12.7. For pH = 11.9 to 12.7, corrections were less than 12% (usually about 6%), depending on both pH and $[H_2O_2]_T$. At pH = 11.5 to 11.6, these corrections ranged between 20 to 50%, depending strongly on $[H_2O_2]_T$. All the corrections were made to increase the observed apparent rate constants, and the percent correction is referred to the uncorrected rate constants.

Treatment of the Data. The effect of pH on the corrected apparent rate constant "$k_{(OH+H_2O_2)}$" is presented in Table I. Each experimental result in the table is an average of two experiments.

The apparent rate constant "$k_{(OH+H_2O_2)}$" is determined by the contributions of Reactions 6, 7, 8, and 9. Since OH and H_2O_2 have their p*K*'s near 11.8, these contributions are expected to be pH dependent in the alkaline pH region. We assume that equilibria of Reactions 5 and 17 are maintained through the course of the reaction

$$H_2O_2 + OH^- \rightleftharpoons HO_2^- + H_2O \quad (17)$$

of hydroxyl radicals with hydrogen peroxide. It can be shown that under such conditions:

$$“k_{(OH+H_2O_2)}” = k_6/((1 + K_5/[H^+]) \times (1 + K_{17}/[H^+])) + k_8/((1 + K_5/[H^+]) \times (1 + [H^+]/K_{17})) + k_9/((1 + [H^+]/K_5) \times (1 + K_{17}/[H^+])) + k_7/((1 + [H^+]/K_5) \times (1 + [H^+]/K_{17})) \quad (18)$$

k_6, k_7, k_8, and k_9 are the rate constants of Reactions 6, 7, 8, and 9 respectively. K_5 is defined as $[H^+] \times [O^-]/[OH]$ and K_{17} as $[H^+] \times [HO_2^-]/[H_2O_2]$, $[H^+]$ is defined as $10^{14}/[OH^-]$.

Equation 18 can be rearranged to the form:

$$“k_{(OH+H_2O_2)}” \times ([H^+]/K_5 + 1) \times (K_{17}/[H^+] + 1) = [H^+] \times k_6 + ((K_{17}/K_5) \times k_8 + k_9) + (K_{17}/[H^+]) \times k_7 \quad (18')$$

Table I. Effect of pH on $“k_{(OH+H_2O_2)}”$

$[OH^-]$[a]	$[H_2O_2]_T \times 10^4$	D_∞[b] $\times 10^2$	D_0[c] $\times 10^2$ when $[H_2O_2] = O$	$“k_{(OH+H_2O_2)}” \times 10^{-9} M^{-1} sec.^{-1}$
3.35×10^{-3}	2.52	2.40	—	2.30
3.50×10^{-3}	1.80	2.10	—	2.40
3.60×10^{-3}	1.02	1.47	0.50	3.05
8.9×10^{-3}	0.93	1.90	—	2.95
9.5×10^{-3}	0.34	2.00	—	2.10
1.03×10^{-2}	0.75	1.31	0.46	3.00
1.03×10^{-2}	1.50	1.56	0.42	2.80
1.57×10^{-2}	1.33	2.20	—	1.40
2.35×10^{-2}	0.61	2.10	—	1.70
2.52×10^{-2}	1.60	2.40	—	1.24
2.57×10^{-2}	2.45	1.62	0.46	2.00
2.91×10^{-2}	2.44	2.20	—	1.08
6.20×10^{-2}	2.93	1.50	—	1.40
9.50×10^{-2}	0.89	1.90	0.57	1.06
9.60×10^{-2}	7.10	1.40	—	0.60
9.70×10^{-2}	2.45	1.60	—	0.93
1.01×10^{-1}	1.23	2.17	0.51	0.90
1.01×10^{-1}	2.44	1.72	—	0.92
1.03×10^{-1}	1.54	2.10	—	1.40
2.88×10^{-1}	1.25	2.50	—	0.85
3.03×10^{-1}	1.28	2.32	—	0.75

[a] $[Ba(OH)_2]/[NaOH] = 3.9 \times 10^{-2}$. (Values ranged from 3.8×10^{-2} to 4.1×10^{-2}.)

[b] The optical density was obtained when practically all of the available hydroxyl radicals had reacted, but before any further change in optical density had taken place because of Reaction 16 or 16′ or because of the decay of O_2^-.

[c] Initial optical density in solutions containing 0.05 atm. N_2O but no initial H_2O_2. (Same pulse intensity as in the corresponding experiments in the presence of H_2O_2.)

Investigations of the effect of pH on "$k_{(OH+H_2O_2)}$" can be used to obtain k_6, $((K_{17}/K_5) \times k_8 + k_9)$, and k_7. However, it is obvious from Equation 18′ that k_8 and k_9 cannot be obtained separately from our experimental results. If "$k_{(OH+H_2O_2)}$" $\times ([H^+]/K_5 + 1) \times (K_{17}/[H^+] + 1) - [H^+] \times k_6$ (in the following will be referred to by y), is plotted *vs.* $(K_{17}/[H^+]) \times 10^{M}$ (in the following will be referred to as x), a straight line should be obtained with a slope equal to $k_{7,0}$ (k_7 at zero ionic strength), and an intercept equal to $((K_{17}/K_5) \times k_8 + k_9)$. M is defined as $1.02 \times \mu^{0.5}/(1 + \alpha\mu^{0.5})$, μ being the ionic strength and α a coefficient, depending on the reaction radius (*8*). K_5 and K_{17}, 1.41×10^{-12} and $2.00 \times 10^{-12}M$ respectively, and $k_6 = 4.5 \times 10^7 M^{-1}$ sec.$^{-1}$ were used.

Least Squares Method. A least squares method was applied to obtain the best line representing y *vs.* x. Let $y = ax + b$ be the theoretical line, and $(x_i y_i)$ an experimental point. The equation

$$\sum_i (y_i - ax_i - b)^2 = \text{a minimum } (25) \qquad (19)$$

does not fit to our case, where $|y_i - y|$ is proportional to $(ax_i + b)$. Therefore, Equation 20 should be used. However, this equation

$$\sum_i ((y_i - ax_i - b)^2/(ax_i + b)^2) = \text{a minimum} \qquad (20)$$

is difficult to treat mathematically. Therefore, a method of successive approximations was used. The values $a = a_1$ and $b = b_1$ were first obtained using Equation 19. Then the results were retreated using Equation 21, and new values $a = a_2$ and $b = b_2$ were obtained. This was repeated until $a_m = a_{m-1}$ and $b_m = b_{m-1}$ resulted. This method will be referred to (in Table II) as S.A.M. The calculation of k_7 and $(k_9 K_{17}/K_5 + k_8)$ using different parameters and calculation methods is presented in Table II.

$$\sum_i ((y_i - ax_i - b)^2/(a_1 x_i + b_1)^2) = \text{a minimum.} \qquad (21)$$

Table II demonstrates that small changes in K_5 and K_{17} have relatively small effects on the values of the calculated rate constants. Also, changing α from 1 to 2 had some effect on the resulting $k_{(O^- + HO_2^-)}$ but practically no effect on the determination of the other rate constants. We prefer calculation no. 3. In Figure 6, the theoretical "$k_{(OH+H_2O_2)}$," calculated on the basis of Table II, no. 3, is plotted *vs.* pH, together with the experimental results of Table I. The fit between the experiments and the theoretical line is satisfactory.

Extinction Coefficients of OH, O^-, O_2^-, and O_3^- at 2600A.

ϵ_{OH} (in Neutral Solutions). Neutral solutions containing either 0.05 atmospheres N_2O or $1.21 \times 10^{-4}M$ hydrogen peroxide were pulsed. The initial optical density (extrapolated to the middle of the electron pulse) at 2600A. was compared with that obtained at 4200A. in a solution containing $5 \times 10^{-4}M$ $K_4Fe(CN)_6$ in 0.05 atmosphere N_2O. In the ferrocyanide system, practically all the OH radicals reacted with ferrocyanide to form ferricyanide. ϵ_{OH} was calculated taking $\epsilon_{(ferricyanide)} = 1000$, $\epsilon_{H_2O_2}^{2600} = 14M^{-1}$ cm.$^{-1}$, $G_{(ferricyanide)} = G(OH) = 5.2$, and $G(H_2O_2) = G_{H_2O_2} = 0.75$ in the N_2O solutions. For the H_2O_2 solutions $G(H_2O_2) = G_{H_2O_2} - G_{e^-_{aq}} = -1.85$. An average of eight independent experiments gave $\epsilon_{OH}^{2600} = 410 \pm 50M^{-1}$ cm.$^{-1}$. The results in N_2O and H_2O_2 solutions were the same, within experimental error.

Table II. Evaluation of k_7 and $(k_9K_{17}/K_5 + k_8)$ Using a Least Square Method

No.	$k_{(O^- + HO_2^-)}$ at $\mu = 0$M^{-1} sec.$^{-1}$	$(k_{(O^- + H_2O_2)} + k_{(OH + HO_2^-)} \times K_{17}/K_5)$M^{-1} sec.$^{-1}$	$K_5 \times 10^{12}$M	$K_{17} \times 10^{12}$M	α
1	3.30×10^8 [a]	9.95×10^9 [a]	1.41	2.00	1
2	3.09×10^8 [b]	8.35×10^9 [b]	1.41	2.00	1
3	2.74×10^8 [c]	1.18×10^{10} [c]	1.41	2.00	1
4	2.47×10^8 [c]	9.66×10^9 [c]	1.41	1.41	1
5	3.27×10^8 [c]	1.16×10^{10} [c]	1.41	2.00	2
6	2.36×10^8 [c]	1.41×10^{10} [c]	1.00	2.00	1
7	3.01×10^8 [c]	1.02×10^{10} [c]	2.00	2.00	1
8	2.95×10^8 [d]	1.10×10^{10} [d]	1.41	2.00	1

[a] Obtained by S.A.M. calculations. Values of "$k_{(OH + H_2O_2)}$" were not corrected for Reaction 3. All the 41 experiments (averages of which gave the data in Table I) were treated as independent experiments.
[b] The condition $\sum_i ((y_i - ax_i - b)^2/y_i^2)$ = a minimum, was applied. Otherwise as (*a*).
[c] Obtained by S.A.M. Calculations: parallel experimental results were averaged and were corrected for Reaction 3 before being processed. (These averages are presented in Table I.)
[d] As (*c*) except that three experiments at pH 11.5–11.6, with the highest correction for Reaction 3 have been omitted.

$\epsilon_{O_2^-}^{2600}$ in Neutral Solutions. The initial (extrapolated to the middle of the pulse) optical densities in air-saturated solutions were compared with the initial optical densities obtained in air-free $1.36 \times 10^{-4}M$ H_2O_2 solutions. Using G and ϵ values as given in the previous section (assuming the primary yields the same for both air-saturated and $1.36 \times 10^{-4}M$ H_2O_2 solutions) and taking $G_H = 0.6$, we obtained $\epsilon_{O_2^-}^{2600} = (1000 \pm 100)$ M^{-1} cm.$^{-1}$. This value is based on $\epsilon_{OH}^{2600} = 410M^{-1}$ cm.$^{-1}$ but the error limits here do not include the error in ϵ_{OH}^{2600}.

$\epsilon_{O_2^-}^{2600}$ in Alkaline Solutions. Four methods have been used to obtain $\epsilon_{O_2^-}^{2600}$ in alkaline solutions.

(1) The optical density at 2600A. after 30 μsec. in a pulsed solution of $2.4 \times 10^{-4}M$ hydrogen peroxide in 0.05 atm. N_2O at pH = 13.0 was

1.3×10^{-2}. Correcting for about 10 per cent of the O^- radical ions which produced O_3^- rather than O_2^-, we obtain a corrected optical density of 1.4×10^{-2}. Under the same conditions the optical density in a solution containing 8.5×10^{-2} atm. O_2 and 0.80 atm. N_2O in $0.092M$ OH^- was 3.2×10^{-2} at 4300A. The absorption at 4300A. is caused by O_3^- and includes a correction for the loss of hydroxyl radicals by reactions competing with Reaction 15 and for H and e^-_{aq} reacting with O_2 rather than with N_2O, using previously known reaction rate constants (*14*). Neglecting any significant contribution of O_3^- to the absorption at 2600A. in the H_2O_2 solutions (this will be justified later) we obtain:

$$(\epsilon^{2600}_{O_2^-} - \epsilon''^{2600}_{H_2O_2}{}'')/\epsilon^{4300}_{O_3^-} = 0.44$$

$\epsilon''^{2600}_{H_2O_2}{}'' = 177$ is the effective extinction coefficient of hydrogen peroxide at pH = 13. Taking $\epsilon^{4300}_{O_3^-} = 2000$ (*4*) we obtain $\epsilon^{2600}_{O_2^-} = (1060 \pm 150)$ M^{-1} cm.$^{-1}$. The radical yields in the nearly N_2O saturated solutions are probably somewhat higher than those used for the present calculations (*9*). Correction for this would increase $\epsilon^{2600}_{O_2^-}$ by up to 15%.

(2) The results in Table I enable a comparison of the final *D* values in the H_2O_2 solutions with the initial *D* values in the H_2O_2 free solutions. The optical densities in the H_2O_2 solutions in Table I must be corrected for loss in OH and O^- radicals by reactions competing with Reactions 7, 8, and 9 as discussed previously. The extinction coefficient of O_2^- at 2600A. was obtained from these results using the relation:

$$D \text{ ratio} = (\epsilon^{2600}_{O_2^-} (G(OH) + G(O^-)) - \epsilon''^{2600}_{H_2O_2}{}'' (G(OH) + G(O)^- - G_{H_2O_2})/$$
$$(\epsilon''^{2600}_{OH}{}'' (G(OH) + G(O^-) + \epsilon''^{2600}_{H_2O_2}{}'' \times G_{H_2O_2}).$$

D ratio is the ratio of the optical density obtained in the hydrogen peroxide solutions after all the hydroxyl radicals reacted (corrected for hydroxyl radicals lost by side reactions) divided by the initial optical density obtained in a solution free of hydrogen peroxide under the same conditions.

$\epsilon''^{2600}_{H_2O_2}{}''$ and $\epsilon''^{2600}_{OH}{}''$ are the effective extinction coefficients of H_2O_2 and OH at 2600A. respectively. We calculated the effective $\epsilon''^{2600}_{H_2O_2}{}''$ and $\epsilon''^{2600}_{OH}{}''$ taking $\epsilon^{2600}_{OH} = 410$, $\epsilon^{2600}_{O^-} = 200$, $\epsilon^{2600}_{HO_2^-} = 185$ and $\epsilon^{2600}_{H_2O_2} = 14M^{-1}$ cm.$^{-1}$, and using $K_5 = 1.41 \times 10^{-12}$ (*32*) and $K_{17} = 2.00 \times 10^{-12}M$ (*23*). $G(OH) + G(O^-) = G_{e^-_{aq}} + G_H + G_{OH} = 5.8$, and $G_{H_2O_2} = 0.7$ were taken for the calculations. We obtain $\epsilon^{2600}_{O_2^-} = 1170 \pm 150M^{-1}$ cm.$^{-1}$ for pH = 11.5 to 13. No systematic change between pH = 11.5 and 13 was observed.

(3) We used N_2O saturated alkaline solutions ($0.095M$ OH^-), containing both O_2 and hydrogen peroxide. Changes in optical density with time were followed simultaneously at 2600 and 4300A. Under our conditions the OH radicals and O^- radical ions are divided between the dissolved oxygen and hydrogen peroxide in less than 30 μsec. These reactions are assumed to produce O_3^- and O_2^- respectively. This process is followed by a relatively slow reaction, in which the optical absorption at 4300A. decays away, together with additional formation of absorption at 2600A. It has been previously shown that the ozonide ion is reactive towards hydrogen peroxide (*12, 16*). We assume that O_2^- is produced according to Reactions 16 or 16′. If O_3^- reacts exclusively with hydrogen

peroxide, producing O_2^- as the only absorbing product at 2600A., then:

$$(\epsilon_{O_2^-}^{2600} - \epsilon_{O_3^-}^{2600} - \epsilon_{\text{hydrogen peroxide}}^{2600})/\epsilon_{O_3^-}^{4300} = \Delta D^{2600}/\Delta D^{4300}$$

ΔD^{2600} and ΔD^{4300} represent the changes of optical density at 2600A. and 4300A. respectively, as Reactions 16 or 16′ proceed, within the same time interval. We find that in a solution containing $3.81 \times 10^{-5}M$ O_2, 3.70 $\times 10^{-4}M$ hydrogen peroxide, and 0.84 atm. N_2O, $D_{\text{maximum}}^{4300} = 0.0150$. While the absorption at 4300A. decayed away, the optical density at 2600A. increased from 0.0125 to 0.0180. Similarly, in a solution containing 1.19 $\times$ $10^{-4}M$ O_2, $3.40 \times 10^{-4}M$ hydrogen peroxide, and 0.77 atm. N_2O: $D_{\text{maximum}}^{4300}$ = 0.0195 and the optical density at 2600A. changed from 0.0082 to 0.0148. From these results, we obtain:

$$(\epsilon_{O_2^-}^{2600} - \epsilon_{O_3^-}^{2600}) = 9 \times 10^2 M^{-1}\ \text{cm.}^{-1}.\ (\text{Based on } \epsilon_{O_3^-}^{4300} = 2000.)$$

These results are not precise, since we have neglected to correct for a fraction of O_3^- which may have decayed away without reacting with H_2O_2, which could have been as much as 18% at the lowest O_2 concentration.

(4) Air-saturated solutions containing neither N_2O nor H_2O_2 have been pulsed at pH = 13. An optical absorption, $D = 0.077$, was formed at 2600A. during the electron pulse. It slowly increased by about 5% within the first msec. and then partially decayed away (down to about 65% of the original optical density) within 100 msecs. Finally it decayed to zero with a half-life of about two secs. Assuming that in the beginning the absorption is caused by molecular H_2O_2, O_3^-, and O_2^-, we were able to calculate $\epsilon_{O_2^-}^{2600}$ by the comparison of these results with initial optical densities (average $D = 0.0165$) obtained by the same pulse intensity in 0.05 atm. N_2O, in the absence of both O_2 and H_2O_2, at pH = 13. This comparison gives $(\epsilon_{O_2^-}^{2600} + 0.8\ \epsilon_{O_3^-}^{2600}) = 1900M^{-1}$ cm.$^{-1}$ (an average of three experiments). Similar experiments at pH = 13 using N_2O and H_2O_2 free, O_2 saturated solutions gave initial optical density = 0.156 at 2600A. compared with initial (extrapolated) $D = 0.055$ in a neutral solution containing 0.05 atm. N_2O but no O_2. These results yield $(\epsilon_{O_2^-}^{2600} + 0.8\ \epsilon_{O_3^-}^{2600})$ = $1900M^{-1}$ cm.$^{-1}$ (an average of two experiments). Experiments carried out in O_2-saturated solutions gave equal initial optical densities at 2600A. and 4300A. $(\epsilon_{O_2^-}^{2600} + 0.8\ \epsilon_{O_3^-}^{2600}) = 1600$ results from these experiments (*see* later discussion).

$\epsilon_{O^-}^{2600}$. The optical densities initially obtained at 2600A. (extrapolated to the middle of the pulse) in solutions of 0.05 atm. N_2O, at pH = 13.0 were compared with those obtained in solutions containing $5 \times 10^{-4}M$ ferrocyanide under the same conditions, but at 4200A. The absorption of ferricyanide was 0.0495, and the initial optical density in the ferrocyanide free solutions was 0.116 (average of four independent experiments). This yields $\epsilon_{O^-}^{2600} = 200M^{-1}$ cm.$^{-1}$.

$\epsilon_{O_3^-}^{2600}$. Only an upper limit for $\epsilon_{O_3^-}^{2600}$ could be obtained. A series of experiments in O_2 containing solutions almost saturated with N_2O was carried out at pH = 13. The optical density of O_3^- at 4300A., formed by Reaction 15 was compared with the optical density at 2600A., produced in the same solution. The absorption at 2600A. is because of three possible products: the molecular hydrogen peroxide, $G_{H_2O_2} = 0.7$, O_2^- (formed mainly by the competition of O_2 for H atoms, $G(O_2^-) = 0.15$ to 0.20, under our conditions, and O_3^-. Some O^- (about 2%) may escape Reaction 15 and may form products absorbing at 2600A. The ratio $D^{2600}/D^{4300} = 6.6 \times 10^{-2}$ ($D^{4300} = 0.037$) was obtained after 30 μsec. in a solution containing 0.87 atm. N_2O and $3.76 \times 10^{-5}M$ O_2 at pH = 13.00. From these results we calculated an upper limit $\epsilon_{O_3^-}^{2600} < 10^2M^{-1}$ cm.$^{-1}$. Similar experiments in $1.2 \times 10^{-4}M$ O_2 and 0.80 atm. N_2O at pH = 13.01 gave $D^{2600}/D^{4300} = 0.12$, ($D^{4300} = 0.0302$). These results give $\epsilon_{O_3^-}^{2600} < 1.5 \times 10^2M^{-1}$ cm.$^{-1}$. For the above calculations, $\epsilon_{O_2^-}^{2600} = 1000$ was used. If $\epsilon_{O_2^-}^{2600} = 2000$ (obtained in the alkaline oxygenated solutions in the absence of H_2O_2) is used, $\epsilon_{O_3^-}^{2600} < 80M^{-1}$ cm.$^{-1}$ results.

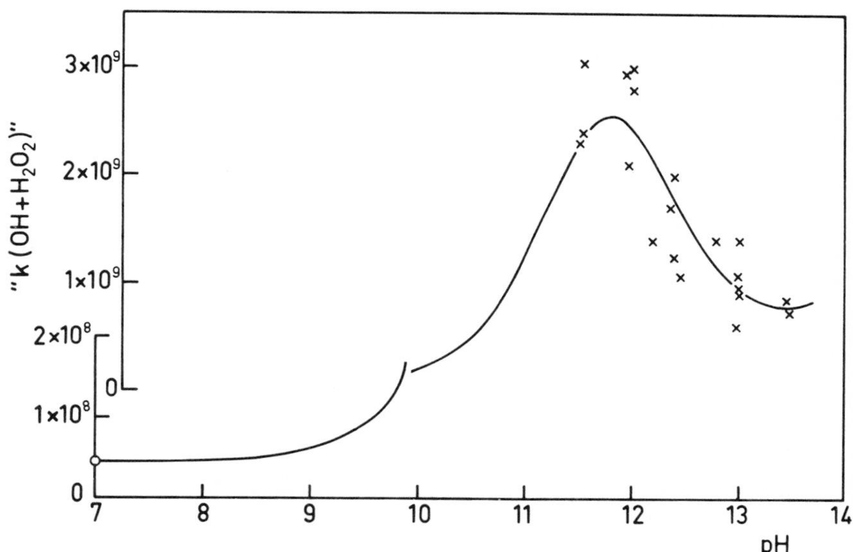

Figure 6. The apparent rate constant for the oxidation of hydrogen peroxide by OH as a function of pH. The experimental results are from Table I. The result at pH = 7 is taken from Ref. 38. The calculated curve is based on Table II, calculation number 3. k(O^- + HO_2^-) *was corrected back to the appropriate ionic strength*

Conclusions

The Absorption Spectrum and Decay in N_2O Alkaline Solutions. The initial ultraviolet absorption formed in N_2O alkaline solutions at pH = 13 (Figure 1), is mainly because of O^- radical ions. The mechanism of O^-decay in alkaline solutions is not fully understood. Reactions 2, 7, 8, 9 and 11 or 12 certainly are important in those solutions. In these reactions, hydrogen peroxide, O_2^- and possibly O_2^{2-} are formed. O_2^{2-} is the doubly ionized hydrogen peroxide. Since HO_2^- does not have a p*K* below 14, O_2^{2-}, if formed, will convert to the more stable form, HO_2^- at pH = 13. O^- may further react with O_2^- and produce O_2 or O_3^{2-}. O_3^{2-} (or HO_3^-) has been suggested previously (*2*). The acid H_2O_3, with p$K \simeq 10$ has been suggested as a product of the reaction between OH and HO_2 (*10*). The formation of O_3^{2-} or HO_3^- can be followed by a reaction with O^-, to form O_3^-.

$$O^- + O_3^{2-} \xrightarrow{H_2O} O_3^- + 2OH^- \qquad (22)$$

The formation of O_3^- has been observed in alkaline solutions containing N_2O (*2*). We have confirmed this observation. O^- may also react with O_3^- to form O_4^{2-}, O_3, or O_2^{2-} and O_2. O_4^{2-} and O_2^{2-} have been suggested as possible intermediates in O_2 containing alkaline solutions (*11*). At present, it is not possible to explain quantitatively the kinetics in alkaline N_2O solutions. In order to be able to do so, one should know all the extinction coefficients of the species involved, and all the individual reaction rate constants. Further work is in progress on the mechanism in irradiated alkaline solutions.

The Extinction Coefficient of O_2^-. In neutral solutions we find $\epsilon_{O_2^-}^{2600} = 1000M^{-1}$ cm.$^{-1}$. Czapski and Dorfman (*11*) reported $\epsilon_{O_2^-}^{2600} = 870M^{-1}$ cm.$^{-1}$. The last value should be corrected for ϵ_{OH}^{2600}, decreasing this value to about $500M^{-1}$ cm.$^{-1}$. We have no explanation for the discrepancy.

At pH = 13, O_2^- radical ions formed in 0.05 atm. N_2O solutions by the reactions of either hydroxyl radicals or O_3^- with hydrogen peroxide, have $\epsilon_{O_2^-}^{2600} \cong 1100M^{-1}$ cm.$^{-1}$. This agrees with our results in neutral pH. However, in solutions containing neither N_2O nor H_2O_2, but saturated with air or oxygen, $\epsilon_{O_2^-}^{2600}$ ranges between 1500 and $2000M^{-1}$ cm.$^{-1}$. These results are in agreement with Czapski and Dorfman (*11*) who observed an increase in the initial optical density in aerated alkaline solutions, as compared with neutral solutions (*see* Figure 7, Reference *11*). Now we know that the dissociation of OH and H_2O_2 to form O^- and HO_2^- respectively, cannot account for the above increase in absorption. In the evaluation of our values for $\epsilon_{O_2^-}^{2600}$, the contributions of OH, O^-, H_2O_2, and HO_2^- were taken into account.

At least one type of the species that we call O_2^- must be something else. In neutral solutions the product of the reduction of O_2 by e^-_{aq} or H is probably O_2^-. In alkaline solutions containing O_2, but no N_2O nor H_2O_2, either a spectral shift, or a stabilization of new species, such as O_4^-, may account for the observations. To explain the results obtained in the solutions containing both H_2O_2 and N_2O we shall have to assume that oxidation of hydrogen peroxide by O_3^- radical ions (and perhaps by hydroxyl radicals as well) does not produce O_2^- in alkaline solutions, but another product—*e.g.*, HO_3^{2-}, which does not form O_4^- in the presence of O_2 and has the same absorption at 2600A. as O_2^-. However, these conclusions are highly speculative, and more work is necessary.

The Reaction of Hydroxyl Radicals with Hydrogen Peroxide. We find $k_{(O^- + HO_2^-)} = 2.74 \times 10^8$ (for zero ionic strength) and ($k_{(O^- + H_2O_2)} + 1.42\ k_{(OH + HO_2^-)}$) $= 1.18 \times 10^{10} M^{-1}$ sec.$^{-1}$. (Table II, No. 3). In a previous paper (*32*), we concluded that OH reacts faster than O^- in electron abstraction reactions with negatively charged ions, while the reactivity of OH and O^- in H abstraction reactions is comparable. The reactivity of hydroxyl radicals towards hydrogen peroxide seems to agree with the above conclusions. It is reasonable to assume that OH and O^- react with H_2O_2 *via* H abstraction, and therefore comparable rates for these two reactions are expected. On the other hand, the reactions of OH and O^- with HO_2^- are probably electron transfer or addition reactions. Using these assumptions, we can obtain the individual rate constants $k_{(O^- + H_2O_2)} \cong 5 \times 10^7$ and $k_{(OH+HO_2^-)} = 8.3 \times 19^9 M^{-1}$ sec.$^{-1}$. The ratio $k_{(OH + HO_2^-)}/k_{(O^- + HO_2^-)} = 30$ (for zero ionic strength) may be compared with $k_{(OH + CNS^-)}/k_{(O^- + CNS^-)} = 6.6$ reported by Adams *et al.* for pH = 13 (*1*). (Both HO_2^- and CNS^- have the same negative charge.) Although corrections for the ionic strength effect at pH = 13 cannot be precise, if we make the same corrections for $O^- + CNS^-$ as made for $O^- + HO_2^-$, we obtain $k_{(OH + CNS^-)}/k_{(O^- + CNS^-)} = 12$ for zero ionic strength, which is comparable with the analogous value of 30 found in the HO_2^- case.

Acknowledgment

The author wishes to thank M. S. Matheson for helpful discussions during the early phases of this work.

Literature Cited

(1) Adams, G. E., Boag, J. W., Currant, J., Michael, B. D., "Pulse Radiolysis," p. 117, Acad. Press, London, 1965.
(2) Adams, G. E., Boag, J. W., Michael, B. D., *Proc. Roy. Soc.* **289,** 321 (1966).
(3) Adams, G. E., Boag, J. W., Michael, B. D., *Nature* **205,** 898 (1965).
(4) Adams, G. E., Boag, J. W., Michael, B. D., *Trans. Faraday Soc.* **61,** 492 (1965).
(5) Anbar, M., Munoz, R. A., Rona, P., *J. Phys. Chem.* **67,** 2708 (1963).
(6) Asmus, K. D., Henglein, A., Beck, G., *Ber. Bunsengesellschaft* **70,** 459 (1966).
(7) Baxendale, J. H., Fielden, E. M., Keene, J. P., "Pulse Radiolysis," p. 207, Acad. Press, London, 1965.
(8) Benson, S. W., "The Foundations of Chemical Kinetics," McGraw-Hill Book Co., Inc., New York, N. Y., 1960.

(9) Czapski, G., ADVAN. CHEM. SER. **81,** 106 (1968).
(10) Czapski, G., Bielski, B. H. J., *J. Phys. Chem.* **67,** 2180 (1963).
(11) Czapski, G., Dorfman, L. M., *J. Phys. Chem.* **68,** 1169 (1964).
(12) Czapski, G., Behar, D. (private communication).
(13) Dainton, F. S., Peterson, D. B., *Nature* **186,** 878 (1960).
(14) Dorfman, L. M., Matheson, M. S., "Progress in Reaction Kinetics," Vol. **3,** G. Porter, ed., Pergamon Press, New York, 1965.
(15) Dorfman, L. M., Taub, I. A., Bühler, R. E., *J. Chem. Phys.* **36,** 3051 (1962).
(16) Felix, W. D., Gall, L., Dorfman, L. M., *J. Phys. Chem.* **71,** 384 (1967).
(17) Gordon, S., Hart, E. J., Matheson, M. S., Rabani, J., Thomas, J. K., *Discussions Faraday Soc.* **36,** 193 (1963).
(18) Gordon, S., Hart, E. J., Thomas, J. K., *J. Phys. Chem.* **68,** 1262 (1964).
(19) Hart, E. J. (private communication).
(20) Hart, E. J., Gordon, S., Thomas, J. K., *J. Phys. Chem.* **68,** 1271 (1964).
(21) Hochanadel, C. J., *Radiation Res.* **17,** 286 (1962).
(22) Jortner, J., Rabani, J., *J. Phys. Chem.* **66,** 2081 (1962).
(23) Jortner, J., Stein, G., *Bull. Res. Counc. Israel* **6A,** 239 (1957).
(24) Jortner, J., Ottolenghi, M., Stein, G., *J. Phys. Chem.* **66,** 2037 (1962).
(25) Keene, J. P., *Radiation Res.* **22,** 1 (1964).
(26) Klotz, I. M., "Chemical Thermodynamics," p. 21, Englewood Cliffs, New Jersey, 1958.
(27) Matheson, M. S., Dorfman, L. M., *J. Chem. Phys.* **32,** 1870 (1960).
(28) Matheson, M. S., Mulac, W. A., Weeks, J. L., Rabani, J., *J. Phys. Chem.* **70,** 2092 (1966).
(29) Matheson, M. S., Rabani, J., *J. Phys. Chem.* **69,** 1324 (1965).
(30) Nielsen, S. O. (private communication).
(31) Rabani, J., ADVAN. CHEM. SER. **50,** 242 (1965).
(32) Rabani, J., *Farkas Symp., Jerusalem, Israel,* Dec., 1967 (in press).
(33) Rabani, J., Matheson, M. S., *J. Am. Chem. Soc.* **86,** 3175 (1964).
(34) Rabani, J., Matheson, M. S., *J. Phys. Chem.* **70,** 761 (1966).
(35) Rabani, J., Mulac, W. A., Matheson, M. S., *J. Phys. Chem.* **69,** 53 (1965).
(36) Schaft, K., Lee, R. M., *Radiation Res.* **16,** 115 (1962).
(37) Schmidt, K. H., *Argonne Natl. Lab. Rept.* **7199** (1966).
(38) Schwarz, H. A., *J. Phys. Chem.* **66,** 255 (1962).
(39) Senvar, C., Hart, E. J., *Proc. 2nd Intern. Conf. Peaceful Uses At. Energy (Geneva)* **29,** 19 (1958).
(40) Thomas, J. K., Rabani, J., Matheson, M. S., Hart, E. J., Gordon, S., *J. Am. Chem. Soc.* **70,** 2409 (1966).
(41) Weeks, J. L., Rabani, J., *J. Phys. Chem.* **70,** 2100 (1966).

RECEIVED January 25, 1968. The experimental work was carried out at the chemistry division, Argonne National Laboratory, Argonne, Ill., under the auspices of the U. S. Atomic Energy Commission.

10

Radiolysis and Photolysis of the Aqueous Nitrate System

MALCOLM DANIELS

Chemistry Department and Radiation Center, Oregon State University, Corvallis, Ore. 97331

Radiolysis of the aqueous nitrate system is discussed in terms of (a) indirect effect in dilute solution, and (b) concurrent indirect and direct effects in concentrated solution. Analysis of energy fractionation breaks down (b), gives $G(NO_2^-)_{NO_3^-} = 4.0$*, and demonstrates stoichiometry for direct effect according to*

$$2\,NO_3^- \rightarrow 2\,NO_2^- + O_2$$

Scavening with H_2 *and* n-*propyl alcohol quantitatively supports this. Pulse radiolysis shows* NO_3 *and* NO_2 *as intermediates,* NO_3 *being characteristic of concentrated solutions. Formation and decay of* NO_3 *is discussed. Primary process of direct radiolysis is formulated as*

$$NO_3^- \xrightarrow{\wedge\!\wedge\!\wedge} (NO_2 + O + e^-)\ \textit{cage, spur}$$

$G(NO_2^-)_{NO_3^-}$ *varies with scavenger and may attain* ~ 17*. From photochemical studies participation of lowest excited state is unlikely, but the second state at 6 e.v. may be involved.*

This paper reviews some of the experimental evidence available concerning the radiolysis of the aqueous nitrate system both by continuous and pulsed beams and correlates it with the available evidence on the ultraviolet photolysis of the same system. Since the early experiments demonstrating that ionizing radiation could indeed cause reduction to nitrite, a considerable amount of information has accumulated, much of it originating in the U.S.S.R. during the last decade. This work has been ably summarized by Pikaev (*14*) and Sharpatyi (*16*). Despite this continuing effort, it was apparent that no satisfactory (*i.e.*, quantitatively and qualitatively self-consistent) account could be given of the radiolytic behavior of this system. This is perhaps not surprising considering the many and varied problems involved, which cover indeed almost the whole gamut of experimental and theoretical activity in radiation chemistry. Thus, to begin to understand this system, it was necessary to start with dilute solutions (which we shall operationally define, from the concentration dependence (*5*) of $G(NO_2^-)$, as less than about 0.1*M*) and elucidate a complete mechanism of radiolysis which, for extension to other situations of high concentration and high intensity, also had to be quantitative. Since the over-all effect of radiation is reduction, the role of the oxidizing OH radicals and the possibility of their reaction with the nitrate ion is critical. Coincidentally, this work is also relevant to the continuing problem of stoichiometry in water radiolysis.

The radiolysis of concentrated nitrate solution is characterized by a yield of nitrite increasing continuously with nitrate concentration up to the solubility limit and the occurrence of O_2 as a major product. This behavior has prompted various suggestions as to its origin. Sworski (*18*), observing the effect indirectly as net reduction of ceric ion over concentrations up to 0.5*M* NO_3^-, suggested that it is caused by the "direct effect" —*i.e.*, the chemical effect of deposition of energy in the nitrate ion, as contrasted with the "indirect effect" manifested in dilute solution. Other suggestions have invoked (a) "sub-excitation elections," (b) excited states of nitrate ion formed either directly in the energy dissipation processes or indirectly by energy transfer from (hypothetical) excited states of water (*16*), (c) collective dissociation processes (*4*). Although attractive and stimulating, such suggestions have generally not been evaluated quantitatively. To do this, the approach must be separated into two stages. First, work must be directed to understanding the chemical processes involved, through stoichiometry, over-all kinetics, and transient kinetics, so that the radiolysis can be described in terms of a particular "primary process." We can then appropriately ask how such a primary process can occur.

We have investigated in detail the parameters affecting the continuous γ-radiolysis of concentrated solutions (intensity, pH, O_2, scavengers, etc.). Transients were investigated by pulsed electron beam radiolysis and kinetic spectroscopy, and the reactions of the optically accessible excited states of nitrate were investigated by conventional photolysis. This paper represents a survey of our recent results which, taken in conjunction with the work of others, allows the construction of a model whereby the main features of this system may be understood and may even be predicted. Literature review is necessarily selective for the present purpose (because of doubtful relevance to liquid state processes, low temperature radiolysis, and hence ESR work has been omitted from consideration). However, we take this opportunity to emphasize some unanswered problems of general interest which arise from the specific system.

γ-*Radiolysis of Dilute Solutions* (5)

The low magnitude of $G(NO_2^-)$ ($\sim$0.5) in dilute solutions immediately suggests that NO_2^- is formed as the result of mutually opposing reduction and oxidation reactions. Before the discovery of the hydrated electron, Bakh (*2*) suggested that the reducing species (then called H atom) could react readily with NO_3^-, and this has been confirmed by direct measurement of the rate constants for reaction of the electron (*3, 19*) with NO_3^- and indirectly for the H atom (*1*). It is clear that except in the most dilute solution, e^- will be scavenged rapidly and completely by NO_3^-

$$e^- + NO_3^- \rightarrow N(IV)\ (NO_3^{2-}, HNO_3^-, NO_2) \qquad (1)$$

The question then concerns the nature of the oxidizing reaction—*i.e.*, what is the fate of the OH radicals? To answer this, it was necessary to distinguish between the following reactions: (a) reaction with nitrate

$$OH + NO_3^- \rightarrow N(VI)\ (NO_3, HNO_4^-) \qquad (2)$$

followed by

$$N(IV) + N(VI) \rightarrow 2NO_3^-$$

(b) reoxidization of the intermediate N(IV)

$$OH + N(IV) \rightarrow NO_3^- \qquad (3)$$

or (c) oxidation of NO_2^-

$$OH + NO_2^- \rightarrow N(IV)\ (NO_2, HNO_3^-) \qquad (4)$$

(In these reactions the unidentified species is symbolized by its formal oxidation number—*i.e.*, NO_3 by N(VI), NO_2 by N(IV), etc.) The clue to the behavior of OH radicals came from the observation that concentration *vs.* dose curves for NO_2^- formation were initially nonlinear until concentrations of NO_2^- reached about 2 μM and were thereafter independent of NO_2^-. This behavior was observed over a wide range of nitrate concentrations from 10^{-3} to 6.0*M*, but the nonlinearity was eliminated by adding small quantities of NO_2^- before irradiation. These facts clearly indicate that Reaction 4 is the fate of the OH radicals, and this was confirmed by demonstrating competition kinetics (*5*) between H_2 and NO_2^- for the OH species. The main features of the radiolysis in dilute solution can thus be accounted for by Reactions 1 and 4, followed by a hydrolytic dismutation process

$$2NO_2 + H_2O \rightarrow 2H^+ + NO_3^- + NO_2^- \qquad (5)$$

The pulse radiolysis work of Pikaev *et al.* (*15*) further verifies this scheme. They measured NO_2^- and H_2O_2 formation as a function of intensity at very high intensities. For dilute solutions both $G(NO_2^-)$ and $G(H_2O_2)$ increased considerably at higher intensities, owing to the incidence of Reaction 6

$$OH + OH \rightarrow H_2O_2 \qquad (6)$$

relative to Reaction 4.

The extensive investigation of the γ-radiolysis has yielded independent relations, allowing the evaluation of the yields of primary species (*5*). In this way the following results were obtained [where $g(H_2)$ is taken from the measurements of Mahlman (*11*)]:

$$g(e^- + H) = 3.41 \qquad g(OH) = 2.53$$

$$g(H_2) = 0.44 \qquad g(H_2O_2) = 0.75$$

These values are based on experiments for this one system, and stoichiometry is not assumed. Indeed these values can be regarded as a test of stoichiometry for conventional species. A small, but unfortunately inescapable difference of about 0.3 exists between the sum (in equivalents) of the reducing species and the oxidizing species. This discrepancy can be resolved if a small amount of oxygen ($g \sim 0.1$) is a product of the radiolysis of water. Evidence to support this suggestion has been presented (*6*), based on (a) determinations of $G(O_2)$ as a function of nitrate concentration, (b) isotopic composition of the evolved oxygen when $H_2{}^{18}O$ was used (*12*).

The understanding which we now have of the mechanism of radiolysis in dilute solution provides an adequate quantitative base for progressing to consideration of the effects in concentrated solution. However, some current gaps exist in our knowledge. As indicated in Reactions 1 and 4, we are still ignorant of the molecular structures of the species denoted by N(IV); interesting ionic relations and differences of reactivity may exist between their various forms. The mechanism of Reaction 5 is somewhat obscure; in fact, actual evidence for it is sparse. These are of course suitable topics for pulse radiolysis experiments, and we expect to be able to clarify them in the near future. Such experiments may also evaluate the extent of Reaction 3 at high intensities and its rate constant.

γ-Radiolysis of Concentrated Solutions

The immediate problem in considering the radiolysis of concentrated solutions is how to account for the water radiolysis process which still undoubtedly accounts for the major part of the energy dissipation. The simplest approach is to assume that the phenomena characteristic of concentrated solution originate independently of water radiolysis; hence, for a product P, formed both in dilute and concentrated solutions, we write:

$$G(P) = G(P)_{H_2O} \cdot f_{H_2O} + G(P)_{NO_3^-} \cdot f_{NO_3^-} \qquad \text{(A)}$$

where $G(P)$ is calculated from total energy absorption (based on electron density), $G(P)_{H_2O}$ is a constant characteristic of dilute solution, and $G(P)_{NO_3^-}$ is a constant characteristic of concentrated solutions. For the weighing coefficients f_{H_2O} and $f_{NO_3^-}$ we have taken the fractions of energy deposition in the water and nitrate components based on electron fractions. There are, of course, considerable theoretical uncertainties in such a procedure, so we can only regard it as semiempirical and judge its utility by its success.

One way to test this formulation is in the rearranged form:

$$\frac{G(P)}{f_{H_2O}} = G(P)_{H_2O} + \frac{f_{NO_3^-}}{f_{H_2O}} \cdot G(P)_{NO_3^-} \qquad \text{(B)}$$

Figure 1 shows the yield of nitrite from 0.1 to 6.0*M* NO_3^- treated in this way (*5, 7*). Considering the difficulties experienced previously in fitting such results, we seem to have found a significant functional relationship. Figure 1 also shows the results of Mahlman (*11*) for $G(O_2)$, which respond even better to this treatment. From the slopes of Figure 1, we obtain $G(NO_2^-)_{NO_3^-} = 4.0$, $G(O_2)_{NO_3^-} = 2.0$, and thus we have the first demonstration of stoichiometry for the processes occurring in concentrated solution, according to

$$2NO_3^- \rightarrow 2NO_2^- + O_2 \qquad (7)$$

Further verification of the simple assumptions involved in this treatment has been obtained by using scavengers. It is known that H_2 is a specific scavenger for OH radicals in dilute solution (*5*); if this holds for concentrated solutions, then the increase in $G(NO_2^-)$ caused by adding H_2 should be a measure of $g(OH)$. Results for 4.0*M* NO_3^- are shown in Figure 2. $G(NO_2^-)$ for H_2-saturated solution is indicated by the horizontal dashed line. Owing to uncertainty in the hydrogen concentration, it was necessary to ensure that scavenging was complete by using *n*-propyl alcohol at various concentrations (in He-swept solution) (Curve A, Figure 2). *n*-Propyl alcohol and H_2 react similarly with OH and give identical stoichiometry (*5*). In this way, we find $g(OH) = 1.9$ for 4.0*M* NO_3^-, which is practically identical with $g(OH)_{H_2O} \cdot f_{H_2O}$. Clearly this indicates that OH is not an intermediate in the concentrated solution processes (at low intensities) and that it is produced solely from water according to the electron fraction.

The close fit between our model and the data would seem to preclude consideration of energy transfer processes, particularly in the higher concentration range above 2*M*. Accordingly, we shall henceforth refer to the characteristic effects in concentrated solutions as "direct effect." Other scavenging work (7) has been done with I^-. In this case, yields were increased considerably beyond those anticipated from $g(OH)_{H_2O}$ and $g(e^-)_{H_2O}$, suggesting that I^- was interfering in the "direct effect." According to the mechanism found in dilute solution, I^- can react efficiently with NO_2

$$NO_2 + I^- \rightarrow NO_2^- + I \quad (8)$$

This behavior then suggests that NO_2 is an intermediate in the "direct effect" (the present behavior could be and probably is caused partly by increased formation of e^- from the nitrate, the electron then reacting *via* Reaction 1, but pulse radiolysis work show this is not a sufficient explanation). Further discussion of I^- scavenging is deferred until a presentation of the results of pulse radiolysis experiments.

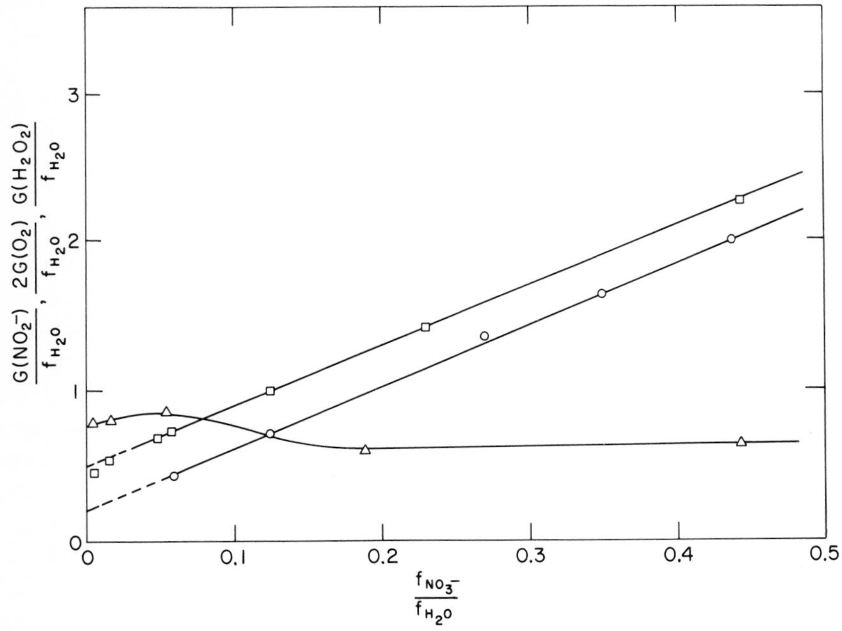

Figure 1. Dependence of $G(NO_2^-)$, $G(O_2)$, *and* $G(H_2O_2)$ *on electron fractions*

□: $G(NO_2^-)$, *corrected for spur scavenging of* H_2 *by nitrate*
○: $G(O_2)$, *data of Mahlman* (11)
△: $G(H_2O_2)$

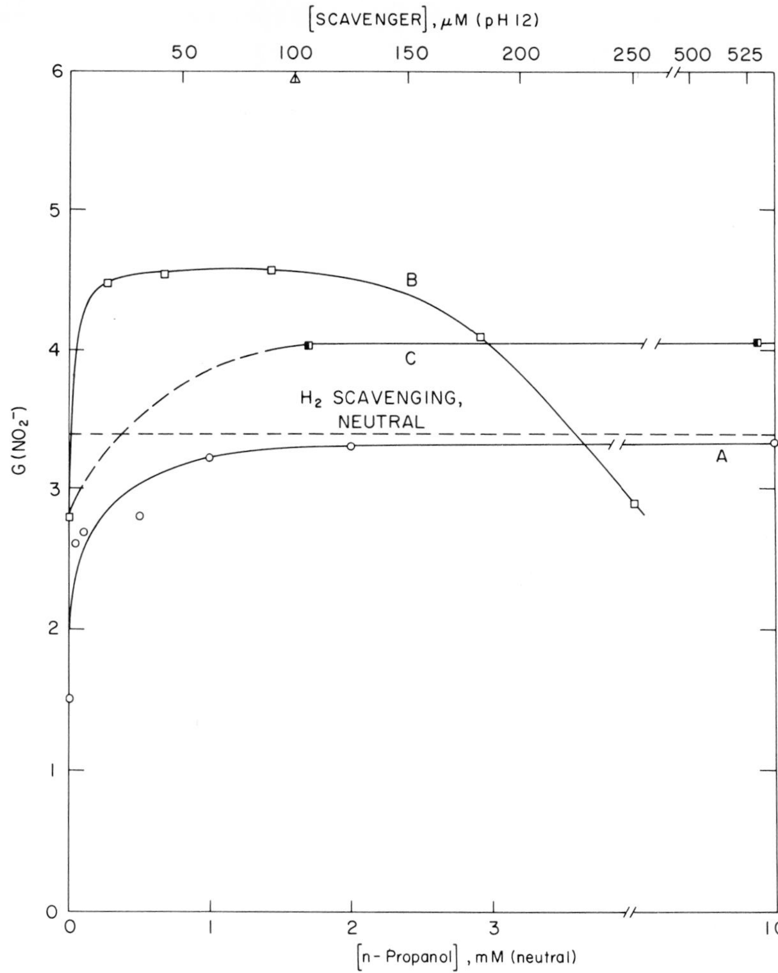

Figure 2. Effect of scavengers on G(NO_2^-) *for He-swept* 4.0M $NaNO_3$

A: n-*Propyl alcohol at neutral pH*
B: H_2O_2 *at pH 12 (upper concentration scale)*
C: n-*Propyl alcohol at pH 12 (upper concentration scale)*
Δ: G(NO_2^-) *at pH 12 for a solution 100 μM in* H_2O_2 *and* 1×10^{-2}M *in* n-*propyl alcohol*

Pulse Radiolysis of Concentrated Solutions

Investigating the pulse radiolysis of aqueous nitrate system by kinetic absorption spectroscopy led to the discovery (*8, 9*) of the characteristic absorption spectrum of the NO_3 radical in neutral solutions—

$> 0.5M$. The amount formed was nonlinear in nitrate concentration but agreed well with Equation B. In itself, this strongly indicated that it was not produced by an OH radical reaction (Reaction 2), and this was confirmed by scavenging studies. However, these studies did show that it has a precursor—*i.e.*, it was not itself a primary species of the "direct effect," formed by a reaction such as

$$NO_3^- \rightarrow NO_3 + e^-$$

A clue to the possible precursor was found from the fact that in the region 380–530 mμ, another transient was found, decaying more slowly than the NO_3 and by second-order kinetics. By comparison with gas-phase spectrum it is believed that this species is NO_2. The amount of NO_2 formed is independent of nitrate concentration (whereas NO_3 increases), implying that as the amount caused by the "indirect effect" decreases, this is balanced by increased formation in the "direct effect." These results agree qualitatively with the deductions from the I^- scavenging experiments that NO_2 is a transient of the "direct effect." Accordingly, it is suggested that NO_3 is formed by Reaction 9,

$$NO_2 + O \rightarrow NO_3 \quad (9)$$

where the precursors originate from a primary process

$$NO_3^- \rightsquigarrow (NO_2 + O + e^-) \quad (10)$$

The iodide scavenging agrees quantitatively with Reaction 10, and further evidence for Reaction 9 is that the formation of NO_3 depends strongly on intensity.

The fate of the NO_3 species is of some interest, particularly since it is characteristic of the "direct effect." Decay kinetics are first order and independent of acidity in acid and neutral solutions. The decay rate increases rapidly in slightly alkaline solutions (such that the species cannot be observed above pH 11) and seems to depend linearly on OH^- concentration. Above pH 9, in the presence of O_2, the characteristic absorption spectrum of O_3^- is seen. All this is consistent with the decay scheme's being

$$NO_3 + OH^- \rightarrow NO_3^- + OH \quad (11)$$

followed by

$$OH \rightarrow H^+ + O^- \quad (12)$$

$$O^- + O_2 \rightarrow O_3^- \text{ etc.} \quad (13)$$

In neutral and acid solution, the relevant process is believed to be

$$NO_3 + H_2O \rightarrow NO_3^- + H^+ + OH \quad (14)$$

If this is true, NO_3 formation leads to a decrease in net formation of nitrite. Here we have an explanation of the results of Pikaev (*15*), who found the over-all $G(NO_2^-)$ to be independent of intensity in concentrated solution. Insofar as the nitrite yield arising from the water fraction was shown to increase at high intensities, this implies that the nitrite yield caused by the "direct effect" decreases at high intensities; this is clearly consistent with our findings that NO_3 increases with intensity, and its decay leads to decreased nitrite yields.

In summary, then we have a reasonably satisfactory working model for the description of the radiolysis of concentrated solutions and the interrelationship of "indirect" and "direct" effects. However, we must consider the remaining problems.

First, the energy absorption caused by the cation (Na) has been largely neglected. At the moment we can say little of the role of the cation, which may indeed have specific effects if it is associated [Ca (*17*)] or reactive [Tl (*4*), Pu (*13*)]. We have begun to investigate this topic.

Secondly, the model presented here suggests that H_2O_2 originates solely from the water as "molecular product." As such, its formation as a function of nitrate concentration should be represented by Equation B by a straight line of zero slope. Although this appears to be the case at higher nitrate concentrations (Figure 1), anomalous behavior is found between 0.1 and 2.0*M* NO_3^-. This may well be correlated with the unusual isotopic results for $G(O_2)$ obtained by Mahlman (*12*), the deviation of nitrite values from strict linearity in this same region (Figure 1), and the effects observed by Mahlman (*11*) in acid solutions of nitrate containing Ce(IV). Further work is needed in this area.

Photolysis of Nitrate Solutions

Although most of the known facts about nitrate radiolysis can be accounted for on the basis of "primary" formation of reactive species suggested to be NO_2, O, and e^-, much less is known about the origin of such species. Also, the possible occurrence of "molecular" processes cannot yet be evaluated. Such a process could, for example, be represented as

$$NO_3^- \rightarrow NO_2^- + O \qquad (15)$$

followed by

$$O + NO_3^- \rightarrow O_2 + NO_2^- \qquad (16)$$

in a solvent cage, where the nitrate of Reaction 16 could be the nearest neighbor of the O atom. The photolysis of nitrate seemed to be a promising way of investigating the occurrence of such processes. In addition, nitrate ion is characterized by a well-defined, relatively forbidden ($f \simeq 10^{-4}$) absorption at about 4 e.v. and might provide interesting results pertinent to consideration of energy transfer effects and the excitation of forbidden levels by subexcitation electrons.

Accordingly, we have begun an extensive investigation of the ultraviolet photolysis of nitrate, under conditions comparable to radiolysis of concentrated solutions. Photolyzing in the first absorption band, it is found (*10*) that nitrite is formed by two processes in neutral solution, an initial rapid rate being self-inhibited and leading to a lower "residual rate" which is independent of most parameters investigated. The quantum efficiency of the initial process is 4×10^{-2} and that of the "residual" is an order of magnitude less. Both processes can be described on the basis of Reactions 15 and 16 together with

$$O + NO_2^- \rightarrow NO_3^- \quad (17)$$

The initial process shows homogeneous competition of Reactions 16 and 17, and the residual process may be described as the occurrence of Reaction 16 as a "solute-cage" reaction.

From the magnitude of the quantum efficiency and the difference in behavior between the photolysis and radiolysis, it seems unlikely that the lowest excited state plays a major role in the radiolytic processes. However, nitrate has another, much stronger ($f \sim 0.3$) absorption at 6 e.v., and we have recently obtained results which suggest that this level may be involved in the radiolysis processes (discussed below).

Magnitude of Direct Effect Radiolysis, $G(NO_2^-)_{NO_3^-}$

The model presented for the direct effect radiolysis is essentially that of self-scavenging by nitrate of its own primary products, suggested in Reaction 10. However, the net observable yield, $G(NO_2^-)_{(NO_3^-)} = 4$, will be determined in great part by the extent of primary recombination —*i.e.*, the reverse of Reaction 10. Such recombination may be interfered by using scavengers which will lead to an increased yield of NO_2^-. Specifically, we have found (*7*) that moderate concentrations of iodide ion and small changes in pH both increase $G(NO_2^-)_{NO_3^-}$ to 8.0. However, a more remarkable effect is found in alkaline solution at pH 12. Measurements of "molecular yield" H_2O_2 show it to be consumed, most probably by OH radicals (or O^-) as in dilute solution. Hence, we have used it as a scavenger. Results for 4.0*M* NO_3^- are shown in Figure 2, Curve B. A typical scavenging curve is not obtained. To investigate this further, we used another scavenger (*n*-propyl alcohol), which we found functioned satisfactorily in neutral solution. A scavenging curve (Curve C, Figure 2) was obtained, whose limit was significantly less than the maximum obtained from H_2O_2. The difference was real as shown by irradiating 4.0*M* NO_3^- at pH 12 in the presence of *n*-propyl alcohol and H_2O_2 simultaneously, each at concentrations corresponding to their maximum effect. This increased $G(NO_2^-)$ by 50% of the value for *n*-propyl alcohol alone (Figure 2). Our present thinking is that the H_2O_2 (as HO_2^-) is acting as scavenger for the O atom,

$$O + HO_2^- \rightarrow O^- + O_2^- + H^+ \qquad (18)$$

and we evaluate $G(NO_2^-)_{NO_3^-}$ to be about 17 under these conditions. This corresponds to 6 e.v. per primary event, which also is the energy of the second ultraviolet absorption band of nitrate. Work in progress on the photolysis may show if this is more than coincidental and may indicate participation of this higher excited state in the radiolysis.

Literature Cited

(1) Appleby, A., Scholes, G., Simic, M., *J. Am. Chem. Soc.* 3891 (1963).
(2) Bakh, N. A., Medvedovskii, V. I., Revina, A. A., Bitiukov, B. D., *Proc. All Union Conf. Radiation Chem., 1st, Moscow, 1957*, p. 45.
(3) Baxendale, J. H., Fielden, E. M., Keene, J. P., *Proc. Roy. Soc. (London)* **A286,** 320 (1965).
(4) Bednar, J., *Proc. Tihany Symp.* 325 (1964).
(5) Daniels, M., Wigg, E. E., *J. Phys. Chem.* **71,** 1024 (1967).
(6) Daniels, M., Wigg, E. E., *Science* **153,** 1533 (1966).
(7) Daniels, M., Wigg, E. E., unpublished results.
(8) Daniels, M., *J. Phys. Chem.* **70,** 3022 (1966).
(9) Daniels, M., unpublished results.
(10) Daniels, M., Meyers, R. V., Belardo, E. V., *J. Phys. Chem.* **72,** 389 (1968).
(11) Mahlman, H. A., *J. Chem. Phys.* **35,** 936 (1961).
(12) Mahlman, H. A., *J. Phys. Chem.* **67,** 1466 (1963).
(13) Miner, F. J., Seed, J. R., *Chem. Rev.* **67,** 299 (1967).
(14) Pikaev, A. K., *Russ. Chem. Rev.* **29,** 235 (1960).
(15) Pikaev, A. K., Gluzanov, P. Y., Yukubovich, A. A., *Kinetics Catalysis (USSR)* **4,** 735 (1963).
(16) Sharpatyi, V. A., *Russ. Chem. Rev.* **30,** 279 (1961).
(17) Sowden, R. G., *Trans. Faraday Soc.* **55,** 2084 (1959).
(18) Sworski, T. J., *J. Am. Chem. Soc.* **77,** 4684 (1955).
(19) Thomas, J. K., Gordon, S., Hart, E. J., *J. Phys. Chem.* **68,** 1262 (1964).

RECEIVED January 9, 1968. Paper prepared with the support of the U. S. Atomic Energy Commission, AEC Document No. RLO-2014-3.

11

Radiation Chemistry of Concentrated $NaNO_3$ Solutions: Dependence of $G(HNO_2)$ on $NaNO_3$ Concentration

T. J. SWORSKI, R. W. MATTHEWS,[1] and H. A. MAHLMAN

Chemistry Division, Oak Ridge National Laboratory, Oak Ridge, Tenn. 37830

*Post-irradiation reduction of cerium(IV) occurs when concentrated sodium nitrate solutions in air-saturated 0.4*M *sulfuric acid containing* 10^{-4}M *cerium(IV) are irradiated with a kilocurie* ^{60}Co *source. A kinetic study of the reaction of cerium(IV) with nitrous acid established that the post-irradiation reaction is reduction of cerium(IV) by nitrous acid. A computer program SLOPULSE was used to determine* G*(*HNO_2*) by kinetic analyses of both the post-irradiation reduction of cerium(IV) and reduction of cerium(IV) by nitrous acid during irradiation. The importance of nitrous acid as an intermediate is evidenced by the high values for* G*(*HNO_2*). For example, about 70% of the reduction of cerium(IV) in 5.0*M *sodium nitrate solutions is caused by nitrous acid with* G*(*Ce^{III}*) = 6.04 and* G*(*HNO_2*) = 2.22.*

Values for $G(Ce^{III})$ of 3.28 in 0.4*M* sulfuric acid and 8.32 in 1.0*M* nitric acid were reported by Challenger and Masters (*7*) for the radiolysis of cerium(IV) solutions with 50 kvp. x-rays. They presented evidence that the larger $G(Ce^{III})$ might be caused by reactions of OH radical with the nitrate ion. We presented definitive evidence (*15, 23*) that the larger $G(Ce^{III})$ in 1.0*M* nitric acid could not be attributed to reaction of OH radical with nitrate ion and proposed an alternative mechanism: the effect of nitrate ion was attributed to excitation of nitrate ion with resultant decomposition to yield nitrite ion which reduces

[1] Guest scientist from Australian Atomic Energy Commission Research Establishment, Sydney, Australia.

cerium(IV). However, no experimental evidence was presented for nitrous acid as a transient intermediate.

This paper establishes the importance of nitrous acid as a transient intermediate in the reduction of cerium(IV). Post-irradiation reduction of cerium(IV) is conveniently observable when concentrated sodium nitrate solutions in 0.4*M* sulfuric acid containing about $10^{-4}M$ cerium(IV) are irradiated with a kilocurie ^{60}Co source. This paper presents kinetic evidence that the post-irradiation reaction is reduction of cerium(IV) by nitrous acid and reports the dependence of $G(HNO_2)$ on sodium nitrate concentration.

Experimental

Materials. Water from a Barnstead still was further purified by successive distillations from an acid dichromate solution, from an alkaline permanganate solution and in an all-silica system to be stored in silica vessels. Solutions were prepared using either Baker and Adamson C. P. or DuPont Reagent sulfuric acid, Fisher certified Reagent 1*N* NaOH solution, either G. Frederick Smith Reagent $Ce(HSO_4)_4$ or Fisher purified ceric ammonium sulfate, either Malinkrodt Analytical Reagent or "Baker Analyzed" Reagent $NaNO_3$, "Baker Analyzed" Reagent $NaNO_2$, Matheson Coleman and Bell Spectroquality Reagent isopropyl alcohol and Fisher purified sodium perchlorate. The cerium(IV) compounds were heated, as recommended by Boyle (*5*), to remove organic impurities before preparation of solutions.

Analytical Procedure. Determinations of $G(Ce^{III})$ were based on molar extinction coefficients for cerium(IV) and iron(III) in 0.4*M* sulfuric acid at 25°C. of 5580 at 320 mμ and 2210 at 305 mμ, respectively. The validity of these molar extinction coefficients relative to each other was previously established (*24*) spectrophotometrically by oxidation of iron(III) by cerium(IV). For cerium(IV) analyses at other sulfuric acid concentrations, the dependence of the molar extinction coefficient for cerium(IV) on sulfuric acid concentration as reported by Boyle (*5*) was used.

Nitrate ion absorption in concentrated sodium nitrate solutions interferes too much for cerium(IV) analyses at 320 mμ so analyses were made at 340 mμ. A molar extinction coefficient of 4860 at 340 mμ was measured for cerium(IV) relative to 5580 at 320 mμ. Sodium nitrate at the concentrations employed has a marked effect on the molar extinction coefficient of cerium(IV) as shown in Figure 1.

Irradiation Procedures. $G(Fe^{III})$ of 15.6 for the ferrous sulfate dosimeter was determined in our laboratory by Hochanadel and Ghormley (*11*). *G*-values reported here are based on total energy absorbed by the solutions. The energy absorbed in concentrated sodium nitrate solutions relative to the ferrous sulfate dosimeter was taken to be in the ratio of electron densities since energy absorption in ^{60}Co irradiations is caused essentially only by Compton recoil electrons.

Air-saturated solutions were placed in Pyrocell cylindrical absorption cells with S 18-260 silica windows such that no air space was present.

Irradiations were within a ^{60}Co source (~ 2000 curies) with a dose rate of about 10^{18} e.v. ml.$^{-1}$ min.$^{-1}$ in the ferrous sulfate dosimeter. Changes in cerium(IV) concentration were followed with a Cary recording spectrophotometer at 340 mμ. No detectable effect on measurements at 340 mμ could be attributed to coloration of the S 18-260 silica windows during irradiation. Therefore, irradiations and spectrophotometric measurements were made in the same cell.

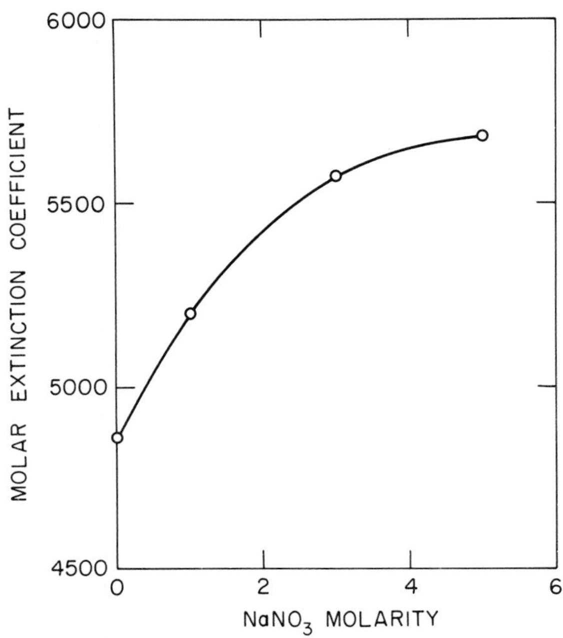

*Figure 1. Effect of sodium nitrate concentration on the molar extinction coefficient of cerium(IV) at 340 mμ in 0.8*N *sulfuric acid*

Thermal Study Procedures. The reduction of cerium(IV) by nitrous acid was investigated in air-saturated sulfuric acid solutions. About 0.05 ml. of a 0.01*N* NaOH stock solution containing 0.01*M* sodium nitrite was added by means of a micropipette to about 4 ml. of a cerium(IV) solution in a 1 cm. square spectrophotometer cell and the chart drive of the spectrophotometer was turned on simultaneously. The square cell was then capped, shaken by hand, and placed in the spectrophotometer. The absorbance of cerium(IV) at either 320 or 340 mμ was then recorded as a function of time after mixing.

Results

Typical experimental data which demonstrate the post-irradiation reduction of cerium(IV) are shown in Figure 2. After an irradiation within a ^{60}Co source, about 13 seconds was required to transfer the irradiated cell to the recording spectrophotometer. Then the total absorbance was recorded as a function of time after irradiation. Such a post-irradiation reaction was not observed in our previous study for three reasons: (a) initial cerium(IV) concentrations were up to fourfold higher; (b) dose rates were about 10^{17} e.v. $ml.^{-1}$ $min.^{-1}$ or about 1/10 of that used in this study; (c) $G(Ce^{III})$ was determined by a series of short intermittent irradiations.

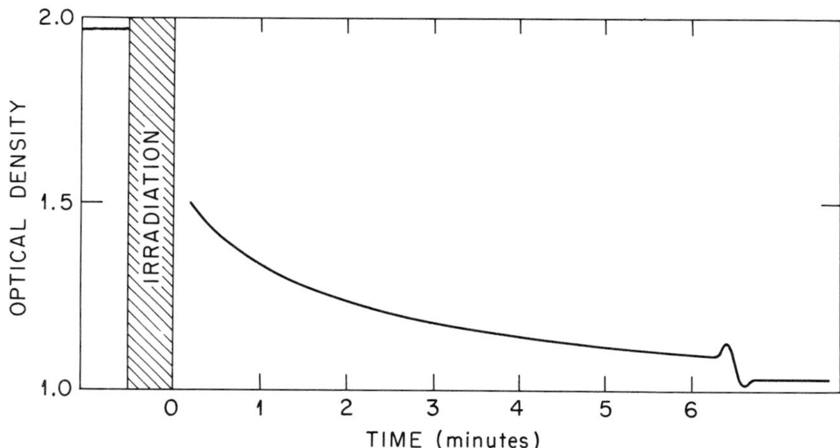

Figure 2. Post-irradiation reduction of cerium(IV) after ^{60}Co gamma radiolysis of air saturated 0.8N sulfuric acid containing 3.0M sodium nitrate and 10^{-4}M cerium(IV) in a 2 cm. cell. Irradiation time was 30.2 sec. Optical densities at 340 mμ were 1.970 initially, 1.029 after post-irradiation reaction was sensibly complete and 0.855 owing to absorption by 0.8N sulfuric acid containing 3.0M sodium nitrate

Reduction of Cerium(IV) by Nitrous Acid: Reaction Kinetics. Since the effect of nitrate ion on $G(Ce^{III})$ was previously attributed (*23*) to intermediate formation of nitrite ion, the thermal reduction of cerium(IV) by nitrous acid was investigated with reactant concentrations comparable with those encountered in the post-irradiation reaction. We discovered that the reduction of cerium(IV) by nitrous acid was slow, with reaction rates comparable with those rates observed in post-irradiation reactions. Typical experimental data are shown in Figure 3. About 5 seconds were required to prepare the mixture before the optical density could be recorded as a function of time after mixing.

In contradiction with our preliminary report (*16*) we shall present evidence of an indirect nature that NO_2 does not reduce cerium(IV) to

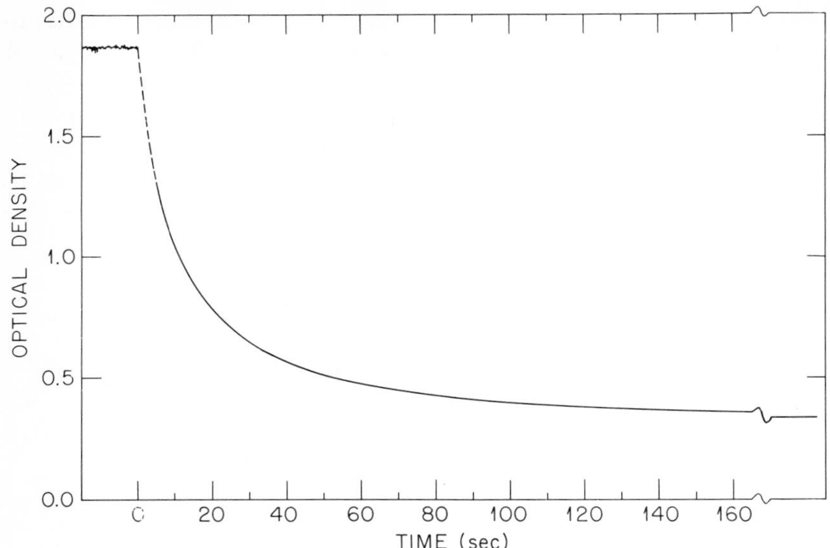

*Figure 3. Thermal reduction of cerium(IV) by nitrous acid in air-saturated 0.8*N *sulfuric acid. Optical density which was measured at 320 mμ is caused by absorption by cerium(IV)*

any measurable extent under our experimental conditions. Our data are consistent with the following reaction mechanism:

$$Ce^{IV} + HNO_2 \rightarrow Ce^{III} + H^+ + NO_2 \quad \text{(a)}$$

$$2NO_2 + H_2O \rightarrow NO_3^- + H^+ + HNO_2 \quad \text{(b)}$$

The rate of reaction adheres well to Equation I:

$$-d[Ce^{IV}]/dt = k_a[Ce^{IV}][HNO_2] \quad \text{(I)}$$

Let $a = [Ce^{IV}]_{t=\infty}$, the concentration of cerium(IV) when reaction is sensibly complete, and let $a + x = [Ce^{IV}]_{t=t}$. Then $[HNO_2] = 0.5x$ and the rate of reaction is given by Equation II:

$$-d[a + x]/dt = 0.5\, k_a[a + x][x] \quad \text{(II)}$$

Integration of Equation II yields Equation III

$$\ln[(a + x)/x]_{t=t} = 0.5a\, k_a t + \ln[(a + x)/x]_{t=0} \quad \text{(III)}$$

where $t = 0$ corresponds either to the time of mixing for the thermal studies or to the end of an irradiation. Figure 4 demonstrates the applicability of Equation III to the experimental data shown in Figure 3.

To determine whether or not the post-irradiation reaction is reduction of cerium(IV) by nitrous acid, the kinetics of the post-irradiation reduction of cerium(IV) and the thermal reduction of cerium(IV) by nitrous

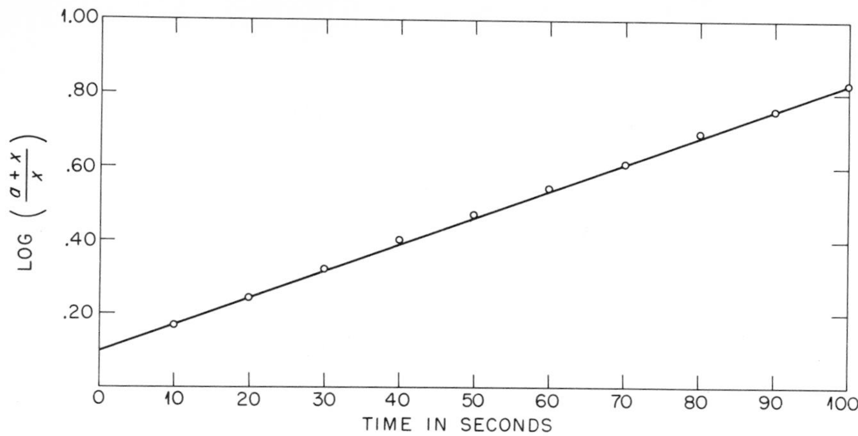

Figure 4. Kinetic evidence that the thermal reduction of cerium(IV) by nitrous acid in air-saturated 0.8N sulfuric acid is first order in both nitrous acid and cerium(IV). Experimental data are the same as shown in Figure 3

acid were compared using aliquots of the same solution. The results are shown in Figure 5 for solutions in which the total concentration of sodium nitrate and sodium perchlorate were held constant at 2.0*M* to maintain the ionic strength approximately constant. The assumption that the post-irradiation reduction of cerium(IV) is reduction by nitrous acid according to Equation III yields values for k_a which are in excellent agreement with the thermal studies. We accept this as kinetic evidence that the post-irradiation reaction is indeed reduction of cerium(IV) by nitrous acid.

To a very good approximation, k_a increases linearly with the reciprocal of the sulfuric acid concentration as shown in Figure 6: $k_a = 240/[H_2SO_4]$ M^{-2} $sec.^{-1}$. $[H^+]$, $[SO_4^{2-}]$, and $[HSO_4^-]$ are approximately equal to 1.3$[H_2SO_4]$, 0.3$[H_2SO_4]$, and 0.7$[H_2SO_4]$, respectively, according to Young, Maranville, and Smith (*32*) over the concentration range of sulfuric acid investigated. Three sets of experiments were conducted at approximately constant ionic strength: k_a was essentially constant when $[H^+]$ and $[HSO_4^-]$ were increased at constant $[H^+]/[HSO_4^-]$; k_a decreased with increased concentrations of $[HSO_4^-]$ and $[SO_4^{2-}]$ at constant $[HSO_4^-]/[SO_4^{2-}]$; and k_a decreased with increasing $[SO_4^{2-}]$; at constant $[H^+][SO_4^{2-}]$. We conclude, therefore, that k_a increases linearly with the reciprocal of the SO_4^{2-} concentration: $k_a[SO_4^{2-}] = 71$ $sec.^{-1}$. This is similar to the dependence on SO_4^{2-} concentration reported for the oxidation of Br^- (*13*) and NH_2OH (*30*) by cerium(IV).

Radiation Chemical Kinetics. A significant amount of nitrous acid must disappear by reduction of cerium(IV) during irradiation. This is apparent from the rate for reduction of cerium(IV) at $t = 0$ as shown in

Figure 2. This must be quantitatively appraised to determine $G(HNO_2)$. This problem is analogous to that solved by Dainton and Sutton (8) who determined $G_{H_2O_2}$ by kinetic analysis of the slow oxidation of iron(II) by hydrogen peroxide.

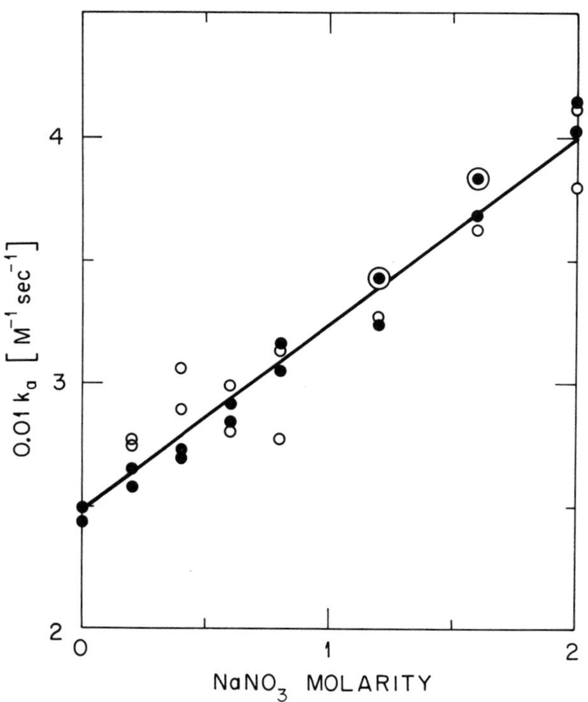

Figure 5. Kinetic evidence that the post-irradiation reduction of cerium(IV) is thermal reduction of cerium(IV) by nitrous acid: ● Thermal reduction of cerium(IV); ○ Post-irradiation reduction of cerium(IV)

Reduction of cerium(IV) during irradiation occurs by fast and slow processes with G-values denoted by $G(Ce^{III})_{fast}$ and $G(Ce^{III})_{slow}$. Since $G(Ce^{III})_{slow}$ equals $2G(HNO_2)$, $G(Ce^{III})$ is given by Equation IV:

$$G(Ce^{III}) = G(Ce^{III})_{fast} + 2G(HNO_2) \qquad (IV)$$

The rates of change in concentration of cerium(IV) and nitrous acid during irradiation are given by Equations V and VI

$$-d[Ce^{IV}]/dt = .01[G(Ce^{III}) - 2G(HNO_2)]I/A + k_a[Ce^{IV}][HNO_2] \qquad (V)$$

$$-d[HNO_2]/dt = .01\, G(HNO_2)I/A - .5k_a[Ce^{IV}][HNO_2] \qquad (VI)$$

in which I is the dose rate in e.v. 1^{-1} sec.$^{-1}$ and A is Avogadro's number.

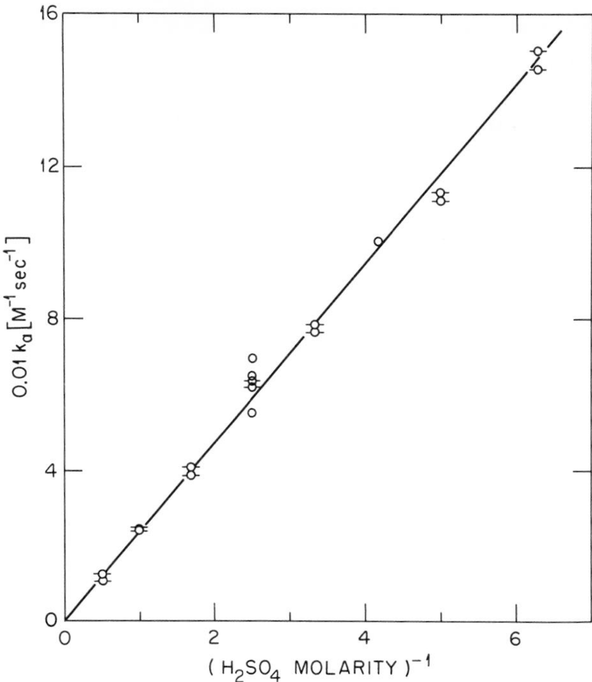

Figure 6. Dependence of k_a on sulfuric acid concentration for the thermal reduction of cerium(IV) by nitrous acid: –○– duplicate experiments with aliquots of the same solution for any particular sulfuric acid concentration; ○ single experiments with any particular solution

Equations V and VI contain five unknowns: $G(Ce^{III})$, $G(HNO_2)$, k_a, $[Ce^{IV}]_{t=t}$ and $[HNO_2]_{t=t}$. For each experiment, k_a and $[HNO_2]_{t=0}$ are obtained by kinetic analysis of the post-irradiation reaction using Equation III while $G(Ce^{III})$ is determined from the $[Ce^{IV}]$ concentrations before irradiation and after the post-irradiation reaction is sensibly complete. We are left with two equations and two unknowns and, therefore, $G(HNO_2)$ can be determined by use of Equations V and VI. This was accomplished by an iterative process in which that value for $G(HNO_2)$ was found which yields $[HNO_2]_{t=0}$ by numerical integration of Equations V and VI by the Runge-Kutta method. A computer program SLOPULSE was written to determine $G(Ce^{III})$, $G(HNO_2)$, and k_a from data such as shown in Figure II. The program SLOPULSE included, as a subroutine, the program of Lietzke (*14*) to fit the post-irradiation data to Equation II by the method of least squares.

The dependence of $G(HNO_2)$ and $G(HNO_2)_{t=0}$ on dose was determined to evaluate the numerical integration of Equations V and VI for correction of the disappearance of nitrous acid during irradiation. $G(HNO_2)_{t=0}$ is based on $[HNO_2]_{t=0}$ and, therefore, contains no correction for nitrous acid disappearance during irradiation. The results are summarized in Figure 7. $G(HNO_2)_{t=0}$ does decrease markedly with dose demonstrating quite clearly the reaction of nitrous acid with cerium(IV) during irradiation. $G(HNO_2)$ scatters randomly about a mean value of 1.77. The rather large scatter in the value of $G(HNO_2)$ and any indication of non-constant value for $G(HNO_2)$ with dose reflects the scatter in corresponding k_a values shown in Figure 8. We do not understand why there is the large scatter in the values for k_a, particularly since each specific value for k_a has a standard error of only 1 to 5%. Furthermore, we occasionally observed serious deviation from adherence of the post-irradiation reaction to Equation III.

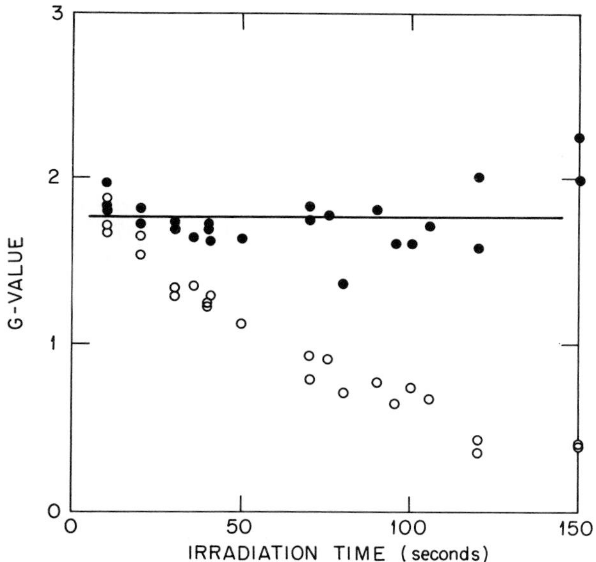

Figure 7. Dependence of G(HNO_2) and G(HNO_2)$_{t=0}$ on irradiation time for 1.0M sodium nitrate solutions: ● *G(HNO_2);* ○ *G(HNO_2)$_{t=0}$*

The dependence of $G(Ce^{III})$, $G(HNO_2)$ and k_a on sodium nitrate concentration was determined in both the presence and absence of $10^{-3}M$ isopropyl alcohol. The results are summarized in Tables I and II. The values for $G(Ce^{III})$ are lower than previously reported (*15, 23*) because we were previously unaware of the dependence of the molar extinction coefficient for cerium(IV) on sodium nitrate concentration. The dependence of k_a on sodium nitrate concentration is probably because of an effect of ionic strength on the bisulfate ion dissociation constant $[H^+][SO_4^{2-}]/[HSO_4^-]$. The data of Yonug, Mananville, and Smith (*32*) indicates that an increase in ionic strength in sulfuric acid equal to that caused by 5.0*M* sodium nitrate would increase the dissociation of HSO_4^- from 30% to about 80%. This correlation can only be qualitative since the dissociation quotient at constant ionic strength has been shown to vary with solution composition (*2*). For this reason, no significance is attached to the dependence of k_a on sodium nitrate concentration as shown in Figure 5.

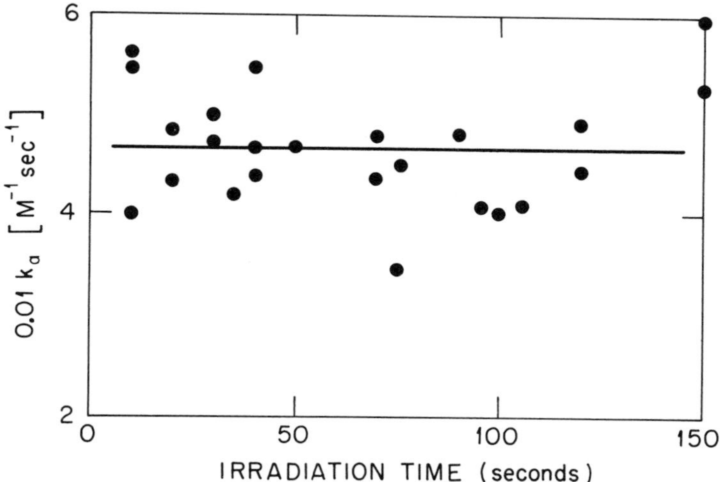

Figure 8. Dependence of k_a *on irradiation time for 1.0*M *sodium nitrate solutions*

Discussion

Post-irradiation reduction of cerium(IV) in concentrated sodium nitrate solutions was previously reported by Pikaev, Glazunov, and Yakubovich (*20*) in pulsed electron irradiations of 0.8*N* sulfuric acid containing 0.5*M* sodium nitrate and $2 \times 10^{-4}M$ cerium(IV). They attributed the post-irradiation reaction to intermediate formation of pernitric acid, originally suggested by Allen (*1*) as an intermediate in the radiolysis of nitric acid solutions. Furthermore, they ruled out nitrous acid since "it has been shown previously that the non-radiolytic reaction between cerium(IV) and nitrous acid goes to completion very quickly under the same conditions." However, they presented no evidence to refute the conclusion of Halfpenny and Robinson (*10*) that there is no good evidence for pernitric acid and that results such as reported by Allen (*1*) are probably caused by pernitrous acid.

Table I. Dependence of $G(Ce^{III})$, $G(HNO_2)$ and k_a on Sodium Nitrate Concentration in Air-saturated 0.8*N* Sulfuric Acid

$[NaNO_3]$, M	$G(Ce^{III})$	$G(HNO_2)$	k_a
0.25 (6)[a]	3.84	1.45	737
0.50 (7)	4.53	1.78	590
0.75 (6)	4.84	1.87	573
1.0 (25)	5.25	1.77	466
2.0 (6)	5.56	1.96	393
3.0 (5)	5.77	2.24	366
4.0 (6)	6.10	2.14	226
5.0 (7)	6.04	2.22	129

[a] Number of experiments from which mean values were obtained are indicated within parentheses.

Table II. Dependence of $G(Ce^{III})$, $G(HNO_2)$ and k_a on Sodium Nitrate Concentration in Air-saturated 0.8*N* Sulfuric Acid Containing 10^{-3}*M* Isopropyl Alcohol

$[NaNO_3]$, M	$G(Ce^{III})$	$G(HNO_2)$	k_a
0.2 (5)[a]	8.91	2.06	657
0.25 (6)	9.25	2.42	662
0.50 (9)	9.78	2.61	518
0.75 (6)	10.26	2.91	508
1.0 (9)	10.28	2.68	419
2.0 (6)	10.82	3.04	322
3.0 (7)	10.83	3.09	269
4.0 (6)	11.00	3.28	181

[a] Number of experiments from which mean values were obtained are indicated within parentheses.

Since we have obtained evidence for nitrous acid as the intermediate which causes post-irradiation reduction of cerium(IV) for ^{60}Co gamma experiments, nitrous acid must also be the intermediate which causes the post-irradiation reaction in the pulsed electron experiments of Pikaev, Glazunov, and Yakubovich (*20*). Their failure to reach this conclusion may be because of non-uniform energy absorption which caused cerium-(IV) concentration gradients in their irradiated solutions and made difficult the duplication of identical conditions for the non-radiolytic reaction between cerium(IV) and nitrous acid. Energy absorption in the Ghormley-Hochanadel (*9*) source, which we used, is essentially uniform.

The dependence of $G(HNO_2)$ on sodium nitrate concentrations is shown in Figure 9. Since there is considerable scatter in the values for

$G(HNO_2)$ as evidenced by Figure 7, the highest and lowest values of $G(HNO_2)$ in addition to the mean values from Tables I and II are shown in Figure 9. $G(HNO_2)$ increases with increasing sodium nitrate concentration in a manner which is strikingly similar to the dependence of $G(Ce^{III})$ on sodium nitrate concentration, previously reported (*15, 23*) and evident also from Tables I and II.

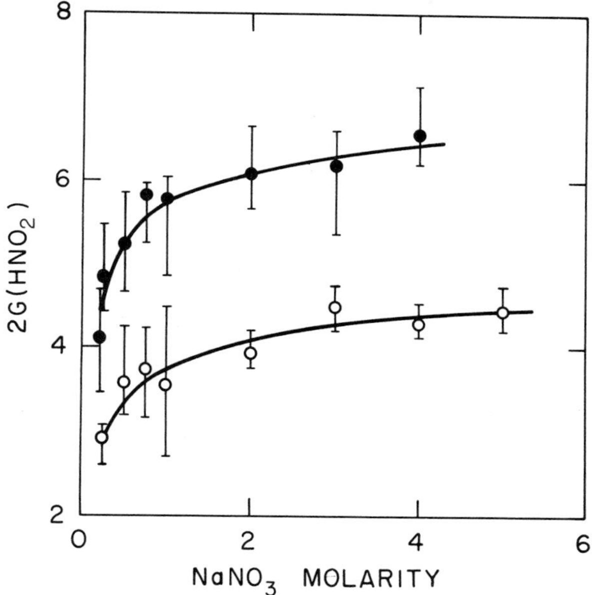

Figure 9. Dependence of G(HNO$_2$) on sodium nitrate concentration: ○ isopropyl alcohol absent; ● 10^{-3}M isopropyl alcohol

In the presence of $10^{-3}M$ isopropyl alcohol, an OH radical scavenger, $G(HNO_2)$ is markedly enhanced as shown in Figure 9. This enhancement requires us to reject the hypothesis of Pikaev, Glazunov, and Yakubovich (*20*) that the increase in $G(HNO_2)$ with increase in sodium nitrate concentration is caused by the reaction of nitrate ion with OH radical

$$H^+ + NO_3^- + OH \rightarrow NO_3 + H_2O \quad (c)$$

which inhibits oxidation of nitrous acid by OH radical.

$$HNO_2 + OH \rightarrow NO_2 + H_2O \quad (d)$$

The enhancement in $G(HNO_2)$ in the presence of $10^{-3}M$ isopropyl alcohol suggests that OH radical, in the absence of isopropyl alcohol, is oxidizing nitrous acid in concentrated sodium nitrate solutions. Therefore, if Reaction c does occur, NO_3 must either oxidize nitrous acid

$$NO_3 + HNO_2 \rightarrow HNO_3 + NO_2 \quad (e)$$

or react with NO_2, formed by reduction of nitrate ion by H atom (*3*),

$$NO_3^- + H \rightarrow NO_2 + OH^- \quad (f)$$

$$NO_3 + NO_2 \rightarrow NO_3^- + NO_2^+ \quad (g)$$

to inhibit nitrous acid formation. Since an increase in $G(Ce^{III})$ is accompanied by an increase in $G(HNO_2)$, our present viewpoint is identical to that which we previously proposed (*15, 23*): the increase in $G(Ce^{III})$ is not because of the reaction of nitrate ion with OH radical.

We have established by additional unpublished research that 2-propanol increases $G(Ce^{III})$ from $2G_{H_2O_2} + G_H - G_{OH}$ to $2G_{H_2O_2} + G_H + G_{OH}$. This effect of isopropyl alcohol is consistent with a reaction mechanism which is similar to that proposed for the effects of thallium(I) (*24*) and formic acid (*26, 27*) on $G(Ce^{III})$. The OH radical reacts with isopropyl alcohol to yield an intermediate which reduces cerium(IV):

$$OH + CH_3CHOHCH_3 \rightarrow H_2O + CH_3\dot{C}OHCH_3 \quad (h)$$

$$CH_3\dot{C}OHCH_3 + Ce^{IV} \rightarrow CH_3COCH_3 + H^+ + Ce^{III} \quad (i)$$

Insight into the processes for cerium(IV) reduction can be obtained from the effect of isopropyl alcohol on $G(Ce^{III})_{fast}$ as shown in Figure 10. In the absence of isopropyl alcohol, $G(Ce^{III})_{fast}$ is, to a first approximation, equal to $2G_{H_2O_2}$ or 1.56 (*25*) suggesting that there are only two intermediates which reduce cerium(IV): nitrous acid and hydrogen peroxide. For cerium(IV) solutions containing $10^{-3}M$ isopropyl alcohol, $G(Ce^{III})_{fast}$ is, to a first approximation, equal to $2G_{H_2O_2} + G_{OH}$ suggesting that there are three intermediates which reduce cerium(IV): nitrous acid, hydrogen peroxide and $CH_3\dot{C}OHCH_3$.

The OH radical can oxidize cerium(III) (*28, 31*), react with sulfuric acid

$$OH + Ce^{III} \rightarrow OH^- + Ce^{IV} \quad (j)$$

to yield HSO_4 which can oxidize cerium(III) (*26, 27*),

$$OH + HSO_4^- \rightarrow OH^- + HSO_4 \quad (k)$$

$$HSO_4 + Ce^{III} \rightarrow HSO_4^- + Ce^{IV} \quad (l)$$

react with nitrate ion to yield NO_3 (*6*) [according to Reaction c] which can oxidize cerium(III) (*19*),

$$NO_3 + Ce^{III} \rightarrow NO_3^- + Ce^{IV} \quad (m)$$

oxidize nitrous acid (*21*) according to Reaction d and react with isopropyl alcohol according to Reaction h. Since nitrous acid and cerium(III) are produced concomitantly as products during an irradiation, they should compete with each other in the absence of isopropyl alcohol for reaction with OH, HSO_4 and NO_3.

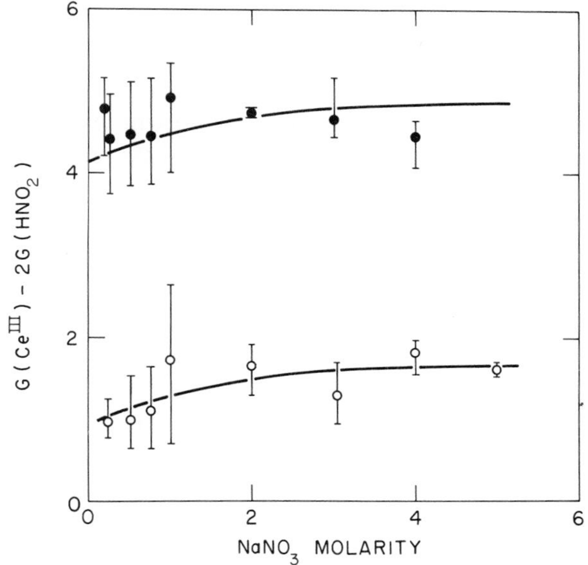

Figure 10. Dependence of $G(Ce^{III})_{fast}$ on sodium nitrate concentration: ○ isopropyl alcohol absent; ● 10^{-3}M isopropyl alcohol

Let us denote the increase in $G(Ce^{III})$, $G(Ce^{III})_{fast}$ and $G(HNO_2)$ induced by $10^{-3}M$ isopropyl alcohol as $\Delta G(Ce^{III})$, $\Delta G(Ce^{III})_{fast}$ and $\Delta G(HNO_2)$, respectively. If all of the OH, HSO_4, and NO_3 radicals preferentially oxidized nitrous acid, then G_{OH} scavenged by isopropyl alcohol would be equal to $0.5\Delta G(Ce^{III})$, $\Delta G(Ce^{III})_{fast}$ and $2\Delta G(HNO_2)$. These three methods of evaluating G_{OH} do not yield the same values as shown in Figure 11. The straight lines in Figure 11 denote mean values for G_{OH} of $0.5\Delta G(Ce^{III}) = 2.6$, $\Delta G(Ce^{III})_{fast} = 3.3$ and $2\Delta G(HNO_2) = 1.9$.

These three conflicting values for G_{OH} are consistent with oxidation of cerium(III) by a significant fraction of the OH, HSO_4 and NO_3 radicals in the absence of isopropyl alcohol. This would cause $G(Ce^{III})_{fast}$ to be less than $2G_{H_2O_2}$ and $G(HNO_2)$ to increase but have no effect on $G(Ce^{III})$. We conclude, therefore, that G_{OH} has a mean value of 2.6 ± 0.2 for sodium nitrate concentrations ranging from $0.25M$ to $4.0M$. Of these 2.6 OH radicals per 100 e.v., 0.7 oxidize cerium(III) and 1.9 oxidize nitrous acid.

Since $G(Ce^{III})_{fast}$ in the presence of $10^{-3}M$ isopropyl alcohol can be attributed to $2G_{H_2O_2} + G_{OH}$, nitrate ion must inhibit reaction of cerium(IV) with H atom. This is consistent with the proposal of Bakh (3) that H atom reduces nitrate ion according to Reaction f. However, NO_2 must not reduce cerium(IV) but forms nitrous acid by combination as proposed by Bakh (3), according to Reaction b. It is the effect of isopropyl alcohol on $G(Ce^{III})_{fast}$ and $G(HNO_2)$ which forces us to propose the sequence of Reactions a and b as the mechanism for reduction of cerium(IV) by nitrous acid.

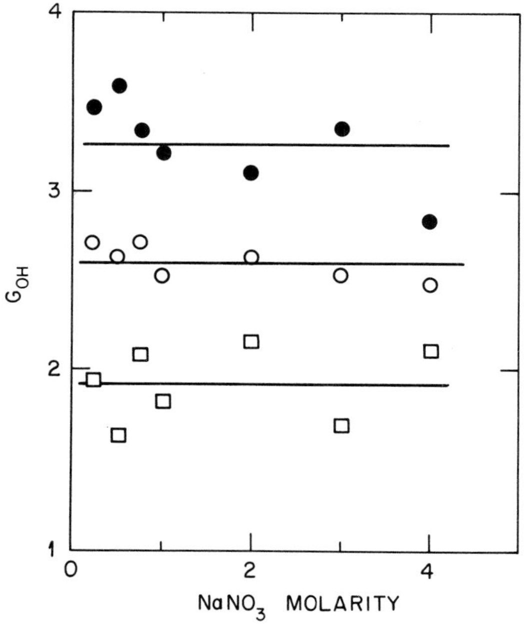

Figure 11. Dependence of G_{OH} on sodium nitrate concentration: ● $G_{OH} = \Delta G(Ce^{III})_{fast}$; ○ $G_{OH} = .5\Delta G(Ce^{III})$; □ $G_{OH} = 2\Delta G(HNO_2)$

The dependence of $G(Ce^{III})_{fast}$ on sodium nitrate concentration, shown by the lower curve in Figure 10, is consistent with an assumption that $G_{H_2O_2}$ may increase from 0.78 in the absence of sodium nitrate (25) to approximately 1.15 in the presence of 5.0M sodium nitrate. The upper curve for the dependence of $G(Ce^{III})_{fast}$ on sodium nitrate concentration in the presence of $10^{-3}M$ isopropyl alcohol represents an increase in

$G(Ce^{III})_{fast} = 2G_{H_2O_2} + G_{OH}$ from $1.56 + 2.60 = 4.16$ to $2.30 + 2.60 = 4.90$.

We assume that the contribution to $G(HNO_2)$ from those free radicals H and OH which escape from the spur in the absence of isopropyl alcohol is about $0.5[G_H - G_{OH} + 0.7] \cong 0.5[3.7 - 2.6 + 0.7] \cong 0.9$. Figure 9 and Table I show that $G(HNO_2)$ is increased from this value of 0.9 to 2.2 by the presence of 5.0*M* sodium nitrate. Two effects of 5.0*M* sodium nitrate are an increase in $G_{H_2O_2}$ *of* $\sim$ 0.4 with concomitant increase in $G(HNO_2)$ of $\sim$ 1.3. These effects of nitrate ion cannot be interpreted quantitatively by the proposal of Bednar (*4*) that nitrous acid formation is accompanied by hydrogen peroxide formation by reaction of nitrate ion with "excited water":

$$H_2O^* + NO_3^- \rightarrow NO_2^- + H_2O_2 \quad \text{(o)}$$

Consideration of material balance leads us to conclude that nitrous acid formation is accompanied by both hydrogen peroxide and oxygen formation.

The simplest model to interpret our results is based on the assumption that the effects of nitrate ion are caused by spur scavenging reactions. We propose that two spur processes are necessary to denote the formation of earliest detectable intermediates in the radiolysis of concentrated sodium nitrate solutions in 0.8*N* sulfuric acid:

$$H_2O \rightsquigarrow H_2, H_2O_2, H_2O, H, OH \quad \text{(p)}$$

$$NO_3^- \rightsquigarrow NO_2^-, O_2 \quad \text{(q)}$$

Reaction q simply denotes the additional products which escape from the spur into the bulk of the solution because of the presence of nitrate ion in solution.

The reported (*17, 22*) decrease in G_{H_2} with increase in sodium nitrate concentration is definitive evidence that nitrate ion interferes with Reaction p. This effect is generally assumed to be because of the reaction of nitrate ion with those reducing species which would otherwise combine in the spur to form hydrogen. Nitrate ion should also react with those reducing species which would otherwise combine with OH radicals in the spur to reform water. Therefore, the limiting effect for reaction of nitrate ion with reducing species in the spur at high sodium nitrate concentration would be to cause spurs with OH and NO_2 radicals.

We assume that OH and NO_2 radicals do not react with each other to reform water and nitrate ion since that would result in no inhibition of water reformation by nitrate ion. Let us consider the formation of pernitrous acid

$$OH + NO_2 \rightleftharpoons HOONO \quad \text{(r)}$$

which has been reported (*10*) to dissociate into OH and NO_2 radicals in acidic solutions. If the lifetime of pernitrous acid were long enough for it to escape by diffusion from the spur before dissociation, then the large increase in $G(HNO_2)$ of 1.3 by 5.0*M* sodium nitrate would be accompanied by a large increase in G_{OH}. Since there is no increase in G_{OH} by 5.0*M* sodium nitrate, we conclude that pernitrous acid formation in the spur is not significant.

Inhibition of water reformation by nitrate ion could cause concomitant high yields of hydrogen peroxide and nitrous acid. The increase in $G_{H_2O_2}$ by 5.0*M* sodium nitrate is significantly less than the increase in $G(HNO_2)$ and may result from secondary reactions of OH radical with hydrogen peroxide in the spur to yield HO_2 radical and oxygen.

Isotopic studies (*18*) have shown that nitrate ion is a precursor of oxygen. This is not consistent with oxygen formation in the spur solely *via* OH radical intermediates from the decomposition of water. Therefore, there must be some oxygen formation resulting from decomposition of excited states of nitrate ion.

$$[NO_3^-]^* \rightarrow NO_2^- + O \qquad (s)$$

$$O + NO_3^- \rightarrow NO_2^- + O_2 \qquad (t)$$

$$[NO_3^-]^* + H^+ \rightarrow NO_2 + OH \qquad (u)$$

$[NO_3^-]^*$ may be formed either by direct action (*18*) or by reaction of NO_3^- with "excited water" (*23, 29*).

Challenger and Masters (*7*) presented excellent evidence to support their viewpoint that the increase in $G(Ce^{III})$ induced by nitrate ion was because of the oxidation of nitrate ion by OH radical: nitrate ion simultaneously reduced the *G*-value for isotopic exchange between radioactive cerium(III) and inactive cerium(IV) induced by oxidation of cerium(III) by OH radical. Although we previously presented (*15, 23*) excellent evidence that any reaction of OH with nitrate ion could not be the cause of the increase in $G(Ce^{III})$, no alternative mechanism was previously proposed for the isotopic exchange results of Challenger and Masters (*7*). We now propose that the lower *G*-value for cerium(III)–cerium(IV) exchange observed in 1.0*M* nitric acid is caused by the reaction of a significant fraction of the OH and NO_3 radicals with nitrous acid.

Hyder (*12*) has assumed that NO_2 is oxidized back to nitrate ion by oxygen. No evidence for such a reaction was obtained in our investigation. This is consistent with our conclusion that cerium(IV), a stronger oxidizing agent than oxygen, does not oxidize NO_2. This apparent disagreement with Hyder (*12*) can be resolved by postulating that NO_3^{2-}, formed by reaction of nitrate ion with the hydrated electron in neutral solutions, can react with O_2 by electron transfer.

$$NO_3^{2-} + O_2 \rightarrow NO_3^- + O_2^- \quad \text{(v)}$$

Acknowledgment

We wish to express our appreciation to J. W. Boyle, C. W. Nestor, Jr., M. H. Lietzke, and D. C. Ramsey of the Oak Ridge National Laboratory for their invaluable assistance in writing the program SLOPULSE.

Literature Cited

(1) Allen, A. O., *J. Phys. Colloid Chem.* **52,** 479 (1948).
(2) Baes, C. F., Jr., *J. Am. Chem. Soc.* **79,** 5611 (1957).
(3) Bakh, N. A., *Conf. Acad. Sci. USSR Peaceful Uses At. Energy,* Moscow, July 1-5, 1955.
(4) Bednar, J., *Collection Czech. Chem. Commun.* **27,** 2204 (1962).
(5) Boyle, J. W., *Radiation Res.* **4,** 483 (1962).
(6) Broskiewicz, R. K., *Intern. J. Appl. Radiation Isotopes* **18,** 25 (1967).
(7) Challenger, G. E., Masters, B. J., *J. Am. Chem. Soc.* **77,** 1063 (1955).
(8) Dainton, F. S., Sutton, H. C., *Trans. Faraday Soc.* **49,** 1011 (1953).
(9) Ghormley, J. A., Hochanadel, C. J., *Rev. Sci. Instruments* **22,** 473 (1951).
(10) Halfpenny, E., Robinson, R. L., *J. Chem. Soc.* **1952,** 928.
(11) Hochanadel, C. J., Ghormley, J. A., *J. Chem. Phys.* **21,** 880 (1953).
(12) Hyder, M. L., *J. Phys. Chem.* **69,** 1858 (1965).
(13) King, E. L., Pandow, M. L., *J. Am. Chem. Soc.* **75,** 3063 (1953).
(14) Lietzke, M. H., Oak Ridge National Laboratory, **ORNL-3259,** March 21, 1964.
(15) Mahlman, H. A., *J. Phys. Chem.* **64,** 1598 (1960).
(16) Mahlman, H. A., Sworski, T. J., *Paper presented 150th Meeting of the ACS,* Atlantic City, N. J., September 1965.
(17) Mahlman, H. A., Boyle, J. W., *J. Chem. Phys.* **27,** 1434 (1957).
(18) Mahlman, H. A., *J. Phys. Chem.* **67,** 1466 (1963).
(19) Martin, T. W., Rummel, R. E., Gross, R. C., *J. Am. Chem. Soc.* **86,** 2595 (1964).
(20) Pikaev, A. K., Glazunov, P. Ya., Yakubovich, A. A., *Kinetika i Kataliz* **4,** 835 (1963).
(21) Schwarz, H. A., Allen, A. O., *J. Am. Chem. Soc.* **77,** 1324 (1955).
(22) Sowden, R. G., *J. Am. Chem. Soc.* **79,** 1263 (1957).
(23) Sworski, T. J., *J. Am. Chem. Soc.* **77,** 4689 (1955).
(24) Sworski, T. J., *Radiation Res.* **4,** 483 (1956).
(25) Sworski, T. J., *J. Am. Chem. Soc.* **76,** 4687 (1954).
(26) *Ibid.,* **78,** 1768 (1956).
(27) Sworski, T. J., *Radiation Res.* **6,** 645 (1957).
(28) Sworski, T. J., *J. Am. Chem. Soc.* **79,** 3655 (1957).
(29) Sworski, T. J., ADVAN. CHEM. SER. **50,** 263 (1965).
(30) Waters, W. A., Wilson, I. R., *J. Chem. Soc. (A)* **1966,** 534.
(31) Weiss, J., Porret, D., *Nature* **139,** 1019 (1937).
(32) Young, T. F., Maranville, L. F., Smith, H. M., "The Structure of Electrolytic Solutions," John Wiley and Sons, New York, N. Y., 1959.

RECEIVED December 20, 1967. Research sponsored by the U. S. Atomic Energy Commission under contract with Union Carbide Corporation.

12

The Radiation Chemistry of Persulfates

MARIA HELENA B. MARIANO

Laboratório de Física e Engenharia Nucleares, Sacavém, Portugal

The effects of peroxydisulfate concentration, of pH, of time of irradiation and of added radical scavengers on the rate of decomposition of peroxydisulfuric acid, in the ^{60}Co γ-radiolysis of this compound are reported. In dilute H_2SO_4 solutions, the rate of $S_2O_8^{2-}$ decomposition is very small. $G(-S_2O_8^{2-})$ decreases with pH and, at constant acidity, increases with $[K_2S_2O_8]$. It is inferred that SO_4^- radicals compete with peroxydisulfate for reaction with HO_2. The reactions

$$SO_4^- + OH \rightarrow HSO_5^- \text{ and } SO_4^- + SO_4^- \rightarrow S_2O_8^{2-}$$

do not take place in the bulk of the solutions. The probability of the dimerization of the sulfate radical within the spurs is small as compared with the probability of occurrence of the other SO_4^- reactions. Peroxydisulfuric acid is protected against radical attack by added Br^- ions or peroxymonosulfate.

For the correct interpretation of the phenomena taking place in the radiolysis of sulfuric acid solutions, a good understanding of the radiolytic behavior of the peroxysulfuric acids, as well as of the ultimate fate of the sulfate radicals is necessary. In fact, the peroxyacids of sulfuric acid are formed during radiolysis with yields which depend on the H_2SO_4 concentration (*1, 4*). In aerated solutions this peroxyacid formation has been considered as the net result of Reactions 1 to 5:

$$OH + HSO_4^- \rightleftarrows SO_4^- + H_2O \quad (7, 10, 15) \tag{1}$$

$$SO_4^- + SO_4^- \rightarrow S_2O_8^{2-} \quad (1, 4) \tag{2}$$

$$SO_4^- + OH \rightarrow HSO_5^- \quad (1, 15, 16) \tag{3}$$

$$S_2O_8^{2-} + HO_2 \rightarrow HSO_4^- + SO_4^- + O_2 \quad (3, 8) \tag{4}$$

$$HSO_5^- + HO_2 \rightarrow HSO_4^- + OH + O_2 \quad (3, 11) \tag{5}$$

A decomposition of $S_2O_8^{2-}$ according to

$$S_2O_8^{2-} + HO_2 \rightarrow HSO_5^- + SO_5^- \ (8) \text{ or } (7)\ S_2O_8^{2-} + OH \rightarrow HSO_5^- + SO_4^- \ (8) \qquad (6)$$

would also account for the production of peroxymonosulfate.

Reactions 2 and 3 are believed to compete with $SO_4^- + H_2O_2 \rightarrow HSO_4^- + HO_2$ in the bulk of the solutions and it is of interest to investigate their relative importance and the possible existence of other mechanisms involving the SO_4^- radicals.

Reaction 2 is still controversial: the yield of peroxydisulfate formation in aerated 0.4*M* H_2SO_4 solutions has been found to be zero (*1, 10*) or very small (*4*) even in the presence of a scavenger of the HO_2 radicals (*1*) despite the fact that, for this acid concentration, all the OH radicals are scavenged by the H_2SO_4 ions, Reaction 1 being shifted to the right (*10, 15*). On the other hand, some authors have failed to observe isotopic exchange between sulfuric acid and peroxydisulfate in the radiolysis of aqueous solutions (*3, 6, 12*). However, such an isotopic exchange does occur during photolysis (*15, 16*) and, according to results obtained in the flash photolysis of persulfate ions, the SO_4^- radicals decay bimolecularly with a rate $k(SO_4^- + SO_4)^- = 3.7 \times 10^8 M^{-1}$ sec.$^{-1}$ (*5*).

A reinvestigation of this problem seems to be desirable. The present paper reports the results we have obtained in the ^{60}Co γ-radiolysis of aerated solutions of potassium peroxydisulfate. The effects of concentration, of pH, of time of irradiation and of added radical scavengers are reported.

Experimental

The irradiations were carried out at room temperature with dose-rates between 0.40×10^{18} and 4.66×10^{18} e.v./ml./hr. The absorbed doses were measured by the use of the Fricke dosimeter, taking $G(Fe^{3+}) = 15.6$ (*9*).

Hydrogen peroxide was determined by cerate oxidimetry measuring the ceric ion absorption at 320 mμ after reduction of the peroxymonosulfate by arsenious oxide (*11*). An excess of a concentrate and deaerated ferrous sulfate solution was then added to the deoxygenated sample and the number of Fe^{3+} ions produced was determined spectrophotometrically at 304 mμ (*11*). After correction for the reaction $Ce^{4+} + Fe^{2+} \rightarrow Ce^{3+} + Fe^{3+}$, the value obtained gives the peroxydisulfate concentration in the sample. The peroxymonosulfate concentration was determined by difference between the total oxidizing power of the solution (obtained in another aliquot after reaction with concentrated $FeSO_4$) and the sum $[H_2O_2] + [H_2S_2O_8]$.

The measurements were performed on a Zeiss PMQ II spectrophotometer equipped with a thermostated cell compartment. The molar extinction coefficients of the ceric and ferric ions were corrected for the acid concentration: in 0.4*M* H_2SO_4, $\epsilon(Ce^{4+})$ was taken as 5,580 liter M^{-1}

cm.$^{-1}$ (*9*) and $\epsilon(Fe^{3+})$ as 2,211 liter M^{-1} cm.$^{-1}$ at 25°C. (*11*). In 5M H_2SO_4, the values used were 6,800 liter M^{-1} cm.$^{-1}$ and 2,874 liter M^{-1} cm.$^{-1}$ respectively (*2, 13*).

All the G values quoted are based on the total quantity of energy absorbed in the system; thus, no attempt was made to calculate the fraction of energy absorbed by the sulfuric acid.

The purification of the water has been previously described (*10*). With the exception of the arsenious oxide (from Carlo Erba, Italy), the chemicals used were Merck analytical products. The peroxymonosulfate samples were obtained from hydrolysis of potassium peroxydisulfate solutions: a $10^{-2}M$ $K_2S_2O_8$ solution in 1M sulfuric acid was heated at 60°C. for 75 minutes and let cool overnight inside the thermostated bath (an ultrathermostat Colora was used). Under these conditions, the peroxydisulfate remaining in the solution, as well as the hydrogen peroxide formed in the simultaneous hydrolysis of the Caro's acid, are small when compared with the resulting peroxymonosulfate concentration.

The solutions were prepared immediately before use with water (conductivity $\sim 1 \times 10^{-6}$ ohm^{-1} cm.$^{-1}$ at 25°C.) purified less than 24 hours before.

Results and Discussion

The Effect of Peroxydisulfate Concentration on the H_2O_2 Yield and on the Rate of Decomposition of the Peroxydisulfuric Acid. The results obtained in the radiolysis of a $10^{-4}M$ and a $5.2 \times 10^{-4}M$ $K_2S_2O_8$ solutions in 0.4M sulfuric acid are plotted in Figures 1 and 2. The comparative analysis of a set of similar curves obtained with different peroxydisulfate concentrations shows that the hydrogen peroxide yield diminishes at a rate comparable with that of the increase in $G(-S_2O_8^{2-})$ (*see* Figure 3), when $[K_2S_2O_8]$ varies from $10^{-5}M$ to $10^{-3}M$. Since no direct interaction between peroxydisulfate and hydrogen peroxide was observed, the results obtained give a strong support to the hypothesis of an interference of $S_2O_8^{2-}$ with the mechanism of H_2O_2 formation, through scavenging of the HO_2 radicals according to Reaction 4. In fact it appears that Reactions 6 and 7 (*8*) have to be ruled out since when $[K_2S_2O_8]$ increases, there is no detectable variation in the yield of peroxymonosulfate which, in each case, was found to be the H_2SO_5 yield measured at zero perdisulfate concentration (Figure 3). If peroxydisulfate is indeed decomposed according to Reaction 4 then, from a similar reasoning, one concludes that Reaction 3 does not take place in the bulk of the solutions. Therefore, the measured H_2SO_5 is a molecular product formed in the spurs.

On the other hand, the very low values of $G(-S_2O_8^{2-})$ lead us also to conclude that, in 0.4M H_2SO_4 solutions, the measured yield of peroxydisulfate formation is small not on account of a radical attack on the peroxyacid (*15*) but because its formation yield is low. In other words,

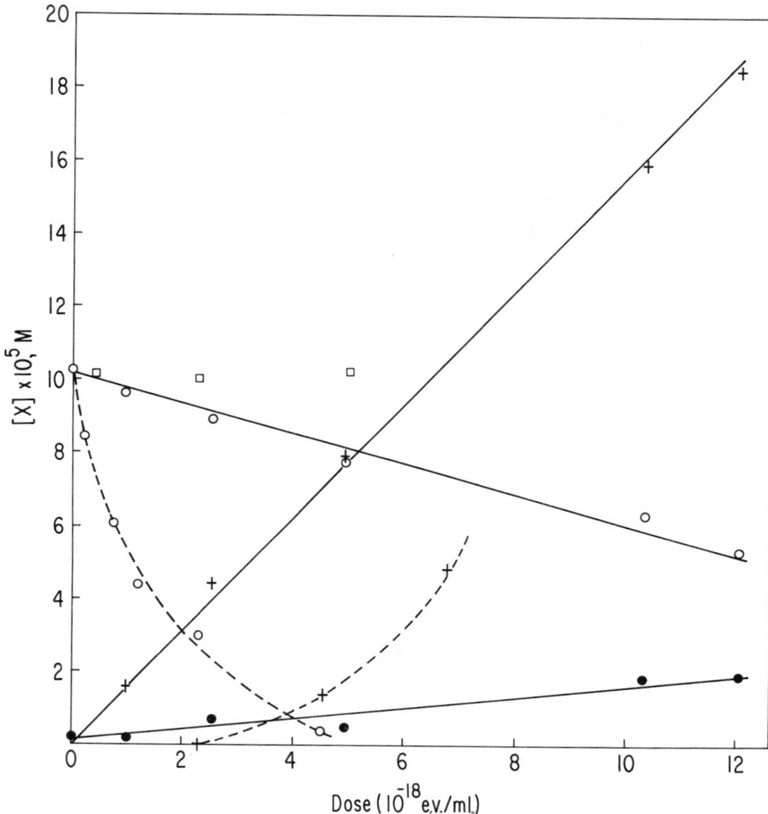

Figure 1. Concentration of H_2O_2, H_2SO_5, and $H_2S_2O_8$ as functions of the absorbed dose in the ^{60}Co γ-radiolysis of an aerated $10^{-4}M$ $K_2S_2O_8$ solution: a) in water (dashed lines); b) in 0.4M H_2SO_4 (full lines)

Dose rate = 0.40×10^{18} e.v./ml./hr.
○ – X = *peroxydisulfate*
● – X = *peroxymonosulfate*
+ – X = *hydrogen peroxide*
□ – X = *peroxydisulfate (in a solution which, at time zero, was $10^{-4}M$ in $K_2S_2O_8$, $10^{-4}M$ in KBr and 0.4M in H_2SO_4).*

the probability of Reaction 2 taking place in dilute sulfuric acid solutions seems to be very low.

The following mechanism is believed to explain the results obtained:

$$OH + SO_4^{2-} \text{ (or } HSO_4^-) + H^+ \rightarrow SO_4^- \text{ (or } HSO_4) + H_2O \quad (8)$$

$$H + O_2 \rightarrow HO_2 \quad (9)$$

$$HO_2 + HO_2 \rightarrow H_2O_2 + O_2 \quad (10)$$

$$S_2O_8^{2-} + HO_2 \rightarrow HSO_4^- + SO_4^- + O_2 \quad (4)$$

$$SO_4^- + HO_2 \rightarrow HSO_4^- + O_2 \ (3, 16) \quad (11)$$

and, possibly, also

$$SO_4^- + H_2O_2 \rightarrow HSO_4^- + HO_2 \quad (12)$$

From this mechanism one deduces a relationship $G(H_2O_2) + G(\text{-}S_2O_8^{2-}) = G_{H_2O_2} + \frac{1}{2}(G_{''H''} - G_{OH})$, the H_2O_2 yield measured in 0.4*M* H_2SO_4 solutions devoid of added solutes, in accordance with the experimental results (Figure 3). ($G_{''H''}$ stands for $G_H + G_{e_{aq}^-}$.)

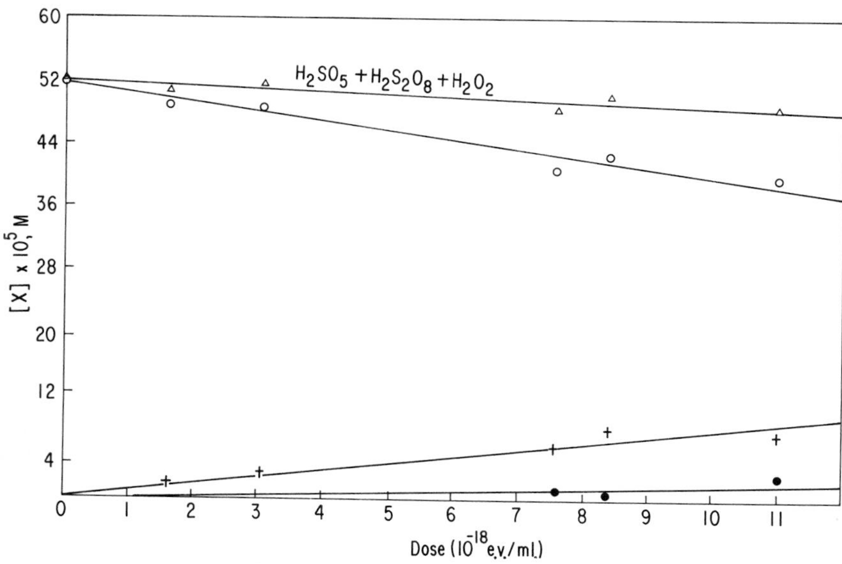

Figure 2. Concentrations of the peroxysulfuric acids and of H_2O_2 vs. absorbed dose in the ${}^{60}Co$ γ-radiolysis of an aerated 5.20 × 10^{-4}M $K_2S_2O_8$ + 0.4M H_2SO_4 solution

Dose rate = 0.40 × 10^{18} e.v./ml./hr.
△ – X = total oxidizing power of the solution
○ – X = peroxydisulfate
+ – X = hydrogen peroxide
● – X = peroxymonosulfate

The Effects of pH and of Time of Irradiation. In Figure 1 are given the results obtained in the radiolysis of a 10^{-4}*M* $K_2S_2O_8$ solution in water. It is seen that the initial rate of decomposition of peroxydisulfate is very high: its value, inferred from the tangent to the curve at time zero, is about 6.0. The H_2O_2 yield is zero for the small doses but it increases as the peroxydisulfate concentration diminishes and, once the peroxyacid has been completely decomposed, regains the value corresponding to pure water. No production of peroxymonosulfate was observed.

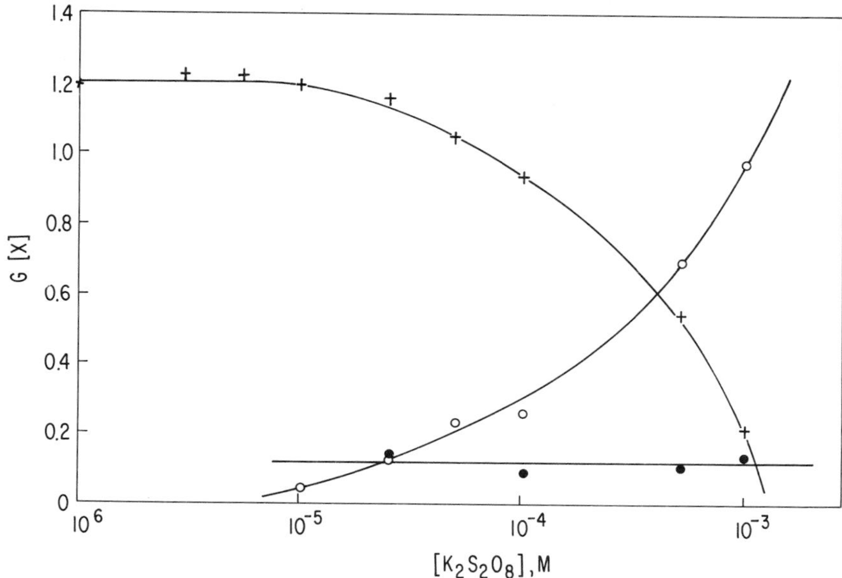

Figure 3. Molecular yields of H_2O_2 and H_2SO_5 and decomposition yield of $S_2O_8^{2-}$ ions vs. *peroxydisulfate concentration in aerated 0.4*M *H_2SO_4 solutions*

Dose rate $= 0.40 \times 10^{18}$ *e.v./ml./hr.*
$+$ – $X = H_2O_2$
○ – $X = -S_2O_8^{2-}$
● – $X = HSO_5^-$

It seems, therefore, that, in the absence of the sulfuric ions, a $10^{-4}M$ $K_2S_2O_8$ solution inhibits completely the reaction $HO_2 + HO_2 \rightarrow H_2O_2 + O_2$ and that the products of this decomposition can destroy the hydrogen peroxide diffusing from the spurs. The results obtained in this aqueous solution, at very small doses may be explained by the following mechanism:

$$H + O_2 \rightarrow HO_2 \quad (9)$$

$$e^-_{aq} + O_2 \rightarrow O_2^- \quad (13)$$

$$H_3O^+ + O_2^- \rightleftarrows HO_2 + H_2O \quad (14)$$

$$S_2O_8^{2-} + HO_2 \rightarrow HSO_4^- + SO_4^- + O_2 \quad (4)$$

$$SO_4^- + H_2O_2 \rightarrow HSO_4^- + HO_2 \quad (12)$$

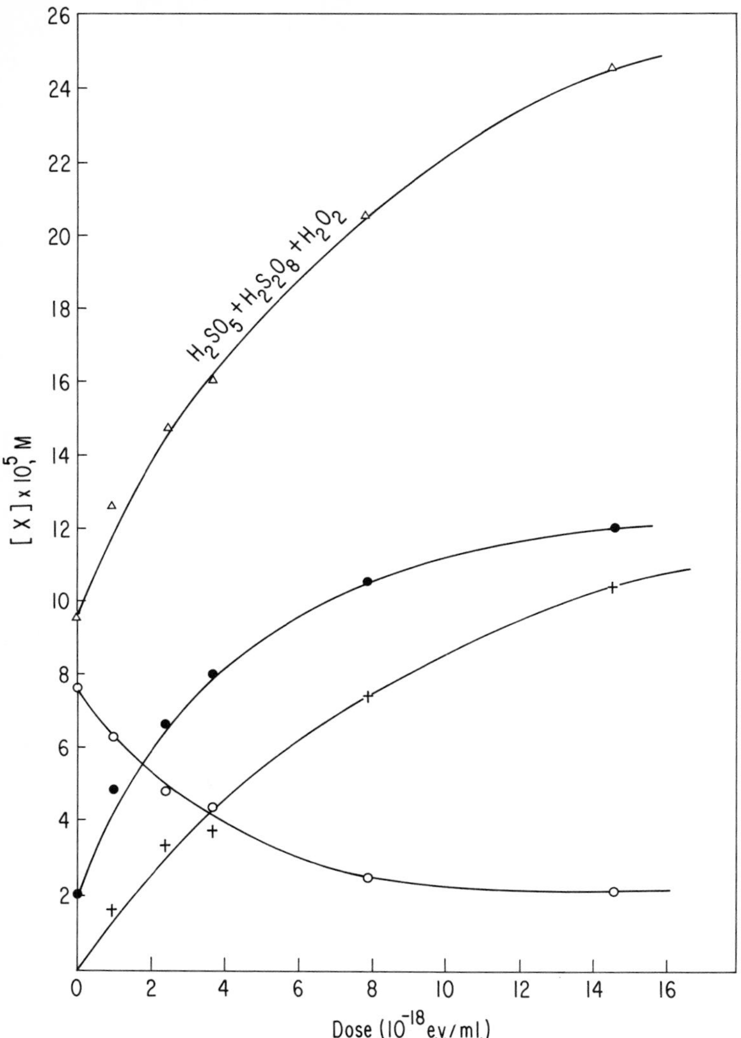

Figure 4. Concentrations of the peroxysulfuric acids and of H_2O_2 as functions of the absorbed dose in the ^{60}Co γ-radiolysis of a 7.6 × 10^{-5}M $K_2S_2O_8$ + 2 × 10^{-5}M H_2SO_5 solution in aerated 5M sulfuric acid

Dose rate = 0.47 × 10^{18} e.v./ml./hr.
△ – *X = total oxidizing power of the solution*
○ – *X = peroxydisulfate*
+ – *X = hydrogen peroxide*
● – *X = peroxymonosulfate*

$$OH + H_2O_2 \rightarrow H_2O + HO_2 \quad (15)$$

$$OH + H_2 \rightarrow H_2O + H \quad (16)$$

(*Note:* The pK of the hydroperoxy radical in Reaction 14 has a value between 4.0 and 4.8 (*17*) and the pH of a $10^{-4}M$ $K_2S_2O_8$ solution in water is 5.35. Thus, the concentrations at equilibrium of the basic and neutral forms of the radical are not very different. It may be that, as Reaction 4 proceeds, the equilibrium represented by Reaction 14 is shifted to the right till all the basic form, O_2^-, is consumed.)

From this, one deduces a yield, $G(-S_2O_8^{2-}) = G_{H_2O_2} + G_{e^-_{aq}} + G_H + G_{OH} = 6.55$ ($G_{H_2O_2} = 0.75$, $G_{e^-_{aq}} + G_H = 3.20$ and $G_{OH} = 2.60$) (*14*), a value to be compared with the experimental one, $G_i(-S_2O_8^{2-}) \simeq 6.0$.

The difference in the rates of decomposition of the peroxydisulfate in water and in acid solutions results, therefore, from the existence a competition between $S_2O_8^{2-}$ and sulfate radicals for reaction with HO_2, this competition being evidenced by the rapid decay of $G(-S_2O_8^{2-})$ with the dose, in the aqueous solution, its decay with the pH and its increase as $[K_2S_2O_8]$ increases at constant sulfuric acid concentration.

Amidst the various possible ways of reaction of the sulfate radicals in the bulk of dilute H_2SO_4 solutions, the most probable seems therefore to be

$$SO_4^- + HO_2 \rightarrow HSO_4^- + O_2 \ (3, 16) \quad (11)$$

Reactions 2 and 3 have to be taken into account when the acidity of the solutions is increased over 0.4*M:* in a 5*M* H_2SO_4 medium, peroxydisulfate builds up in the solution and there is a fivefold increase in the initial yield of formation of peroxymonosulfate (*see* Figure 5). These variations are certainly the result of a direct effect of the radiation on the sulfuric acid ions leading to an intraspur formation of both peroxyacids. It must be pointed out that, in concentrated sulfuric acid solutions, the radiolytic phenomena are masked by the high rate of hydrolysis of the peroxyacids (*11*) so that the interpretation of the experimental data is markedly dependent on the time factor. To illustrate this, a mixture of peroxydisulfate ($\sim 8.10^{-5}M$) and peroxymonosulfate ($2.10^{-5}M$) in a 5*M* H_2SO_4 solution was irradiated with dose-rates differing by a factor of $\sim$ 10: the results have been plotted in Figures 4 and 5, showing a striking difference in the pattern of the curves obtained. In Figure 5 are also given these results after correction for the effect of hydrolysis (by measuring the blank at the same time as the irradiated solution). From this figure it is inferred that the rate of peroxydisulfate formation is $G(S_2O_8^{2-}) = 0.18$ and that the initial yield of production of peroxymonosulfate equals 0.60 in very good agreement with data of Boyle (*1*).

The Effects of Added Ce^{3+} and Br^- Ions. Ce^{3+} and Br^- ions are good scavengers of OH radicals and are likely to interfere with the phenomena

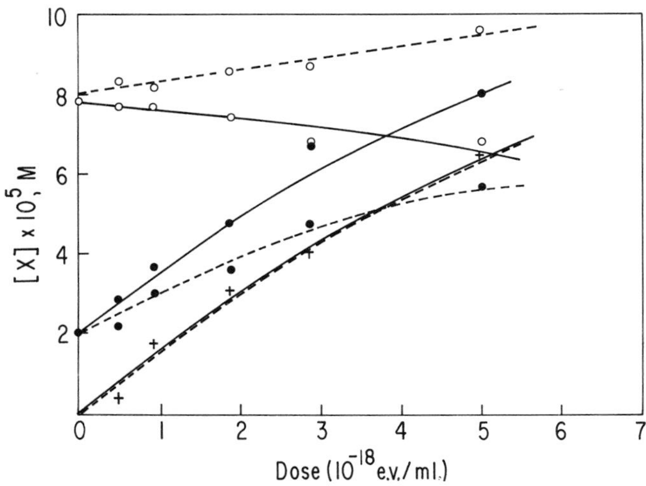

Figure 5. Concentration of the peroxysulfuric acids and hydrogen-peroxide, vs. *absorbed dose, in the radiolysis of a 7.8* 10^{-5}M $K_2S_2O_8$ *+ 2.10*$^{-5}$M H_2SO_5 *solution in aerated* 5M *sulfuric acid: a) values actually measured (full lines); b) values obtained after correction for the hydrolysis of the peroxysulfuric acids (dashed lines)*

Dose rate $= 4.47 \times 10^{18}$ *e.v./ml./hr.*
○ – *X = peroxydisulfate*
● – *X = peroxymonosulfate*
+ – *X = hydrogen peroxide*

taking place in the radiolysis of potassium peroxydisulfate. To test the validity of the hypothesis concerning the competition represented by Reactions 4 and 11 we have studied the effects of $10^{-3}M$ Ce^{3+} and $10^{-4}M$ Br^- when added to $10^{-4}M$ $K_2S_2O_8$ solutions in 0.4*M* sulfuric acid. (At the concentrations used both Ce^{3+} and Br^- ions do not interfere with the phenomena taking place within the spurs.) In the samples containing cerous ions there was no variation in the rate of decomposition of peroxydisulfate (neither on the yields of formation of the other products of radiolysis) as it was to be expected from the sequence of reactions

$$Ce^{3+} + OH \text{ (or } SO_4^-) \rightarrow Ce^{4+} + OH^- \text{ (or } SO_4^{2-}) \text{ and}$$

$$Ce^{4+} + HO_2 \rightarrow Ce^{3+} + H^+ + O_2$$

which has the same effect as that of Reaction 11.

In what concerns the solution containing bromide ions a marked sensitization of the rate of decomposition of perdisulfate was expected to occur as a result of the well known reactions

$$Br^- + OH \rightarrow Br + OH^-$$

and

$$Br + H_2O_2 \rightarrow Br^- + H^+ + HO_2 \ (18)$$

Rather surprisingly, however, we did verify that peroxydisulfate was efficiently protected by Br^- ions against radical attack (Figure 1). This indicates that bromine atoms react *via* $Br + HO_2 \rightarrow Br^- + H^+ + O_2$ rather than with hydrogen peroxide.

The Effect of Added Peroxymonosulfate. Caro's acid also acts as a protecting agent against decomposition of peroxydisulfate by hydroperoxy radicals. Even at equimolecular concentrations, $G(-S_2O_8^{2-})$ drops to zero or very low values in the presence of peroxymonosulfate. This, along with the fact that the peroxymonoacid presents a greater rate of decomposition as compared with that of equal molar concentrations of $S_2O_8^{2-}$, indicates that H_2SO_5 is a better HO_2 scavenger than peroxydisulfate.

On the other hand, the measured $G(HSO_5^-)$ values are greater than those corresponding to peroxydisulfate (Figure 5 and Reference 1). It appears, therefore, that the initial yield of peroxymonosulfate formation in sulfuric solutions far exceeds that of peroxydisulfate.

These first conclusions drawn from the results obtained in the radiolysis of mixtures of both peroxyacids have to be completed with a more thorough study. In fact, the problems involved in the radiolysis of peroxymonosulfate deserve further attention and will be considered in a later paper.

Acknowledgment

We are thankful to M. Coimbra for his skillful technical assistance.

Literature Cited

(1) Boyle, J. W., *Radiation Res.* **17,** 427 (1962).
(2) Boyle, J. W., Mahlman, H. A., *Radiation Res.* **16,** 416 (1962).
(3) Buu, A., Pucheault, J., *J. Chim. Phys.* **63**, 1037 (1966).
(4) Daniels, M., Lyon, J., Weiss, J., *J. Chem. Soc.* **1957,** 4388.
(5) Dogliotti, L., Hayon, E., *J. Phys. Chem.* **71,** 2511 (1967).
(6) Eager, R. L., McCallum, K. J., *Can. J. Chem.* **32,** 692 (1954).
(7) Giuliano, R., Schwartz, N., Wilmarth, W. K., *J. Phys. Chem.* **63,** 353 (1959).
(8) Hart, E. J., *J. Am. Chem. Soc.* **83,** 567 (1961).
(9) Hochanadel, C. J., Ghormley, J. A., *J. Chem. Phys.* **21,** 880 (1953).
(10) Mariano, M. H., Santos, M. L., *Radiation Res.* **32,** 905 (1967).
(11) Mariano, M. H., *Anal. Chem.* (in press, 1968).
(12) Riesebos, P. C., Aten, A. H. W., *J. Am. Chem. Soc.* **74,** 2440 (1952).
(13) Scharf, K., Lee, R. M., *Radiation Res.* **16,** 115 (1962).
(14) Thomas, J. K., "Proceedings of the Third International Congress of Radiation Research," p. 179, North-Holland Publishing Company, Amsterdam, 1967.
(15) Tsao, M.-S., Wilmarth, W. K., *J. Phys. Chem.* **63,** 346 (1959).

(16) Tsao, M.-S., Wilmarth, W. K., *Discussions Faraday Soc.* **29,** 137 (1960).
(17) Czapski, G., Bielski, B. H. J., *J. Phys. Chem.* **67,** 2180 (1963).
(18) Sworski, T. J., *J. Am. Chem. Soc.* **76,** 4687 (1954).

RECEIVED February 5, 1968.

13

A Pulse Radiolysis Study of Bivalent and Zerovalent Gold in Aqueous Solutions

A. S. GHOSH-MAZUMDAR

Bhabha Atomic Research Centre, Trombay, Bombay, India

EDWIN J. HART

Chemistry Division, Argonne National Laboratory, Argonne, Ill. 60439

Transient bivalent gold ions and two unidentified species, possibly Au°, were prepared and stiuded in different aqueous matrices by pulse radiolysis. Their absorption spectra and rate constants of formation and decay are reported. Bivalent gold was prepared by the oxidation of $Au(CN)_2^-$ in neutral chloride solutions of N_2O, and also by the reduction of $AuCl_4^-$ in the presence of CH_3OH. The kinetics of its decay indicates disproportionation. The reduced species of $Au(CN)_2^-$ from H atoms is different from that obtained with e^-_{aq}, the latter being attributed to an electron adduct. Both of these species decay, forming colloidal gold.

The technique of pulse radiolysis, besides having direct importance to basic radiation chemistry, is being successfully employed for the study of unstable intermediates in both organic and inorganic chemistry. Thus, for several metal ions, hitherto unknown oxidation states have been well characterized by their kinetic properties (*1, 4, 6, 7, 8, 10, 21*). The present work deals with the pulse radiolysis of aqueous gold salts.

The steady state radiolysis of gold compounds is mainly concerned with the reduction of trivalent gold to the metal (*13, 16*). The reported yield, $G(\text{-Au}^{III})_{eq} = 2.3 \pm 0.2$ (*16*), has been interpreted to arise from $2G_{H_2O_2} + G_H - G_{OH}$, where the *G*'s stand for the primary radiolytic yields. From the point of view of pulse radiolytic investigation, Au^I is, however, more interesting. Since monovalent gold is unstable except when complexed (*17*), the choice of a suitable compound is very limited.

In this work, we used $KAu(CN)_2$. We also used Au^{III} (chloroauric acid) to confirm some of our results relating to Au^{II} but obtained with Au^{I}.

Bivalent gold is extremely rare in compounds and is practically nonexistent in aqueous solutions although it has been postulated in a few kinetic studies (*16, 22*). Rich and Taube (*22*) reported that the induced exchange of Cl^- and $AuCl_4^-$ is markedly increased by a one electron reductant like Fe^{2+}, as compared with the two electron reductants Sn^{II} and Sb^{III}. According to these authors, the observed effect is because of transient formation of Au^{II}. It is now finally settled that $AuCl_2$ or $AuAuCl_4$ does not exist in the solid state (*11*). A few organic complexes of Au^{II}, such as the dithiomaleonitrile complex and the phthalocyanine complex have, however, been reported (*9, 25*). In the present studies we have been able to characterize Au^{II} by its spectrum in aqueous solutions for the first time. Its kinetic properties have also been studied.

Baxendale, Fielden, and Keene (*7*) identified a transient lower oxidation state of silver obtained by reaction of Ag^+ solutions with hydrated electrons or atomic H. In the present work, similarly, transient—*i.e.*, chemically reactive species of the lower oxidation state of gold were obtained by reducing Au^{I}. Kinetic properties of these species, which might be of zero valency have, moreover, been examined.

Transient absorption bands centered around 300–400 n.m. have been reported to be produced by the action of the hydrated electron on different metal ions. As mentioned earlier, they are ascribed to the lower oxidation states (*1, 4, 6*). In view of the general similarity of the spectra of these ions, it has been suggested that they may be some electron adduct of the type $M^{n+} \ldots e^-_{aq}$ (*15*). Evidence seems to be accumulating that these electron aducts may not occur commonly (*3, 10, 18, 20, 21*). Our results, on the other hand, suggest that with the gold cyanide system, at least in neutral and alkaline matrices, such a possibility does exist.

Experimental Procedure

Hydrated electrons and OH radicals were generated in aqueous solutions by a single 0.4 μsec. pulse of 15 Mev. electrons from a linear accelerator (*12*). By putting quartz or aluminum diffusers of suitable thickness at the exit port, the concentration of the primary reactive species was varied by a factor of 8. Irradiations were carried out in a 4 cm. long cylindrical cell having Suprasil end windows. Formation and decay of transient species were followed by absorption spectrophotometry using a 450-watt xenon lamp as an analyzing light source. A Bausch and Lomb monochromator followed by a 1P28 photomultiplier and a Type 555 Tektronix oscilloscope fitted with a Polaroid camera were used for recording the absorption changes in the solution. Oscilloscope traces thus obtained were analyzed by the CDC 3600 computer by the use of available programs (*23, 24*).

Unless otherwise mentioned, all spectra were obtained with a "split beam" arrangement. In this system, a constant fraction of the analyzing light beam entered a second monochromator kept at a fixed wavelength, then to a photomultiplier and finally to the above mentioned oscilloscope. With this arrangement it was easy to monitor the electron pulse intensity, and to make suitable corrections, if necessary.

Because of the high reactivity of hydrated electrons toward oxygen and carbon dioxide, work was done with deaerated solutions prepared with triply distilled water and handled by the syringe technique (*14*). In general, reagent quality chemicals were used without further purification. Nitrous oxide was condensed in a liquid nitrogen trap, evacuated further, and then a solution was prepared by saturation at a pressure of 1 atm. The source of Au^{I} was Fluka reagent grade $KAu(CN)_2$; that of Au^{III} was Merck chloroauric acid, $AuCl_3HCl\ H_2O$.

The hydrated electron concentration/pulse was monitored for each set of runs by the absorption produced in deaerated 1m*M* NaOH containing 1-2m*M* CH_3OH, the extinction coefficients assumed being $\epsilon_{550} = 0.818 \times 10^4$, $\epsilon_{575} = 1.1 \times 10^4$ (*12*). The initial concentration of e^-_{aq} was of the order of $10^{-6}M$. Nitrous oxide was used for converting the hydrated electrons to "OH" radicals.

$$e^-_{aq} + N_2O \rightarrow N_2 + OH^- + OH \qquad (1)$$

Irradiations at 110–115 atm. hydrogen were carried out in a specially designed cell, detail of which will be described elsewhere.

Bivalent Gold

Results. (1) OXIDATION OF Au^{I} IN THE PRESENCE OF N_2O. Hydrated electrons react not only with N_2O according to Reaction 1 ($k_{N_2O} = 5.6 \times 10^9 M^{-1}\ sec.^{-1}$), but also with Au^{I}, producing elemental gold ($k_{Au^{I}} = 8 \times 10^9\ M^{-1}\ sec.^{-1}$). In order to keep the competition in favor of Reaction 1, the solute concentration was maintained at 100μM or less, while N_2O was used in the 1 to 15m*M* range. Under these conditions, the oxidizing yield is $G(e^-_{aq} + OH)$.

In all cases, transients were produced by irradiations carried out in different matrices. Typical transient spectra obtained are shown in Figures 1, 2, and Curve I of Figure 3. The decay characteristics of the transients at their absorption maxima were also followed. The spectra from neutral 0.01*M* KCl, acidic chloride (0.009*M* KCl + 0.001*M* HCl), and 0.01*M* HCl matrices, each saturated with N_2O, have maxima near 300–325 n.m., while those in neutral (2m*M* N_2O + 5m*M* K_2SO_4), alkaline (1m*M* NaOH + 1–15m*M* N_2O), acid (0.01*N* H_2SO_4) and (0.01*M* KF), each saturated with N_2O, have maxima at 270–280 n.m. Moreover, the spectra obtained in chloride solutions decay according to a second order law, while those in other matrices follow either a first order or some other mixed law. We attribute the spectrum reported in Figure 2 to Au^{II}, most probably as a chloro complex, since the same spectrum was not obtained in chloride-free matrices. The peak height remains unaltered (within experimental error of ±10%) when the $Au(CN)_2^-$ concentration is changed from $50\mu M$ to $100\mu M$. The extinction coefficient, $\epsilon_{325\ n.m.}$ is $(5.8 \pm 0.5) \times 10^3\ M^{-1}\ cm.^{-1}$, on the assumption that $G(Au^{II}) = G(e^-_{aq} + OH) = 5.4$.

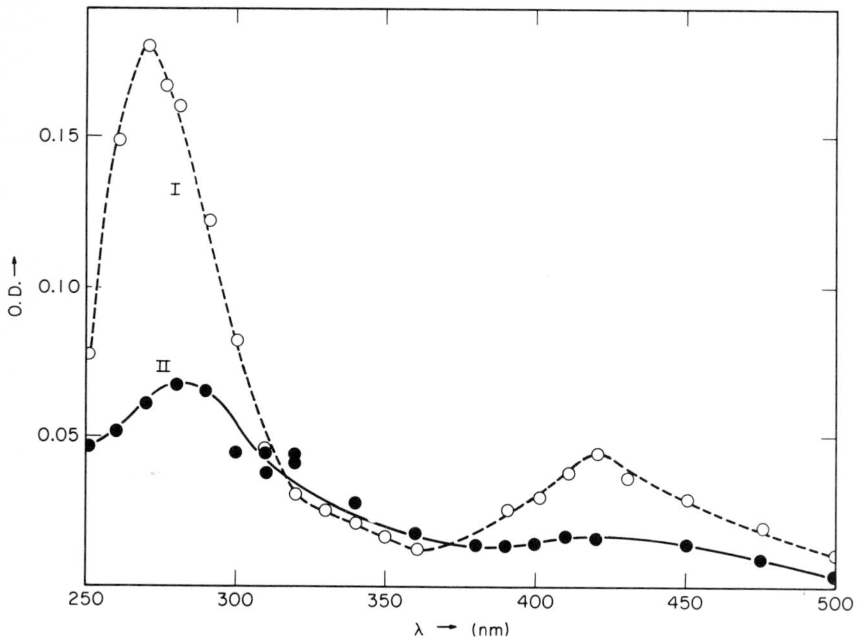

Figure 1. Spectra of oxidized gold species, $Au(CN)_2^-$, 0.1mM

I. Matrix, 0.01N H_2SO_4, N_2O saturated, $[OH] = \sim 2.8\mu M$/pulse.
II. Matrix, 1mM NaOH + 1mM N_2O, $[OH] = 2.1\mu M$/pulse.

The strongly absorbing (2) transient Cl_2^- is absent in our irradiations. Some pulse irradiations of N_2O-saturated neutral chloride solutions, free from Au^I, were run. We confirmed that there was no significant absorption caused by Cl_2^- in the spectrum being reported.

(2) Reduction of Au^{III} in the Presence of Methanol. In order to confirm the spectrum of Au^{II}, Au^{III} solutions containing 0.002 to $0.02M$ methanol were irradiated in a neutral $0.01M$ KCl matrix. Under these conditions, the primary OH radicals are scavenged and the system behaves as a source of hydrated electrons in neutral, or of atomic H in acid solutions. The reducing yield is about one half of the oxidizing yield (in presence of N_2O). A typical spectrum is shown in Curve II of Figure 3, and the second order decay appears in Figure 4 (Curve I). In Figure 3

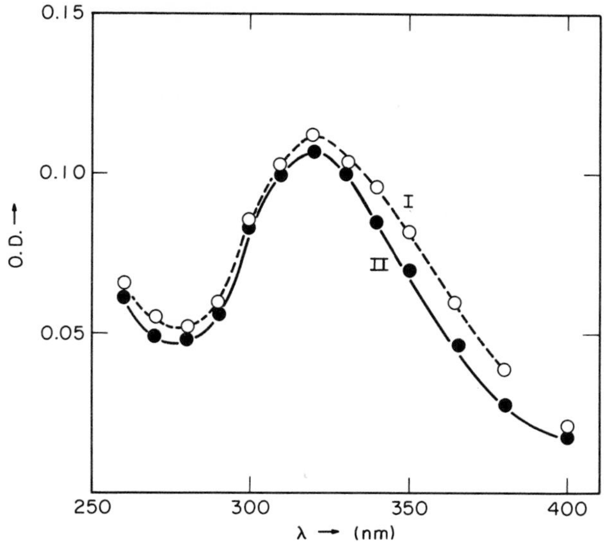

Figure 2. Absorption spectrum of Au^{II} in 0.01M HCl solution, N_2O saturated. $Au(CN)_2^-$, 0.1M. [OH] = ~2.3μM/pulse

I. Maximum O.D. (with Cl_2^-).
II. O.D. after 35 μsec. (Au^{II} free from Cl_2^-).

we corrected dotted Curve II for the loss of absorption by the pulse caused by the disappearance of Au^{III}, whose absorption peak under our conditions is around 300 n.m. Note that the shape of the corrected spectrum (solid curve of Figure 3) is similar to that obtained from $N_2O + Au^I$. Furthermore, as expected, its optical density per pulse at the peak is roughly one half that of the former. The peak lies very close to 325 n.m. The slope of the second order decay curve is $(2.1 \pm 0.4) \times 10^4$ sec.$^{-1}$, the same as that obtained in Curve II, Figure 4.

(3) Growth and Decay of the Transients Formed in Neutral 0.01*M* KCl Matrix. The growth of the transients was followed at 330 nm., at 2 to 10 μsec. sweep rates, and at gold concentrations of 25μ*M* and 50μ*M*. From the growth curves the rate constants for the reactions:

$$Au^I \text{ (as } Au(CN)_2^-) + OH \rightarrow Au^{II} + OH^- \quad (2)$$

and

$$Au^{III} \text{ (as } AuCl_4^-) + H \text{ (or } e^-_{aq}) \rightarrow Au^{II} + H^+ \text{ (or } H_2O) \quad (3)$$

are

$$k_2 = (4.7 \pm 0.8) \times 10^9 \ M^{-1} \text{ sec.}^{-1};$$

and

$$k_3 = (5.7 \pm 1.5) \times 10^9 \ M^{-1} \text{ sec.}^{-1}.$$

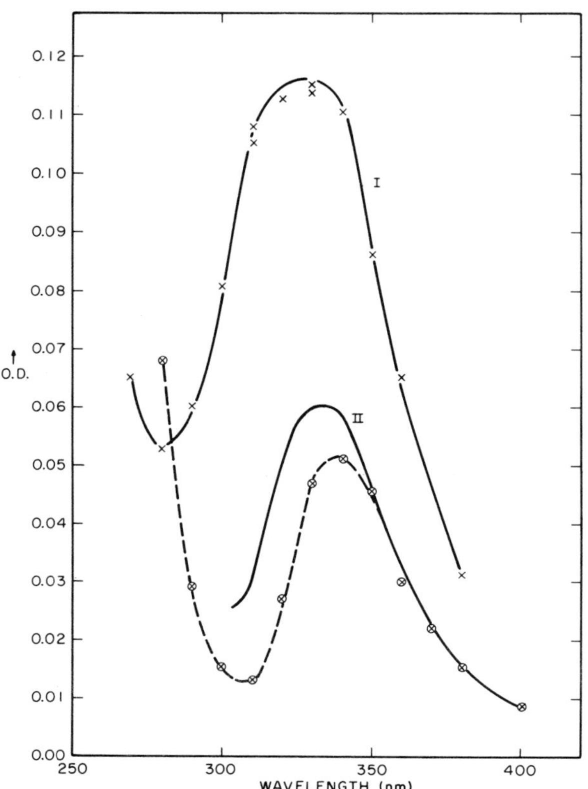

*Figure 3. Absorption spectra of Au^{II} in neutral 0.01*M *KCl solutions*

I. N_2O + 50μM $Au(CN)_2^-$, [OH] = 2.48μM/pulse.
II. 50μM, $AuCl_4^-$ + CH_3OH, $[e^-_{aq}]$ = 1.24μM/pulse.
Continuous line: corrected. Broken line: experimental.

Table I. Rate Constants of Formation

Reaction	k ($\times 10^{-9}$ M^{-1} *sec.*$^{-1}$)
$Au^{I} + OH \rightarrow Au^{II} + OH^-$	(4.7 ± 0.8)
$Au^{I} + OH \rightarrow Au^{II} + OH^-$	2.6
$Au^{III} + H(e^-_{aq}) \rightarrow Au^{II} + H^+$	(5.7 ± 1.5)
$2Au^{II} \rightarrow Au^{I} + Au^{III}$	(0.48 ± .12)
$2Au^{II} \rightarrow Au^{I} + Au^{III}$	~(0.24 ± .06%)
$Au^{I} + e^-_{aq} \rightarrow (Au^\circ)_{e^-_{aq}}$	(8.0 ± 0.5)
$(Au^\circ)_{e^-_{aq}} + (Au^\circ)_{e^-_{aq}} \rightarrow$ Product	(3.2 ± 0.9)
$(Au^\circ)_{e^-_{aq}} + (Au^\circ)_{e^-_{aq}} \rightarrow$ Product	(2.9 ± 0.8)
$(Au^\circ)_H + (Au^\circ)_H \rightarrow Au_2$	(5.0 ± 1.0)

[a] From growth of the transient product.
[b] Solute, $AuCl_4^-$. In all other cases the solute is $Au(CN)_2^-$.

The decay of the transients was also followed at 330 n.m. The transients formed either from $Au(CN)_2^-$ + N_2O or from $AuCl_4^-$ + CH_3OH decay according to a second order rate law (*see* Figure 4) up to about 70% of the maximum optical density. The slopes of a number of such decay curves pertaining to both the two systems average around $(2.1 \pm 0.4) \times 10^4$ sec.$^{-1}$, and they are the same at $25\mu M$ and $50\mu M$ gold concentrations which are much in excess of the free radicals or hydrated electrons produced per pulse. The second order decay indicates a disproportionation reaction

$$2Au^{II} \rightarrow Au^{I} + Au^{III}, \quad (4)$$

having a rate constant of $(4.8 \pm 1.2) \times 10^8\ M^{-1}$ sec.$^{-1}$ in a chloride matrix.

Discussion. (1) NEUTRAL CHLORIDE MATRIX. We attribute the spectra observed in 0.01*M* KCl to Au^{II} because (a) identical spectra were obtained in N_2O solutions by the oxidation of Au^I with OH, as by the reduction of Au^{III} by e^-_{aq}; (b) the yield in the former case was twice that of the latter as expected because of Reaction 1; (c) in both cases, the transients decayed by a second order rate law, as expected from Reaction 4 (*17*); and (d) the disproportionation rate constants were the same. We further confirmed that there was no contribution to the optical density owing to Cl_2^- likely to be formed by the action of OH on Cl^-. However, it is known (*2*) that the reaction between OH and Cl^- is favored by H^+. Though the pH of the solutions with $KAu(CN)_2$ was very close to 7, yet that with the Au^{III} (chloroauric acid) was near 4, because of the acidic reaction of the latter. Blank runs with Au^{III}-free solutions, but containing CH_3OH were carried out at this pH and showed no significant contribution owing to Cl_2^-.

The two systems, N_2O + $Au^I(CN)_2^-$ and CH_3OH + $Au^{III}Cl_4^-$, are not exactly identical. The former contains cyanide having a much stronger

and Decay of Au^{II} and Au°

Matrix	*pH*	*Remarks*
0.01*M* KCl (+ N_2O)	7	a
0.01*N* H_2SO_4 (+ CH_3OH)	2	d
0.01*M* KCl (+ CH_3OH)	4	a, b
0.01*M* KCl (+ N_2O or CH_3OH)	4, 7	c
0.01*M* HCl (+ N_2O)	2	c
1m*M* NaOH (+ CH_3OH)	11	c
1m*M* NaOH (+ CH_3OH)	11	c
100m*M* NaOH (+ high press H_2)	13	c
0.01*N* H_2SO_4 (CH_3OH or high press)	2	c

[c] From decay of the transient.
[d] By the method of competition kinetics.

complexing property than chloride and with a pH near 7. On the other hand, the latter is free from cyanide ions but with a pH of about 4. Nevertheless, because of the rapidity of the reactions there can be but little question that Au^{II} forms in this range of pH either when Au^{III} is reduced, or Au^{I} is oxidized. However, there may be complications in a complete comparison between the spectra of these two systems because of ligand transformations or of disproportionation products. The Au^{II} species is probably a chloride complex. We have, moreover, not investigated whether H or e^{-}_{aq} were responsible for the production of Au^{II} from $AuCl_4^-$. At pH 4, e^{-}_{aq} would certainly react at least partially with H^+ producing H. In any case, the reducing character of the solution is not thereby affected.

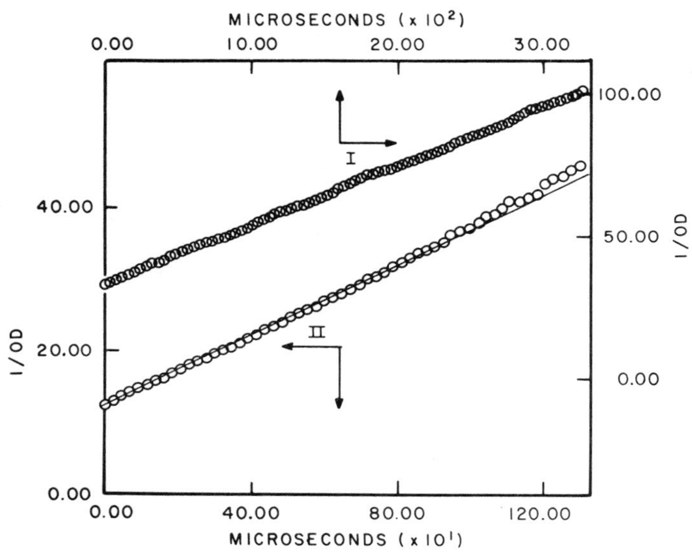

Figure 4. Decay of Au^{II} transient

I. From 50μM $AuCl_4^-$.
II. From 50μM $Au(CN)_2^-$.

(2) HYDROCHLORIC ACID MATRIX. The spectrum obtained on pulse irradiating Au^{I} in N_2O-saturated 0.01*M* HCl, is similar to that obtained in N_2O-saturated 0.01 KCl. In these solutions the transient Cl_2^- ion forms a peak at 340 n.m. However, the final yield of Au^{II} remains unaltered because of the reaction

$$Cl_2^- + Au^{I} \rightarrow Au^{II} + 2Cl^-. \tag{5}$$

The formation and decay of Cl_2^- was readily observed in our spectra.

The decay of this gold transient follows a second order law as one would expect from disproportionation of Au^{II}, but its slope is only half of that in neutral solution. This indicates that the species which are formed in acid solutions are more stable than those in neutral solution, probably because of differences in the chloride complexes. In spite of these differences, the observed similarity of the spectra seem to indicate that the transitions responsible for the spectra are possibly the same, maybe from the ligand to the central metal atom, as has been suggested for the case of the chloride complex of the trivalent gold (25).

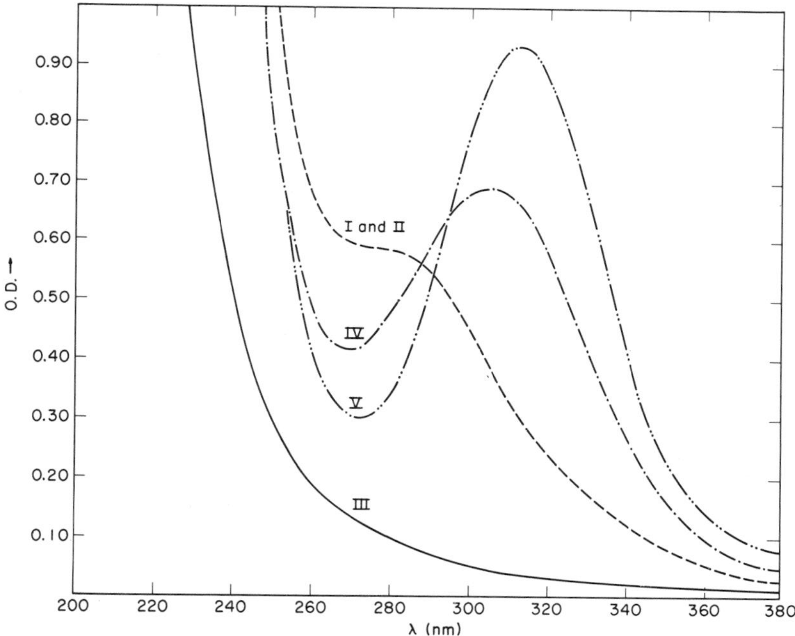

Figure 5. Absorption spectra of $Au^{III}Cl_4^-$ in various matrices (with Cary 14 Recording Spectrophotometer). 0.1mM Au^{III}, 1 cm. optical path

I. Neutral water.
II. 0.01M $KClO_4$.
III. 1mM NaOH.
IV. 0.01N H_2SO_4.
V. 0.01M KCl.

(3) CHLORIDE-FREE MATRICES. In these chloride-free solutions, whether acidic (0.01*N* H_2SO_4), neutral (5m*M* K_2SO_4 or pure water) or alkaline (1m*M* NaOH), the transient spectra from $Au(CN)_2^-$ show peaks near 270–280 n.m. rather than at 325 n.m. Moreover, they do not decay by a second order rate law. Instead the decay is nearly first order,

and, therefore, it is not caused by pure disproportionation reaction, contrary to what one would expect from Au^{II}. Though we do not rule out the possibility of the formation of Au^{II}, in these matrices, yet it was difficult to establish Au^{II} unequivocally. The complication arises because Au^{III}, one of the disproportionation products, also absorbs in the same region (*see* Figure 5). Furthermore, Au^{III} has hydrolyzed species having a narrow range of stability with respect to pH (9). From the spectra reproduced in Figure 5 (Curves 1 and 2) having a plateau near 280 n.m., it would appear that at least one of the hydrolyzed species absorbs strongly near 280 n.m. The observed first order decay in the alkaline medium, which is incidentally relatively very slow (half-life nearly 2 seconds), is possibly caused by the hydrolysis of Au^{III}, following its formation from Au^{II}. No further work has been done on this point.

Zero Valent Gold

Results. (1) REDUCTION OF Au^{I} BY HYDRATED ELECTRONS. Irradiations were carried out either in neutral or alkaline matrices, in the presence or absence of CH_3OH (used as an OH scavenger). The spectrum

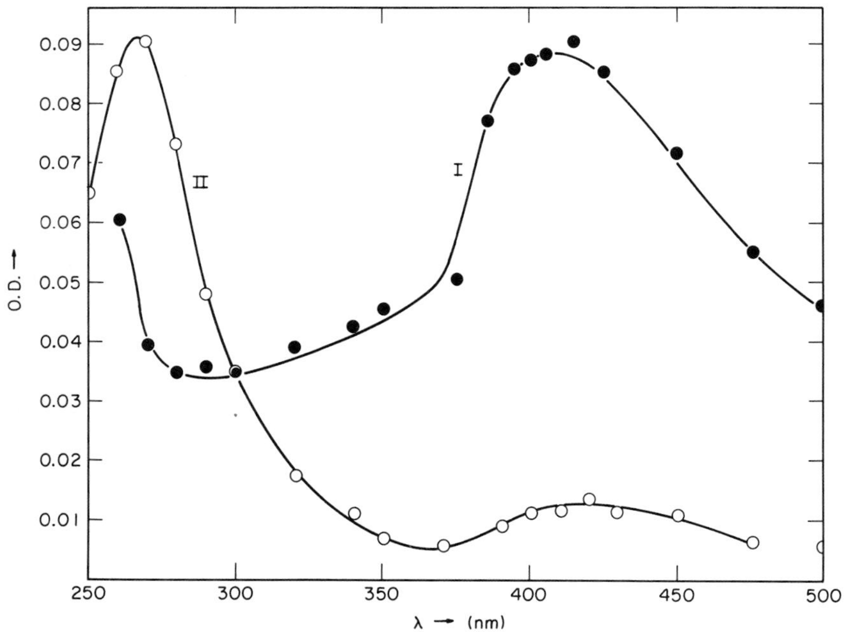

*Figure 6. Absorption spectra of Au°. 0.1m*M *$Au(CN)_2^-$*

*I. 1m*M *NaOH + 2m*M *CH_3OH.*
*II. 0.1*N *H_2SO_4 without CH_3OH.*

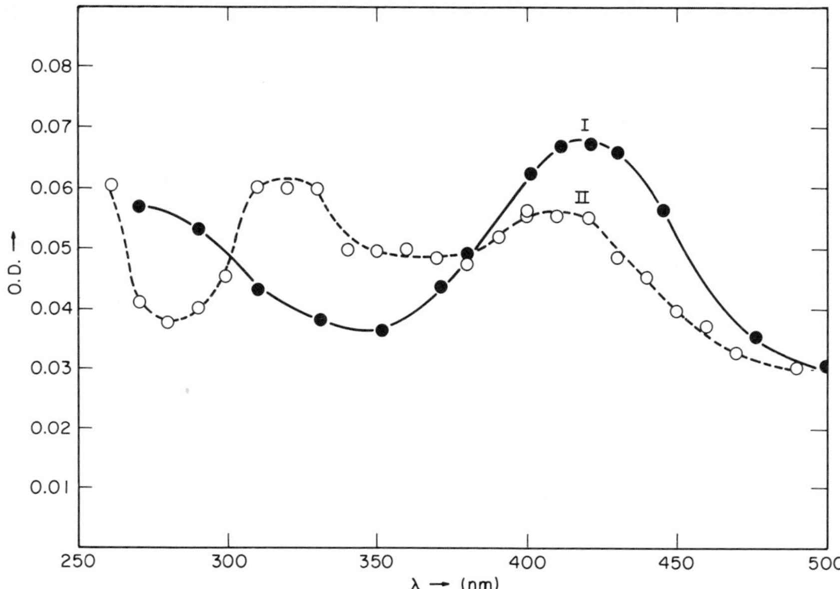

Figure 7. Absorption spectra of gold transient in neutral solution. 0.1mM $Au(CN)_2^-$

I. Neutral water matrix. $[e^-_{aq}] = 1.3\mu M$*/pulse.*
II. Neutral 0.01M KCl. $[e^-_{aq}] = 0.95\mu M$*/pulse.*

(Figure 6, Curve I) obtained in 1mM NaOH, containing 2mM CH_3OH has a strongly absorbing peak at about 410 n.m. Over the range of 20 to 100μM $Au(CN)^{2-}$, the molar extinction coefficient is $(7.5 \pm 1.1) \times 10^3$ M^{-1} cm.$^{-1}$, on the assumption that $G(Au°)_{e^-_{aq}} = G(e^-_{aq}) = 2.7$. On repeated pulsing, red colloidal gold appears. This band is clearly caused by the species formed by reaction with e^-_{aq}.

In a pure water matrix, a species having a similar spectrum was obtained (Figure 7, Curve I). However, in neutral 0.01M chloride (not containing alcohol), a double humped spectrum forms (Figure 7, Curve II). The peak near 410 n.m. corresponds to the one in pure water or alkali owing to reduction by hydrated electrons and that near 325 n.m. to oxidation by OH radicals.

The growth and decay of the transient which we shall designate by $(Au°)_{e^-_{aq}}$ was followed at 410 n.m. in 1mM alkaline solutions at different concentrations of $Au(CN)_2^-$. From the growth curves obtained at Au^I concentrations in the range from 20 to 100μM, at low sweep rates, the rate constants for the reactions:

$$e^-_{aq} + Au^I \rightarrow (Au°)_{e^-_{aq}} \quad (6)$$

equals $(8.0 \pm 0.5) \times 10^9\ M^{-1}$ sec.$^{-1}$, in the presence of 2mM CH_3OH, and $(8.5 \pm 0.9) \times 10^9\ M^{-1}$ sec.$^{-1}$, in the absence of alcohol.

In the absence of alcohol and in 1mM NaOH matrix, the decay of $(Au°)_{e^-_{aq}}$ at 410 n.m. does not follow either a first or a second order rate law. However, in the same matrix and in the presence of alcohol, the decay up to about 70% is nearly second order. From the average slopes which are measured at two concentrations [50μM and 100μM $Au(CN)_2^-$] and the extinction coefficient, the second order rate constant is $(3.2 \pm 0.9) \times 10^9 M^{-1}$ sec.$^{-1}$.

The reactivity of $(Au°)_{e^-_{aq}}$ toward O_2, $K_3Fe(CN)_6$, and N_2O was measured from the first order decay curves after introducing the additives in concentrations, high in comparison with the transient concentration, but not high enough to react appreciably with e^-_{aq}. The observed rate constants are shown in Table II, which also includes, for comparison, previous data involving e^-_{aq} and monovalent cations like Zn^+ and Cd^+.

Table II. A Comparison of Specific Reaction Rates of Some Electron Scavengers with $(Au°)_{e^-_{aq}}$ and with Other Transient Monovalent Cations[a]

Additive	$(Au°)_{e^-_{aq}}$	e^-_{aq} [b]	Zn^+	Cd^+
O_2	3.6×10^9	1.9×10^{10}	2.4×10^9 [c] 3.3×10^9 [d]	2.4×10^9 [c] 3.3×10^9 [d]
N_2O	5.5×10^8	5.6×10^9	$\leqslant 1.3 \times 10^7$ [c]	$\leqslant 2 \times 10^6$ [c] 1×10^6 [e]
$K_3Fe(CN)_6$	5.5×10^8	3×10^9	—	—

[a] In units of M^{-1} sec.$^{-1}$.
[b] Ref. 3.
[c] Ref. 21.
[d] Ref. 8.
[e] Ref. 10.

In order to eliminate possible effects of CH_2OH radicals in the experiments described above, we irradiated our solutions in the presence of high pressure hydrogen ($\sim$98mM dissolved H_2) as OH scavenger in lieu of CH_3OH. The pH of the solution was raised from 11 to 13 in order that the H and OH radicals were converted to e^-_{aq} *via* H atoms with a half-life $< 10^{-6}$ sec. The 410 n.m. absorption band remains unchanged. Moreover, the decay is second order over two half-lives and the slope of the plot, $1/D$ *vs.* t, is 9.8×10^4 sec.$^{-1}$. From this slope and the extinction coefficient, the second order rate constant is $(2.9 \pm 0.7) \times 10^9\ M^{-1}$ sec.$^{-1}$. From these results we conclude that CH_2OH radicals do not significantly affect the observed kinetics.

(2) REDUCTION OF Au^I BY ATOMIC H. Irradiations carried out in $0.01N$ H_2SO_4 provide atomic H for the reducing agent.

$$e^-_{aq} + H^+ \rightarrow H \quad (7)$$

Under conditions where the concentration of Au^I is about 1/100th of $[H^+]$, the direct reaction between $e^-_{aq} + Au^I$ is negligible. The transient species having an absorption peak near 270 n.m. (Curve II of Figure 6), forms by the following reaction:

$$Au^I + H \rightarrow (A°)_H + H^+ \quad (8)$$

From the present work, it is not possible to say anything definite about its structure. It could be a hydride complex. On repeated pulsing, colloidal gold forms.

The spectrum of Figure 6, Curve II, is completely different from that of $(Au°)_{e^-_{aq}}$. On the other hand, its peak is in practically the same position as that for N_2O saturated $0.01N$ H_2SO_4 (Curve I of Figure 1), that is of Au^{II}. The addition of $2mM$ CH_3OH lowers the peak height considerably as expected. At constant CH_3OH concentration, the peak height increases gradually with an increase of the Au^I concentration, obviously caused by competition reactions of the OH radicals between CH_3OH and Au^I. In the same way, at constant Au^I concentration, and increasing CH_3OH concentration, the optical density drops at first and then reaches a plateau (Figure 8). At still higher concentrations, the optical density falls further because of the loss of H atoms by reaction with CH_3OH, $k_{H+CH_3OH} = 1.7 \times 10^6$, $k_{OH+CH_3OH} = 4.7 \times 10^8$ (*3*). Making the reasonable assumption that the optical density at the plateau represents $(Au°)_H$ only, we calculate its molar extinction coefficient at 280 n.m. as $(2.6 \pm 0.4) \times 10^3$ and at 270 n.m. as $(3.2 \pm 0.5) \times 10^3$ M^{-1} cm.$^{-1}$ on the assumption that $G_H = 3.2$.

From the dependence of optical density on CH_3OH concentration we calculate the rate constant for the reaction

$$OH + Au^I \rightarrow Au^{II} + OH^-$$

by the method of competition kinetics and obtain a value of $2.6 \times 10^9 M^{-1}$ sec.$^{-1}$.

The same spectral absorption at 270 n.m. was observed by reaction of $Au(CN)_2^-$ with H atoms generated in an altogether different way in neutral medium. Irradiations were carried out in triply distilled water saturated with N_2O but under a high pressure of hydrogen. Under these conditions, the hydrated electrons are converted to OH radicals by Reaction 1, and then the OH radicals are converted to H by the H_2 dissolved under high pressure as explained before. In neutral water the conversion of H atoms to e^-_{aq} is negligible.

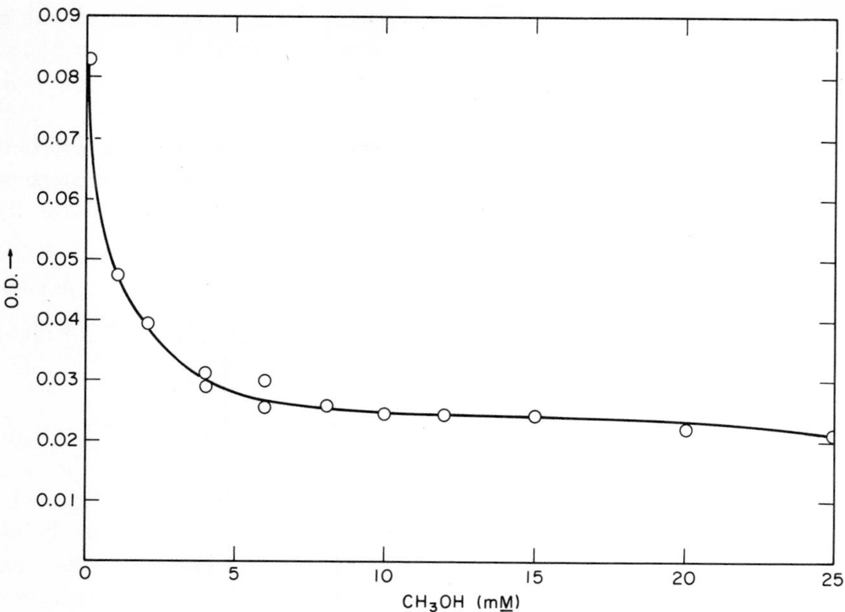

Figure 8. Effect of CH_3OH concentration on the O.D. of the gold transient obtained by pulse radiolysis in 0.01N H_2SO_4, 0.1mM $Au(CN)_2^-$

Table III. Extinction Coefficients

Species	*Conditions*	*pH*	*Solute*	λ*max* (*n.m.*)	ϵ ($\times 10^{-3}$ M^{-1} *cm.*$^{-1}$)
$(Au^\circ)_{e^-_{aq}}$	1m*M* NaOH + 2m*M* CH_3OH	11	$Au(CN)^{2-}$	410	(7.5 ± 1.1)
$(Au^\circ)_H$	0.01*N* H_2SO_4 + 10m*M* CH_3OH	2	$Au(CN)^{2-}$	270	(3.2 ± 0.5)
Au^{II}	0.01*M* KCl + 15m*M* N_2O	7	$Au(CN)^{2-}$	325	(5.8 ± 0.5)
Au^{II}	0.01*M* KCl + 2–20m*M* CH_3OH	4	$AuCl_4^-$	325	(5.8 ± 0.5)

Decay of the 270 n.m. band was followed in the acid matrix in the presence of either CH_3OH or high pressure hydrogen. With 10–15m*M* CH_3OH and 50–100μM $Au(CN)_2^-$, the slope of $1/D$ *vs.* t plot was (4.0 ± 0.4) × 10^5 sec.$^{-1}$, from which the second order rate constant of (5.0 ± 1.0) × 19^9 M^{-1} *sec.*$^{-1}$ is calculated for the reaction

$$2Au^\circ \rightarrow Au_2 \qquad (9)$$

When the alcohol concentration was lowered to 2m*M*, or the gold concentration was raised to 1m*M*, the $1/D$ *vs.* t. plots remain linear but the slopes decrease indicating an interfering reaction, the product of which also absorbs at 270 n.m. We have seen earlier that Au^{II} and then Au^{III} form by oxidation of Au^{I} by unscavenged OH radicals. Each of these species has a strong absorption at this wavelength that complicates our decay curve.

With 110 atm. of hydrogen and 50μM of Au^{I} at pH 2, when roughly 10% of the OH radicals remain unscavenged, the $1/D$ *vs.* t plots are linear, having slopes of $(3.2 \pm 0.3) \times 10^5$ sec.$^{-1}$. With 40 atm. of H_2, when the Au^{II} formed by the $\sim$ 25% unscavenged OH is more, the slope of the second order plot is only 2.0×10^5 sec.$^{-1}$. These results indicate that the effect, if any, of CH_2OH radicals may not be appreciable in the formation and decay of $(Au°)_H$ at least under the present experimental conditions. Our estimate for the best value for k_9 is $(5.0 \pm 1.0) \times 10^9$ M^{-1} sec.$^{-1}$.

Discussion

It has been shown (*8, 10, 21*) that the species obtained by the action of e^-_{aq} on Cd^{2+} or Zn^{2+} react readily with O_2, yet they are rather unreactive toward e^-_{aq} scavengers like N_2O or H_3O^+. These results support the conclusion that the reduced species are really monovalent cations, and not some type of electron adduct like $M^{n+} \ldots e^-_{aq}$, as has been suggested (*15*). Our work with $(Au°)_H$ also indicates that the species obtained by the action of atomic H on Au^{I} is rather unreactive toward N_2O. By contrast, the reactivity of $(Au°)_{e^-_{aq}}$ (whose spectrum is also different from $(Au°)_H$) is reminiscent of the reactivity of e^-_{aq}, particularly towards N_2O and $K_3Fe(CN)_6$ (*see* Table II). We suggest that, although the formation of electron adducts is not general, $Au(CN)_2^-$ appears to form one. The structure of these adducts is not known but it may be represented as $Au(CN)_2^- \ldots e^-_{aq}$.

This conclusion is supported, though in a qualitative way, by the results of an experiment based on the ability of N_2O to extract the adduct electron and convert it to an OH radical. We carried our irradiation in neutral Au^{I}—0.01*M* KCl matrix, in which extra OH formed oxidizes Au^{I} to Au^{II}. In order to observe this effect we studied the formation of Au^{II} at its 325 nm. peak (Figure 7, II). The amount of N_2O added was sufficiently high to react with the transient $(Au°)_{e^-_{aq}}$ but not high enough to react appreciably with e^-_{aq}. The results are shown in Figure 9. Note that a rapid initial growth is followed by a slower one. In the rapid growth, Au^{II} forms by the primary OH radicals and also by Reaction 1 from the

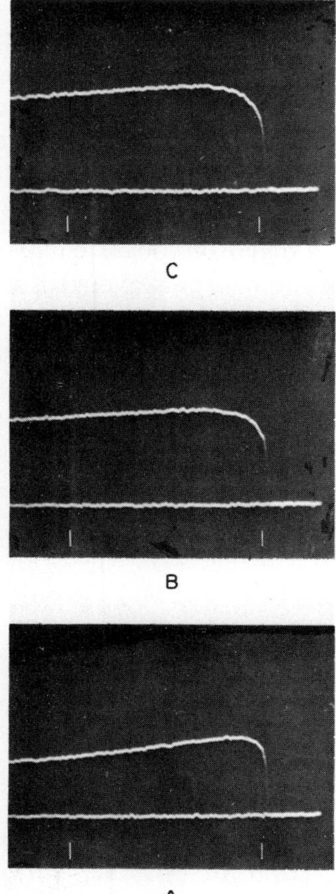

Figure 9. Effect of N_2O on the formation of Au^{II} from $(Au^\circ)_{e^-_{aq}}$. $\lambda = 320$ n.m., sweep rate = 10 μsec./cm. Matrix, 0.01M KCl. $[e^-_{aq}] = 0.95$ μM/pulse. $[Au(CN)_2^-] = 100$μM; $[N_2O]$, A = 0, B = ~30μM, C = ~100μM

primary e^-_{aq} on N_2O. We calculate from the rate constants and concentrations of Au^I and N_2O that reaction of these species with e^-_{aq} has a half-life < 0.4 μsec. The slower additional growth for 15 μsec., however, confirms our prediction since it indicates abstraction of e^-_{aq} from $(Au^\circ)_{e^-_{aq}}$ and its conversion to OH by N_2O, followed finally by more Au^{II}.

The observed second order decay may arise by the spin pairing of Au° atoms forming the normal diamagnetic metal, or by the bimolecular reaction of the electron adduct species which also produces the metal. Second order decay of Au° caused by disproportionation reactions, as has been suggested for monovalent Cd^+, Zn^+, etc. (*1, 5*) is not applicable in the present case. The transient obtained with H atoms is probably atomic Au, and therefore, spin pairing mechanism would be applicable, whereas in the e^-_{aq} product, a bimolecular mode of decay is more probable.

Acknowledgments

We wish to acknowledge with thanks the valued help and suggestions of M. Sauer and J. K. Thomas, the technical assistance of R. Clarke and P. Walsh, and finally the cooperation of the Linac crew, particularly B. Clifft and B. Naderer.

Literature Cited

(1) Adams, G. E., Baxendale, J. H., Boag, J. W., *Proc. Chem. Soc.* **1963**, 241.
(2) Anbar, M., Thomas, J. K., *J. Phys. Chem.* **68**, 3829 (1966).
(3) Anbar, M., Neta, P., *Intern. J. Appl. Radiation & Isotopes* **18**, 493 (1967).
(4) Baxendale, J. H., Dixon, R. S., *Proc. Chem. Soc.* **1963**, 148.
(5) Baxendale, J. H., Fielden, E. M., Keene, J. P., *Proc. Chem. Soc.* **1963**, 242.
(6) Baxendale, J. H., Fielden, E. M., Keene, J. P., *Proc. Roy. Soc.* **A286**, 320 (1965).
(7) Baxendale, J. H., Fielden, E. M., Keene, J. P., "Pulse Radiolysis," p. 207, M. Ebert, J. P. Keene, A. J. Swallow, J. H. Baxendale, eds., Academic Press, London, 1965.
(8) Baxendale, J. H., Keene, J. P., Stott, D. A., *Chem. Comm.* **1966**, 715.
(9) Bjerrum, N., *Bull. Soc. Chim. Belg.* **57**, 432 (1948).
(10) Buxton, G. H., Dainton, F. S., Thielens, G., *Chem. Comm.* **1967**, 201.
(11) Corbett, J. D., Druding, L. F., *J. Inorg. Nucl. Chem.* **2**, 20 (1959).
(12) Dorfman, L. M., Matheson, M. S., "Progress in Reaction Kinetics," p. 239, G. Porter, ed., Pergamon, London, 1965, **3**.
(13) Fujita, H. Izaisa, M., Yamazaki, H., *Chem. Abs.* **64**, 15226a (1966).
(14) Hart, E. J., Gordon, S., Thomas, J. K., *J. Phys. Chem.* **68**, 1271 (1964).
(15) Hart, E. J., "Actions Chimiques et Biologiques des Radiations," Vol. X, M. Haissinsky, ed., Masson et Cie, Paris, 1966.
(16) Koulkes-Pujo, A. M., Ziemecki, S., *J. Chem. Phys.* **59**, 843 (1962).
(17) Latimer, L. M., "Oxidation Potentials," 2nd Ed., p. 192, Prentice Hall, New York (1952).
(18) Low, W., Suss, J. T., *Physics Letters* **7**, 310 (1963).
(19) MacCragh, A., Koski, W. S., *J. Am. Chem. Soc.* **87**, 2496 (1965).
(20) Moorthy, P. N., Weiss, J. J., *Nature* **211**, 1317 (1964).
(21) Meyerstein, D., Mulac, W. A., *J. Phys. Chem.* **72**, 784 (1968).
(22) Rich, R. L., Taube, H., *J. Phys. Chem.* **58**, 6 (1954).
(23) Sauer, M., *Argonne Natl. Lab. Reports,* **ANL-7113** (1965).
(24) *Ibid.,* ***ANL-7146*** (1966).
(25) Vlcek, A. S., Beran, P., *Chem. Listy* **50**, 1306 (1956).
(26) Waters, J. H., Gray, H. B., *J. Am. Chem. Soc.* **87**, 3534 (1965).

RECEIVED January 8, 1968. Based on work performed under the auspices of the U. S. Atomic Energy Commission.

14

Radiolytic Transients from *p*-Nitrophenol and Their Inter- and Intramolecular Reactions

B. CERCEK and M. EBERT

Paterson Laboratories, Christie Hospital and Holt Radium Institute, Manchester 20, England

The reactions of hydrated electrons, H and OH radicals with p-*nitrophenol have been studied using the technique of pulse radiolysis. The H and OH radicals react with the nitro-group to produce in acid solutions the radicals* $HOC_6H_4NO_2H\cdot$ *and* $HOC_6H_4NO_3H\cdot$ *or in neutral solutions the anion radicals* $HOC_6H_4NO_2^-\cdot$ *and* $HOC_6H_4NO_3^-\cdot$*, respectively. The optical absorption spectra and molar extinction coefficients of these species as well as their rates of formation and decay have been obtained and the* pK *values for the protonation of the anion radicals estimated. An intramolecular rearrangement of the anion radical* $HOC_6H_4NO_3^-\cdot$ *has been observed.*

Aqueous solutions of the anion-radicals of *p*-nitrophenol, namely $HOC_6H_4NO_2^-\cdot$ and $HOC_6H_4NO_3^-\cdot$ as well as their protonated forms $HOC_6H_4NO_2H\cdot$ and $HOC_6H_4NO_3H\cdot$ were studied using the technique of pulse radiolysis.

In this contribution the optical absorption spectra, pH dependent equilibra and reactions of these radicals will be described. An unexpected intramolecular rearrangement of the anion-radical $HOC_6H_4NO_3^-\cdot$ is discussed.

Experimental

Irradiation Facilities. Details of the experimental arrangement have been described (*18*). Single 2 μsec. pulses of 4 Mev. electrons were used, giving doses from 50 to 3000 rad per pulse. The slit width of the analyzing monchromator was normally kept at 5 n.m.

Dosimetry. The dose given by each pulse was monitored with a secondary emission chamber (abbr. SEC). The SEC was calibrated by means of a modified Fricke dosimeter ($10^{-2}M$ ferrous sulfate in $0.8N$ sulfuric acid solution saturated with oxygen) using the value 15.6 for $G(Fe^{3+})$ (*13*).

Materials. All solutions were prepared using distilled water redistilled from alkaline permanganate. The quality of the water was checked by measuring the half-life of the hydrated electron in deaerated water. It was at a dose of about 30 rad per 2 μsec. pulse at least 100 μsec. The reagents (*p*-nitrophenol and sulfuric acid) were of AnalaR grade and were used without further purification.

Results and Discussion

Identification of the Transients. NEUTRAL SOLUTIONS. In deaerated $5 \times 10^{-5}M$ *p*-nitrophenol solution at pH 7, the absorption spectrum with a maximum at 290 n.m. was observed about 20 μsec. after the end of the radiation pulse (Figure 1-A) when all the hydrated electrons, H and OH radicals have reacted with the *p*-nitrophenol. The spectra shown in Figure 1-A and 1-B were corrected for the decrease in optical density owing to solute destruction. The *G*-value for the destruction of *p*-nitrophenol was assumed to be equal to the sum of $G(e^-_{aq}) + G(OH) + G(H) = 6.0$ (*2, 15, 19*). The corrections had a maximum value at 400 n.m. namely, 103% and 130% of the observed optical densities and decreased to 40% and 81% at 290 n.m. for spectrum A and B, respectively. When hydrated electrons are converted to OH radicals by reaction with N_2O (*11*), the absorption at 290 n.m. decreases and the maximum shifts towards 300 n.m. (Figure 1-B). It can be concluded, therefore, that the transient species produced by hydrated electrons as well as OH radicals have an optical absorption in the same wavelength region.

ACID SOLUTIONS. In deaerated $5 \times 10^{-5}M$ *p*-nitrophenol solutions at pH 1.3, the absorption spectrum with a maximum at 290 n.m. was observed about 20 μsec. after the end of the radiation pulse (Figure 1-C) when all the H and OH radicals have reacted with the *p*-nitrophenol. The spectra in Figures 1-C and 1-D were corrected for the decrease in optical density owing to the destruction of *p*-nitrophenol. No correction for the formation of the radical HO_2 was applied as its contribution to the optical densities above 280 n.m.—*i.e.*, region of the absorption maxima—could be neglected. The *G*-value for the destruction of *p*-nitrophenol was assumed to be 6.2 and 2.9 for deaerated and oxygenated solutions, respectively (*2*). The corrections had a maximum value at 310 n.m. At this wavelength the observed optical densities were 30% of the corrections. When the solution is saturated with oxygen ($1.3 \times 10^{-3}M$ O_2) the absorption at 290 n.m. decreases by a factor of two and the maximum shifts to 310 n.m. (Figure 1-D). Oxygen reacts rapidly with H radicals ($k(H + O_2) = 2 \times 10^{10}M^{-1}$ sec.$^{-1}$ (*3*), but slowly with the OH radical reaction products

($k(HOC_6H_4NO_3^{-}\cdot + O_2) = 1.7 \times 10^6 M^{-1}$ sec.$^{-1}$ (*see* Section on Reaction Kinetics). It can be concluded, therefore, that both H and OH radicals produce transients which absorb in the same wavelength region and that oxygen by converting H radicals to radicals HO_2 protects the *p*-nitrophenol.

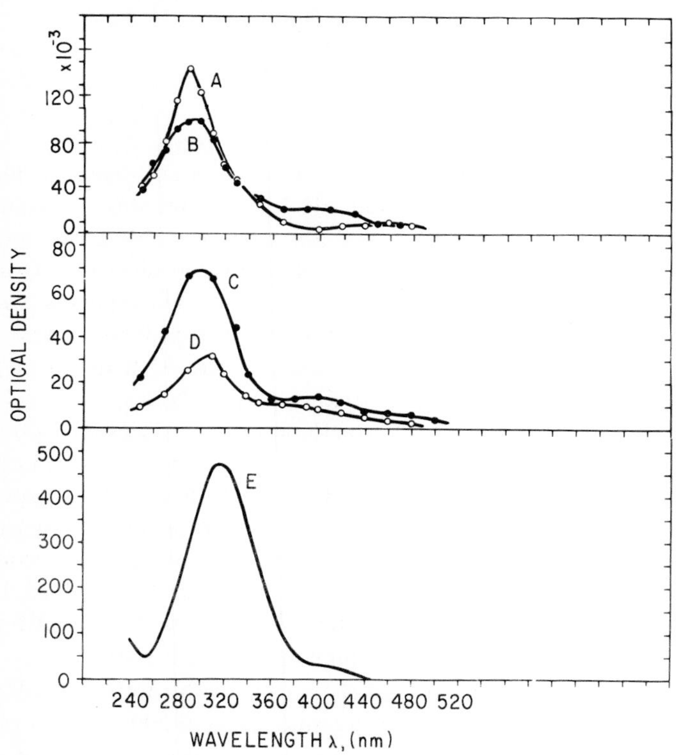

Figure 1. Transient spectra in 5 × 10⁻⁵M p-*nitrophenol solution observed after a 2 μsec. pulse of radiation of approximately 500 rads*

pH 7: A, deaerated; B, deaerated and N_2O-saturated.
pH 1.3: C, deaerated; D, in the presence of 1.3×10^{-3}M O_2;
E, 5×10^{-5}M p-nitrophenol for pHs 1 to 6, unirradiated.
Spectra are corrected for solute destruction. For this purpose the spectrum of the p-*nitrophenol shown in block E has been used.*
Ordinate: Optical density
Abscissa: Wavelength, n.m.

Structure of the Transients. SPECIES PRODUCED BY e^-_{aq}. Hydrated electrons react with the *p*-nitrophenol to form the radical anion $HOC_6H_4NO_2^{-}\cdot$ (*14*). This transient can become protonated to form the radical $HOC_6H_4NO_2H\cdot$ depending on the pH of the solution. This is analogous to the well established reaction of e^-_{aq} with nitrobenzene (*5*).

SPECIES PRODUCED BY OH RADICALS. OH radicals could react with the *p*-nitrophenol in the following ways:

(*1a*) by hydrogen abstraction from the benzene ring and/or OH group,

(*1b*) by addition to the benzene ring,

(*1c*) by π-complex formation,

(*1d*) by a reaction with the nitro-group.

Mechanism *1a* has been disproved earlier (*14*). Mechanism *1b* is also unlikely for the following reasons: the bathochromic shifts of the hydroxy-cyclohexadienyl radicals are linearly correlated to the parent molecules (*7*) and additive for substituents in disubstituted benzenes (*17*). The hydroxy-cyclohexadienyl radical of the *p*-nitrophenol is expected to have an absorption maximum at 420 n.m. in contrast to the observed one at 295 n.m. Furthermore, the OH addition products—*i.e.*, cyclohexadienyl radicals—are known to react by a second order process (*6, 8, 12*), whereas the OH radical reaction product of the *p*-nitrophenol decays by a first order process (*see* Section on Reaction Kinetics). Thus, both on the basis of the optical properties and the kinetic behavior, Mechanism *1b* is not favored. Mechanism *1c*, π-complex formation between the OH radical and the *p*-nitrophenol, is not probable for the following reasons: the OH radical, a reactive electrophilic species (*4*), attacks preferentially positions of high electron density. The nitro group is a strong electron-withdrawing substituent (*16*). If a complex would be formed between the radical OH and the *p*-nitrophenol, then it would probably involve the electron-rich nitro-group rather than the electron-depleted benzene ring. In fact similar optical absorption spectra (Figures 2 and 3) and pH-effects (Figure 4) for H and OH radical adducts suggest a related structure of the transients—*i.e.*, $HOC_6H_4NO_2H\cdot$ and $HOC_6H_4NO_3H\cdot$ respectively. We favor Mechanism *1d*, namely, a reaction of the OH radical with the nitro-group leading to the anion radical $HOC_6H_4NO_3^{-}\cdot$ or its protonated form the radical $HOC_6H_4NO_3H\cdot$.

SPECIES PRODUCED BY H RADICALS. H radicals could react with *p*-nitrophenol in the following ways:

(*2a*) by hydrogen abstraction from the benzene ring and/or the OH group,

(*2b*) by addition to the benzene ring,

(*2c*) by a reaction with the nitro-group.

According to Mechanism *2a*, the hydrogen gas yield in deaerated *p*-nitrophenol solutions of high acidity is expected to be close to 3 H_2 molecules per 100 e.v. However, the hydrogen gas yield was found to be 0.33 $\pm$ 10% H_2 molecules per 100 e.v. in an aqueous degassed $10^{-2}M$ *p*-nitrophenol solution at pH 0.5. Obviously, Mechanism *2a* does not apply.

H and OH adducts to the benzene ring of nitrobenzene as well as other benzene derivatives have identical optical absorption spectra (*6*). By analogy the OH and H addition products of *p*-nitrophenol are expected to have identical spectra, with a maximum at about 420 n.m. However, no absorption was observed in this wavelength region. On this basis, Mechanism *2b* can be excluded. A reaction of the H radicals with the nitro-group, Mechanism *2c,* is a likely explanation. It is supported by experiments in which deaerated $5 \times 10^{-5}M$ *p*-nitrophenol solutions at pH 1 were irradiated in the presence of $10^{-1}M$ isopropyl alcohol. In this system all e^{-}_{aq}, OH, and H radicals are converted to isopropyl alcohol radicals. These radicals reduce the nitro-group of aromatic compounds forming the anion radical $HOC_6H_4NO_2^{-}\cdot$ (*5*). Identical spectra were obtained when *p*-nitrophenol was reduced by isopropyl alcohol radicals and protonated to yield the radicals $HOC_6H_4NO_2H\cdot$ (Figure 3-A), or by H radical addition to the nitro-group (Figure 1, spectrum D subtracted from C).

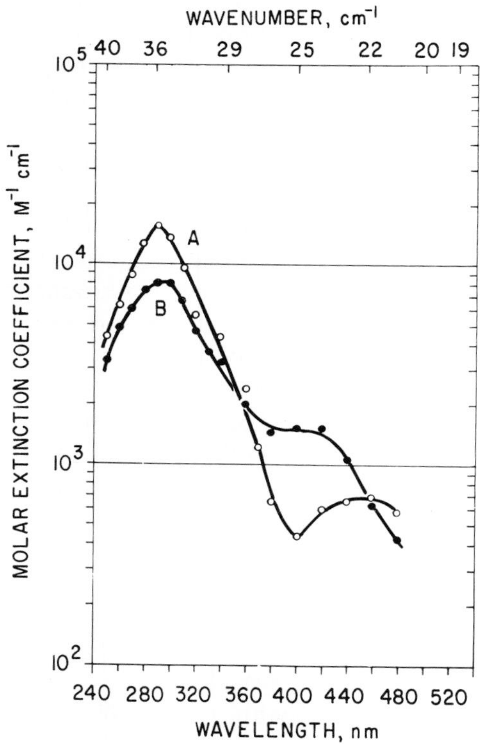

Figure 2. Absorption spectra of the anion radicals at pH 7: A, $HOC_6H_4NO_2^{-}\cdot$ *and B,* $HOC_6H_4NO_3^{-}\cdot$

Ordinate: Molar extinction coefficient, M^{-1} *cm.*$^{-1}$
Abscissa: Wavelength in n.m. or wave numbers in cm.$^{-1}$

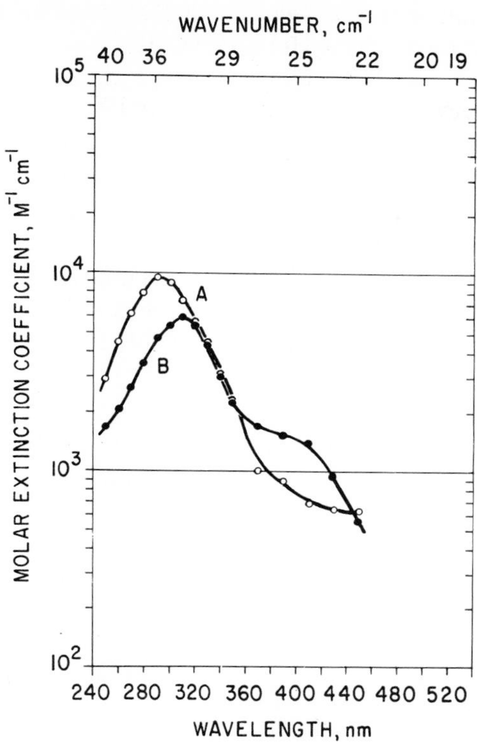

Figure 3. Absorption spectra of the protonated anion radicals at pH 1.3: A, $HOC_6H_4NO_2H\cdot$ and B, $HOC_6H_4NO_3H\cdot$

Ordinate: Molar extinction coefficient $10^{-3} \times M^{-1}$ cm.$^{-1}$ Abscissa: Wavelength in n.m. or wave numbers in cm.$^{-1}$

Absorption Spectra and Molar Extinction Coefficients of the Transients. $HOC_6H_4NO_2H\cdot$ AND $HOC_6H_4NO_2^{-}\cdot$. The optical absorption spectrum of the anion radical $HOC_6H_4NO_2^{-}\cdot$ (Figure 2-A) was obtained in N_2O-saturated $5 \times 10^{-5}M$ *p*-nitrophenol solutions in the presence of $10^{-1}M$ isopropyl alcohol. The spectrum of the radical $HOC_6H_4NO_2H\cdot$ was observed in similar solutions, but at pH 1.3 and is shown in Figure 3-A. Under these conditions all hydrated electrons, H and OH radicals are converted to isopropyl alcohol. These reduce the *p*-nitrophenol to the anion radical $HOC_6H_4NO_2^{-}\cdot$ which on protonation in solutions of high acidity yields the radical $HOC_6H_4NO_2H\cdot$. To calculate the molar extinction coefficients it was assumed that the yield of $HOC_6H_4NO_2^{-}\cdot$ was equal to the sum of $G(e^{-}_{aq}) + G(OH) + G(H) = 6.0$ (*2, 15, 19*) at neutral pH and that of $HOC_6H_4NO_2H\cdot$ to the sum $G(OH) + G(H) = 6.2$ at pH 1.3 (*2*). On this basis the molar extinction coefficients at

290 n.m. were estimated to be 15,800 ± 3,000M^{-1} *cm.*$^{-1}$ for $HOC_6H_4NO_2^{-}\cdot$ and 9,500 ± 2,000M^{-1} cm.$^{-1}$ for $HOC_6H_4NO_2H\cdot$.

$HOC_6H_4NO_3H\cdot$ AND $HOC_6H_4NO_3^{-}\cdot$. The optical absorption spectra of radicals $HOC_6H_4NO_3H\cdot$ and $HOC_6H_4NO_3^{-}\cdot$ are obtained when e^{-}_{aq} and H radicals are scavenged with oxygen. Oxygen reacts slowly with these organic radicals (*see* Section on Reaction Kinetics). The spectrum seen at the end of the radiation pulse was that of $HOC_6H_4NO_3H\cdot$ at pH 1.3 and that of $HOC_6H_4NO_3^{-}\cdot$ at pH 7 (Figures 3-B and 2-C). It was assumed that the OH radical yield, G(OH), equals 2.9 and is pH independent (*1, 9*). The molar extinction coefficients at 290 n.m. were calculated to be 8,200 ± 2,000M^{-1} cm.$^{-1}$ for $HOC_6H_4NO_3^{-}\cdot$ and 4,700 ± 1,000M^{-1} cm.$^{-1}$ for $HOC_6H_4NO_3H\cdot$.

Reaction Kinetics. FORMATION OF $HOC_6H_4NO_2^{-}\cdot$. Transients produced by hydrated electrons and OH radicals absorb in the same wavelength region, but *p*-nitrophenol reacts about one-tenth as fast with OH radicals (*see* below) than with hydrated electrons. Therefore, it is possible in deaerated 5 × 10^{-6}*M* *p*-nitrophenol solutions at pH 7 to observe the formation of the anion radical $HOC_6H_4NO_2^{-}\cdot$ without the interference of the OH radical reaction product. From the exponential rate of formation of the anion radical $HOC_6H_4NO_2^{-}\cdot$ at 290 n.m., the rate constant k_1 was calculated to be (3.5 ± 0.6) × 10^{10}M^{-1} sec.$^{-1}$.

$$e^{-}_{aq} + HOC_6H_4NO_2 \rightarrow HOC_6H_4NO_2^{-}\cdot \quad (1)$$

Kinetic analysis of the simultaneous decay of the hydrated electron at 650 n.m. gave rate constants which were within ± 10% of this value.

PROTONATION OF $HOC_6H_4NO_2^{-}\cdot$. In N_2O-saturated 5 × 10^{-5}*M* *p*-nitrophenol solutions in the presence of 10^{-1}*M* isopropyl alcohol the anion radical $HOC_6H_4NO_2^{-}\cdot$ is the only species seen by the end of the radiation pulse. As the pH is decreased below 5 the $HOC_6H_4NO_2^{-}\cdot$ is gradually protonated and the optical absorption decreases (Figure 4-A). From the point of inflexion in Figure 4-A the pK for Reaction 2 was estimated to be 4.1 ± 0.2

$$HOC_6H_4NO_2H\cdot \rightleftarrows HOC_6H_4NO_2^{-}\cdot + H^{+} \quad (2)$$

DECAY OF $HOC_6H_4NO_2^{-}\cdot$ AND $HOC_6H_4NO_2H\cdot$. At all of the pHs studied, the transients $HOC_6H_4NO_2^{-}\cdot$ and $HOC_6H_4NO_2H\cdot$ decay by a second order process, but the second order rate constant, $2k_3$, changes from 7 × 10^{6}M^{-1} sec.$^{-1}$ at pH 6 to 6 × 10^{9}M^{-1} sec.$^{-1}$ at pH 2.5. The electrochemically produced anion radical $HOC_6H_4NO_2^{-}\cdot$ at pH 12.8 has been found to decay with a second order rate constant of 20M^{-1} sec.$^{-1}$ (*10*); it therefore appears that, although at pH 6 over 99% of the radicals are in the anionic form, the anion radicals $HOC_6H_4NO_2^{-}\cdot$ do not react with each other, but decay *via* Reaction 2 and Reaction 3. This mechanism is analogous to a similar second order disappearance of the $C_6H_5NO_2^{-}\cdot$ species (*5*).

$$2\ HOC_6H_4NO_2H\cdot \rightarrow HOC_6H_4NO_2 + HOC_6H_4NO + H_2O \qquad (3)$$

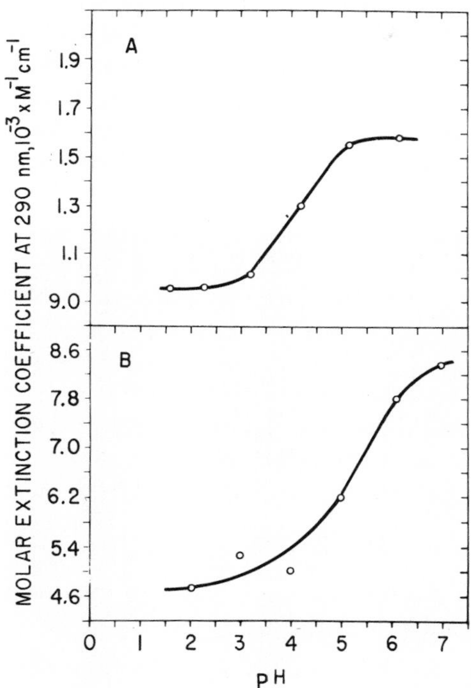

*Figure 4. Extinction at 290 n.m. as a function of pH in 5 × 10⁻⁵*M *p-nitrophenol solution: A, deaerated and N_2O-saturated in the presence of 10^{-1}*M *isopropyl alcohol; B, in the presence of 1.3 × 10^{-3}*M *oxygen*

Ordinate: Molar extinction coefficient $10^{-3} \times M^{-1}$ cm.$^{-1}$
Abscissa: pH

FORMATION OF $HOC_6H_4NO_3^{-}\cdot$. The formation of $HOC_6H_4NO_3^{-}\cdot$ can be observed when e^{-}_{aq} are either converted with N_2O to OH radicals or scavenged with oxygen. The rate of formation of the anion radical $HOC_6H_4NO_3^{-}\cdot$ at 290 n.m. and the decrease in optical density at 400 n.m. caused by the destruction of the *p*-nitrophenol were recorded. It was found that the rate of formation of $HOC_6H_4NO_3^{-}\cdot$ followed a first order rate law. From the half-life of the exponential increase of the 290 n.m. absorption or decrease of the 400 n.m. absorption after a pulse of radiation, a rate constant, $k_4 = (3.8 \pm 0.6) \times 10^9 M^{-1}$ sec.$^{-1}$ was calculated for Reaction 4:

$$HO + HOC_6H_4NO_2 \rightarrow HOC_6H_4NO_3^{-}\cdot + H^+ \qquad (4)$$

DECAY OF $HOC_6H_4NO_3^{-}\cdot$. In N_2O-saturated neutral $5 \times 10^{-5}M$ *p*-nitrophenol solutions, all hydrated electrons are converted to OH radicals. When the small amounts of $HOC_6H_4NO_2^{-}\cdot$ caused by the reaction of H radicals ($G(H)$ being 0.6) are neglected, the anion radical $HOC_6H_4NO_3^{-}\cdot$ is the only transient present in the solution shortly after the pulse. The changes in optical transmission accompanying the disappearance of the anion radical $HOC_6H_4NO_3^{-}\cdot$ and formation of the products are shown in Figure 5. The kinetic analysis of the curves in Figure 5

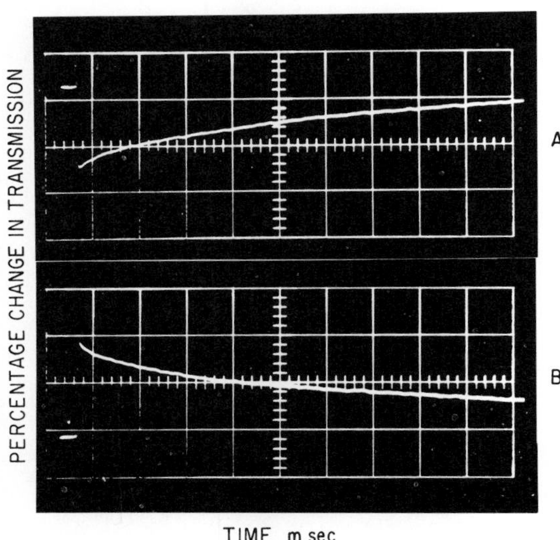

Figure 5. Typical traces used for kinetic analysis after a dose of approximately 500 rad

Deaerated and N_2O-saturated 5×10^{-5}M p-nitrophenol solution. Wavelength: A, 290 n.m.; B, 400 n.m.
Ordinate: Percentage change in transmission, 6.67% per large division.
Abscissa: 20 msec. per large division.

revealed a first order process. From the half-life of the exponential decay of the optical density at 290 n.m., the rate constant $k_6 = 14 \pm 2$ sec.$^{-1}$ was calculated. An identical rate constant was obtained from the half-life for the exponential increase of the optical density at 400 n.m.

Product analysis for aqueous *p*-nitrophenol solutions in which all e^-_{aq} were converted to OH radicals with N_2O showed that the *G*-value for the hydroxylated products equals about half the sum of $G(e^-_{aq})$ + $G(\mathrm{OH})$ (*20*). On this basis the following reaction was suggested:

NO_2 NO_2 NO_2

2 [ring] OH, H → [ring] + [ring] OH + H_2O **5**

OH OH OH

Both the steady state (*20*) and the pulse radiolysis results can be accounted for on the assumption that the primary OH radical addition product $HOC_6H_4NO_3^{-}\cdot$ undergoes the intramolecular rearrangement Reaction 6. It produces the OH benzene ring addition product

$$HOC_6H_4NO_3^{-}\cdot + H^+ \rightarrow \cdot HO(HO)C_6H_4NO_2 \qquad (6)$$

$\cdot HO(HO)C_6H_4NO_2$ and disproportionates *via* Reaction 5. This reaction scheme can explain the experimental results and this was checked by the Manchester University Atlas Computer. The decay of the anion radical $HOC_6H_4NO_3^{-}\cdot$ and the formation of products were used to obtain the value of k_5. Complete agreement between the kinetic analysis of computed and experimental data from Figure 5 was obtained for $k_5 = 1 \times 10^9 M^{-1}$ sec.$^{-1}$. This is a reasonable value compared with some other rate constants for the decay of monosubstituted hydroxycyclohexadienyl radicals which range from $4 \times 10^9 M^{-1}$ sec.$^{-1}$ to $16 \times 10^9 M^{-1}$ sec.$^{-1}$ (*8*).

REACTION OF $HOC_6H_4NO_3^{-}\cdot$ WITH O_2. In O_2-saturated $5 \times 10^{-5}M$ *p*-nitrophenol solution, the hydrated electrons are scavenged with oxygen and only the OH radicals react with *p*-nitrophenol. Under these conditions the optical absorption at 290 n.m. caused by $HOC_6H_4NO_3^{-}\cdot$, decays in a first order way, but 160 times faster than Reaction 6. From the half-life of the exponential decay of the 290 n.m. absorption after a pulse of radiation and the concentration of oxygen, a rate constant k_7 of $(1.7 \pm 0.2) \times 10^6 M^{-1}$ sec.$^{-1}$ was calculated for the reaction:

$$HOC_6H_4NO_3^{-}\cdot + O_2 \rightarrow \text{Products} \qquad (7)$$

An identical rate constant was obtained from the simultaneous increase of the optical density at 400 n.m.

PROTONATION OF $HOC_6H_4NO_3^{-}\cdot$. As shown in Figure 4-B the optical density caused by the anion radical $HOC_6H_4NO_3^{-}\cdot$ decreases with increasing acidity of the solution. This is attributed to the protonation of the anion radical $HOC_6H_4NO_3^{-}\cdot$. From the point of inflexion in Figure 4-B the pK for the Reaction 8 can be derived to be 5.3 ± 0.2.

$$HOC_6H_4NO_3H\cdot \rightleftarrows HOC_6H_4NO_3^{-}\cdot + H^+ \quad (8)$$

Conclusion

Rate constants and pK values for the following radiolytic processes in aqueous *p*-nitrophenol solutions were obtained:

Reaction	*Rate Constants*	*pK*
(1) $e^-_{aq} + HOC_6H_4NO_2 \rightarrow HOC_6H_4NO_2^{-}\cdot$	$(3.5 \pm 0.6) \times 10^{10} M^{-1}$ sec.$^{-1}$	——
(2) $HOC_6H_4NO_2^{-}\cdot + H^+ \rightleftarrows HOC_6H_4NO_2H^+$	——————	4.1 ± 0.2
(3) (a) $2HOC_6H_4NO_2^{-}\cdot \rightarrow$ PRODUCTS	7×10^6	——
(b) $2HOC_6H_4NO_2H\cdot \rightarrow HOC_6H_4NO + HOC_6H_4NO_2 + H_2O$	$6 \times 10^9 M^{-1}$ sec.$^{-1}$	——
(4) $HO + HOC_6H_4NO_2 \rightarrow HOC_6H_4NO_3^{-}\cdot + H^+$	$(3.8 \pm 0.6) \times 10^9 M^{-1}$ sec.$^{-1}$	
(5) $2\cdot HO(HO)C_6H_4NO_2 \rightarrow HOC_6H_4NO_2 + (HO)_2C_6H_4NO_2 + H_2O$	$1 \times 10^9 M^{-1}$ sec.$^{-1}$ (by computer analysis)	——
(6) $HOC_6H_4NO_3^{-}\cdot + H^+ \rightarrow \cdot HO(HO)C_6H_4NO_2$	14 ± 2 sec.$^{-1}$	——
(7) $HOC_6H_4NO_3^{-}\cdot + O_2 \rightarrow$ PRODUCTS	$(1.7 \pm 0.2) \times 10^6 M^{-1}$ sec.$^{-1}$	——
(8) $HOC_6H_4NO_3^{-}\cdot + H^+ \rightleftarrows HOC_6H_4NO_3H\cdot$	——————	5.3 ± 0.2

This study has demonstrated the usefulness of pulse radiolysis as a probe for the investigation of molecular re-arrangements of short lived intermediates such as the radical anion $HOC_6H_4NO_3^{-}\cdot$.

Literature Cited

(1) Adams, G. E., Boag, J. W., Current, J., Michael, B. D., "Pulse Radiolysis," p. 117, M. Ebert, J. P. Keene, A. J. Swallow, J. H. Baxendale, eds., Academic Press, London and New York, 1965.
(2) Allen, A. O., "The Radiation Chemistry of Water and Aqueous Solutions," pp. 47, 64, Van Nostrand, New York, Toronto, London, 1961.
(3) Anbar, M., Neta, P., *Intern. J. Appl. Radiation Isotopes* **16**, 227 (1965).
(4) Anbar, M., Meyerstein, D., Neta, P., *J. Phys. Chem.* **70**, 2660 (1966).

(5) Asmus, K. D., Wigger, A., Henglein, A., *Ber. Bunsenges. Physik Chem.* **70,** 862 (1966).
(6) Asmus, K. D., Cercek, B., Ebert, M., Henglein, A., Wigger, A., *Trans. Faraday Soc.* **63,** 2435 (1967).
(7) Cercek, B., *J. Phys. Chem.* **71,** 2354 (1967).
(8) Cercek, B., *J. Phys. Chem.* (in press).
(9) Cercek, B., Ebert, M., Gilbert, C. W., Swallow, A. J., "Pulse Radiolysis," p. 83, M. Ebert, J. P. Keene, A. J. Swallow, J. H. Baxendale, eds., Academic Press, London and New York, 1965.
(10) Corvaja, C., Farna, G., Vianello, E., *Electrochim. Acta* **11,** 919 (1966).
(11) Dainton, F. S., Paterson, D. B., *Proc. Roy. Soc. A* **267,** 443 (1962).
(12) Dorfman, L. M., Taub, I. A., Bühler, R. E., *J. Phys. Chem.* **36,** 305 (1962).
(13) Gordon, S., Hart, E. J., Matheson, M. S., Rabani, J., Thomas, J. K., *J. Am. Chem. Soc.* **85,** 1375 (1963).
(14) Grässlin, D., Merger, F., Schulte-Frohlinde, D., Vollart, O., *Z. Physik Chem. (Neue Folge)* **51,** 84 (1966).
(15) Hayon, E., *Trans. Faraday Soc.* **61,** 723 (1964).
(16) Hine, J., "Physical Organic Chemistry," p. 87, McGraw-Hill Book Co., Inc., New York, N. Y., 1962.
(17) Jaffe, H. H., Orchin, M., "Theory and Application of Ultraviolet Spectroscopy," p. 260, John Wiley and Sons Inc., New York, London, 1964.
(18) Keene, J. P., *J. Sci. Instr.* **41,** 493 (1964).
(19) Rabani, J., Mulac, W. A., Matheson, M. S., *J. Phys. Chem.* **69,** 53 (1965).
(20) Volkert, O., Termens, G., Schulte-Frohlinde, D., *Z. Physik. Chem. (Neue Folge)* **56,** 261 (1967).

RECEIVED January 2, 1968.

15

Pulse Radiolysis Studies. XIII. Rate Constants for the Reaction of Hydroxyl Radicals with Aromatic Compounds in Aqueous Solutions

P. NETA and LEON M. DORFMAN

The Ohio State University, Columbus, Ohio 43210

Absolute rate constants have been determined for the reaction of the hydroxyl radical with a variety of aromatic compounds in aqueous solution. The rate constants obtained are significantly higher than values previously reported. Rate constants for the reaction of the hydroxyl radical with methyl alcohol and ethyl alcohol have also been determined by competition kinetics using three of these absolute rate constants as reference values. Comparison of our results with the published values from competition kinetics suggests that the rate constants for the reaction of hydroxyl radicals with iodide ion and thiocyanate ion are significantly higher than reported in earlier work. The ultraviolet absorption bands of the various substituted hydroxycyclohexadienyl radicals formed have been observed.

Absolute rate constants for the reaction of hydroxyl radicals with aromatic compounds in aqueous solution have been determined in a number of pulse radiolysis investigations (*6, 10, 11, 15*). The rate constants were obtained directly from the formation curves of the hydroxycyclohexadienyl adduct free radical. Recent observations in this (*22*) and other laboratories (*6, 15, 18*) have shown that the cyclohexadienyl radical formed by H-atom addition has an ultraviolet absorption band which overlaps that of the hydroxycyclohexadienyl radical and is equally intense. The rate constants for the addition of hydrogen atoms to benzene and toluene (*18*), to phenol (*15*) and to benzoic acid (*16*) in water appear to be significantly lower than the rate constants for hydroxyl radical addition. It appeared worthwhile, therefore, to determine absolute rate constants for OH-addition for benzoate ions, benzene and a number of other aromatic compounds from the formation curves in systems in which the hydrogen atoms have been essentially eliminated or at least sharply reduced in concentration. Solutions containing a sufficient concentration of nitrous oxide to scavenge the hydrated electron and convert it to hydroxyl radical at pH 6 to 9 have been used for this purpose.

Relative reactivities of organic compounds toward hydroxyl radicals have also been determined by competition kinetics using carbonate ions (*1*), thiocyanate ions (*1, 2, 19*), and iodide ions (*21*) as the reference reactant. However, the values reported for carbonate differ by a factor of two (*1, 21, 23*) and the values for both iodide and thiocyanate have been questioned (*7, 12*) since there is a possibility that diiodide formation rather than iodine atom formation may be rate determining (*12*) and the analogous possibility has been suggested (*7*) for thiocyanate. There appears to be a need for further work to establish accurate values for a number of rate constants which may serve as reference values.

Relative reactivities of substituted benzenes and benzoate ions toward hydroxyl radicals have been correlated (*4*) with Hammett's equation. In the present work such a correlation has also been carried out using absolute rather than relative values.

In the course of this work the absorption spectra for the various substituted hydroxycyclohexadienyl radicals have been determined.

Experimental

The detailed experimental technique, using a Varian V-7715A linear accelerator has been outlined (*13*). 3.5 to 4 Mev. electrons were used with pulse duration of 50 to 100 nsec. during most of the work, although occasionally pulses as long as 0.5 μsec. were used. The pulse current was in the range 310 to 330 ma. The dose with the 50 nsec. pulse at maximum current is 3×10^{16} e.v./gram as determined with the modified Fricke dosimeter previously discussed (*9*). Taking $G_{OH} + G_{e^-_{aq}} = 5.2$ molecule/100 e.v., this gives an initial OH concentration of $3 \times 10^{-6}M$. The detection system used was for the most part as described (*13*), but a few runs in cases which exhibited higher rate constants were done with a nanosecond detection system (*20*) similar to that designated by Hunt and Thomas (*14*). The irradiation cell was 2 cm. long, using a double pass of the analyzing light beam and 0.8 cm. deep in the direction of the electron beam.

The concentration range of the aromatic compound in each case was at least threefold and at least four runs were done at each concentration. Depending upon the rate constant the concentrations varied from 5×10^{-5} to $5 \times 10^{-4}M$. The carboxylic acids were neutralized with sodium hydroxide to pH 6 to 8, and some were also irradiated at pH 9.4 in borax buffered solution.

In the case of volatile compounds of low solubility such as benzene and anisole, the solution was made up as follows. The stock solution was made up by pipetting the solute into a large volumetric flask in which the remaining gaseous volume was very small compared with the liquid volume. The water was first deaerated by bubbling N_2O through it and was thus also saturated with N_2O at atmospheric pressure. The stock solution was then pipetted in and the final reaction solution transferred to the cell using a large syringe. It would appear that any non-random uncertainty in the solute concentrations would tend to give a rate constant on the low side.

The nitrous oxide was passed through two successive alkaline pyrogallol solutions and finally through triply distilled water. The aromatic compounds were either Baker Analyzed reagents or Baker Grade reagents.

Results and Discussion

Under our experimental conditions the hydrated electron is effectively scavenged by nitrous oxide in competition with the reactions with hydrogen ion and with the aromatic molecule:

$$e^-_{aq} + N_2O = N_2O^- \quad (1)$$

At one atmosphere pressure the N_2O concentration exceeds $10^{-2}M$ and $k_1[N_2O]$ is thus much greater than $k_{e^-_{aq}+H}$ $[H^+]$ at pH 6 to 9 and $k_{e^-_{aq}+\text{aromatic}}$ [aromatic] at the solute concentrations used. There is ample evidence (*3, 13, 17*) that the lifetime of N_2O^- is very short and that OH is rapidly formed (*17*) either through O^- formation followed by protonation involving water or by direct protonation of the nitrous oxide anion involving water. The yield of hydroxyl radical is approximately doubled, and the yield of hydrogen atom is thus about one-tenth the total hydroxyl radical yield under these conditions. The system is then very nearly a one-radical system in which the hydroxycyclohexadienyl radical is the observed species formed in the reaction:

$$OH + C_6H_5COO^- = (OH)C_6H_5COO^- \quad (2)$$

The nitrous oxide does not interfere with the hydroxyl radical kinetics as is shown in this and earlier work (*17*).

Absorption Spectra. The absorption spectra of the various hydroxycyclohexadienyl radicals, in accord with earlier work (*6, 8, 10, 11, 15*), show a strong band in the ultraviolet. The absorption bands for eleven different compounds have been determined in this investigation and are shown in Figure 1. The wavelength corresponding to the maximum for each band is also given in Table I. The contribution of the hydrogen atom adduct to these absorption bands is very small, and its effect may be neglected in view of the low yield of hydrogen atoms although the hydrogen adduct spectrum is similar in its wavelength maximum as well as extinction coefficient (*6, 15, 22*). Calculation of the bathochromic shifts showed a fair agreement with the results of Chutny (*8*).

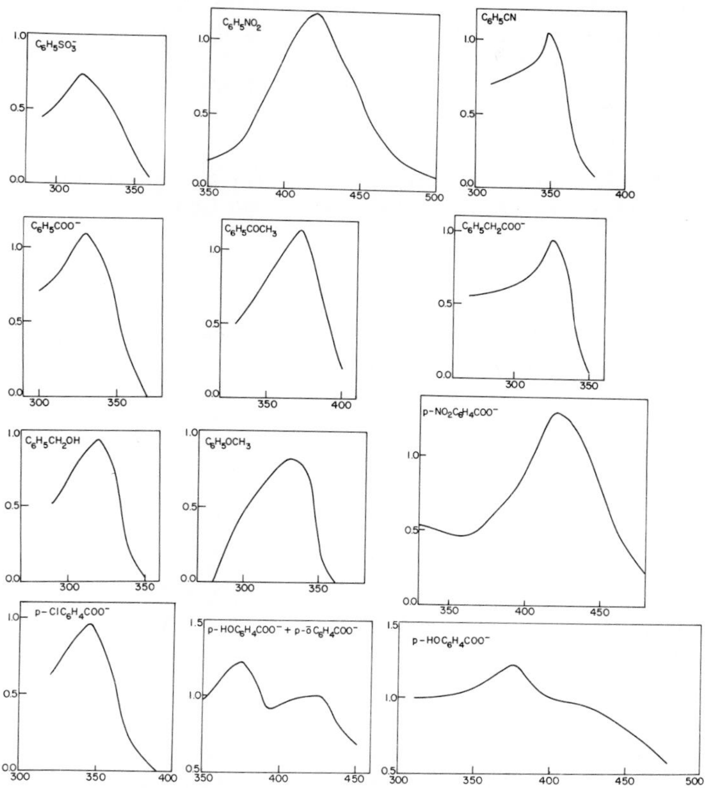

Figure 1. Ultraviolet absorption bands of various hydroxycyclohexadienyl radicals in aqueous solution containing nitrous oxide at neutral pH. The ordinate gives the relative optical density and the abscissa the wavelength in n.m.

Absolute Rate Constants. Absolute rate constants for the hydroxyl radical reactions, as determined from the formation curves of the hydroxycyclohexadienyl radicals, are summarized in Table I. Detailed data for benzoate ion are shown in Table II. In all cases the rate curves fit closely to a first order rate law. A detailed examination of this case seems warranted not only as an example of the data, but because of the possible use of this reaction as a reference reaction in competition kinetics.

As mentioned in the experimental section, the initial OH concentration with the 50 nsec. pulse is $3 \times 10^{-6}M$. Thus, the ratio $[OH]_0/[C_6H_5COO^-]$ is 0.03 and 0.06 for the 50 nsec. and 100 nsec. pulse respectively at $1 \times 10^{-4}M$ benzoate ion, the lowest concentration used. Since $k_{OH+OH} = 1.2 \times 10^{10}\ M^{-1}\ sec.^{-1}$ (*17*), the initial rate for OH recombination is 0.07 and 0.13 of the OH-addition rate for this initial OH-concentration, and falls to considerably less over the region of rate curve analysis. The effect on the observed rate constant is thus on the order of 1 to 2% for the lowest benzoate concentration.

Table I. Absolute Rate Constants for the Reactions of Hydroxyl Radical with Aromatic Compounds

Compound	*Wavelength Maximum of OH-Adduct Radical (nm.)*	*pH*	*Absolute Rate Constant*[c] $(M^{-1}\ sec.^{-1} \times 10^{-9})$	$\log \frac{k_{OH+PhX}}{k_{OH+PhH}}$
$C_6H_5NO_2$	410	7	3.2 ± 0.4	−0.39
$C_6H_5SO_3^-$	315	7	4.7 ± 0.6	−0.22
C_6H_5CN	348	7	4.9 ± 0.6	−0.20
C_6H_5COOH[a]	347	3	4.3 ± 0.8	−0.26
$C_6H_5COO^-$	330	6–9.4	6.0 ± 0.7	−0.11
$C_6H_5COCH_3$	372	7	6.5 ± 0.7	−0.08
$C_6H_5CH_2COO^-$	325	6–8	7.9 ± 1.1	−0.005
C_6H_6	313	7	7.8 ± 1.1	0.00
$C_6H_5CH_2OH$	320	7	8.4 ± 1.2	0.03
$C_6H_5OCH_3$	330	7	12 ± 3	0.19
C_6H_5OH[b]	330	7.4–7.7	14 ± 3	0.25
$C_6H_5COO^-$	330	6–9.4	6.0 ± 0.7	0.00
p-$NO_2C_6H_4COO^-$	420	6–9.4	2.6 ± 0.4	−0.36
p-$ClC_6H_4COO^-$	345	6–9.4	5.0 ± 0.8	−0.08
p-$OHC_6H_4COO^-$	375	7	9 ± 2	−0.17
p-$^-OC_6H_4COO^-$	425	9.4	—	—

[a] Taken from Ref. 22.
[b] Taken from Ref. 15.
[c] The correction for the effect upon the value for the OH-addition rate constant (as determined graphically) of the two reactions OH + aromatic and OH + OH has been estimated using an Electronic Associates Incorporated, Model TR-20 analog computer, and is included in this table. It ranges from +10% to +8% with decreasing concentration of the aromatic compound, the correction for OH + OH ranging from 0 to −2%.

No pH effect was found for the reaction with benzoate ion in the region of pH 6–9.4, as may be seen in Table II. This was also found to be the case for the other compounds listed. It should be noted that the rate constants for benzoic acid (*22*) and benzoate ion show a slight difference. In the case of benzoate ion the same rate constant was obtained when chloroform (at a concentration five times that of benzoate) was used as a scavenger for the hydrated electron instead of nitrous oxide. This demonstrates that the presence of N_2O has no effect upon the rate constant as has been shown in another reaction investigated by Rabani and Matheson (*17*).

Table II. Absolute Rate Constant for the Reaction of Hydroxyl Radicals with Benzoate Ion

Benzoate Ion Concentration ($M \times 10^4$)	*Scavenger*	*pH*	*Rate Constant* (M^{-1} $sec.^{-1} \times 10^{-9}$)
1.0	N_2O (1 atm.)	9.4	6.6
1.0	N_2O	6	6.9
2.0	N_2O	6	7.2
2.0	N_2O	9.4	6.6
2.0	$CHCl_3$ (1m*M*)	6	6.6
2.5	N_2O	6	5.2
2.5	N_2O	9.4	6.1
3.0	N_2O	6	6.5
3.0	N_2O	9.4	5.9
3.0	$CHCl_3$ (1.5m*M*)	6	5.8
4.0	N_2O	6	5.3
5.0	N_2O	6	4.8
5.0	N_2O	9.4	5.4
5.0	$CHCl_3$ (2.5m*M*)	6	5.6
average		6–9.4	6.0 ± 0.7

The absolute rate constants determined in this investigation are significantly higher (*see* Reference 5 for comparison) than those determined by competition kinetics with iodide ion (*21*) and thiocyanate ion (*2*) as well as those determined absolutely by formation kinetics (*10, 11*). In the latter case this may be understood from the fact that the addition of hydrogen atoms to the aromatic ring, as has been shown for benzene and toluene (*18*) and benzoic acid (*16*) has a much lower rate constant than the addition of hydroxyl radicals. Since the H-adduct free radical has a similar absorption, and is formed in comparable amount in acidic solution (*11*) in the absence of an electron scavenger, its observation concurrently with the OH-adduct would give an apparent lower rate constant. Our value for nitrobenzene is, however, lower than the recent value of Asmus, *et al.* (*6*). With respect to results from competition kinetics, the difference shown in the results of this investigation indicates that there may still be some uncertainty in the value of the rate constants of the reference reactions used.

A plot of log $\frac{k_{OH+PhX}}{k_{OH+PhH}}$ from these

absolute values for monosubstituted benzene and *p*-substituted benzoate ions as well as the value for phenol (*15*) and for benzoic acid (*22*) against the Hammett σ values is shown in Figure 2. This correlation has been discussed (*4*). The ρ value obtained from the slope is -0.5, in good agreement with th evalue -0.4 previously obtained (*4*). The contribution of the aliphatic side chain to the overall rate appears to be very small, comparing $k_{OH+aromatic}$ with $k_{OH+methyl\ alcohol}$, $k_{OH+acetate}$ or $k_{OH+acetone}$ (*5*).

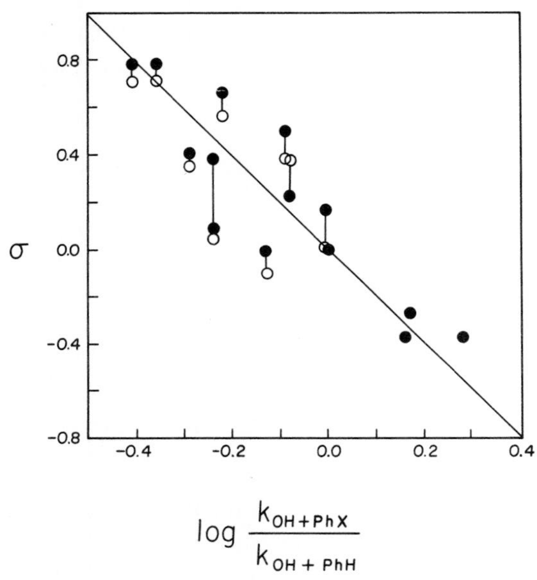

Figure 2. Plot of correlation with Hammett's equation

σpara, ●, and σmeta, ○, are used as discussed in Ref. 4

Competition Kinetics. Since the foregoing absolute rate constants have been determined independently, and appear to be accurate values, it is of interest to carry out competition kinetics with some reactants for which relative rate constants have been determined by competition kinetics with iodide ion and thiocyanate ion as the reference reactants. In this way, some assessment may be made of the validity of the existing values for the rate constants of the reactions:

$$OH + I^- = OH^- + I \qquad (3)$$

and

$$OH + SCN^- = OH^- + SCN \qquad (4)$$

Rate constants for methanol and ethyl alcohol relative to those for benzoate ion, phenylacetate ion and *p*-nitrobenzoate ion are shown in Table III. Each value in the table consists of experiments at five separate concentration ratios. The random uncertainty in each value is less than ±10%. In determining these rate constants from optical density ratios it was necessary to make a small correction for the contribution to the optical density by the H-adduct free radical. The molar extinction coefficients at 340–350 mμ for the H-adduct and OH-adduct are similar for benzoic acid (*22*) and were assumed to be comparable for the other two aromatic ions in the table. The correction is necessary since the rate constants for the reaction of hydrogen atoms with the alcohols used are two orders of magnitude lower than the rate constants for hydrogen atom addition to the aromatic ring, while the analogous hydroxyl rate constants are roughly comparable.

The data in Table III show excellent self-consistency for the three aromatic rate constants, the individual values of which are nevertheless quite different. Comparison with rate constants determined by iodide ion competition kinetics (*21*) indicates that the absolute values determined in this work are higher for benzene, ethyl alcohol, and methyl alcohol. Comparison with the rate constants determined by thiocyanate ion competition kinetics (*1, 2*) indicates that our absolute values are higher for benzene, benzoate ion, methyl alcohol and ethyl alcohol. This comparison indicates that the actual rate constants for Reactions 3 and 4 may be higher than the values which have been determined (*1, 2, 21*) from the formation curves of the optically absorbing product by as much as a factor of 1.6 to 2.3 in the former case and 1.7 in the latter case. That is, the true values may be nearer $k_3 \cong 2 \times 10^{10}$ and $k_4 = 1.2 \times 10^{10}$ M^{-1} sec.$^{-1}$ at 25°C. This same qualitative conclusion for the case of thiocyanate has recently been reached by a different method by Baxendale and Stott (*7*) whose suggested value for k_4 is approximately $2 \times 10^{10} M^{-1}$ sec.$^{-1}$. The difficulties in the direct absolute determination lie in the complexities of the kinetics and hence in the interpretation of the formation rate curves.

Table III. Rate Constants for the Reaction of Hydroxyl Radicals with Methanol and Ethyl Alcohol Determined by Competition Kinetics

Reference Aromatic Compound	k_{OH+CH_3OH} $(\times 10^{-8} M^{-1}$ *sec.*$^{-1})$	$k_{OH+C_2H_5OH}$ $(\times 10^{-8} M^{-1}$ *sec.*$^{-1})$
$C_6H_5COO^-$	8.5	18.5
$C_6H_5CH_2COO^-$	8.3	18.3
p-$NO_2C_6H_4COO^-$	8.4	18.1
average	8.4 ± 1	18.3 ± 2

Acknowledgment

This report is based upon work supported by the U.S. Atomic Energy Commission. The assistance obtained from the Graduate School of the Ohio State University in supporting P. N. as a visiting scientist under the University Postdoctoral Program is gratefully acknowledged. We are indebted to E. G. Wendell for his operation and maintenance of the linear accelerator and the electronic detection equipment. We are grateful to C. J. Geankoplis for his helpful advice concerning the use of the EAI analog computer.

Literature Cited

(1) Adams, G. E., Boag, J. W., Michael, B. D., *Trans. Faraday Soc.* **61,** 1417 (1965).
(2) Adams, G. E., Boag, J. W., Currat, J., Michael, B. D., "Pulse Radiolysis," p. 131, Baxendale, Ebert, Keene, Swallow, eds., Academic Press, New York, N. Y., 1965.
(3) Adams, G. E., Boag, J. W., Michael, B. D., *Proc. Royal Soc. (London)* **A289,** 321 (1966).
(4) Anbar, M. Meyerstein, D., Neta, P., *J. Phys. Chem.* **70,** 2660 (1966).
(5) Anbar, M., Neta, P., *Intern. J. Appl. Radiation Isotopes* **18,** 493 (1967).
(6) Asmus, K. D., Cercek, B., Ebert M., Henglein, A., Wigger, A., *Trans. Faraday Soc.* **63,** 2435 (1967).
(7) Baxendale, J. H., Stott, D. A., *Chem. Commun.* ***1967,*** 699.
(8) Chutny, B., *Nature* **213,** 593 (1967).
(9) Dorfman, L. M., Taub, I. A., *J. Am. Chem. Soc.* **85,** 2370 (1963).
(10) Dorfman, L. M., Taub, I. A., Buhler, R. E., *J. Chem. Phys.* **36,** 3051 (1962).
(11) Dorfman, L. M., Taub, I. A., Harter, D. A., *J. Chem. Phys.* **41,** 2954 (1964).
(12) Dorfman, L. M., Firestone, R. F., *Ann. Rev. Phys. Chem.* **18,** 177 (1967).
(13) Felix, W. D., Gall, B. L., Dorfman, L. M., *J. Phys. Chem.* **71,** 384 (1967).
(14) Hunt, J. W., Thomas, J. K., *Radiation Res.* **32,** 149 (1967).
(15) Land, E. J., Ebert, M., *Trans. Faraday Soc.* **63,** 1181 (1967).
(16) Neta, P., Dorfman, L. M. (to be published).
(17) Rabani, J., Matheson, M. S., *J. Phys. Chem.* **70,** 761 (1966).
(18) Sauer, M. C., Jr., Ward, B., *J. Phys. Chem.* **71,** 3971 (1967).
(19) Scholes, G., Shaw, P., Willson, R. L., Ebert M., "Pulse Radiolysis," p. 151, Baxendale, Ebert, Keene, Swallow, eds., Academic Press, New York, N. Y., 1965.
(20) Shank, N., Dorfman, L. M. (to be published).
(21) Thomas, J. K., *Trans. Faraday Soc.* **61,** 702 (1965).
(22) Wander, R., Neta, P., Dorfman, L. M., *J. Phys. Chem.* **72** (in press).
(23) Weeks, J. L., Rabani, J., *J. Phys. Chem.* **70,** 2100 (1966).

RECEIVED January 2, 1968.

16

Pulse Radiolysis Studies of Deaerated Aqueous Salicylate Solutions

C. B. AMPHLETT

Chemistry Division, A.E.R.E., Harwell, Berkshire, England

G. E. ADAMS and B. D. MICHAEL

Research Unit In Radiobiology, B.E.C.C., Mount Vernon Hospital, Northwood, Middlesex, England

Salicylate ion forms transient adducts with H atoms, OH radicals and e^-_{aq} when deaerated solutions are irradiated with a pulse of 1.8 Mev. electrons. The absorption band due to the electron adduct is centered on 4400 A., while the H and OH adducts absorb between 3500 and 4000 A. The rates of formation of the adducts, determined directly and by competitive methods, are k(H + salicylate) = 1.4×10^9, k(OH + salicylate) = 1.2×10^{10} and k(e^-_{aq} + salicylate) $\sim 10^{10}$ liter mole^{-1} sec.$^{-1}$. The electron adduct is rapidly protonated. All three adducts disappear principally by second-order reactions with half-lives which decrease markedly in acid solution compared with their values in neutral solution.

Irradiation of aqueous solutions of aromatic solutes is believed to lead initially to adding H atoms and OH radicals to the ring to form cyclohexadienyl radicals, which then react further to form the observed products (*17, 21, 34*). The hydrated electron can also react to form transient negatively-charged entities (*8, 29, 40*) which may either be protonated by reaction with the solvent molecules (*8, 40, 41*) or else dissociate to form a stable anion and a substituted phenyl radical (*8*). In some systems (*12, 41*) the lifetime of the electron adduct is sufficient for its detection by pulse radiolysis techniques, but in many cases only the protonated species is seen. The rates of reaction of H atoms, OH radicals and hydrated electrons with aromatic solutes vary widely, but some success has been achieved (*8, 10, 29, 40*) in correlating these rates with accepted theories of aromatic reactivity.

Aromatic carboxylic acids have not been studied in detail. They are interesting in that they undergo decarboxylation as well as hydroxylation, hydrogenation, and dimerization, although the effects of structure and substituents upon decarboxylation are unknown. Steady-state studies of dilute benzoic acid solutions (*22*) in aerated solutions at pH 4 or 9 showed that G(-PhCOOH) = 2.6 and $G(CO_2)$ = 0.73; all three isomeric hydroxyacids were formed with G values (pH unspecified) of 0.74, 0.42, and 0.33 for the ortho, meta and para derivatives respectively. Aerated solutions of calcium benzoate at pH 6 gave (*13*) G(-benzoate) = 2.05, G(ortho) = 0.67, G(meta) = G(para) = 0.37, $G(H_2O_2)$ = 2.30, G(PhOH) = 0.05. In separate experiments with 300 Kev. x-rays at pH 0.4 $G(CO_2)$ = 0.43 and $G(H_2)$ = 0.62 in degassed 1 m*M* solutions, and $G(CO_2)$ = 0.68 in the presence of O_2; these results are in reasonable agreement with those of Downes (*22*). Matthews and Sangster (*31*) found that $G(CO_2)$ = 0.9 − 1.0 in γ-irradiated solutions of benzoate at pH 3 to 11, although some of this was formed in relatively slow post-irradiation reactions. Although they did not measure any other products arising from the solute, they showed that the sum of their CO_2 yields and of the yields of hydroxy-acids reported by Downes and by Armstrong *et al.* were approximately equal to G(OH). Aerated aqueous benzoate solutions were studied over a wide concentration range by Loeff and Swallow (*30*), who found that, while the hydroxy-acids were formed solely by an indirect mechanism, CO_2 appeared to arise *via* both indirect and direct processes. They also observed the formation of a dialdehyde ($G \sim 0.5$), which has not been reported by other workers; its formation resembles that of mucondialdehyde (*38*) in the radiolysis of aerated benzene solutions. The formation of dimeric products was reported by Sakumoto and Tsuchihashi (*35*), who found that in aerated solutions benzoic acid produced salicylate, but that in the absence of oxygen the salicylate yield was reduced and diphenylcarboxylic acids were formed instead. This behavior parallels the formation of phenol and diphenyl in aerated and degassed solutions of benzene, respectively. Unfortunately there have been no studies of benzoate solutions in which all the products have been unambiguously identified.

Sangster (*36*) has investigated the transient spectra observed following the pulse radiolysis of degassed aqueous benzoate solutions at pH 12.8. A band at 3280 A. was ascribed to the OH radical adduct and two bands at 3220 and 4440 A. to the protonated form of the electron adduct. These wavelengths slightly differ from those given by Chutny (*20*) for the primary bands, *viz.* OH-adduct 3450 A., H-adduct 3450 A., electron adduct 3130 A., but this may arise in part from differences in pH.

There is evidence from other systems (*15*) that the spectrum of the protonated form of an electron adduct may differ significantly from that of an H atom adduct.

Little work has been reported on salicylate solutions; Downes (*22*) found $G(CO_2) = 1.53$ in aerated alkaline solutions, and reported the formation of 2,3- and 2,5-dihydroxybenzoic acids. In a reference (*30*) to unpublished work by Capellos and Swallow, all three isomeric hydroxybenzoic acids were reported to undergo further hydroxylation; salicylic acid gave the 2,3-, 2,4- and 2,5-dihydroxybenzoic acids. More detailed studies (*37*) have indicated that in deaerated solutions of salicylate at pH 6.3 there is no detectable hydroxylation, the products being almost exclusively CO_2 and dihydroxydiphenyl with the simple stoichiometry G(-salicylate) $= G(CO_2) = 1.6 = 2G$(dihydroxydiphenyl). In both acid and alkaline solutions a wider range of products was found, including dihydroxybenzoic acids, benzoic acid, phenol and catechol. The formation of catechol from salicylic acid has also been reported by Matthews and Sangster (*31*).

Radiolytic decarboxylation has been discussed by Anbar *et al.* (*9*), who consider that the enhanced reactivity of certain carboxylate anions towards OH radicals may be owing to the additional pathway provided by electron transfer, *viz.*

$$R.COO^- + OH \rightarrow OH^- + R.COO\cdot \rightarrow OH^- + R\cdot + CO_2$$

This sequence of reactions resembles the production of CO_2 and hydrocarbons when carboxylate ions are discharged at an anode, as in the Kolbe synthesis. Certain acids such as acetic (*23, 24*) give low yields of CO_2 on irradiation, and tend to form H_2 plus dibasic acids, while radiation-induced carboxylation is observed when CO_2-saturated aqueous solutions of some organic compounds are irradiated (*25, 26, 33*). Appreciable yields of CO_2 are observed either when the resulting radical R is resonance-stabilized or when the alternative reaction is unlikely for steric reasons; acids possessing no C–H groupings—*e.g.*, tetrahydroxysuccinic acid—are very reactive towards OH radicals.

Brimacombe and Milner (*19*) found that the liquid phase products from the γ-radiolysis of aqueous mandelic acid solutions could be explained on the basis of the formation of the radicals $Ph\dot{C}(OH)COOH$ and $Ph\dot{C}HOH$, the latter presumably arising from the decarboxylation of the former; unfortunately CO_2 production was not studied. Norman and Pritchett have studied decarboxylation in more detail (*32*), using the reagent Ti^{3+}/H_2O_2 as a source of OH radicals to oxidize substituted benzene derivatives and examining transient ESR spectra in a fast flow system. Depending upon the pH, oxidation gave either substituted cyclohexadienyl radicals by OH radical addition to the ring or radicals formed by loss of a side-chain grouping, which was COOH in the carboxylic acids. For example, in $>10^{-2}M$ H_2SO_4 phenylacetic acid gave only $PhCH_2\cdot$ radicals, with no trace of $Ph\dot{C}HCOOH$, while at lower acidities the ESR spectrum was attributed to OH radical adducts such as

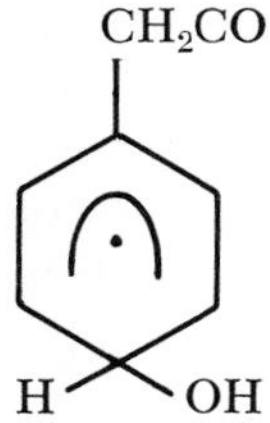

CH_2COOH

H OH

These authors postulate that even in the stronger acid solutions the initial product is the OH adduct. This then undergoes acid-catalyzed heterolytic bond fission in which the significant step is the loss of OH^- from the ring, initiated by an electron switch from the side-chain, leading ultimately to a resonance-stabilized radical—*e.g.*,

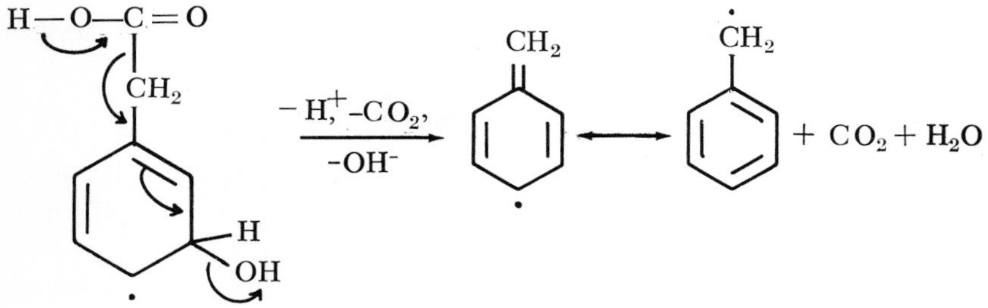

H—O—C=O CH_2 H OH $\xrightarrow[-OH^-]{-H^+, -CO_2,}$ CH_2 $\dot{C}H_2$ $+ CO_2 + H_2O$

Meta-Adduct

Similar elimination reactions involving loss of water only have been postulated for other aromatic solutes such as phenol (*6*), hydroquinone (*5*), phenylhydroxylamine (*43*), and *p*-nitrophenol (*27*).

The present work was designed to study the initial stages of the reaction in deaerated salicylate solutions by pulse radiolysis techniques, as an aid to unravelling some of the complexities of the steady-state radiolysis. A longer-term aim is to investigate the effect of substituents, particularly OH groups in different positions, on the decarboxylation reactions.

Experimental Details

Details of the accelerator, the procedure for irradiation, and the methods used to prepare and degas solutions, are described elsewhere

(2, 28). Irradiations were carried out with single 0.2 μsec. pulses of 1.8 Mev. electrons, the dose per pulse being varied over the range 0.15–2 krad. Variations between individual pulses, which rarely exceeded a few per cent, were corrected by measuring the charge collected on a grounded plate (2), calibrated against a thiocyanate dosimetric solution (4) using a value of $\epsilon(CNS)_2^- = 7.1 \times 10^3 M^{-1}$ cm.$^{-1}$ at 5000 A.

Salicylic acid and sodium salicylate were recrystallized from triply-distilled water. The absorption spectrum of sodium salicylate solution, measured on a Hilger Uvispek spectrophotometer, gave $\lambda_{max} = 2950$ A. and $\epsilon_{max} = 3560 \pm 10 M^{-1}$ cm.$^{-1}$, compared with literature values (39) of 2960 A. and $3510 M^{-1}$ cm.$^{-1}$; salicylic acid gave an identical spectrum.

Results

Transient Spectra. Three distinct spectral regions are distinguishable in neutral (pH 6.3), N_2-saturated 1 m*M* salicylate solutions (Figure 1), *viz.*

(1) a broad band of relatively low intensity centered around 5800 A.;

(2) an intense absorption between 4200 and 5000 A., $\lambda_{max} \sim 4400$ A., with some structure;

(3) a fairly intense absorption extending from $\sim$ 4000 A. to shorter wavelengths, ultimately merging with the longer wavelength band of the salicylate ion itself.

In neutral N_2O-saturated solutions or N_2-saturated solutions at pH 2 the first of these regions shows a relatively unchanged spectrum, the second practically disappears, and the third shows an enhanced absorption (Figure 1). This suggests that the band centered on 4400 A. is attributable to an electron adduct, and that the spectrum below 4000 A. is caused by both OH radical and H atom adducts. Since the spectra in N_2O-saturated and in acid solutions are not identical the OH and H adduct spectra must be different. The broad, low-intensity band at longer wavelengths results presumably from all three adducts (H, OH, e^-_{aq}) with similar spectra; it has not been investigated further.

Careful examination of the spectra below 4000 A. shows (a) that the enhancement of optical density in acid relative to neutral solution is greater than that produced when N_2O is added to a neutral solution, and (b) that the absorption maximum is shifted towards longer wavelengths in the former case. This suggests that the H atom adduct is more intensely absorbing than that of the OH radical adduct, with the absorption maximum of the former at a slightly longer wavelength. Further resolution was attempted by taking difference spectra between pairs of the following solutions:

A. 1 m*M* salicylate, N_2, pH 2

B. 1 m*M* salicylate, N_2, pH 6.3

C. 1 mM salicylate, N_2O, pH 6.3

Representing the primary yields by g_e, g_H and g_{OH}, and the extinction coefficients of the adducts at a given wavelength by ϵ_e, ϵ_H and ϵ_{OH}, we have the following relationships between the observed optical densities per unit path length (D/1):

$$D_{A/1} = g_{OH}\epsilon_{OH} + (g_H + g_e)\epsilon_H$$

$$D_{B/1} = g_{OH}\epsilon_{OH} + g_H\epsilon_H + g_e\epsilon_e$$

$$D_{C/1} = (g_{OH} + g_e)\epsilon_{OH} + g_H\epsilon_H$$

These relationships assume that (a) the intermediates e^-_{aq}, H and OH are removed by the solute with equal efficiency over this pH range, (b) the primary yields g_H and g_{OH} are independent of pH over this range, and (c) there is no significant change in transient spectra because of pH alone.

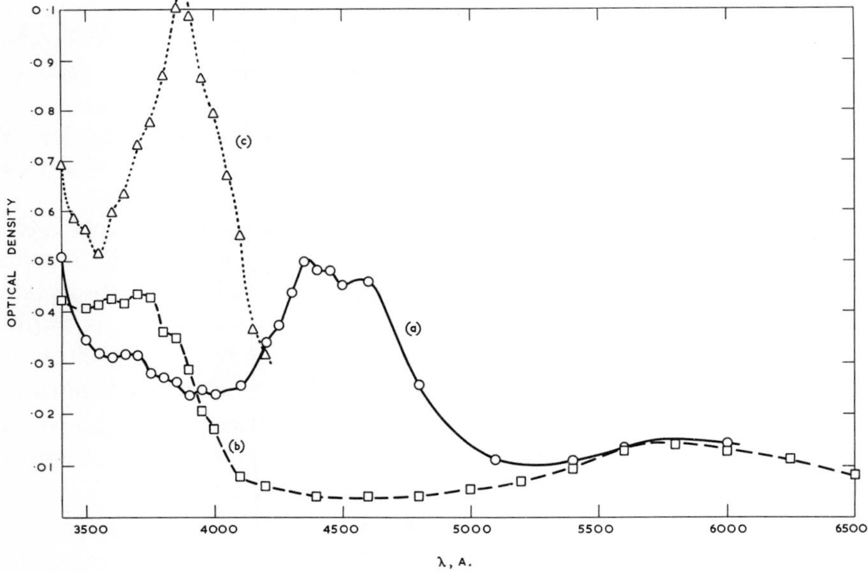

Figure 1. Transient spectra in 1 mM. *salicylate solutions after a single 0.2 μsec. pulse*

(a) N_2-saturated, pH 6.3
(b) N_2O-saturated, pH 6.3
(c) N_2-saturated, pH 2

The first assumption is satisfied by data on the concentration dependence of the transient spectra; changes in the primary yields between pH 2 and 4 will affect the absolute values of extinction coefficients, but should not alter the general validity of the conclusions. There are at present no data which would enable the third assumption to be tested. An overriding assumption which is also made, which can not be proved at this stage but which is probably justified, is that the whole of the primary product yield gives adducts whose extinction is measured. If this were not so, and if the proportion of primary product yield reacting to form the adduct varies with pH, correction terms would be required in the above relationships.

Difference spectra (Figure 2) were obtained as follows:

$$(D_A - D_B)/1 = g_e(\epsilon_H - \epsilon_e)$$

$$(D_C - D_B)/1 = g_e(\epsilon_{OH} - \epsilon_e)$$

$$(D_A - D_C)/1 = g_e(\epsilon_H - \epsilon_{OH})$$

Since the intensity of the electron adduct band decreases rapidly below 4000 A. the first two spectra approximate to those of the H atom and OH radical adducts, while the third represents the difference between them. The qualitative conclusions drawn from visual examination of the gross spectra are confirmed; the H atom adduct spectrum reaches a peak at ~3900 A. compared with ~3600–3800 A. for the much broader, less intense OH radical adduct spectrum, while the negative values of $g_e(\epsilon_{OH} - \epsilon_e)$ above 3900 A. suggest that the electron adduct spectrum extends a little below 4000 A., although its intensity is much less than that of the H atom adduct. From the measured dose in the pulse, calibrated against thiocyanate, and assuming the primary yields to be $g(OH) = 2.9$, $g(H) = 0.6$, $g(e^-_{aq}) = 2.3$, we calculate the following approximate values for the extinction coefficients of the transients:

$$\epsilon_{OH}^{3750} = 950, \ \epsilon_H^{3900} = 4900, \text{ and } \epsilon_e^{4400} = 4000 M^{-1} \text{ cm.}^{-1}.$$

If we assume that the observed optical density at 5800 A. is caused by all three transients, with a combined yield of $G = 5.8$, then $\epsilon^{5800} \sim 430 M^{-1}$ cm.$^{-1}$.

When the spectrum of 1 m*M* salicylate in N_2-saturated solution at pH 2 is compared with that of N_2-saturated 1 m*M* salicylic acid at pH 3.5 (Figure 3) a further fact emerges. In both solutions the electron adduct band is absent and the spectrum below 4000 A. is enhanced in intensity. If we take $k(e^-_{aq} + H_3O^+) = 2.3 \times 10^{10}$ liter mole^{-1} sec.$^{-1}$ (*42*) and $k(e^-_{aq}$ + salicylate) ~10^{10} liter mole^{-1} sec.$^{-1}$ (*see* below), then the relative rates of the reaction of e^-_{aq} with salicylate and with H_3O^+ will be 0.05:1 and 1.6:1 at pH 2 and pH 3.5 respectively. Thus, while we would not expect to observe the electron adduct at pH 2, its absorption should only be reduced by ~35% at pH 3.5 if the only reaction leading to its non-appearance is the removal of e^-_{aq} by reaction with H_3O^+ ions. We conclude therefore that the electron adduct is readily protonated to give the conjugate acid, as seen in several other systems including benzoate (*36*), nitrobenzene (*15, 16*), nitrosobenzene (*14*), and some keto-compounds (*1*). Comparison of the spectra at pH 2 and 3.5 suggests that the protonated form of the electron adduct formed at the latter pH is not identical with the H atom adduct formed at pH 2; a similar difference has been reported in the case of nitrobenzene (*15*).

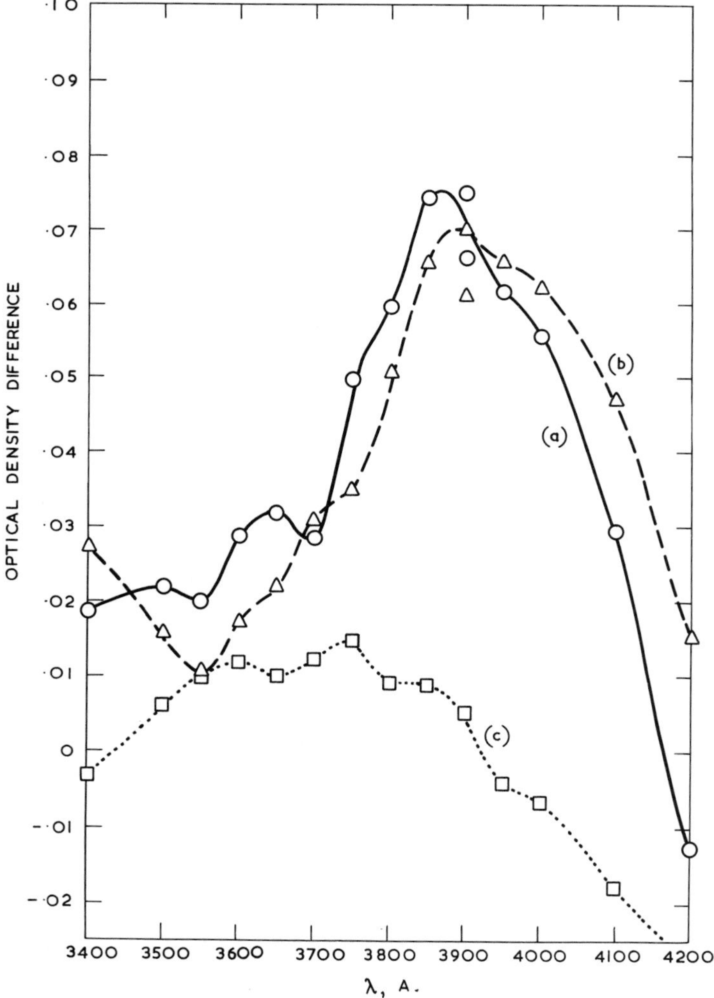

Figure 2. Difference spectra for transients in 1 mM. *salicylate solutions after a single 0.2 μsec. pulse*

(a) [S–*H*] – [S–*e*⁻]
(b) [S–*H*] – [S–*OH*]
(c) [S–*OH*] – [S–*e*⁻]

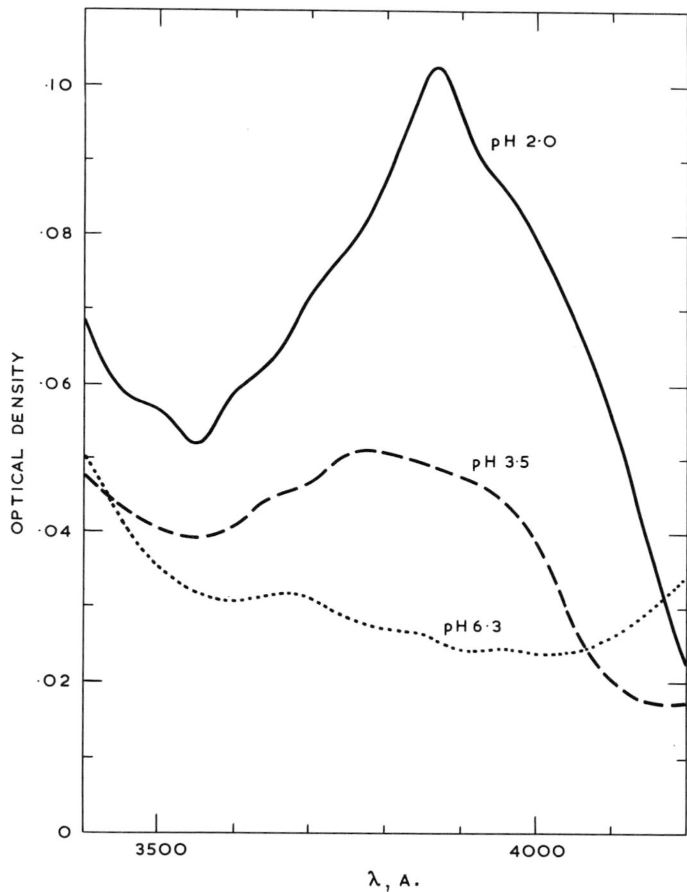

Figure 3. Transient spectra in 1 mM., N_2-saturated salicylate solutions as a function of pH

Rates of Formation of Transient Species. Rate constants for the formation of transient species were determined as follows:

(1) Competitive studies with CNS^- to determine $k(OH + \text{salicylate})$;

(2) Competition with methyl alcohol and with ethyl alcohol in neutral and in acid solutions in an attempt to derive both $k(OH + \text{salicylate})$ and $k(H + \text{salicylate})$.

(3) Observation of the direct buildup of the two transient spectra in the region 3500–4000 A. to obtain $k(OH + \text{salicylate})$ and $k(H + \text{salicylate})$.

(4) Decay of the solvated electron spectrum at 7000 A. as a function of salicylate concentration to give $k(e^-_{aq} + \text{salicylate})$. Direc

observation of the formation of the electron adduct at 4400 A. is precluded by the strong absorption due to e^{-}_{aq} itself.

Competition studies in air-saturated neutral solutions of 1–2m*M* CNS- gave reciprocal plots according to the usual competition kinetics from which was derived a value of $k(\mathrm{OH} + \text{salicylate}) = 1.2 \pm 0.1 \times 10^{10}$ liter mole^{-1} sec.$^{-1}$, based on a value of $k(\mathrm{OH} + \mathrm{CNS}^{-}) = 6.6 \times 10^{9}$ liter mole^{-1} sec.$^{-1}$ (*3*) (Figure 4). Attempts to confirm this value by competitive experiments with ethyl alcohol (0–1000 m*M*) in neutral, N_2O-

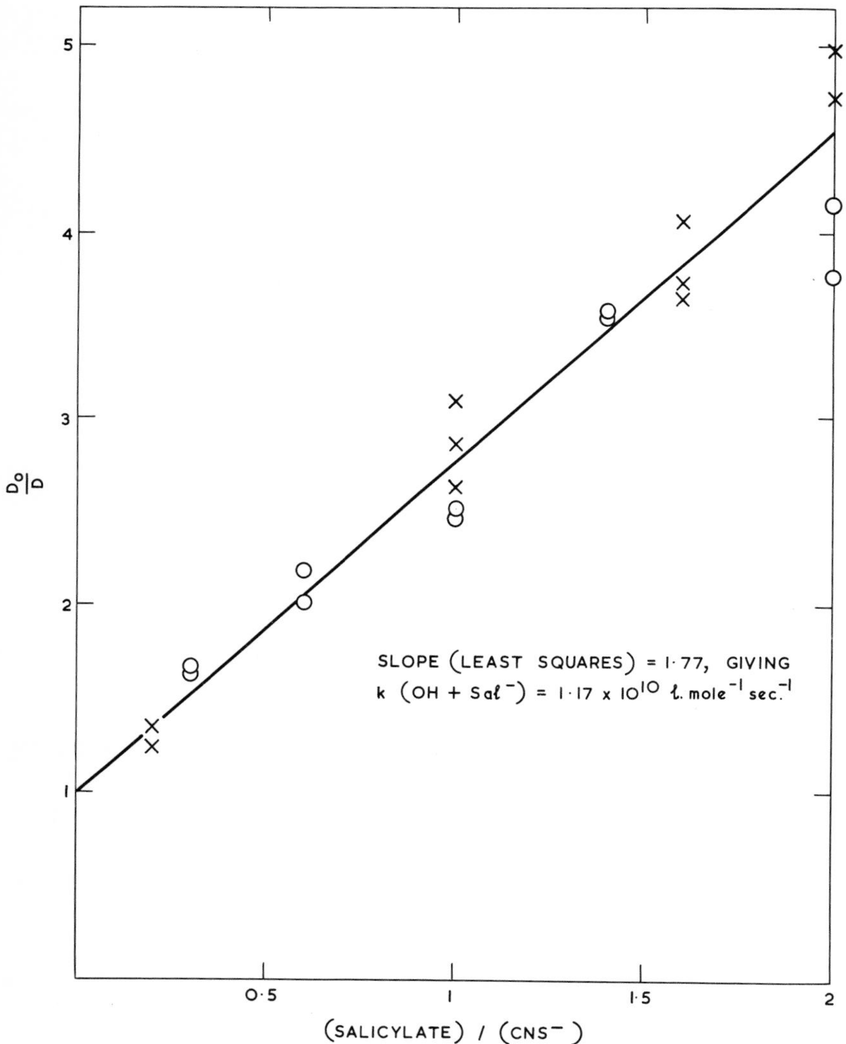

Figure 4. Thiocyanate competition experiments: reciprocal plot

saturated 0.5 m*M* salicylate solutions, in which the absorption at 3750 A. was measured, gave reciprocal plots which curved markedly at an early stage. The competition betwen the two solutes continued over the whole range of concentrations; moreover, in neutral, N_2O-saturated solutions the optical density showed a more rapid and extensive decrease as the alcohol concentration was increased, compared with N_2-saturated solutions at pH 2, where a steep initial reduction was followed by a prolonged, more gradual decrease. This suggests that ethyl alcohol and salicylate are competing for both OH radicals and H atoms, and that $k(OH + \text{salicylate}) > k(H + \text{salicylate})$. Better results were expected from the use of methyl alcohol, since published data (7) show that $k(OH + CH_3OH)/k(H + CH_3OH) \approx 350$ and $k(OH + C_2H_5OH)/k(H + C_2H_5OH) \approx 75$. However, the two regions of scavenging still overlapped when methyl alcohol was used (Figure 5), although the degree of curvature of the reciprocal plots was less serious. Better results might be expected with *tert*-BuOH as scavenger, where $k(OH + ROH)/k(H + ROH) \approx 2800$, but this has not yet been tried.

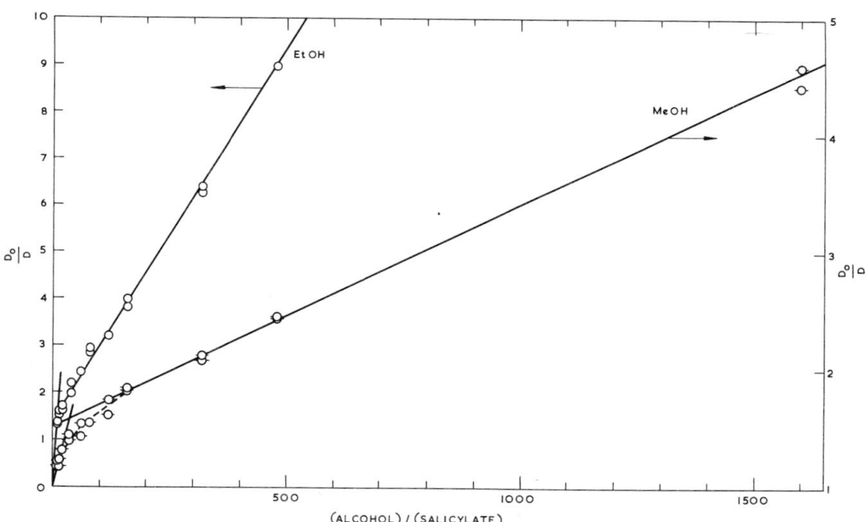

Figure 5. Alcohol competition studies: reciprocal plots to high scavenger concentrations. 0.5 mM. salicylate, N_2-saturated, pH 2; λ3750A.

Methyl Alcohol: right-hand ordinate
Ethyl Alcohol: left-hand ordinate

A crude analysis of the linear portions of the reciprocal plots at low and at high scavenger concentrations (Figure 6) gave the following approximate values based on $k(OH + CH_3OH) = 5 \times 10^8$ liter mole^{-1}

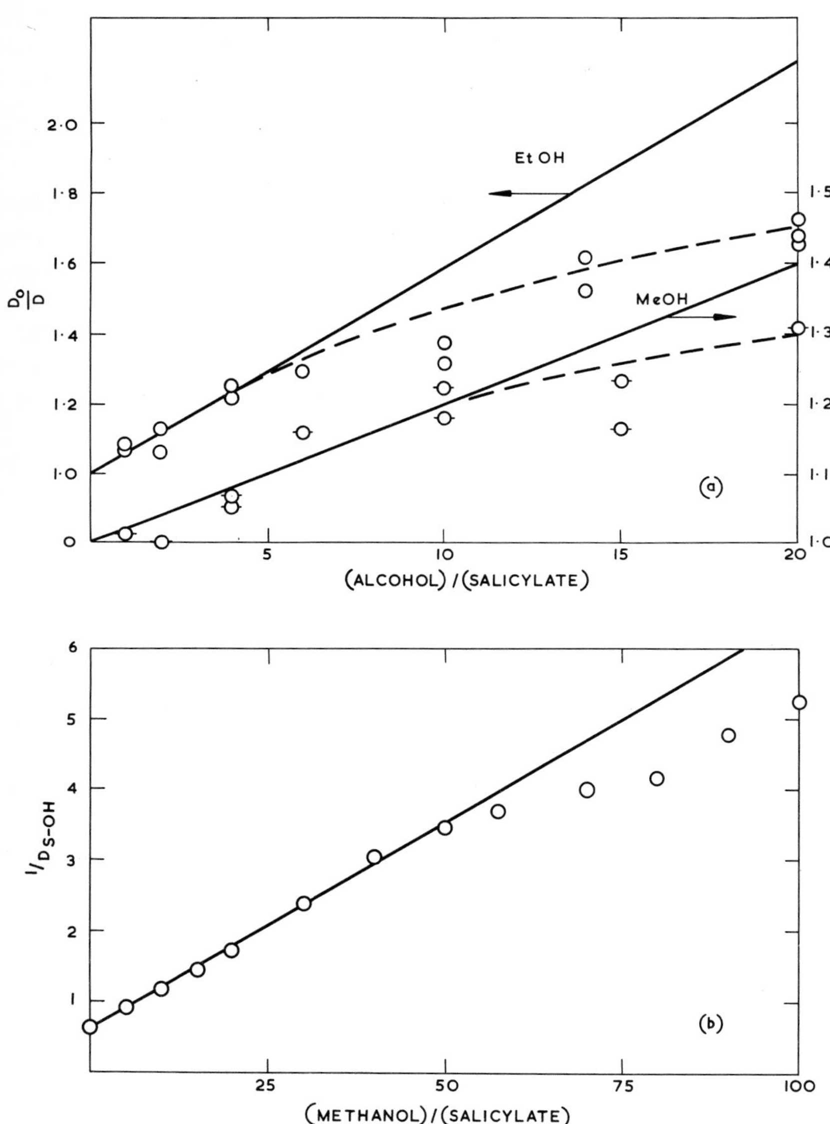

Figure 6. Alcohol competition studies: reciprocal plots at low scavenger concentrations. Conditions as in Figure 5

(a) Uncorrected values of total optical density
Ethyl Alcohol: left-hand ordinate
Methyl Alcohol: right-hand ordinate
(b) Using values of D *for S–OH only, obtained as described in text*

sec.$^{-1}$ (*9*), $k(H + CH_3OH) = 1.6 \times 10^6$ (*11*), $k(OH + C_2H_5OH) = 1.1 \times 10^9$ (*3*) and $k(H + C_2H_5OH) = 1.6 \times 10^7$ liter mole^{-1} sec.$^{-1}$ (*11*).

Reaction	*k*, liter mole^{-1} sec.$^{-1}$	
	Based on CH_3OH	Based on C_2H_5OH
OH + salicylate	2.5×10^{10}	1.0×10^{10}
H + salicylate	8.5×10^{8}	1.0×10^{9}

While the determination of k(H + salicylate) presents little difficulty, the initial curvature introduces considerable errors in the calculation of k(OH + salicylate) by this method. The procedure was therefore refined by extrapolating the final linear portion of the curve to zero alcohol concentration, on the assumption that there was no residual permanent absorption at 3750 A. If we assume that this represents H atom scavenging we can subtract the optical densities caused by the H atom adduct from the total densities and thereby obtain those caused by the OH radical adduct alone. When these are plotted on a reciprocal plot a good straight line is obtained for methyl alcohol over a much wider range of concentration, from which a value of $k(OH + \text{salicylate}) = 1.4 \times 10^{10}$ liter mole^{-1} sec.$^{-1}$ is derived. Less satisfactory results were obtained with ethyl alcohol, possibly because the initial linear portion of the overall scavenging curve is much shorter. Despite the more satisfactory nature of the value obtained with methyl alcohol, attempts to synthesize the overall scavenging curves from their components were not completely successful, and the results suggest that there may be a small residual absorption at 3750 A.

Visual inspection of the buildup curves in N_2-saturated solutions at low doses and slow sweep speeds in the region 3500–4000 A. also suggested that two processes were operative. A rapid initial buildup was followed by an appreciably slower rate of increase; the importance of the latter increased considerably on changing from neutral to acid solution. This suggests a rapid formation of the OH radical adduct followed by slower formation of the H atom adduct, in agreement with the alcohol scavenging data. The rapid initial buildup was followed at 3500 A. as a function of salicylate concentration (20-100 μM) in N_2O-saturated, neutral solution (to enhance OH addition still further relative to H addition), using low doses (150–200 rads/pulse) to minimize second-order reactions. Good first-order plots were obtained (Figure 7a), and a plot of half-life *vs.* reciprocal of the salicylate concentration (Figure 7b) gave a value of $k(OH + \text{salicylate}) = 1.2 \times 10^{10}$ liter mole^{-1} sec.$^{-1}$.

Analysis of the slow stage of the buildup of the transient spectrum from 3550 to 4050 A. in N_2-saturated, 300 μM salicylate solution at pH 2 (to convert e^-_{aq} to H atoms and thereby enhance the contribution of the H atom adduct) showed first-order kinetics with $k = 2.8 \pm 0.5 \times 10^9$

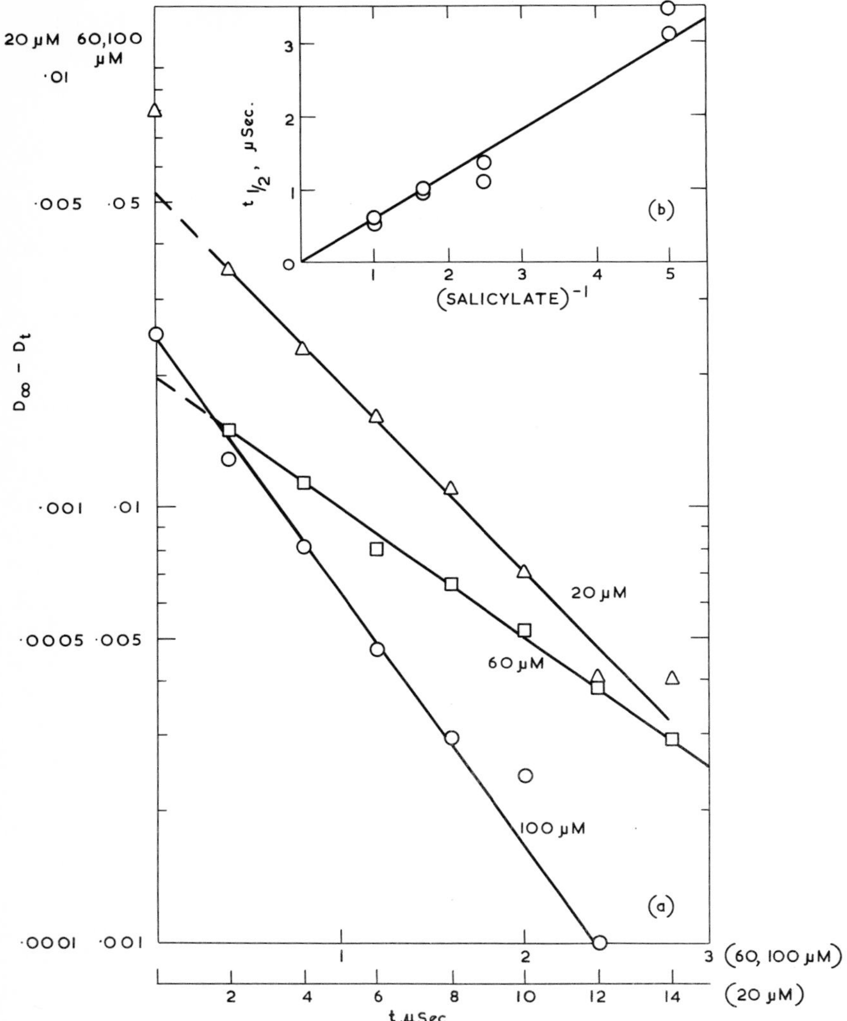

Figure 7. Formation of hydroxyl radical adduct in N_2O-saturated solution at pH 6.3

(a) First-order plots at 3500A. for different concentrations of salicylate
(b) Half-life vs. *[Salicylate]$^{-1}$*

liter mole^{-1} sec.$^{-1}$; a study of the concentration dependence of the half-life at 3900 A. at salicylate concentrations from 100 to 500 μM gave a value of $k(\mathrm{H} + \text{salicylate}) = 2.4 \pm 0.4 \times 10^9$ liter mole^{-1} sec.$^{-1}$ (Figure 8).

The rate constant for formation of the electron adduct was determined by following the decay of the hydrated electron absorption at 7000 A. as the concentration of salicylate was varied from 10 to 40 μM

in neutral, N_2-saturated solutions. Good first-order decay plots were obtained which gave values for $k(e^-_{aq} + \text{salicylate}) = 1.8_3, 0.9_6$ and $1.4_7 \times 10^{10}$ liter mole^{-1} sec.$^{-1}$; in view of their spread these must be regarded as preliminary figures.

Table I summarizes the different values of the rate constants for forming the three transient species.

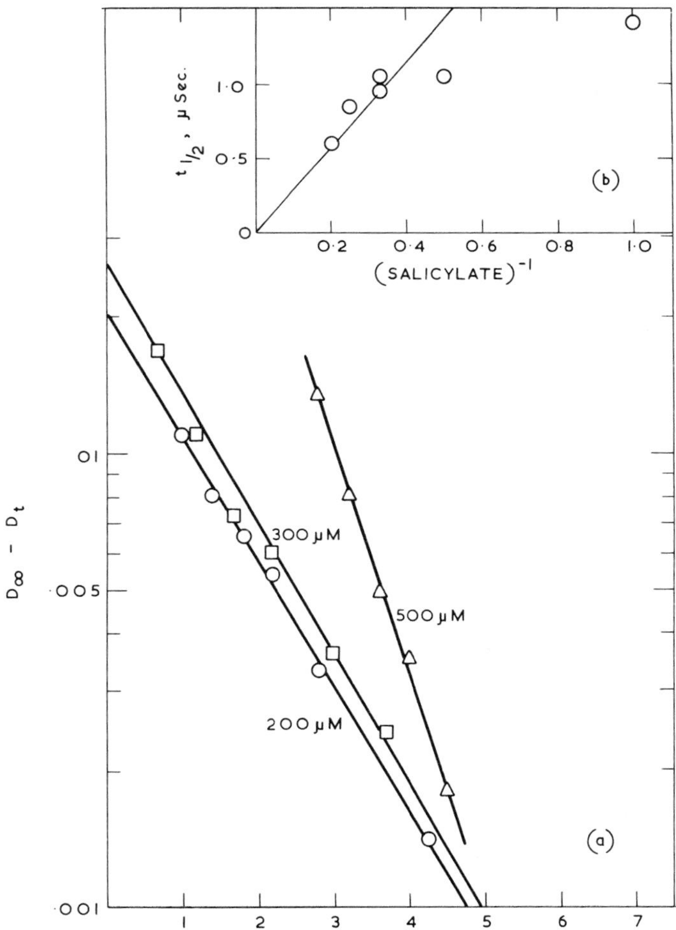

Figure 8. Formation of hydrogen atom adduct in N_2-saturated solution at pH 2

(a) First-order plots at 3900A. for different salicylate concentrations
(b) Half-life vs. *[Salicylate]$^{-1}$*

Table I. Formation of Transient Species on Irradiation of Salicylate Solutions

Reaction	*Method Used to Determine k*	*k, liter mole^{-1} sec.$^{-1}$*
OH + salicylate	Competition with CNS^- in aerated, neutral solution	1.2×10^{10}
	Competition with EtOH in N_2-saturated solution, pH 2	1.0×10^{10}
	Competition with MeOH in N_2-saturated solution, pH 2	1.4×10^{10} (corrected)
	Direct buildup in N_2O-saturated, neutral solution	1.2×10^{10}
H + salicylate	Competition with EtOH in N_2-saturated solution, pH 2	1.0×10^{9}
	Competition with MeOH in N_2-saturated solution, pH 2	8.5×10^{8}
	Direct buildup in N_2-saturated solution, pH 2	2.4×10^{9}
e^-_{aq} + salicylate	Decay of e^-_{aq} at 7000A. in N_2-saturated, neutral solution	$\sim 1 \times 10^{10}$

Decay of Transient Spectra. The decay of the transient spectra, containing two or more components, is complex, but the following broad generalizations emerge.

N_2-SATURATED SOLUTIONS, pH 6.3. Second-order decay was found between 3400 and 3800 A., and from 4200 to 4600 A. A narrow region of first-order decay appears to exist between 3900 and 4100 A., and from 5400 to 6000 A. the decay is probably second-order.

N_2O-SATURATED SOLUTIONS, pH 6.3. Second-order decay between 3400 and 3700 A., and probably from 5400 to 5800 A. The decay is complex between 3800 and 3900 A. and was not resolved.

N_2-SATURATED SOLUTIONS, pH 2 and 3.5. Complex second-order decay between 3400 and 4100 A. with two components, except at 3900 and possibly 4000 A., where a single straight line is obtained on a second-order plot.

In neutral solutions the initial values of $t_{1/2}$ in all second-order processes studied range from 150 to 200 μsec. for comparable doses in the pulse. Assuming a value of $G(\text{radicals}) = 6$ and the disappearance of transients by pairwise combination reactions, this would indicate a second-order rate constant of $2k = 1.4 \times 10^9$ liter mole^{-1} sec.$^{-1}$. In acid solutions the first half-life decreases to $\sim 70 - 100$ μsec. at pH 3.5 and $\sim 35 - 70$ μsec. at pH 2 (these figures refer to the initial linear portion of the second-order plot). A more detailed study of the electron adduct peak gave a value of $t_{1/2} = 189 \pm 11$ μsec. between 4300 and 4600 A. in N_2-saturated, neutral solutions, corresponding to $2k = 1.3 \times 10^9$ liter mole^{-1} sec.$^{-1}$ for disappearance of the species, assuming that $g(e^-_{aq}) = 2.3$. The value of $2k$ at 4500 A. was constant at $1.3 \pm 0.2 \times 10^9$ liter mole^{-1} sec.$^{-1}$ from pH 6 to 12, but it increased markedly to $8.8 \pm 0.2 \times 10^9$ liter mole^{-1} sec.$^{-1}$ at pH 3.4; this increase is accompanied by a nearly fourfold fall in the optical density which, as indicated above, is considerably greater than we would expect on the basis of competition between salicylate and hydrogen ions for e^-_{aq}, and presumably indicates that the electron adduct undergoes rapid protonation in acid solution. The more rapid decay in acid solution compared with that in neutral solution suggests, as does the spectral evidence (*see* above) that the protonated form of the electron adduct is not identical with the H atom adduct.

Discussion

The first stage of ionization of salicylic acid is characterized by a value of $pK_1 = 2.97$. Except for the results at pH 2, where $\sim 90\%$ of the solute is present as the undissociated acid, the predominant species will be the salicylate ion (OH, COO^- substituted benzene ring), and this is assumed to be the species taking part in the reactions studied.

Adducts are formed between salicylate ion and all three reactive intermediates H, OH and e^-_{aq}, that with e^-_{aq} apparently undergoing rapid protonation at acid pH values to give a product which is not identical with the H atom adduct formed under conditions where e^-_{aq} reacts with hydrogen ions rather than with salicylate. The rates of formation of the transient species approach diffusion-controlled values (*see* Table I).

The tabulated data of Anbar and Neta (7), in which original references are given, give only one value for reaction of a related carboxylic acid with H atoms, *viz.* 8.7×10^8 liter mole^{-1} sec.$^{-1}$ for benzoate at pH 7, a figure which is not significantly different from that given above for salicylate. The above value for the reaction with OH radicals is greater than those quoted for benzoate (2.1×10^9 at pH 3, 3.8×10^9 at pH 7) and for other substituted benzoic acids—*e.g.*, 4.5×10^9 liter mole^{-1} sec.$^{-1}$ for *o*-iodobenzoate at pH 9, 1.2-3.2 $\times 10^9$ liter mole^{-1} sec.$^{-1}$ for *m*- and *p*-substituted derivatives. Comparison of rate constants for OH radical reactions with aromatic compounds indicates that the COOH group does not activate the benzene ring towards OH addition, but an ortho-substituted OH group appears to increase the reactivity, as may be seen by comparing benzoate with salicylate.

More data are available on electron adduct reactions, although they are mainly confined to alkaline solutions. $k(e^-_{aq}$ + benzoate) decreases from 5.4 to 2.9 × 10^9 between pH 5.4 and 14, while values for substituted benzoic acids range from 4 × 10^8 for *p*-hydroxybenzoate at pH 7 to 1.3 × 10^{10} for *m*-iodobenzoate at pH 11. The value quoted for salicylate, 3.2 × 10^9 liter $mole^{-1}$ $sec.^{-1}$ at pH 11, is much lower than that found in this work, but the preliminary nature of our own figure and the marked pH effect found in other carboxylic acids make comparison difficult. Other aromatic acids such as phthalic and trimesic acids also give values between 10^9 and 10^{10} liter $mole^{-1}$ $sec.^{-1}$, the former decreasing threefold between pH 5.6 and 12.8. Carboxyl groups activate the benzene ring markedly towards electron addition, provided that the carboxyl unsaturation is conjugated with that of the ring, as shown by the following data for the rate constants:

Solute	*Benzene*	*Benzoate*	*Phenyl-acetate*	*Cinnamate*	*Hydro-cinnamate*
$k(e^-_{aq}$ + solute)	<7 × 10^6 (pH 7)	5.4 × 10^9 (pH 5.4)	5.1 × 10^7 (pH 5.4)	6.8 × 10^9 (pH 7.2)	4.9 × 10^7 (pH 5.4)

A similar degree of activation is seen when we compare the value for phenol (< 4 × 10^6 liter $mole^{-1}$ $sec.^{-1}$ at pH 11) with that for salicylate.

The good agreement obtained in this work between the value of *k*(OH + salicylate) determined by competition studies and by direct methods is interesting, in view of discrepancies in other systems when data obtained by the thiocyanate competition method are compared with those obtained by other techniques (*15, 18*); a reason for these discrepancies has been suggested (*18*).

The adducts disappear predominantly by second-order reactions, presumably of combination and disproportionation, but the nature of the reaction(s) in which CO_2 is eliminated has not been established. There is some evidence for first-order disappearance between 3900 and 4100 A. in neutral, N_2-saturated solutions, but the complexity of the spectrum in this region and the small contribution made by H atoms under these conditions make it difficult to analyze the decay unambiguously. In acid solutions there is no evidence of first-order decay. No evidence was obtained for the intermediate formation of other transient species during decay or of permanent absorption after decay, although if these were present below 3500 A. they would be masked by the intense absorption of the salicylate ion. Stoichiometrically we may write second-order reactions of combination in which CO_2 and dihydroxydiphenyl are formed (*37*) as follows:

$$2\ \cdot HOC_6H_4(OH)COOH \rightarrow (\cdot C_6H_4OH)_2 + 2CO_2 + 2H_2O$$

$$2\ \cdot H{\cdot}C_6H_4(OH)COOH \rightarrow (\cdot C_6H_4OH)_2 + 2CO_2 + 2H_2$$

$$\cdot HO{\cdot}C_6H_4(OH)COOH + \cdot H{\cdot}C_6H_4(OH)COOH \rightarrow (\cdot C_6H_4OH)_2 + 2CO_2 + H_2 + H_2O$$

Similar equations may be written for disproportionation to give CO_2, H_2, phenol and cyclohexadienol; the last two compounds have not been observed in steady-state studies at neutral pH, although phenols have been found in acid solution (*37*).

The electron adduct also disappears by a second-order process, which is much more rapid in acid solutions; the reaction may occur in two stages, a rapid protonation followed by a rate-determining second-order reaction —*i.e.*,

$$[C_6H_4(OH)COOH]^- + H_2O \overset{\text{fast}}{\rightleftharpoons} \cdot H\cdot C_6H_4(OH)COOH + OH^-$$

$$2\ \cdot H\cdot C_6H_4(OH)COOH \rightarrow \text{products (rate-determining)}$$

There is no parallel in the work of Sitharamarao (*37*) on the steady-state radiolysis of salicylate solutions to the observation by Sakumoto and Tsuchihashi (*35*) that diphenylcarboxylic acids are formed from benzoate solutions, but in view of the complexity of the analytical problems and the lack of total material balances this remains an open question. If indeed diphenylcarboxylic acids or their hydroxyl derivatives are formed in irradiated salicylate solutions, it may be that the H atom adduct and the protonated electron adduct behave differently, one giving dihydroxydiphenyl, CO_2 and H_2 and the other diphenylcarboxylic acids and water. More data are required on the steady-state radiolysis to clear up this point.

The decrease in the half-life of the OH radical adduct from ~200 μsec. at pH 6.3 to ~60 μsec. at pH 2 indicates that the second-order rate constant for its disappearance must increase accordingly, but the similar decrease in the half-life of the H atom adduct implies a small decrease (~40%) in the second-order rate constant at pH 2, since the concentration of the adduct will be increased about five-fold on converting e^-_{aq} to H atoms.

Literature Cited

(1) Adams, G. E., Baxendale, J. H., Boag, J. W., *Proc. Roy. Soc. A* **277**, 549 (1964).
(2) Adams, G. E., Boag, J. W., Michael, B. D., *Trans. Faraday Soc.* **61**, 492 (1965).
(3) *Ibid.*, **61**, 1417 (1965).
(4) *Ibid.*, **61**, 1674 (1965).
(5) Adams, G. E., Michael, B. D., *Trans. Faraday Soc.* **63**, 1171 (1967).
(6) Adams, G. E., Michael, B. D., Land, E. J., *Nature* **211**, 293 (1966).
(7) Anbar, M., Neta, P., *Intern. J. Appl. Radiation Isotopes* **18**, 493 (1967).
(8) Anbar, M., Hart, E. J., *J. Am. Chem. Soc.* **86**, 5633 (1964).
(9) Anbar, M., Meyerstein, D., Neta, P., *J. Chem. Soc. (B)* **1966**, 742.
(10) Anbar, M., Meyerstein, D., Neta, P., *J. Phys. Chem.* **70**, 2660 (1966).
(11) Appleby, A., Scholes, G., Simic, M., *J. Am. Chem. Soc.* **85**, 3891 (1963).
(12) Arai, S., Dorfman, L. M., *J. Chem. Phys.* **41**, 2190 (1964).

(13) Armstrong, W. A., Black, B. A., Grant, D. W., *J. Phys. Chem.* **64,** 1415 (1960).
(14) Asmus, K.-D., Beck, G., Henglein, A., Wigger, A., *Ber. Bunsen. physik. Chem.* **70,** 869 (1966).
(15) Asmus, K.-D., Cercek, B., Ebert, M., Henglein, A., Wigger, A., *Trans. Faraday Soc.* **63,** 2435 (1967).
(16) Asmus, K.-D., Wigger, A., Henglein, A., *Ber. Bunsen. physik. Chem.* **70,** 862 (1966).
(17) Barelko, E. V., Kartasheva, L. I., Novikov, P. D., Proskurnin, M. A., *Proc. All-Union Conf. Radiation Chem., 1st, Moscow, 1957,* p. 89.
(18) Baxendale, J. H., Stott, D. A., *Chem. Commun.* **1967,** 699.
(19) Brimacombe, J. S., Milner, D. J., *Nature* **209,** 1232 (1966).
(20) Chutny, B., *Nature* **213,** 593 (1967).
(21) Dorfman, L. M., Taub, I. A., Bühler, R. E., *J. Chem. Phys.* **36,** 3051 (1962).
(22) Downes, A. M., *Australian J. Chem.* **11,** 154 (1958).
(23) Garrison, W. M., Raymond, H. R., Morrison, D. C., Weeks, B. M., Gile-Melchert, J., *J. Am. Chem. Soc.* **75,** 2459 (1953).
(24) Garrison, W. M., Bennett, W., Cole, S., Raymond, H. R., Weeks, B. M., *J. Am. Chem. Soc.* **77,** 2720 (1955).
(25) Getoff, N., Gütlbauer, F., Schenck, G. O., *Intern. J. Appl. Radiat. Isotopes* **71,** 341 (1966).
(26) Getoff, N., Schenck, G. O., *Radiation Res.* **31,** 486 (1967).
(27) Grässlin, D., Merger, F., Schulte-Frohlinde, D., Volkert, O., *Z. physik. Chem. (Frankfurt)* **51,** 84 (1966).
(28) Hart, E. J., Boag, J. W., *J. Am. Chem. Soc.* **84,** 4090 (1962).
(29) Hart, E. J., Gordon, S., Thomas, J. K., *J. Phys. Chem.* **68,** 1271 (1964).
(30) Loeff, I., Swallow, A. J., *J. Phys. Chem.* **68,** 2470 (1964).
(31) Matthews, R. W., Sangster, D. F., *J. Phys. Chem.* **69,** 1938 (1965).
(32) Norman, R. O. C., Pritchett, R. J., *J. Chem. Soc. (B)* **1967,** 926.
(33) de la Paz, L. R., Getoff, N., *Radiation Res.* **28,** 567 (1966).
(34) Phung, P. V., Burton, M., *Radiation Res.* **7,** 199 (1957).
(35) Sakamoto, A., Tsuchihashi, G., *Bull. Chem. Soc. Japan* **34,** 660 (1961).
(36) Sangster, D. F., *J. Phys. Chem.* **70,** 1712 (1966).
(37) Sitharamarao, D. N. (unpublished work at A.E.R.E., Harwell).
(38) Stein, G., Weiss, J., *J. Chem. Soc.* **1951,** 3265.
(39) Stevenson, G. W., *Anal. Chem.* **32,** 1522 (1960).
(40) Szutka, A., Thomas, J. K., Gordon, S., Hart, E. J., *J. Phys. Chem.* **69,** 289 (1965).
(41) Taub, I. A., Harter, D. A., Sauer, M. C., Dorfman, L. M., *J. Chem. Phys.* **41,** 979 (1964).
(42) Thomas, J. K., Gordon, S., Hart, E. J., *J. Phys. Chem.* **68,** 1524 (1964).
(43) Wigger, A., Henglein, A., Asmus, K.-D., *Ber. Bunsen. physik. Chem.* **71,** 513 (1967).

RECEIVED January 31, 1968.

17

The Sensitizing Effect of N_2O on X-ray Induced Degradation of Benzoic Acid and Anthranilic Acid

K. F. NAKKEN, T. BRUSTAD, and A. KARTHUM HANSEN

Norsk Hydro's Institute for Cancer Research, The Norwegian Radium Hospital, Montebello, Norway

To shed light on the proposed reaction:

$$N_2O + e^-_{aq} \rightarrow N_2O^- \xrightarrow{H^+} N_2 + OH$$

effects of the electron scavengers O_2, N_2O, NO_3^-, and H_2O_2 on x-ray induced degradation of anthranilic acid (AA) and benzoic acid (B) were studied. AA ($2 \times 10^{-5} - 3 \times 10^{-4}$M) was degraded with G-values of 0.25 in N_2, 1.2 in O_2, 1.2–1.6 in N_2O, and 2.2 with nitrate (1×10^{-2}M) in N_2. For B (6×10^{-4}M) the G-values of hydroxybenzoic acids were 0.20 in N_2, 1.19 in O_2, 0.45 in N_2O and 0.88 with H_2O_2 ($4.4 \times 10^{-3}M$) in N_2. Thus, O_2 is able to oxidize B radicals. All electron scavengers studied suppress e^-_{aq} induced back reactions, but only H_2O_2 converts e^-_{aq} into OH. N_2O converts e^-_{aq} into a radical less reactive than NO_3^{2-} and OH.

Nitrous oxide has been used extensively in radiation chemical studies, because it interacts rapidly with hydrated electrons, more slowly with hydrogen atoms, and not at all with OH radicals (*15, 16, 17, 18, 22*). It seems to follow from the stoichiometry of radiation induced radicals and products formed in neutral water solution (*15, 16, 17, 18*), and from the reaction rates in various chemical systems (*1, 2, 3, 21, 37*) that N_2O^- spontaneously gives rise to an OH radical according to the following equation:

$$e^-_{aq} + N_2O \xrightarrow{k_1} N_2O^- \xrightarrow{H^+} N_2 + OH \qquad (1)$$

The evidence for Reaction 1 is very strong. There are, however, systems where the results are difficult to explain on the assumption that nitrous oxide does transform hydrated electrons into OH radicals (*5, 6, 8, 30, 31, 32, 34*). For this reason it was decided to study the effect of N_2O and various other electron scavengers on the x-ray induced degradation and hydroxylation of benzene derivatives. Radiation induced hydroxylation of aromatic compounds is initiated by addition of an OH radical to the benzene nucleus (*19*). Phenol derivatives are formed in subsequent dismutation reactions (*26*), or through oxidation of the intermediate aromatic radicals (*35*). Electron scavengers may increase the yield of phenols by: (1) interfering with back reactions, (2) oxidizing intermediate aromatic radicals, and (3) giving rise to OH radicals.

Mechanism (1) is common to all electron scavengers, mechanism (2) is typical for oxygen, and mechanism (3) is typical for hydrogen peroxide, which acts according to Equation 2:

$$e^-_{aq} + H_2O_2 \rightarrow H_2O_2^- \rightarrow OH^- + OH \qquad (2)$$

In general, electron scavengers which do not exert their effect according to mechanism (2) or mechanism (3) may react according to Equation 3:

$$e^- + A \rightarrow A^- \qquad (3)$$

Some A^- radicals dismutate (as O_2^-), others may act as oxidizing or reducing agents.

In the present paper radiation chemical studies are presented on the x-ray induced degradation of anthranilic acid and hydroxylation of benzoic acid. The effect of the electron scavenger N_2O is compared with that of NO_3^-, H_2O_2, and O_2. The results suggest that N_2O^- (or N_2OH) radicals do not spontaneously give rise to OH radicals in solutions of benzoic acid or anthranilic acid.

Materials and Methods

Chemicals. Low Conductivity Water. This was obtained by double distillation from all-glass equipment.

Anthranilic Acid (AA). This was obtained from Hoffman-La Roche (Basel), and recrystallized twice from low conductivity water. The molar extinction coefficient in 0.067*M* phosphate buffer, pH 7.0, was $2.900M^{-1}$ $cm.^{-1}$ at 310 $m\mu$.

3-Hydroxyanthranilic Acid. This was obtained from Hoffman-LaRoche (Basel) and used as purchased.

5-Hydroxyanthranilic Acid (5-OH-AA). This was synthesized from *m*-hydroxybenzoic acid by coupling with diazotized rosaniline and subsequent reduction with sodium dithionite. The recrystallized product had a melting point of 242°C. (dec.).

SALICYLIC ACID, *m*-HYDROXYBENZOIC ACID AND *p*-HYDROXYBENZOIC ACID. These were obtained from Fluka AG (Buchs, Switzerland), and recrystallized before use.

SODIUM BENZOATE. This was obtained from British Drug Houses Ltd., England.

The above compounds were dissolved in low conductivity water and neutralized to pH 7.0 with NaOH.

NITROUS OXIDE, OXYGEN, AND NITROGEN. These were obtained from Norsk Surstof og Vandstoffabrik A/S, Oslo, Norway. The nitrous oxide was of anaesthetic grade and the nitrogen was highly purified (containing less than 0.005% O_2, according to analysis by the manufacturer). The routine procedure was to flush N_2O through pyrogallol solution, although this did not affect the results.

Irradiation Procedure. Irradiation was carried out with a Siemens x-ray set operated at 220 kv. and 20 ma., with 2 mm. Al filtration. The sample solutions in irradiation vessels of borosilicate glass (*23*) were flushed with appropriate gases before and during irradiation. The dose rate for each irradiation vessel was determined with the Fricke dosimeter (*36*), assuming 15.5 molecules of Fe^{3+} (*36*) formed per 100 e.v. absorbed energy. The dose rate was 1.94 krad $min.^{-1}$.

Analytical Procedure. METHOD FOR DETERMINATION OF AA. Residual AA was determined immediately after irradiation by spectrophotofluorometry. In general the solutions were acidified to pH = 2.8 and analyzed using $\lambda_{exit} = 342$ and $\lambda_{emit} = 428$ mμ. To avoid quenching of the fluorescence because of AA, the irradiated solutions were diluted to an initial concentration of $2 \times 10^{-5}M$ AA. In experiments with nitrate, residual AA was determined by two different spectrophotofluorometric procedures. In the first method, carried out as described above, it was necessary to correct for a decrease in fluorescence caused by radiation induced nitrite which slowly diazotized AA. This reaction was followed with time and AA at the time of acidification was determined by extrapolation. In the second method, AA was determined by fluorescence assay of the diluted neutral solution ($\lambda_{exit} = 290$ mμ and $\lambda_{emit} = 340$ mμ). The radiation products (aniline 3-hydroxy- and 5-hydroxyanthranilic acid) did not interfere in either method, and both gave the same value for residual AA in the irradiated solutions (*33*).

With oxygen present during irradiation a dicarbonyl compound is formed. This compound might possibly interfere in the fluorescence assay. Consequently, residual AA was also determined by diazotization and coupling with *N*-1-naphthylethylenediamine as described by Bratton and Marshall (*14, 29*). The coupling reaction was, in this case, allowed to proceed for 120 minutes before the optical density was read at 545 mμ. Control experiments revealed that aniline, 3-hydroxy- and 5-hydroxyanthranilic acid did not interfere with determining residual AA. In a series of experiments, the Bratton-Marshall procedure and the fluorescence assay gave the same value for residual AA. Thus, it seemed reasonable to use the fluorescence assay as the general procedure. Throughout this work, residual AA was determined from a standard curve which showed a linear relationship between the concentration of AA and the relative fluorescence.

METHODS FOR DETERMINATION OF *o*-, *m*-, AND *p*-HYDROXYBENZOIC ACID. The x-ray induced formation of *o*-, *m*-, and *p*-hydroxybenzoic acid was determined by spectrophotofluorometry (*10*) immediately after irradiation. In all experiments light was carefully excluded from the sample solution. Solutions containing H_2O_2 give rise to OH radicals when exposed to ultraviolet light, and it was therefore necessary to perform the fluorescence assay with a minimum of ultraviolet-exposure. By repeating the assay several times for each sample, small corrections for ultraviolet-induced hydroxylation were found by extrapolation to zero ultraviolet-exposure.

The quantum yield of fluorescence from *p*-hydroxybenzoic acid is low (*10*). It was found that this fluorescence was subject to strong quenching in irradiated solutions. In the fluorescence assay, therefore, *p*-hydroxybenzoic acid was added as an internal standard. The *G*-values so obtained were in agreement with those obtained by spectrophotometric assay at an isobestic point.

Absorption spectrophotometry and spectrophotofluorometry were carried out with a Zeiss recording spectrophotometer (RPQ20), with a fluorescence attachment (ZFM 4C).

Results

X-ray Induced Total Degradation of AA. When dilute solutions of AA were exposed to x-rays, no characteristic change in the absorption spectrum of AA occurred, except for a broadening of the 310 mμ absorption peak towards higher wavelengths (Figure 1A). This is not surprising, since it has been shown by paper chromatography that 3-hydroxy- and 5-hydroxy AA represent the main products; these compounds have absorption peaks at slightly higher wavelengths than does AA (Figure 1B). The yield of total degradation of AA was, however, determined conveniently by fluorescence assay or by diazotization and coupling as described above.

Figures 2A and 2B show typical results of the fluorescence assay of AA in irradiated solutions. When AA was irradiated in solutions continuously flushed with air, a strong decrease in the fluorescence peak was observed (Figure 2A). Residual AA was found to decrease exponentially with dose (Figure 2B). A summary of the results obtained is shown in Figure 3. Here the D_{37} dose is plotted as a function of the initial concentration of AA. *G*-values can be calculated from the slope of the curves and are thus corrected for radical-radical interactions at low concentrations of AA (*24*). This procedure cannot be adopted for the N_2O results, where the relationship between D_{37} dose and initial concentration of AA is non-linear.

OXYGEN AS ELECTRON SCAVENGER. In the case of oxygen there is a linear relationship between D_{37} dose and initial concentration of AA with only a small intercept at the ordinate (Figure 3). The *G*-value for total degradation of AA in presence of oxygen is equal to 1.2. Since G_{OH} = 2.25 (*4*) it follows that one molecule of AA is degraded per two radiation induced OH radicals. The end products of the degradation reaction are probably formed from dismutation reactions of intermediate aromatic radicals, a mechanism previously suggested for *p*-aminobenzoic acid (*29*). In a nitrogen atmosphere the *G*-value for total degradation of AA was found to be 0.25 and is thus only 20% of the value obtained in oxygen. The most likely explanation for this low *G*-value under anoxia is that AA itself may act as a scavenger of e^-_{aq}, thereby giving rise to radicals which may participate in back reactions.

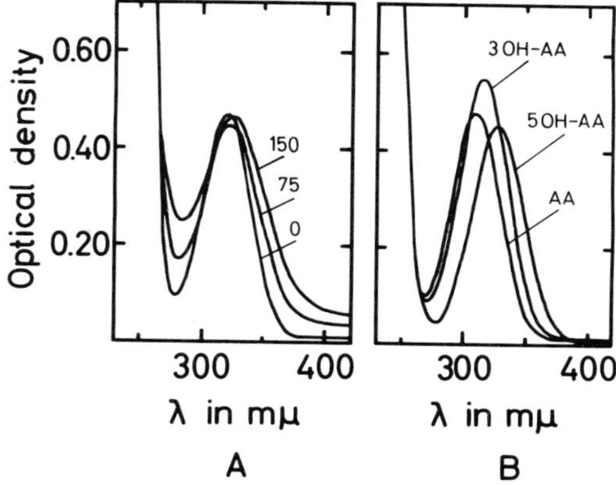

Figure 1. A. Absorption spectra of unirradiated and irradiated solutions of anthranilic acid containing oxygen, $(AA)_0 = 1.6 \times 10^{-4}$M. *Dose, in krads, is indicated by numbers on the figure*

B. *Absorption spectra of unirradiated AA, 3-hydroxyanthranilic acid (3-OH-AA) and 5-hydroxyanthranilic acid (5-OH-AA). The concentration of solutes was* 1.6×10^{-4}M *in 0.067*M *phosphate buffer, pH = 7.0*

NITRATE AS ELECTRON SCAVENGER. In the case of nitrate, a linear relationship between the D_{37} dose and the initial concentration of AA was found, as shown in Figure 3. The curve passes through the origin, and its slope corresponds to a *G*-value for total degradation nearly twice that in oxygen, namely *G*(-AA) = 2.2. At neutral pH, hydrated electrons and OH-radicals are both known to be formed with *G*-values of about 2.25. The present result would therefore suggest that hydrated electrons are transformed by nitrate into a radical which behaves as if it were stoichiometrically equivalent to OH. It may be assumed that this radical is NO_3^{2-}, which might oxidize AA and/or AA radicals, thereby giving rise to NO_2^-. This assumption is supported by the finding that the fluorescence of AA shows no decrease with time at neutral pH, but decreases rapidly at pH 2.7, as would be expected if the irradiated solution contained NO_2^-. Furthermore, such an after-effect in acidified solutions was observed only in experiments with NO_3^- and not with any of the other electron scavengers.

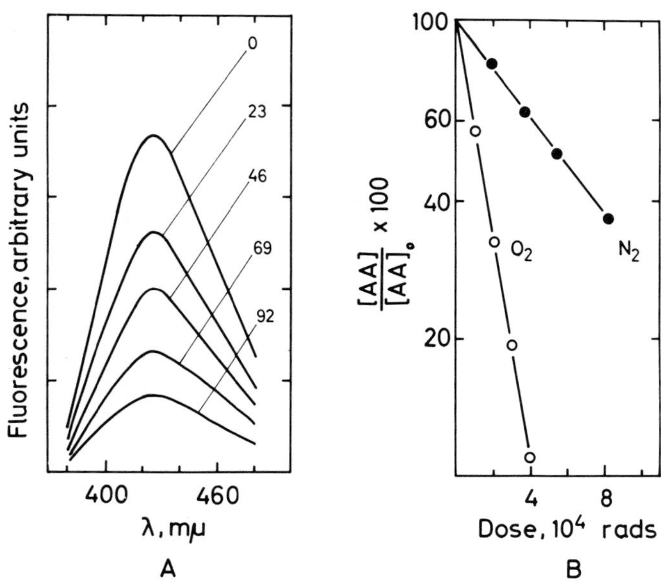

Figure 2. X-ray induced degradation of anthranilic acid (AA)

A. *Fluorescence spectra of remaining AA in irradiated neutral solutions equilibrated with air,* $(AA)_0 = 5.8 \times 10^{-5}$M $(\lambda_{exit} = 342\ m\mu,\ pH = 2.8)$. *The dose, in krads, is indicated by numbers on the figure*

B. *Remaining AA as a function of radiation dose.* $(AA)_0 = 2.0 \times 10^{-5}$M. *The solutions were flushed with* O_2 *and* N_2 *respectively, as indicated in the text. Fluorescence assay with* $\lambda_{exit} = 342\ m\mu$, $\lambda_{emit} = 428\ m\mu$ *and* $pH = 2.8$

NITROUS OXIDE AS ELECTRON SCAVENGER. In solutions saturated with nitrous oxide $(1.6 \times 10^{-2}M)$ all e^-_{aq} is scavenged by N_2O, giving rise to N_2O^- or N_2OH radicals. If OH radicals were formed rapidly from N_2O^-, according to Equation 1, a plot of D_{37} *vs.* initial concentration of AA should be a straight line, with a slope corresponding to a *G*-value of about 2. Neither of these expectations was confirmed in our experiments

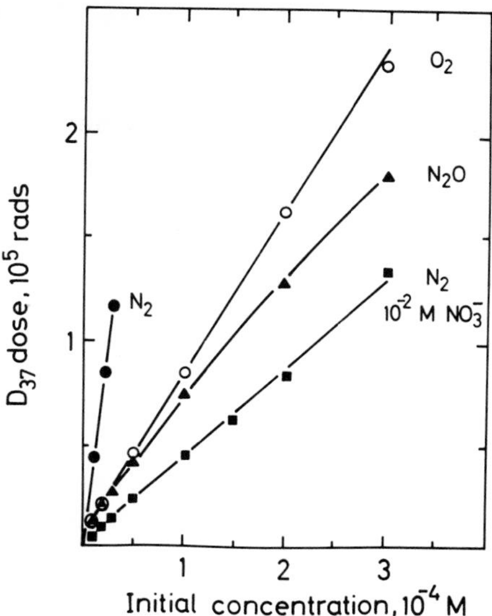

Figure 3. D_{37} dose as a function of initial concentration of anthranilic acid. The solutions were flushed with either N_2, O_2, or N_2O, before and during irradiation. After the sample solution had been diluted to 2×10^{-5}M initial concentration of AA, remaining AA was determined by fluorescence assay, as in Figure 2 B

(*see* Figure 3). The data here presented show that the slope decreases steadily with increasing concentration of AA. The slope corresponds to a *G*-value of 1.2 at low concentration which increases steadily in the concentration range studied without, however, reaching the value 2.

Our studies lend support to the assumption that N_2O^- (or N_2OH) radicals may interact with AA in a slow reaction, strongly dependent on the concentration of AA:

$$AA + N_2OH \underset{(slow)}{\xrightarrow{k_4}} N_2 + H_2O + AA^\circ \quad (4)$$

where k_4 is the rate constant of a rather slow reaction probably involving hydrogen abstraction from AA. At high concentrations of AA Reaction 4 may compete effectively with a dismutation reaction of the N_2OH radicals:

$$2\ N_2OH \underset{(fast)}{\xrightarrow{k_5}} N_2 + N_2O + H_2O \quad (5)$$

The present data may be explained if N_2O^- (or N_2OH) radicals act as oxidizing radicals of low reactivity. Thus, our results give no evidence for a conversion of hydrated electrons into OH radicals in irradiated solutions of AA containing nitrous oxide. Furthermore, in the present system, N_2O^- (or N_2OH) does not seem to behave as stoichiometrically equivalent to OH.

It may be suggested that the aromatic amino group of AA acts as an electron acceptor in the electron transfer reaction:

$$N_2O^- + AA \rightarrow N_2O + AA^-, \qquad (6)$$

prior to the assumed spontaneous decomposition of N_2O^-. Such an explanation seems unlikely, however, in view of the above finding that the yield of total degradation of AA decreases, whereas the probability of formation of OH radicals from N_2O^- increases for decreasing concentrations of solute. Nevertheless, it seemed necessary to study the effect of nitrous oxide on the x-ray induced degradation of an aromatic compound without the amino group, such as benzoic acid.

X-ray Induced Hydroxylation of Benzoic Acid. It is well known that irradiation of benzoic acid in dilute solutions gives rise to decarboxylation as well as to hydroxylation in the ortho-, meta-, and para-positions (*10, 27*). From these investigations it follows that radiation induced formation of hydroxybenzoic acids in neutral aqueous solutions accounts for about 50% of the total degradation. In order to shed more light on the ability of N_2O to convert hydrated electrons into oxidizing radicals, it was decided to compare the effect of nitrous oxide with that of hydrogen peroxide under anoxic conditions. If Reaction 1 and 2 occur rapidly, the effect of nitrous oxide would be expected to be similar to that of hydrogen peroxide, except that the latter compound may also convert H atoms into OH radicals.

Throughout the present experiments benzoic acid was irradiated at a concentration of $6 \times 10^{-4}M$. It follows from the rate constants in Table I that benzoic acid, under the present experimental conditions, will scavenge nearly all OH radicals, whereas e^-_{aq} will react almost quantitatively with O_2, H_2O_2, or N_2O. The x-ray induced formation of *o*-, *m*-,

Table I. Rate Constants for Reactions of e^-_{aq}, H°, and OH° with Solutes (in Units of 10^9M^{-1} sec.$^{-1}$)

Solute (pH = 7.0)	e^-_{aq}	H°	OH°	*References*
Benzoic acid	3.1	0.87	3.3	1, 9
O_2	20	20	—	12
N_2O	8.7	0.0002	—	9, 22
H_2O_2	13	0.10	0.045	9, 12

and *p*-hydroxybenzoic acid as a function of dose is given in Figure 4 for a variety of experimental conditions. In all cases linear dose response curves passing through the origin were obtained. From the slopes of these curves the *G*-values for formation of the various hydroxybenzoic acids can be calculated. The values so obtained are presented in Table II.

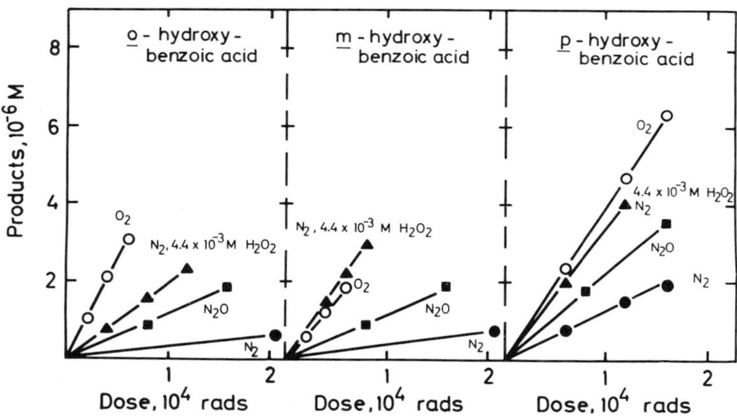

Figure 4. X-ray induced formation of o-, m- *and* p-*hydroxybenzoic acid as a function of dose. Samples were flushed with either* N_2, O_2, *or* N_2O, *before and during irradiation. The hydroxybenzoic acids formed were determined by fluorescence assay* (10, 33). *In the case of* p-*hydroxybenzoic acid, an internal standard was added to the irradiated sample. In the experiments with* H_2O_2 *(4.4 ×* 10^{-3}M) *the solution was flushed with* N_2; *the yields were corrected for ultraviolet induced hydroxylation as described in the text*

In solutions flushed with N_2, and without other electron scavengers present, the *G*-value for hydroxybenzoic acids was found to be 0.20. This low *G*-value may be ascribed to e^-_{aq} and H, being scavenged by benzoic acid, and giving rise to radicals which participate in back reactions.

EFFECTS OF O_2. In the presence of oxygen ($1.5 \times 10^{-3} M$), e^-_{aq} and H will react with oxygen whereas all OH radicals react with benzoic acid. The *G*-value for hydroxybenzoic acids under these conditions ($G =$ 1.19) is six times higher than that in nitrogen.

The sensitizing effect of oxygen may be ascribed partly to scavenging by oxygen of e^-_{aq} and H, thus interfering with back reactions (*29*). This effect alone is not sufficient to explain the *G*-value for total degradation of benzoic acid, which is 2.45 in the presence of oxygen (*27*). Armstrong *et al.* (*10, 11*) who performed their experiments with benzoic acid in N_2

and O_2, and obtained results similar to ours, concluded that oxygen also may participate in reactions with intermediate benzoic acid radicals.

Effects of H_2O_2 and N_2O. When benzoic acid is irradiated in the presence of H_2O_2 ($4.4 \times 10^{-3}M$) or N_2O ($1.6 \times 10^{-2}M$) these solutes will compete for the radiation induced radicals. From the concentrations of the solutes and their rate constants given in Table I, the amount of each radical species which interacts with benzoic acid, H_2O_2 and N_2O can be calculated. In the case of H_2O_2, 97% of e^-_{aq} and 46% of H will be scavenged by H_2O_2 and thus be converted into OH radicals (*36*) according to Equation 2. About 91% of all OH radicals formed will be scavenged by benzoic acid. The remaining OH radicals (about 9%) may be scavenged by H_2O_2, and give rise to equivalent amounts of O_2^-.

Table II. X-ray Induced Hydroxylation of Benzoic Acid[a]

	G *(Hydroxybenzoic Acid)*			
	(N_2)	*(O_2)*	*($N_2 + 4.4 \times 10^{-3}M\ H_2O_2$)*	*(N_2O)*
o-hydroxybenzoic acid	0.03	0.49	0.19	0.11
m-hydroxybenzoic acid	0.04	0.31	0.37	0.12
p-hydroxybenzoic acid	0.13	0.39	0.32	0.22
o-, *m*- and *p*-hydroxybenzoic acid	0.20	1.19	0.88	0.45

[a] Solutions of sodium benzoate in water ($6.0 \times 10^{-4}M$, pH = 7.0) were irradiated at room temperature with x-rays (220 Kev., 2 mm. Al filter) at a dose rate of 1.94 krads min.$^{-1}$. The solutions were flushed continuously with N_2, O_2, or N_2O (1 atm.) as indicated in parentheses above. The hydroxybenzoic acids were determined by spectrophotofluorometry immediately after irradiation (*10, 33*). The yield values were obtained from 2 or 3 dose-response curves. In the determination of *p*-hydroxybenzoic acid an internal standard was added to the irradiated sample.

In the presence of N_2O essentially all OH (and H) radicals will interact with benzoic acids while all e^-_{aq} will be scavenged by N_2O.

The extent to which e^-_{aq} is transformed into OH radicals according to Equation 1 is at present unknown, but may be assessed by comparison of the yields of hydroxybenzoic acid formed when benzoic acid is irradiated in the presence of H_2O_2 or N_2O.

Let us assume that N_2O is able to transform e^-_{aq} into OH radicals according to Equation 1 with a *G*-value G_1. For a given dose the ratio (*F*) of OH radicals interacting with benzoic acid in the presence of H_2O_2 or N_2O, is given by:

$$F = \frac{0.91\ (G_{OH} + 0.97\ G_{e^-_{aq}} + 0.46\ G_H)}{G_{OH} + G_1} = \frac{4.47}{2.25 + G_1} \qquad (7)$$

where $G_{OH} = 2.25$, $G_{e^-_{aq}} = 2.27$, and $G_H = 0.48$ (*4*). If G_1 is equivalent to $G_{e^-_{aq}}$—*i.e.*, all e^-_{aq} being transformed into OH radicals, then F ≈ 1. If N_2O is unable to transform e^-_{aq} into OH, then F ≈ 2.

In our experiments hydroxybenzoic acids were formed with a *G*-value of 0.45 in presence of N_2O, whereas the corresponding yield in the presence of H_2O_2 was 0.88—*i.e.*, nearly twice that in N_2O.

When the present result is compared with the ratio *F* (given in Equation 7) it seems to follow that $G_1 \approx 0$—*i.e.*, N_2O is unable to transform e^-_{aq} into OH in the present system.

The following arguments should be considered:

Firstly, 0.33 and 0.48 reducing species per 100 e.v. absorbed energy may participate in back reactions in the H_2O_2 and the N_2O systems, respectively, and thus decrease slightly the yields of phenol derivatives. The ratio of phenol derivatives formed in the two benzoic acid systems will, however, barely be affected by this small amount of back reactions.

Secondly, in the H_2O_2 system 9% of OH radicals are transformed into O_2^- radicals which may give rise subsequently to O_2 through dismutation. Because of the low dose rate and the continuous nitrogen flushing during irradiation, it does not seem likely that the small amount of radiation induced oxygen can explain the finding that the yield of phenol derivatives formed in H_2O_2 was twice that in N_2O.

Thirdly, if H_2O_2 were able to oxidize intermediate benzoic acid radicals, this would give rise to OH radicals and thus to a chain reaction. However, neither in the present system nor in the benzene system studied by Baxendale and Magee (*13*) is there any evidence for H_2O_2 induced chain reactions.

Thus, the sensitizing effect of N_2O on x-ray induced degradation of benzoic acid, anthranilic acid and *p*-aminobenzoic acid (*34*) gives no evidence for a conversion of hydrated electrons into OH radicals by N_2O.

Discussion

Kartasheva *et al.* (*26*) were the first to suggest that x-ray induced hydroxylation of benzene is initiated by the addition of an OH radical to the benzene ring, and that phenol is formed in a subsequent dismutation reaction of intermediate radicals. Subsequently, pulse radiolysis experiments (*19*) have demonstrated that OH radicals give rise to an addition product with benzene ($k = 4 \times 10^9 M^{-1}$ sec.$^{-1}$). Studies of the ability of various solutes to compete for radiation induced OH radicals have shown that *p*-aminobenzoic acid (PABA) is able to interact with OH radicals at a high rate ($k = 2 \times 10^{10} M^{-1}$ sec.$^{-1}$) (*31*), and that AA probably interacts with OH radicals at nearly the same rate as does PABA (*25*). The interaction of OH radicals with low molecular thiols proceeds at a rate 1/3–1/6 of the rate of interaction of OH with PABA (*31*). It is, therefore, likely that hydrogen abstraction reactions are of little importance in the first step of degradation of aminobenzoic acid derivatives (*3, 19, 29*), although this mechanism may partly operate with benzoic acid.

Radiation Chemistry of Aminobenzoic Acids. Previous work (*29, 33*) has demonstrated that aromatic amines are hydroxylated exclusively in the positions *o*- and *p*- to the amino group. This may be ascribed to the strong electrophilic reactivity of the OH radical (*3, 7, 29, 33, 38*). The positions *o*- to the amino group are strongly favored for interaction with OH radicals. Thus, for anthranilic acid, the ratio *G*(3-OH-AA)/*G*(5-OH-AA) was found to be 4:1. The degradation of AA may be accounted for by the formation of 3-OH-AA (40%), 5-OH-AA (10%), and ringsplitting and decarboxylation (50%). In the case of PABA, hydroxylation *o*- to the amino group accounts for 80% of the degradation observed. *p*-Aminosalicylic acid is not formed and *p*-aminophenol is formed only in a low yield.

The first step in the x-ray induced degradation and hydroxylation of aminobenzoic acid derivatives is therefore assumed to be an addition of the OH radical to electro-negative sites of the benzene nucleus:

$$RH + OH^\circ \rightarrow RH\text{-}OH^\circ \quad (8)$$

In solutions flushed with oxygen the intermediate RH-OH° radicals seem to participate in dismutation reactions—*e.g.*,

$$2\ RH\text{-}OH^\circ \rightarrow RH + \text{products} \quad (9)$$

consistent with the finding that *G*(-AA) and *G*(-PABA) is equal to 1/2 G_{OH} (Table III).

Table III. X-ray Induced Degradation of Benzoic Acid, Anthranilic Acid and *p*-Aminobenzoic Acid

	G (-Solute)		
Condition	*Benzoic acid*	*Anthranilic acid*	p-*Aminobenzoic acid*
N_2	0.4[a]	0.25	0.2[c]
N_2O (1 Atm.)	1.2[a]	1.2-1.6[b]	0.9[c]
$N_2 + 10^{-2}M\ NO_3^-$	—	2.2	0.8[c]
O_2 (1 Atm.)	2.45[a] (27)	1.2	1.2[c]

[a] These *G*-values include $G(CO_2) = 0.20$ in N_2, $G(CO_2) = 0.79$ in N_2O and $G(CO_2) = 0.72$ in O_2 (Ref. 28).
[b] *G*-value calculated from $(AA)_o/D_{37}$, $(AA)_o = 3 \times 10^{-4}M$.
[c] Ref. 32.

The low yield of x-ray induced degradation in solutions flushed with N_2 (Table III) is probably caused by a back reaction (Equation 11):

$$RH + e^-_{aq} \rightarrow RH\text{-}e^- \quad (10)$$

$$RH\text{-}e^- + RH\text{-}OH^\circ \rightarrow 2\ RH + OH^- \quad (11)$$

EFFECTS OF O_2, N_2O, AND NO_3^-. It would have been of interest to have compared the effect of nitrous oxide with that of hydrogen peroxide in the AA system. This was, however, difficult to do because AA was easily oxidized by H_2O_2, even in the dark. The effect of N_2O was therefore compared with those of oxygen and nitrate, which also are excellent scavengers of e^-_{aq} (*5, 12, 22*).

The main effect of O_2, N_2O, and NO_3^- seems to involve scavenging of e^-_{aq}, thus suppressing Reaction 11. This mechanism could explain the values of G(-AA) and G(-PABA) (Table III). Oxygen has been assumed to interact directly with intermediate aryl radicals (*35*). It may, however, be concluded that neither oxygen, O_2^- nor radiation induced H_2O_2 participates in the x-ray induced hydroxylation and degradation of *o*- and *p*-aminobenzoic acid derivatives.

The reactivity of the radicals O_2^-, N_2O^- (or N_2OH), and NO_3^{2-} seems to increase in the above mentioned order. The O_2^- radical is probably unable to oxidize the intermediate radicals formed. Thus, for PABA it was found that $G(H_2O_2) = G_{H_2O_2} + 1/2\ G_{e^-_{aq}+H}$ (*29*), and for benzoic acid $G(H_2O_2)$ was only slightly higher (*10*). The N_2O^- (N_2OH) radical seems unable to oxidize PABA-radicals (*34*) and AA-radicals under our experimental conditions. However, as was discussed above, N_2O^- (N_2OH) may be able to oxidize AA at concentrations of AA greater than $5 \times 10^{-5}M$. It seems to follow that N_2O^- does not give rise to OH radicals in this system. The present results with NO_3^- demonstrate that NO_3^{2-} is able to oxidize AA (or AA radicals) even when $(AA)_0 = 2 \times 10^{-5}M$, and that NO_3^{2-} behaves stoichiometrically equivalent to OH in the presence of AA.

Radiation Chemistry of Benzoic Acid. Benzoic acid (BH) is of particular interest since the yields of three different hydroxybenzoic acids can be determined independently, in the presence as well as in the absence of electron scavengers.

EFFECTS OF O_2, N_2O, AND H_2O_2. The finding that the G-value for degradation of benzoic acid in O_2 is 2.45 (*27*), whereas dimers are found in extremely small yields, may be explained if nearly all intermediate benzoic acid radicals interact with O_2 according to Equations 12 or 13.

$$BHOH^\circ + O_2 \rightarrow \text{products} \qquad (12)$$

$$BHOH^\circ \rightarrow B^\circ + H_2O \qquad (13a)$$

$$B^\circ + O_2 \rightarrow \text{products} \qquad (13b)$$

The occurrence of Reactions 12 and 13 may also explain the present observation that G(hydroxybenzoic acids) was higher in O_2 than in presence of H_2O_2, although the number of OH radicals interacting with benzoic acid in the latter experiment was increased by a factor of two.

Benzoic acid in aqueous anoxic solution reacts rapidly not only with OH°, but also with e^-_{aq} and H (Table I). It follows that in anoxia oxidized and reduced benzoic acid radicals may interact and give rise to back reactions, thus reducing the yield of total degradation.

The effect of N_2O on x-ray induced hydroxylation and degradation of benzoic acid could be explained by suppression of Reaction 10 and thus of Reaction 14:

$$BH\text{-}e^- + BH\text{-}OH^\circ \rightarrow 2\ BH + OH^- \quad (14)$$

Since G(hydroxybenzoic acids) in presence of H_2O_2 was greater by a factor of two than that in N_2O, it seems to follow that suppression of Reactions 10 and 14 may be the only effect of N_2O in the benzoic acid system.

The yield of *m*-hydroxybenzoic acid was three times higher in the presence of H_2O_2 than in N_2O, the yields of the other isomers being increased only by a factor of 1.5–1.7 (Table II). This may indicate that the $H_2O_2^-$ radical, which is formed according to Equation 2, may have sufficient lifetime to react with benzoic acid (or benzoic acid radicals). Since $H_2O_2^-$ is probably less reactive than OH, the former may be expected to oxidize preferentially the more electronegative meta positions, and thus increase the yield of *m*-hydroxybenzoic acid relative to the yields of the other isomers.

It should be noted that the relative rates of attack of OH at the ortho-, meta-, and para-positions of benzoic acid cannot be derived from the observed G-values of end products in anoxia. The G-values will be influenced strongly by the redox potentials of the intermediate radicals as well as by steric factors. From our results it appears that the *p*-hydroxybenzoic acid radical probably acts as a reducing agent, whereas *o*-, and *m*-hydroxybenzoic acid radicals probably are oxidizing entities in "dismutation reactions" taking place in anoxia.

The present results with N_2O strongly conflict with those of other workers, who have presented evidence that N_2O is able to convert e^-_{aq} into OH radicals in many systems (*1, 2, 3, 16, 18, 21, 37*). Our results appear difficult to interpret on this basis. It therefore seems important that more work be conducted on radiation chemical systems containing N_2O, particularly with reference to chemical reactions specifically involving OH radicals.

Acknowledgment

The authors take pleasure in expressing their gratitude to M. Ebert for stimulating discussions during an early stage of this work. Financial support from The Nansen Scientific Fund and from The Norwegian Cancer Society is also gratefully acknowledged.

Literature Cited

(1) Adams, G. E., "Current Topics in Radiation Research," Vol. 3, Chap. II, p. 35, M. Ebert, A. Howard, eds., North Holland Publishing Co., Amsterdam, 1967.
(2) Adams, G. E. (personal communications).
(3) Adams, G. E., Boag, J. W., Currant, J., Michael, B. D., "Pulse Radiolysis," p. 117, M. Ebert, J. P. Keene, A. J. Swallow, J. H. Baxendale, eds., Academic Press, London, 1965.
(4) Allen, A. O., "Actions Chimiques et Biologiques des Radiations," Series 5, Chap. I, p. 9, M. Haïssinsky, ed., Masson et Cie, Paris, 1961.
(5) Anbar, M., ADVAN. CHEM. SER. **50,** 55 (1965).
(6) Anbar, M., Meyerstein, D., Neta, P., *J. Phys. Chem.* **68,** 2967 (1964).
(7) Anbar, M., Meyerstein, D., Neta, D., *Nature* **209,** 1348 (1966).
(8) Anbar, M., Munoz, R. A., Rona, P., *J. Phys. Chem.* **67,** 2708 (1963).
(9) Anbar, M., Neta, P., *Intern. J. Appl. Radiation Isotopes* **16,** 227 (1965).
(10) Armstrong, W. A., Black, B. A., Grant, D. W., *J. Phys. Chem.* **64,** 1415 (1960).
(11) Armstrong, W. A., Facey, R. A., Humphreys, W. G., *Radiation Res.* **19,** 120 (1963).
(12) Baxendale, J. H., "Pulse Radiolysis," p. 15, M. Ebert, J. P. Keene, A. J. Swallow, J. H. Baxendale, eds., Academic Press, London, 1965.
(13) Baxendale, J. H., Magee, J., *Discussions Faraday Soc.* **14,** 160 (1953).
(14) Bratton, C. A., Marshall, E. K., *J. Biol. Chem.* **128,** 527 (1939).
(15) Dainton, F. S., Peterson, D. B., *Nature* **186,** 878 (1960).
(16) Dainton, F. S., Peterson, D. B., *Proc. Roy. Soc.* **267A,** 443 (1962).
(17) Dainton, F. S., Watt, W. S., *Nature* **195,** 1294 (1962).
(18) Dainton, F. S., Watt, W. S., *Proc. Roy. Soc.* **275A,** 447 (1963).
(19) Dorfman, L. M., Taub, I. A., Buhler, R. E., *J. Chem. Phys.* **36,** 3051 (1962).
(20) Downes, A. M., *Australian J. Chem.* **11,** 154 (1958).
(21) Ebert, M. (personal communications).
(22) Gordon, S., Hart, E. J., Matheson, M. S., Rabani, J., Thomas, J. K., *Discussions Faraday Soc.* **36,** 193 (1963).
(23) Howard-Flanders, P., Alper, T., *Radiation Res.* **7,** 199 (1959).
(24) Hutchinson, F., Ross, D. A., *Radiation Res.* **10,** 477 (1959).
(25) Kalkwarf, D. R., *2nd Intern. Conf., Peaceful Uses At. Energy, Geneva* **29,** 379 (1958).
(26) Kartasheva, L. I., Bulanovskaya, Z. S., Barelko, E. V., Varshavskii, Ya. M., Proskurnin, M. A., *Dokl. Akad. Nauk. SSSR* **136,** 143 (1961).
(27) Loeff, L., Swallow, A. J., *J. Phys. Chem.* **68,** 2470 (1964).
(28) Matthews, R. W., Sangster, D. F. (personal communication).
(29) Nakken, K. F., *Radiation Res.* **21,** 446 (1964).
(30) Nakken, K. F., *Strahlentherapie* **129,** 586 (1966).
(31) Nakken, K. F., "Current Topics in Radiation Research," Vol. 1, Chap. 2, p. 49, M. Ebert and A. Howard, eds., North Holland Publishing Co., Amsterdam, 1965.
(32) Nakken, K. F., Thesis, University of Oslo, Norway, 1966.
(33) Nakken, K. F., Brustad, T., *4th Meeting of the Federation of European Biochem. Soc.* **Abstr. 151,** 38, Oslo, 1967.
(34) Nakken, K. F., Pihl, A., *Radiation Res.* **26,** 519 (1965).
(35) Phung, P. V., Burton, M., *Radiation Res.* **7,** 199 (1957).

(36) Spinks, J. W. T., Woods, R. J., "An Introduction to Radiation Chemistry," John Wiley & Sons, Inc., New York, 1964.
(37) Thomas, J. K., *Trans. Faraday Soc.* **61,** 702 (1965).
(38) Williams, G. H., "Homolytic Aromatic Substitution," Pergamon Press, Oxford, 1960.

RECEIVED January 5, 1968.

18

A Compact Apparatus for Photogeneration of Hydrated Electrons

KLAUS SCHMIDT and EDWIN J. HART

Chemistry Division, Argonne National Laboratory, Argonne, Ill. 60439

A new flash photolysis instrument, especially designed to generate hydrated electrons and study their reactions, is described in detail. With a new three-dimensional multiple reflection cell and its capacity to produce up to 10^{-7}M e^-_{aq} *in a single 40-μsec. light pulse, this instrument provides adequate sensitivity for determining* e^-_{aq} *rate constants and for use in analytical chemistry. With this instrument less than* 10^{-9}M e^-_{aq} *may be detected.*

The hydrated electron, a newly discovered, highly reactive negative ion, has broad potential uses in chemistry. In water it is a more powerful reducing agent than the hydrogen atom by 0.6 volt. It is the dominant reducing species in irradiated water, and after its rate constants were established it helped to explain many radiolytic mechanisms. Since it is liberated by photochemical, thermal, and electrolytic reactions, it is a species important throughout the several branches of chemistry (*7, 8*).

As promising as this species is in contributing to advances in chemistry, its usefulness is hampered by its 10^{-3}-sec. lifetime and by the expensive and hazardous methods needed for its generation. Its brief lifetime is overcome by using the modern techniques of flash photolysis and pulse radiolysis (*1, 2, 10, 12*). While pulse radiolysis provides an unexcelled way of producing it in adequate concentrations for research, it is an impractical method for general usage. For this reason we have devised a relatively simple, safe, and inexpensive apparatus for studying its reactions by absorption spectroscopy. Only a flash of ultraviolet light is required to produce the hydrated electron in our equipment. Its properties are studied by following the decay of its optical absorbance by using the special flash spectrophotometric array described in this paper. Our instrument provides students of advanced physical chemistry with a practical way to study the properties of the hydrated electron. Besides, the radiation chemist may obtain kinetic data on the hydrated electron without using costly linear accelerators.

Theory and General Layout

Hydrated electrons are generated in a H_2-saturated alkaline solution by a flash of ultraviolet light (*7, 13*). Our apparatus may be used to study its chemical properties, to measure its rate constants, or to analyze solutions for low concentrations of its scavengers (*9*). The well-established reactions producing e^-_{aq} are:

$$OH^- + h\nu \rightarrow OH + e^-_{aq} \qquad (1)$$

$$OH + H_2 \rightarrow H_2O + H \quad 4.5 \times 10^7 M^{-1} \text{ sec.}^{-1} \qquad (2)$$

$$H + OH^- \rightarrow e^-_{aq} \quad 2.0 \times 10^7 M^{-1} \text{ sec.}^{-1} \qquad (3)$$

Each light quantum effective in Reaction 1 eventually produces a second e^-_{aq} *via* Reactions 2 and 3 (*7*), but scavengers such as O_2, when present even in submicromolar concentrations, profoundly affect its formation and decay. To eliminate them we preirradiate our solutions with a second ultraviolet mercury lamp. After "cleanup" we can inject scavengers at micro- and submicromolar levels. During preirradiation and after the injection of samples, the solution in the cell is mixed by means of a small glass-encased iron rod, activated by a solenoid that receives repetitive pulses from a pulse-generating circuit.

The apparatus consists of a xenon flash lamp, a mercury ultraviolet lamp, a Suprasil quartz irradiation cell, a tungsten lamp, optical system, red filters, photomultiplier, and an oscilloscope. A block diagram of the apparatus is shown in Figure 1.

The hydrated electron concentration is followed by monitoring the light transmission of the solution at 700 nm., near its optical absorption maximum. At this wavelength, its molar extinction coefficient is $1.85 \times 10^4 M^{-1}$ cm.$^{-1}$. For increased sensitivity, the narrow analyzing light beam from a tungsten lamp is passed through the cell seven times. Next, the light goes through a red filter combination and then into the cathode of a photomultiplier tube. The transient absorption signal is finally displayed on an oscilloscope and recorded, if desirable.

Details

Optical Arrangement. A new three-dimensional multiple reflection design has been devised for the analyzing light beam in our apparatus. This design permits a larger diameter of the light beam for a given number of passes to reduce photomultplier shot noise.

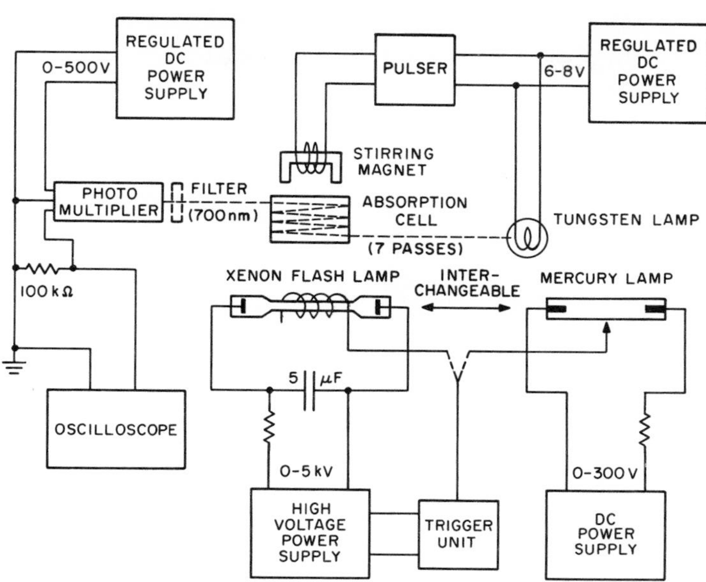

Figure 1. Block diagram of the apparatus for the photogeneration of hydrated electrons

In the "classical" multiple reflection arrangement (*18*) the axis of the light beam passing through the cell remains in a plane. Thus, only a small portion of the cell cross section is utilized for the passage of light, and the light spots lie on a straight line. In an improved version (*13*) the light spots occupy two parallel straight lines on the window, thus about doubling the cross section of the analyzing light beam. Our three-dimensional arrangement permits a further increase of this cross section. It uses two fixed concave mirrors as opposed to the split mirrors in the previous arrangements. The light beam is reflected between these mirrors in such a way that it "rotates around the axis" of the mirrors, as shown in Figure 2. As mirrors, plano-concave lenses of borosilicate glass are used, whose concave sides are silvered except for a 90° sector through which the entering and exit light beam passes.

The three-dimensional multiple reflection from concave mirrors is illustrated in Figure 2. The right half of this figure shows the geometrical conditions for a light ray coming from point 1 to be reflected to point 2 on mirror M_2 in such a way that it passes through point 3 having the same axial distance as point 1. The ratio, $\phi/2$ is the angle of rotation per reflection. If N is the (odd) number of passes, then $\phi/2 = 2\pi/(N + 1)$. In our apparatus $N = 7$, so $\phi = \pi/2$. Thus, the radius of curvature of the mirrors must be 3.414 times their distance. In practice, this ratio is not very critical. [The distance, d, is the equivalent distance in a material with the same refractive index as that adjacent to the reflecting mirror surfaces. If n_o is this refractive index, a layer of thickness, t, and refractive index, n, has the equivalent thickness, $t_o = tn_o/n$.]

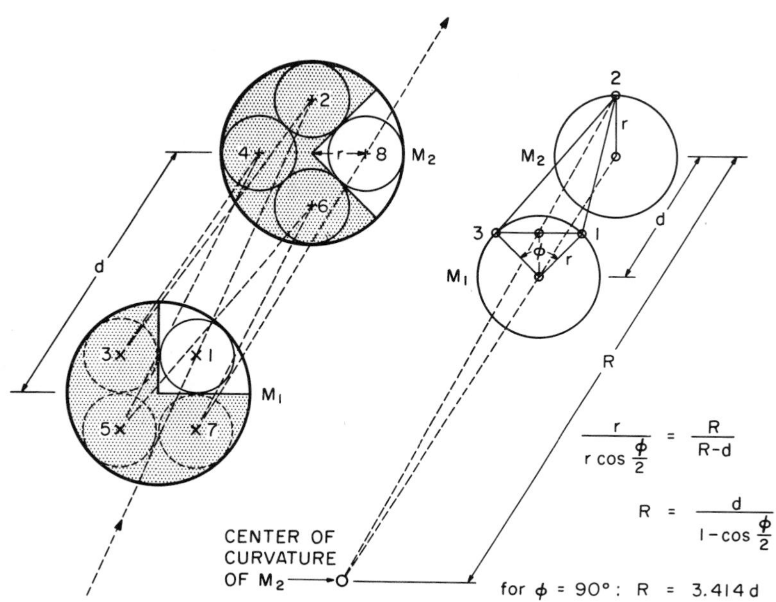

Figure 2. Three-dimensional multiple reflection on concave mirrors

The left half of Figure 2 shows how the light beam is reflected back and forth between mirrors M_1 and M_2. The beam enters through M_1 at the bottom and emerges through M_2 at the top. The beam follows the course 1 . . . 8. The upper part of Figure 3 shows the schematic arrangement of the optical elements in the analyzing light beam. The lower part of this figure depicts the unfolded light beam on its path through the multiple pass system, the loci of the lamp filament F, and of the aperture limiting stop D_1. The total path length in the cell is 35 cm. Although the reflection losses at the quartz-air interfaces add up to about 50%, we obtain sufficient light intensity on the photomultiplier cathode so that a water immersion system (*13*) is unnecessary.

Flash Irradiation. A Novatron 277 xenon capillary flash tube of 4-cm. arc length supplies the light flash. It is encased in a stainless steel reflector which has been polished and vacuum-coated with aluminum. Figure 4 shows its geometrical arrangement. The contour of the cylindrical reflector consists of three circular arcs forming three images, L_1', L_2', and L_3' of the light source L. The cross section of each light beam from the source is also indicated. The Hanovia 612-C mercury lamp used for preirradiation is mounted into a similar reflector.

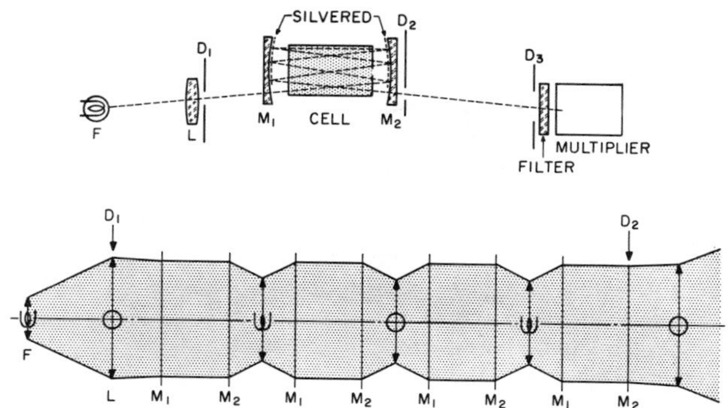

Figure 3. Path of analyzing light beam

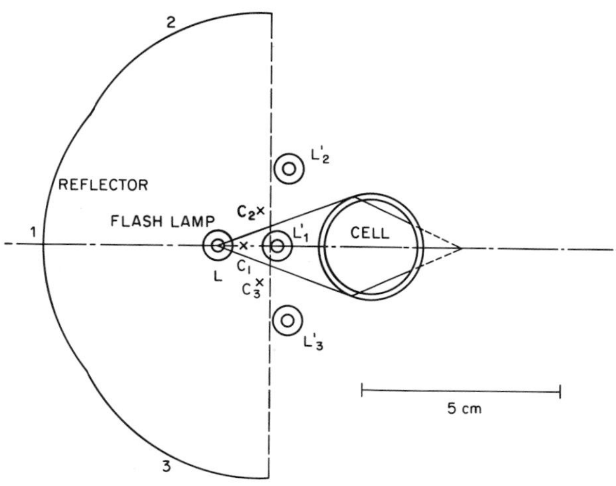

Figure 4. Reflector geometry

An interesting feature of this optical arrangement is that two segments of the cell receive no light from the primary or image beams (*see* Figure 4). Their size is independent of the position of the light source. For this reason, the portion of the cell diameter usable for the analyzing light beam is reduced by approximately 20%. The three images of the light source give rise to similar light beams. All four beams converge, and this, in part, compensates for the absorption loss in the solution.

An approximate calculation taking into account the measured absorption spectrum of 0.001*M* NaOH solution and the relative spectral emission of the xenon lamp in the useful 185–220-nm. range shows that homogeneity is sufficient for measuring second-order rate constants (*14*).

Electronic Circuitry. For the mercury lamp, a filtered d.c.-power supply is used, although an a.c.-power supply would be adequate. The mercury lamp is started by using the trigger circuit for the xenon lamp. In our first experiments we tested the Hanovia 612-C mercury lamp for flash irradiation by superimposing a condenser discharge on its normal operating current (*15*). While satisfactory e^-_{aq} signals are obtained, the lamps have a limited lifetime, and the arc is often extinguished by the flash discharge so that the lamp has to be restarted. Hence, we changed to our present two-lamp system.

The xenon flash lamp is operated with single discharges of a 5–μF condenser at 4–5 kvolts. The condenser is connected directly to the lamp. After the condenser has been charged, the lamp is triggered by feeding a pulse from a tesla coil to a thin wire wound around the capillary portion of the lamp. Although this method has proved satisfactory, an improved circuit using a triggered spark gap is being constructed.

The tungsten lamp (General Electric type 1962 tungsten iodide) operates on a regulated low voltage power supply. A standard circuit with six transistors is used. The voltage is usually set at 7 volts, although the maximum permissible voltage is 8.5. By using the lower voltage we increase considerably the lamp life with only a moderate intensity loss in the red spectral range.

A simple astable multivibrator circuit provides the pulsed voltage for the stirring coil. It operates at a pulse frequency of about 2 cycles per sec. from voltage taken from the tungsten lamp power supply.

A photomultiplier type 7102 (RCA) tube serves as a detector for the analyzing light beam. It receives its power from a Hewlett Packard type 711A regulated power supply. The last three dynodes are connected to the anode; the operating voltage is approximately 450 volts. With a load resistor of 100 kohms it provides sufficient output voltage for an oscilloscope without further amplification, and adequate time resolution. We use a Tektronix type 564 storage oscillosope with a 2A63 plug-in amplifier operated in the d.c. mode and a 2B76 time base. However, any d.c. oscilloscope with a minimum sensitivity of 10 mv./cm. and a risetime of as much as 5 μsec. would be adquate. For calibration, the multiplier operating voltage is adjusted so that a 2-volt deflection on the oscilloscope corresponds to 100% transmission. For e^-_{aq} experiments, a 2-μF coupling capacitor is inserted between the multiplier and the oscilloscope.

Mechanical Construction. A photograph of the entire apparatus is shown in Figure 5. The flash unit is on the left, the relay rack in the center, and the oscilloscope on the right. The relay rack contains all the electronic circuitry except that of the photomultiplier power supply (located on the top of the relay rack) and the photomultiplier circuit. The latter is built into the small aluminum box (left) attached to the photomultiplier tube housing. The red filter is hidden by the light tunnel between the cell and the photomultiplier.

Figure 5. Over-all view of apparatus for the photogeneration of e^-_{aq}

Figure 6 shows more detail of the flash unit. The two interchangeable ultraviolet lamp assemblies have been turned on their sides for a better view. The tungsten lamp housing with lens attachment, the cell holder, the cell and the injection device may now be seen. The concave mirrors are mounted into the aluminum rings protruding from both ends of the cell holder, and a small cooling fan is mounted below. Grooves are provided in the cell housing for inserting light filters, and this figure shows a 1-mm. fused quartz square with negligible ultraviolet absorption in the filter holder. Its purpose is to improve the cooling efficiency of the air from the fan. The Suprasil quartz irradiation cell has an outer diameter of 25 mm. and an over-all length of 52 mm. The stirring rod, which cannot be seen in the figure, consists of a cut-off nail sealed into 3-mm. borosilicate glass tubing. Tests showed that it does not interfere with the analyzing light beam when idle.

Figure 6. Close-up view of absorption cell and light sources

Solution Preparation. The matrix is a $10^{-3}M$ NaOH solution saturated with hydrogen. Triply distilled water, 1*M* NaOH stock solution, and prepurified hydrogen (Matheson) are used in its preparation (*4*). Figure 7 illustrates our procedure for saturating the solution with H_2 and filling the irradiation cell. We bubble hydrogen through the water in the modified 250-ml. wash bottle for about 2 minutes to remove the bulk of air and CO_2. Then 0.25 ml. of the 0.1*M* NaOH solution is added, and H_2 is bubbled again through the bottle for 15 minutes. After flushing the cell with H_2, the H_2-saturated solution from the bottle is forced into the cell. This solution is expelled from the cell with H_2, and the cell filled again. At this point, the solution contains less than $10^{-6}M$ O_2.

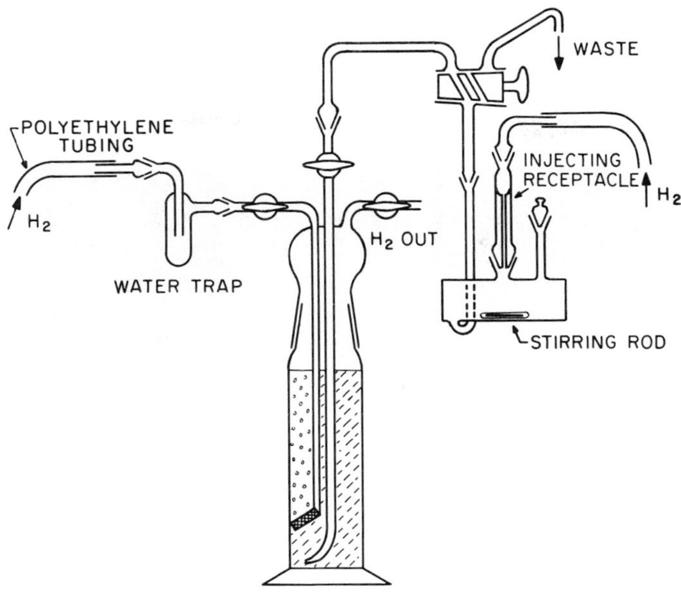

Figure 7. Arrangement for filling the cell

The 20-μM H_2O_2 used in the injection experiment is prepared from a 30% H_2O_2 (Superoxol, Merck) by diluting it with triply distilled water. This solution is then H_2-saturated in the same manner as the matrix. Up to 1 ml. of these solutions is injected into the cell by an all-borosilicate glass syringe provided with an adapter having a long glass needle. The H_2O_2 solution from the wash bottle is forced through the needle into the syringe. After thoroughly flushing the syringe with the plunger removed, it is reinserted, the solution is expelled from the syringe, and then the syringe is refilled (9). Thus, a virtually air-free filling is obtained. The syringe is next inserted into the injecting receptacle (Figures 6 and 7) attached to the cell by a ground-glass joint. The length of the needle and the needle adapter are adjusted so that the tip of the needle protrudes about 1 mm. into the cell. In this way the scavenger solution is injected directly into the matrix. For injections, the stopcock on the right sidearm is opened, and the stirring mechanism is activated. Care must be taken so that the level of the matrix solution is well above the capillary portion of the injecting receptacle before inserting the needle. Otherwise, the matrix will be contaminated with air. Before use, the cell and all the glassware are thoroughly cleaned, rinsed with triply distilled water, and heated to about 450°C.

Results

Analysis of Decay Curves. The decay curves obtained immediately after filling the cell with matrix solution have small amplitudes and half-lives of only a few tenths of a millisecond. This is caused by impurities, particularly oxygen. From the e^-_{aq} half-life and its rate constant of $2 \times 10^{10} M^{-1}$ sec.$^{-1}$ (2), we calculate an impurity (O_2) concentration of 1–2 $\times 10^{-7} M$ O_2. To remove this trace of O_2 we preirradiate the matrix for 2 minutes with light from the mercury lamp which operates at 100 watts to avoid heating the solution. This procedure effectively removes oxygen from the solution by a mechanism analogous to that of preirradiation with γ-rays (*4*, *9*). After preirradiation we obtain e^-_{aq} signals with considerably larger amplitudes and longer half-lives (*see* Figure 8). The curve with the larger amplitude was recorded at minimum flash lamp distance (Figure 4), the one with the smaller amplitude at a distance of approximately 10 cm. The oscilloscope sensitivities were 50 and 10 mv./cm., respectively. From the half-lives of these two curves we calculate the first- and second-order components of the e^-_{aq} decay, using machine-computed tables described elsewhere (*16*). From the second-order component, we obtain $k(e^-_{aq} + e^-_{aq}) = 6 \times 10^9 M^{-1}$ sec.$^{-1}$ at about 25°C., which agrees well with reported values (*5*). The first-order component is equivalent to about 3nM O_2.

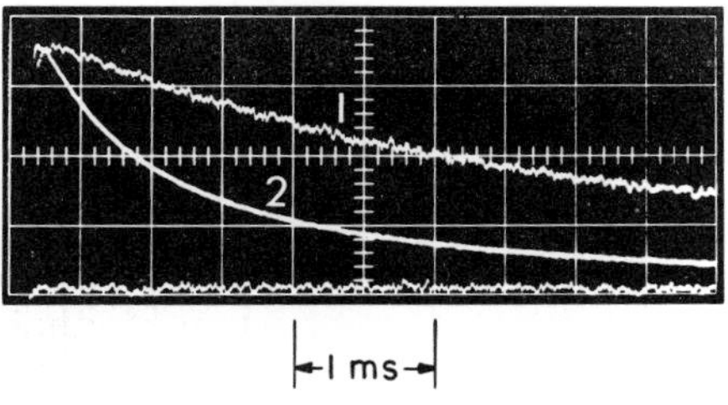

Figure 8. e^-_{aq} *Decay curves*

1: *16n*M $[e^-_{aq}]_o$
2: *80n*M $[e^-_{aq}]_o$

Reaction of e^-_{aq} with H_2O_2. In another series of experiments, we injected various amounts of 20-μM H_2O_2 into the matrix to study the mechanism of the $H_2 + H_2O_2$ reaction. In Figure 9 the first-order component of the electron decay curve is plotted *vs.* the initial H_2O_2 concentration. $k[X]$ is the measured first-order rate constant, formally written as the product of a second-order rate constant, k, and the concentration of an unknown reaction partner, X. The figure also shows the effect of injecting hydrogen-saturated water as a control. The injected volumes of water are those used for injecting the amounts of H_2O_2 given by the abscissa. Further tests prove that the impurities introduced by this injection technique are usually smaller than indicated by the blank curve.

The H_2O_2 points were obtained by injecting up to 1 ml. of the stock solution in volumes of 0.1 or 0.05 ml. and recording an oscilloscope trace after each addition. After the first 0.5 ml. had been injected, the cell with the syringe in place was irradiated with the mercury lamp. This brought the decay curve back to its original shape. Next, a second series of points was obtained by injecting the remaining 0.5 ml. of the stock solution in the same way. Since no significant difference could be observed between the first and second series of points, all the points of several such experiments were plotted on one graph.

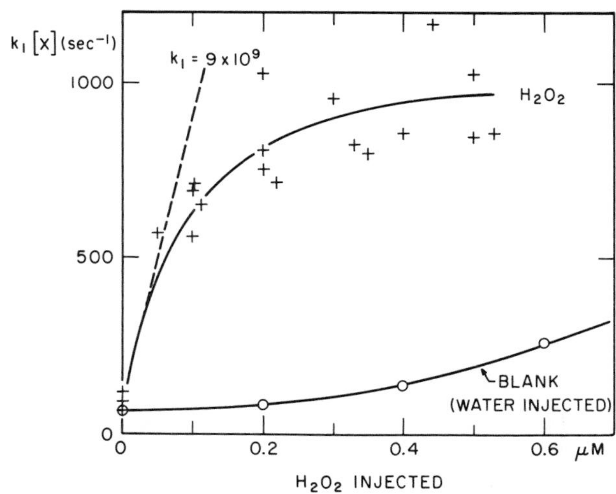

Figure 9. Effect of H_2O_2 concentration on the first-order decay of $[e^-_{aq}]$ in the system H_2O_2–H_2 at pH 11

Discussion

In a hydrogen-saturated pH 11 matrix, a chain decomposition mechanism initiated by Reaction 1 and followed by Reactions 2, 3, and 4 is expected.

$$e^-_{aq} + H_2O_2 \rightarrow OH^- + OH \qquad 1.2 \times 10^{10} M^{-1}\ \text{sec.}^{-1} \qquad (4)$$

The quantum yield of Reaction 1 in our 185–200-nm. wavelength range is unknown, but it is sufficiently high with our 100-joule pulse to provide an initial $10^{-7}M$ e^-_{aq} concentration. A loss of e^-_{aq} or, which is equivalent under our conditions, a loss of H or OH radicals, can therefore only occur in second-order reactions such as 5 and 6.

$$OH + OH \rightarrow H_2O_2 \qquad 5.5 \times 10^{9} M^{-1}\ \text{sec.}^{-1} \qquad (5)$$

$$e^-_{aq} + OH \rightarrow OH^- \qquad 3.0 \times 10^{10} M^{-1}\ sec.^{-1} \qquad (6)$$

However, owing to the low concentrations involved, these reactions are too slow to account for the observed effect of H_2O_2. We carried out a computer calculation (*17*) of the expected e^-_{aq} decay curve, taking into account not only the above reactions but also other possible chain terminating reactions, including reactions of e^-_{aq} with O^- and HO_2^- which cannot be neglected at pH 11. Owing to their low concentrations and relatively low extinction coefficients, the over-all light absorption by OH and H_2O_2 is at least 2 orders of magnitude less than the absorption by OH^-. Therefore, light absorption by these species may be neglected. According to the computer result, a H_2O_2 concentration as large as $1\mu M$ should change the half-life by only a few percent. On the other hand, the initial slope of the H_2O_2 curve in Figure 9 corresponds to an apparent rate constant, k, of $9 \times 10^9 M^{-1}$ sec.$^{-1}$. This agrees well with the literature values (*3, 7*) of k_4 and $k(e^-_{aq} + HO_2^-) = 3 \times 10^9 M^{-1}$ sec.$^{-1}$, considering the fact that at pH 11 about 20% of the H_2O_2 is dissociated. It, therefore, seems that at low H_2O_2 concentrations the species X is identical with H_2O_2—*i.e.*, the chain reaction sequence: Reactions 2, 3, and 4, is prevented for some unknown reason. Previous experiments on the same chemical system with γ-ray pulses yielded a similar result (*9*). It was to explain these unexpected results that we started the H_2O_2 experiments described here.

Acknowledgments

We thank Edmund E. Klocek and his staff for making the mechanical parts of the apparatus, and Steve G. Petrek for building the electronic circuitry.

Literature Cited

(1) Boag, J. W., "Actions Chimiques et Biologiques des Radiations," Sixieme Serie, M. Haissinsky, ed., Chap. I, p. 1, Masson, Paris, 1963.
(2) Dorfman, L. M., Matheson, M. S., *Progr. Reaction Kinetics* (1965).
(3) Felix, W. O., Gall, B. H., Dorfman, L. M., *J. Phys. Chem.* **71**, 384 (1967).
(4) Fielden, E. M., Hart, E. J., *Radiation Res.* **32**, 564 (1967).
(5) Gottschall, W. C., Hart, E. J., *J. Phys. Chem.* **71**, 2102 (1967).
(6) Hart, E. J., *J. Am. Chem. Soc.* **73**, 68 (1951).
(7) Hart, E. J., "Actions Chimiques et Biologiques des Radiations," Dixieme Serie, M. Haissinsky, ed., Chap. I, p. 1, Masson, Paris, 1966.
(8) Hart, E. J., *Record Chem. Prog.* **28**, 25 (1967).
(9) Hart, E. J., Fielden, E. M., ADVAN. CHEM. SER. **50**, 253 (1965).
(10) Keene, J. P., "Pulse Radiolysis," M. Ebert, J. P. Keene, A. J. Swallow, J. H. Baxendale, eds., p. 1, Academic Press, London and New York, 1965.
(11) Matheson, M. S., Mulac, W. A., Rabani, J., *J. Phys. Chem.* **67**, 2613 (1963).

(12) Porter, G., Technique of Organic Chemistry, 2nd Ed., Vol. VIII, Part 2, p. 1055, Interscience, New York, 1963.
(13) Rabani, J., Mulac, W. A., Matheson, M. S., *J. Phys. Chem.* **69**, 53 (1965).
(14) Sauer, M. C., Jr., *Argonne Natl. Lab. Rept.* **ANL-7327** (1967).
(15) Schmidt, K., *Strahlentherapie* **124,** 127 (1964).
(16) Schmidt, K., *Argonne Natl. Lab. Rept.* **ANL-7400** (1968).
(17) *Ibid.,* **ANL-7199** (1966).
(18) White, J. U., *J. Opt. Soc. Am.* **32,** 285 (1942).

RECEIVED January 15, 1968. Work performed under the auspices of the U. S. Atomic Energy Commission.

19

Molecular and Radical Product Yields in Alpha-Radiolysis of 0.8*N* H_2SO_4

M. V. VLADIMIROVA

State Committee of Utilization of Atomic Energy, Moscow, USSR

The paper discusses the newest and most reliable results of investigations of α-radiolysis of 0.8N H_2SO_4 as well as $FeSO_4$ and $Ce(SO_4)_2$ solutions. Based on the results discussed the yields were calculated of radical products of radiolysis and the yield of water decomposition that proved equal to 3.35 molecule/100 e.v. in aerated solution. This $G(-H_2O)$ value is lower than those determined before (3.5–3.7). The paper gives the values of the yields of intratrajectory reactions (H_2O_2 + OH, H_2 + OH, H_2O_2 + H) calculated from the experimental data as well as the yield of track reaction (H + OH) calculated from the above relationship between the yields of radiolysis products and the LET value. The initial yields of water decomposition in α-radiolysis are calculated; the yields of intratrajectory reactions (G_{-H_2O} = 4.35 molecule/100 e.v.) and the yield of H + OH reaction (G_{-H_2O} = 7.0 molecule/100 e.v.) taken into account.

This paper analyzes some experimental data obtained in the radiolysis of 0.8*N* H_2SO_4 effected by α-radiation of dissolved Po; the yields of some radiolysis products are estimated on their basis.

Two sufficiently complete reviews are available where experimental data are collected on α-radiolysis of aqueous solutions (*7, 14*). It follows from these reviews that the yields are established with reasonable accuracy: $G(Fe^{3+})_{O_2} = 5.1$ ion/100 e.v. (*2, 8, 9, 12*) in aerated and $G(Fe^{3+}) = 3.53$–3.57 ion/100 e.v. (*8, 9, 12*) in deaerated 0.8*N* H_2SO_4 solutions, hydrogen yields $G(H_2) = 1.40$ molecule/100 e.v. (*9, 11*), $G(H_2)/Fe^{2+} = 1.60$ molecule/100 e.v. (*12*), and $G(HO_2) = 0.2$ rad/100 e.v. (*5*).

The yields of other α-radiolysis products have been recently refined after the appearance of the above reviews.

After careful determination of Ce^{4+}-ion reduction yield in aerated $0.8N$ H_2SO_4 solution under the influence of dissolved Po the workers (*2*) offered the yield value $G(Ce^{3+})$ equal to 2.94 ± 0.06 ion/100 e.v. This value ranged formerly within 3.05–3.3 ion/100 e.v. (*14*).

The $G(Ce^{3+})$ value found in (*1*) appears to be most reliable since it is equal to Ce^{3+} yields determined when other types of radiation are used whose LET value ranges within 2–25 e.v./A. In the same work (*2*) the H_2O_2 yield was found in $0.8N$ H_2SO_4 which proved equal to 1.41 + 0.06 molecule/100 e.v. at the radiation doses of $(4\text{–}10) \times 10^{17}$ e.v./ml. In previous work (*4*) $G(H_2O_2)$ was found equal to 1.20 ± 0.1 molecule/100 e.v. We cited the yield values that are not only newer but are also more reliable. Unfortunately, in some of the latest monographs on radiation chemistry old data is given on α-radiolysis of $0.8N$ H_2SO_4, although new and more accurate results are already available.

The question of determining water decomposition yield in α-radiolysis and difficulties in correlating the values of the yields of radiolysis radical products obtained in investigating various chemical systems have been repeatedly discussed in literature.

To calculate H, OH, and H_2O_2 yields in deaerated solutions the following equations are used:

$$G(Fe^{3+}) = 2G(H_2O_2) + G(OH) + 3G(HO_2) + G(H) \qquad (1)$$

$$G(Ce^{3+}) = 2G(H_2O_2) - G(OH) + G(HO_2) + G(H) \qquad (2)$$

$$2G(H_2O_2) + G(OH) + 3G(HO_2) = 2G(H_2) + G(H) \qquad (3)$$

In (*2*) the authors did not determine the Ce^{3+} yield in a deaerated solution, however, it can be estimated from the fact that the ratio of $G(Ce^{3+})O_2$ to $G(Ce^{3+})$ found for α-radiation (*6*) and other types of radiation equals $\sim$1.05. Substituting the known values into Equations 1–3 one finds the yields in a deaerated $0.8N$ H_2SO_4 solution:

$$G(H_2O_2) = 1.20,\ G(-H_2O) = 3.0 \text{ molecule/100 e.v.}$$

$$G(OH) = 0.2,\ G(H) = 0.4 \text{ rad/100 e.v.,}$$

The values obtained differ from those previously reported by us (*12, 14*).

The yield of H radicals determined by calculation is shown to equal 0.4 rad/100 e.v. At the same time the discrepancy between the hydrogen yields, determined with and without Fe^{2+} ions being present in the solution and characterizing the H radical yield is equal to only 0.2. Thus, in deaerated solutions there is a disagreement between $G(H)$, found by experiment and calculation. Added investigations are needed to clarify this disagreement.

To determine the yields in aerated solutions the following equations are used:

$$G(Fe^{3+})O_2 = 2G(H_2O_2)O_2 + G(OH)O_2 + 3G(HO_2) + 3G(H)O_2 \quad (4)$$

$$G(Ce^{3+})O_2 = 2G(H_2O_2)O_2 + G(H)O_2 + G(HO_2) - G(OH)O_2 \quad (5)$$

$$2G(H_2O_2)O_2 + G(OH)O_2 + 3G(HO_2) = 2G(H_2) + G(H)O_2 + 2[G(H_2O_2)O_2 - G(H_2O_2)] \quad (6)$$

The last term of Equation 6 expresses the yield of H radicals that took part in the additional formation of H_2O_2 in aerated solutions. The H_2O_2 formation may proceed in tracks or in a track region by the following reactions:

$$H + O_2 \rightarrow HO_2,\ HO_2 + H \rightarrow H_2O_2.$$

Since $G(H_2O_2)O_2$ depends on the radiation dose and ranges within 1.4–1.2 molecule/100 e.v., this yield will be considered a sought quantity, satisfying Equations 4, 5, and 6.

By substituting the known quantities into these equations the yields are found in aerated solutions: $G(OH)O_2 = 0.35$, $G(H)O_2 = 0.55$ rad/100 e.v. $G(H_2O_2)O_2 = 1.30$, $G(-H_2O)O_2 = 3.35$ molecule/100 e.v. When calculating the yields in aerated solutions the $G(H_2)$ and $G(HO_2)$ values were taken identical to those in deaerated ones. The OH yield value turned out to be lower than the value that we gave before (*12*). The observed yield of water decomposition (3.35 molecule/100 e.v.) also proved lower than the values (3.5–3.6) that were widely used until recently. However, this yield $G(-H_2O)O_2$, equal to 3.35 molecule/100 e.v. agrees very well with what we found by using a different independent procedure.

Based on numerous experimental data on H_2 and Fe^{3+} yields in 0.8*N* H_2SO_4 for different types of radiation the $G(H_2)$, $G(Fe^{3+})O_2$, $G(H)O_2$ and $G(-H_2O)O_2$—LET/e.v./A. of radiation relationships were derived (*10, 13*).

In LET region 3.0–25 e.v./A. these relationships take the form:

$$G(H_2) = 1.1 + 0.02\ (LET) \quad (7)$$

$$G(H)O_2 = 1.50 - 0.25\sqrt{(LET)} \quad (8)$$

$$G(-H_2O)O_2 = 3.65 - 0.195\sqrt{(LET)} + 0.03(LET) \quad (9)$$

As calculated by Equation 9, the observed yield of water decomposition is equal to 3.33 molecule/100 e.v. It should be noted that the radical product yields in α-radiolysis are different in deaerated and aerated solutions.

The above yields of water decomposition were observed and obtained when using scavengers of radical and molecular products—Fe^{2+} and Ce^{4+} ions. When using the same scavengers in γ-radiolysis the yield of water decomposition is known to equal 4.4 molecule/100 e.v. The observed yield of water decomposition and the yields of α-radiolysis products depend largely on the presence of various substances in solution that are capable of interacting with radicals. This was explained by Pucheault who considered it to be governed by intra-trajectory reactions taking place in a region of high local concentration of molecular and radical products.

$$H_2O_2 + OH \rightarrow HO_2 + H_2O \quad (a)$$

$$H_2 + OH \rightarrow H + H_2O \quad (b)$$

$$H_2O_2 + H \rightarrow OH + H_2O \quad (c)$$

One of the evidences for the occurrence of intra-trajectory reactions may be an increase of the yields of radiolysis molecular products in the presence of substances in solution that are scavengers of H or OH radicals and suppress Reactions a, b, or c.

We have shown that the H_2O_2 yield in 0.8N H_2SO_4 solution with glucose, methylene blue, and hydrogen present is increased substantially (*11*). This experimental data permitted the yield of Reaction a to be found; it is equal to 0.2. Our results agree well with the results of Hart (*5*).

Experiments on determination of H_2 yield in presence of some scavengers of OH radicals permitted the yield of Reaction b to be found, that proved equal to 0.35–0.4 (*11*).

The question of the amount of the initial yield of water decomposition or of the initial yields of H and OH radicals is of interest. These yields include the yield of those radicals that take part in alpha-particle tracks in recombination reactions (H + H, OH + OH), in a track region in reactions of radiolysis molecular product decomposition (H_2O_2 + OH, H_2O_2 + H, H_2 + OH), and in a solution volume—in reactions with solutes. Only the recombination reaction H + OH was not taken into account.

The initial yield of water decomposition is G_{-H_2O} and is presented in the following way:

$$G_{-H_2O} = G_H = 2G(H_2) + G(H) + G(b) + G(c) + G(a) - G(a) = G(-H_2O) + G(a) + G(b) + G(c) \quad (10)$$

$$G_{-H_2O} = G_{OH} = 2G(H_2O_2) + G(OH) + 3G(a) + G(b) + G(c) = G(-H_2O) + G(a) + G(b) + G(c) \quad (11)$$

To find the initial yield of water decomposition in α-radiolysis one should know the yields of intra-trajectory reactions and the observed yield of water decomposition.

By substituting the values of $G(-H_2O) = 3.35$, $G(a) = 0.2$, $G(b) = 0.4$ and $G(c) = 0.35$ ($G(c)$—according to Pucheault) into equation for G_{-H_2O} one obtains $G_{-H_2O} = 4.3$ molecule/100 e.v. Thus, the initial yield of water decomposition in α-radiolysis is almost the same as in γ-radiolysis. However, in γ-radiolysis all radicals and molecular products are readily used up in reactions with dissolved substances, and in α-radiolysis they partially take up one another. When investigating α-radiolysis of various systems we may have the value of the water decomposition yield in the range $\sim$ 3.2–4.3 molecule/100 e.v.

Now the problem is to find the experimental evidence for the value $G_{-H_2O} = 4.3$ molecule/100 e.v. when investigating α-radiolysis of solutions containing energetic scavengers of H or OH radicals. We have recently obtained such evidence when investigating α-radiolysis of acid NH_4CNS solutions. Using the mechanism of radiation-chemical reactions in these solutions, proposed by Duflo (*3*), we found the H radical yield in deaerated NH_4CNS solution concentrated to $0.1M$ to equal 1.65 rad/100 e.v., whereas the yield of water decomposition, calculated as the sum of $2\,G(H_2) + G(H)$ equals 4.2 molecule/100 e.v.

For the sake of comparison it may be said that the yield of water decomposition in γ-radiolysis of similar solutions proved equal to 4.35 molecule/100 e.v.

Developing the idea of the initial yield of water decomposition in α-radiolysis one may say that taking into account H + OH reaction that was not discussed above, it should be even more than the yield of water decomposition in γ-radiolysis. Based on the H_2 and $G(-H_2O)$ yield–LET relationship (*13*) derived by us, we have performed a preliminary calculation, assuming conventionally the value of $G_{-H_2O}\,\gamma = 6.0$ molecule/100 e.v.; it showed that in going from γ- to α-radiation the $G(H + OH)$ yield is increased from 1.5 to 2.7 and the yield of water decomposition from 6.0 to 7.0 molecule/100 e.v. Such an increase of the yield of water decomposition in α-radiolysis is in accordance with the idea suggested by Allen (*1*) about the origin of some new way of water decomposition in case of dense tracks.

Summing up the material discussed, it may be said that the experimental data obtained supports the early assumptions of the proximity of the initial yield of water decomposition in α-radiolysis to the yields of water decomposition in γ-radiolysis.

The use of the recent experimental data on α-radiolysis of $0.8N$ H_2SO_4 containing $FeSO_4$ and $Ce(SO_4)_2$ permitted the refinement of the value of the observed water decomposition yield and the radical product yields.

The application of the calculation method based on derived relationships between the yields of some radiolysis products and the amounts of linear energy transfer (LET) made it possible to determine the value of the observed yield of water decomposition in aerated solutions. The value obtained is in agreement with the quantity $G(-H_2O)O_2$, found by the equation of material balance.

Literature Cited

(1) Allen, Augustine O., "The Radiation Chemistry of Water and Aqueous Solutions," D. Van Nostrand Company, Inc., Princeton, N. J., 1961.
(2) Anta, M. C., Mariano, M. H., Santos, M. Z., *J. Chim. Phys.* **61** (4), 577 (1964).
(3) Duflo, M., *Ann. Chim.* **10,** 551 (1965).
(4) Ershova, Z. V., Valdimirova, M. V., *At. Energ. (USSR)* **5,** 546 (1958).
(5) Hart, E., *Radiation Res.* **2,** 33 (1955).
(6) Lefort, M., Tarrago, X., *J. Phys. Chem.* **63,** 833 (1959).
(7) Pucheault, J., *Actions Chim. Biol. Radiations* **5,** 31 (1961).
(8) Steyn, J., *J. S. African Chem. Inst.* **14,** 93 (1961).
(9) Trumbore, C., Hart, E., *J. Phys. Chem.* **63,** 867 (1959).
(10) Valdimirova, M. V., *At. Energ. (USSR)* **17** (3), 222 (1964).
(11) Vladimirova, M. V., Ershova, Z. V., "Transactions of 2nd All-Union Conference on Radiation Chemistry," p. 162, Pub. Acad. Sci., Moscow, USSR, 1962.
(12) Vladimirova, M. V., Kulikov, I. A., Shulyatikova, L. G., *Radiokhimya* **8** (2), 226 (1966).
(13) Vladimirova, M. V., *Radiokhimiya* **9** (3), 386 (1967).
(14) Vladimirova, M. V., *Usp. Khim.* **4,** 462 (1964).

RECEIVED February 7, 1968.

Biology

20

Electron Transfer Studies by Pulse Radiolysis

G. E. ADAMS, B. D. MICHAEL, and R. L. WILLSON

British Empire Cancer Campaign for Research, Research Unit in Radiobiology, Mount Vernon Hospital, Northwood, Middlesex, England

A general review of pulse radiolysis studies on electron transfer in solution is presented together with some recent unpublished data. Electron transfer processes occurring in irradiated solutions of metal ions, inorganic anions, and various aliphatic and aromatic organic compounds are discussed with respect to general redox phenomena in radiation and free radical chemistry. Specific topics include the measurement of peroxy radical formation, the use of nitrous oxide in alkaline radiation chemistry, and cascade electron transfer processes. Some implications of the kinetics of electron transfer are discussed briefly.

Considerable effort has been devoted to studying electron transfer reactions in inorganic and organic systems. Several techniques, including polarography and electron spin resonance (ESR), have been used to investigate the spontaneous formation of radical anions, their acid-base properties, both inter- and intramolecular charge transfer phenomena and the compilation of relative electron affinities.

In particular, Russell and co-workers (*37*) have made extensive ESR studies on electron transfer from carbanions and nitranions to various acceptors including azobenzenes, diaryl ketones, and nitroaromatics. Some one-electron transfer processes have been investigated using a combination of electrochemical and ESR techniques (*26*). In these experiments, radical anions were produced electrochemically and introduced into a mixing chamber containing an aromatic electron acceptor. Electron transfer was indicated by the formation of the ESR spectrum of the resultant radical anion. It was verified that the direction of transfer between two reactants could be predicted from E_0' values derived from polarographic data.

Table I lists the experimental E_o' values for a number of aromatic solutes in *N,N*-dimethylformamide. The anion radical of each compound reacted with compounds below it in the table to form the anion radical of lesser E_o. Although this list was somewhat limited, no anomalies were found.

Table I. Reaction Potentials of Aromatic Systems in DMF

Parent compd.		
No.	*Name*	$E^{\circ\prime}$ [a]
1	*trans*-Stilbene	−2.22
2	1,5-Naphthalenedisulfonate	−2.15
3	Pyrazine	−2.09
4	Anthracene	−1.95
5	*p*-Nitroaniline	−1.41
6	9-Fluorenone	−1.29
7	*p*-Nitrotoluene	−1.18
8	Nitrobenzene	−1.13
9	*p*-Chloronitrobenzene	−1.04
10	9,10-Anthraquinone	−0.87
11	*p*-Nitrobenzonitrile	−0.83
12	*p*-Nitropyridine *N*-oxide	−0.78
13	*p*-Benzoquinone	−0.48

[a] $E^{\circ\prime}$ in volts *vs.* standard calomel electrode. Data from Ref. *26*.

This paper attempts to illustrate, using both published and some recent unpublished data, how pulse radiolysis is being used to contribute to an understanding of the underlying principles of electron transfer phenomena, particularly in aqueous solution.

The technique of pulse radiolysis affords the possibility of studying one-electon transfer processes directly. Observations are made under nonequilibrium conditions, and thus the rate data, essential for a complete understanding of the mechanisms involved, can be obtained directly. The formulation of a reaction mechanism in radiation chemistry usually depends upon the determination of relative rate constants for reactions between radical precursors and component solutes or the solvent. Recently, however, several independent suggestions have been made that the relative efficiency of two or more solutes competing for thermal electrons, including solvated electrons, depends on differences in electron affinity rather than on relative rate constants.

Consider two solutes, A and B, competing for solvated electrons

$$A + e^-_{sol} \xrightarrow{k_1} A^- \quad (1)$$

$$B + e^-_{sol} \xrightarrow{k_2} B^- \quad (2)$$

Clearly, the initial reaction path of the electron is governed by the relative magnitude of the two terms k_1 [A] and k_2 [B]. If, however, solutes A and B differ in electron affinity, anionic transfer can occur—*i.e.*,

$$A^- + B \rightarrow B^- + A \tag{3}$$

or

$$B^- + A \rightarrow A^- + B \tag{4}$$

and thus the ultimate reaction mechanism will be affected.

This general type of process has been discussed with respect to the radiation chemistry of aqueous solutions (*1, 7, 11, 20, 22, 24, 31*) organic liquids (*9*), gas-phase mixtures (*29*), a model for radiobiological sensitization (*1, 6*), and with respect to some apparent conflicts between steady-state radiation chemistry and pulse radiolysis (*22, 24*). In this paper, some examples of electron transfer in pulse radiolysis have been chosen to illustrate various features of this phenomenon.

Inorganic Ions

The transient univalent states of certain metals—*e.g.*, Zn^+, Ni^+, Pb^+, Cd^+, Co^+, etc.—can be produced in aqueous solution by reducing the corresponding M^{2+} ions by hydrated electrons (*15*). These unstable cations absorb strongly in the ultraviolet, and their reactions can be followed conveniently by pulse radiolysis (*2, 17*). At neutral pH, the lifetimes of the transient absorptions depend upon the experimental conditions, but initial half-lives of 50 μsec. or more can be obtained routinely. However, in the presence of other oxidizing cations, the lifetimes decrease considerably owing to the onset of electron transfer reactions of the type

$$M^+ + M'^{2+} \rightarrow M^{2+} + M'^+ \tag{5}$$

These reactions can be used in some instances to determine the sequence of relative potentials for the M^+/M^{2+} couples (*20*). Rate constants for a number of such reactions are listed in Table II.

The rate of electron transfer to oxygen approaches that of a diffusion-controlled reaction (*20*).

$$Zn^+ + O_2 \rightarrow Zn^{2+} + O_2^- \tag{6}$$

The rate constants for reaction between two metal ions are, however, somewhat lower as might be expected in view of the charge factor. With respect to the quantitative determination of relative potentials of the various couples, the variation in the rate data are of little value, although the direction of the electron transfer illustrates the order of the relative value of $E°$.

$$E°(Pb^+/Pb^{2+}) > E°(Cd^+/Cd^{2+}) > E°(\dot{Z}n^+/Zn^{2+})$$

The solutes N_2O, H_2O_2, nitrate, nitrite, bromate, iodate, and permanganate oxidize transient univalent metal ions (*19, 22, 32*). With little doubt, the mechanisms involve electron transfer, although in some cases precise details of the reactions are lacking.

Table II. Rate Constants for Some Inorganic Electron-Transfer Reactions[a]

Donor	*Acceptor*	*Rate Constant* $\times 10^{-9}$ M^{-1} *sec.*$^{-1}$	*Reference*
Cd^+	Pb^{2+}	0.75	*20*
	O_2	3.3	*20*
	O_2	2.4	*32*
	H_2O_2	2.8	*22*
	N_2O	0.001	*22*
	MnO_4^-	13.	*19*
	NO_3^-	0.35	*32*
	NO_2^-	2.0	*32*
	BrO_3^-	0.13	*32*
	IO_3^-	2.3	*32*
Zn^+	Pb_2^+	0.4	*20*
	O_2	3.3	*20*
	NO_3^-	2.1	*32*
	BrO_3^-	2.1	*32*
	H_2O_2	1.8	*32*
Ni^+	MnO_4^-	7.2	*19*
	N_2O	0.05	*22*
	H_2O_2	0.21	*22*
	O_2	2.2	*20*
	IO_3^-	0.22	*32*
Co^+	MnO_4^-	10.	*19*
	N_2O	0.7	*22*
	H_2O_2	1.9	*22*
O_2^-	$C(NO_2)_4$	6.	*39*

[a] Ambient temperature at neutral pH.

Reactions involving the ferrocyanide/ferricyanide couple are of current interest. The oxidation of ferrocyanide ion by OH radicals has been studied in detail by both pulse radiolysis (*5, 34*) and steady-state methods (*23, 25, 30, 35*). The reaction, which involves electron transfer to OH can be followed conveniently by directly observing the buildup of the ferricyanide ion

$$[Fe(CN)_6]^{4-} + OH \rightarrow [Fe(CN)_6]^{3-} + OH^- \qquad (7)$$

At high pH, the corresponding reaction of the anion of the OH radical, O^-, is very slow, and thus by studying the effect of pH on the experimental rate constant, Rabani and Matheson (*34*) were able to calculate the pK_a of the OH radical (11.9). This value has since been verified by an independent method (*4*).

Ferricyanide ion is reduced by e^-_{aq} in a diffusion-controlled reaction whose rate constant is $3.0 \times 10^9 M^{-1}$ sec.$^{-1}$ (*27*). The oxidation of various organic radicals and radical ions by ferricyanide has been observed directly by pulse radiolysis by Adams *et al.* (*8*), Henglein (*28*), and others [Chambers, K. W., Collinson, E., Dainton, F. S., Seddon, W. A., Wilkinson, F., *Trans. Faraday Soc.* **63**, 1699 (1967)]—the reaction being followed by measuring the decrease in light absorption of the ferricyanide complex at 4100 A. (*see* Table III).

Table III. Rate Constants for Some Organic-Inorganic Electron-Transfer Reactions[a]

Doner Radical	*Acceptor*	*pH*	$\times 10^{-9}$ M^{-1} *sec.*$^{-1}$ *Rate Constant*
$\dot{C}H_2OH$	$Fe(CN)_6^{3-}$	Neutral	4.0
$\dot{C}H_2O^-$	$Fe(CN)_6^{3-}$	13	3.1
$(CH_3)_2COH$	$Fe(CN)_6^{3-}$	Neutral	4.7
Polyethylene oxide	$Fe(CN)_6^{3-}$	Neutral	3.2
Acetophenone$^-$	$Fe(CN)_6^{3-}$	12.3	1.9
Glycollate$^-$	$Fe(CN)_6^{3-}$	Neutral	0.4
CO_2^-	$Fe(CN)_6^{3-}$	Neutral	0.56
Nitrobenzene-[b]	$Fe(CN)_6^{3-}$	Neutral	1.5
	KIO_4	Neutral	0.16
	$KMnO_4$	Neutral	1.1

[a] Solvent, water; Data from Ref. *8*.
[b] Data from Ref. *28*.

The organic radicals were produced in neutral and alkaline solution by reaction of OH radicals with the parent solute. The oxidation rates are first order in ferricyanide concentration as shown in Figure 1. The bimolecular rate constants obtained from the slopes are given, with other examples, in Table III.

This oxidation of the methanol radical, originally postulated by Hughes and Willis (*30*) is almost diffusion controlled.

$$\dot{C}H_2OH + [Fe(CN)_6]^{3-} \rightarrow CH_2O + H^+ + [Fe(CN)_6]^{4-} \quad (8)$$

In strongly alkaline solution, where the methanol radical is ionized [pK $CH_2OH = 10.6$ (*13*)], the reaction is somewhat slower.

$$CH_2O^{\cdot -} + [Fe(CN)_6]^{3-} \rightarrow HCHO + [Fe(CN)_6]^{4-} \quad (9)$$

A similar reaction has been observed for both the ionized and unionized isopropyl radical produced, either by reduction of acetone by e^-_{aq}, or by oxidation of isopropyl alcohol in N_2O-saturated solution (*8*)

$$\begin{array}{l} (CH_3)_2CHOH \\ \quad\downarrow\ OH \\ (CH_3)_2\dot{C}OH + [Fe(CN)_6]^{3-} \rightarrow (CH_3)_2C{=}O + [Fe(CN)_6]^{4-} \\ \quad\rightleftharpoons \\ (CH_3)_2\dot{C}{-}O^- \\ \quad\uparrow\ e^-_{aq} \\ (CH_3)_2CO \end{array} \qquad (10)$$

The oxidation of formate radical ion, CO_2^-, previously postulated from steady-state studies (*23*), is less than diffusion controlled. The rate is influenced, presumably by the charge factor,

$$CO_2^- + [Fe(CN)_6]^{3-} \rightarrow CO_2 + [Fe(CN)_6]^{4-} \qquad (11)$$

Electron transfer to ferricyanide is being used as a reference system for studying and measuring reactions involving peroxy radical formation of the type

$$R + O_2 \rightarrow RO_2 \qquad (12)$$

e.g., in the pulse radiolysis of a neutral N_2O-saturated solution of methanol ($0.1M$) containing a low concentration of ferricyanide ion and some oxygen, the CH_2OH radicals are either oxidized by ferricyanide, or react with oxygen to form a hydroxyperoxy radical

$$CH_2OH + O_2 \rightarrow \begin{array}{c} O_2 \\ | \\ CH_2OH \end{array} \qquad (13)$$

Since the peroxy radicals do not appear to react with ferricyanide, the decrease in absorption at 4100 A. is a direct measure of the extent of the competition between Reactions 8 and 13.

The usual simple competition kinetics can be applied. If D_o is the decrease in optical density of ferricyanide after irradiation of a N_2O-saturated solution in the absence of oxygen, and D is the corresponding decrease when a given concentration of oxygen is present, it can be shown that

$$\frac{D_o}{D} = 1 + \frac{k_{13}[O_2]}{k_8[[Fe(CN)_6]^{3-}]} \qquad (14)$$

Figure 2 shows the test of this equation in the competition of oxygen and ferricyanide for the methanol radical in neutral solution. The plot is linear, as required and from the slope the rate constant ratio, k_{13}/k_8, and hence the absolute rate constant for the oxygen reaction, can be obtained directly. Table V list someexamples of reactions of this type.

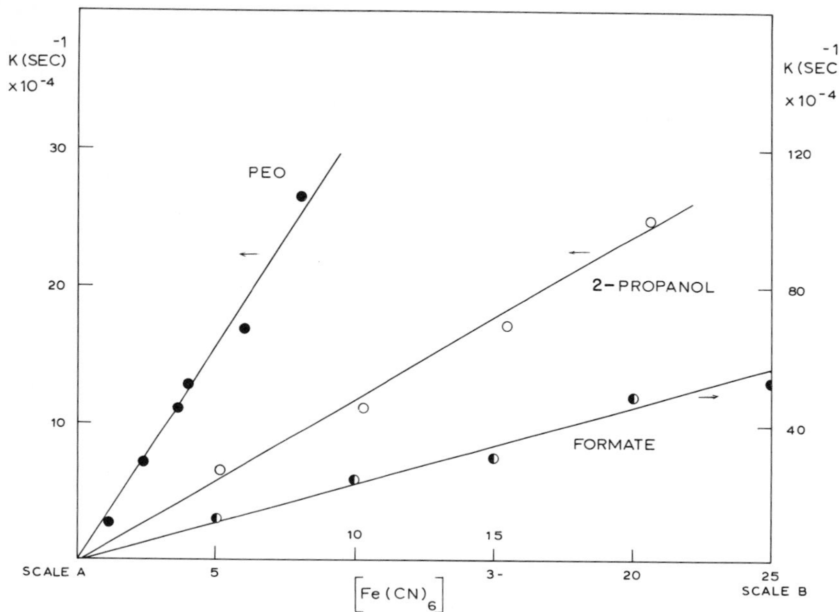

Figure 1. Electron transfer from organic radicals to ferricyanide ion. First-order dependence on $[Fe(CN)_6]^{3-}$ *in neutral solution*

●: *Polyethylene oxide*
○: *Isopropyl alcohol*
◐: *Formate ion*

Electron Transfer to Organic Solutes

One of the earliest observations of this phenomenon was made by Henglein and co-workers working with nitromethane solutions (*11*). In alkaline solutions the radical anion, $CH_3NO_2^-$, absorbs at 2700 A. (ϵ = $1800M^{-1}$ cm.$^{1-}$). In the presence of a much lower concentration of tetranitromethane, electron transfer from $CH_3NO_2^-$ was indicated by the buildup at 3500 A. of an absorption assigned to the radical ion $C(NO_2)_3^-$

$$CH_3NO_2^- + C(NO_2)_4 \rightarrow CH_3NO_2 + C(NO_2)_3^- + NO_2 \qquad (15)$$

The value of k_{15} was $6.6 \times 10^9 M^{-1}$ sec.$^{-1}$.

Electron transfer from the protonated species, $CH_3NO_2 \cdot H$ was also reported (*11*).

A series of nondissociative electron transfer reactions involving aromatic radical ions produced by electron attachment in isopropyl alcohol solutions, have been studied by pulse radiolysis by Dorfman and co-workers (*9*). Donor radical anions were derived from diphenyl,

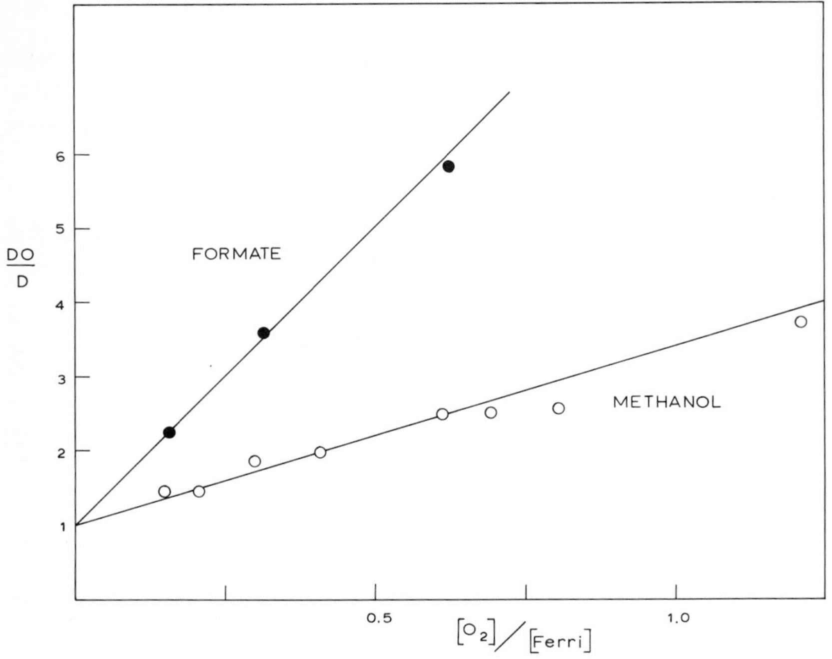

Figure 2. Reactions of organic radicals with oxygen. Competition between oxygen and ferricyanide ion in neutral solution

●: *Formate ion*
○: *Methanol*

p-terphenyl, *m*-terphenyl, and *o*-terphenyl while the acceptors were naphthalene, anthracene, phenanthrene, pyrene and *p*-terphenyl. Figure 3 shows an example of electron-transfer spectra, observed in an isopropyl alcohol solution containing diphenyl ($3.5 \times 10^{-3}M$) and pyrene ($2.1 \times 10^{-5}M$) irradiated with a single electron pulse. Spectrum a observed 2.9 μsec. after the pulse is that of the diphenylide ion. This absorption decays and is replaced 12.9 μsec. later, by the spectrum of the pyrene radical anion (Spectrum b). The formation and decay kinetics are equal and first order in acceptor concentration. The bimolecular rate constants are listed in Table IV. Most, but not all, of the rate constants are near diffusion controlled values. During this work complications arising from radical-anion formation by direct oxidation of the solvent radicals by the acceptor molecule do not appear to be present; however, such reactions do occur with some electron acceptors, particularly quinones (*18*), and should be considered particularly in alcoholic solution. Reactions of this type are discussed below.

Electron Transfer in Aqueous Solutions of Organic Molecules

Nitrobenzene (*14*) and nitrosobenzene (*10*) each reacts rapidly with e^-_{aq} to produce the corresponding negative radical ions. $C_6H_5NO_2^-$ absorbs strongly at 2900 A. with a subsidiary peak near 4600 A., while for $C_6H_5NO_2^-$, the maximum is at 2850 A.

The pK of the protonated species, $C_6H_5NO_2 \cdot H$, was 3.2 (*14*).

In alkaline solutions containing various alcohols, the ionized alcohol radicals produced by OH reaction with the solute, are oxidized rapidly by electron transfer to nitrobenzene (*14*).

$$RCHO^- + C_6H_5NO_2 \rightarrow RCHO + C_6H_5NO_2^- \qquad (16)$$

For all alcohols studied, a diffusion-controlled transfer rate constant of about $3 \times 10^9 M^{-1}$ sec.$^{-1}$ was found in alkaline solution. In less basic solutions, however, where the alcohol radical was not dissociated, the transfer rate constant for the reaction

$$RCHOH + C_6H_5NO_2 \rightarrow RCHO + C_6H_5NO_2^- + H^+ \qquad (17)$$

depended strongly on the structure of the alcohol, consistent with the inductive influence of the alcohol side groups. Similar reactions were

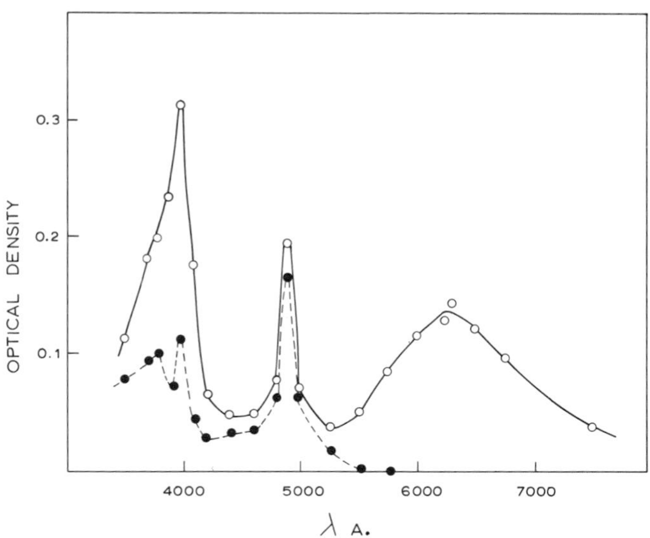

Figure 3. Absorption spectra from an irradiated isopropyl alcohol solution containing diphenyl (3.5 mM) and pyrene (2.1 × 10⁻⁵M). Data from Ref. 9

○: *2.9 μsec. after pulse*
△: *12.9 μsec. after pulse*

observed in nitrosobenzene solutions. In addition electron transfer from the formate radical-ion, CO_2^- was observed for which $k = 4.0 \times 10^9 M^{-1}$ sec.$^{-1}$ (*10*).

Electron Transfer Involving Ketyl Radicals

Because of ground state electron delocalization, conjugation between electron acceptor groups greatly enhances the electron affinity of organic compounds. Some aromatic ketones—*e.g.*, acetophenone (*8*), benzophenone (*3*), benzil, and certain α-diketo molecules—*e.g.*, diacetyl (*8*)—react with solvated electrons to produce relatively long-lived ketyl radical anions, particularly in solutions of high pH. In general, these transient species show intense absorption bands in the visible region of the spectrum, which can be studied conveniently by pulse radiolysis. Some of the spectra were in fact first characterized by flash photolysis methods where the ketyl anion is derived from the corresponding neutral radical formed by interaction of an excited ketone molecule with the organic solvent (*21, 23*).

Figure 4 shows electron attachment spectra from several deoxygenated aqueous alkaline solutions of some conjugate ketones irradiated with a single 0.2-μsec. pulse of 1.3 Mev. electrons (*9, 8*) (*e.g.*, Reaction 18).

$$\mathrm{C_6H_5{-}C({=}O){-}C_6H_5} \xrightarrow{e^-_{aq}} \mathrm{C_6H_5{-}C(O){-}C_6H_5} \qquad (18)$$

Electron transfer involving ketyl anions of this type has been reported (*7*). In Figure 4a, Curve i is the transient spectrum observed 1 μsec. after the pulse, from 3.34 m*M* acetophenone at pH 13. Curve ii is the spectrum obtained when 16.6-m*M* acetone is present in the solution. The maximum at 4400 A. is that of the acetophenone ketyl anion (*21*),

$$CH_3COC_6H_5 + e^-_{aq} \rightarrow [CH_3COC_6H_5]^- \qquad (19)$$

while the peak at 3700 A. is caused by the OH adduct, a substituted cyclohexadienyl radical. In the presence of a high concentration of acetone (Curve ii), the latter peak is suppressed because the precursors, OH radicals, are scavenged by acetone. The peak at 4400 A., however, is virtually unaffected. Since both solutes react with e^-_{aq} at or near diffusion-controlled rates and since acetone is greatly in excess, direct electron attachment to acetophenone cannot take place. The peak at 4400 A. in Curve ii is caused by electron transfer

$$[\text{Acetone}]^- + \text{Acetophenone} \rightarrow [\text{Acetophenone}]^- + \text{Acetone} \qquad (20)$$

Similar data for benzophenone are reproduced in Figure 4b for benzophenone and acetone mixtures. Again, acetone does not suppress the formation of the spectrum of the benzophenone ketyl. Both transfer reactions were first order in phenone concentration, and the bimolecular rate constants are given in Table IV.

Table IV. Rate Constants for Some Organic Electron-Transfer Reactions

Donor	*Acceptor*	*Solvent*	*pH*	*Rate Constant* $\times 10^{-9}$ M^{-1} *sec.*$^{-1}$	*Reference*
Diphenylide$^-$	Naphthalene	2-Propanol	Neutral	0.26	9
Diphenylide$^-$	Phenanthrene			0.6	9
Diphenylide$^-$	*p*-Terphenyl			3.2	9
Diphenylide$^-$	Anthracene			6.4	9
p-Terphenylide$^-$	Anthracene			5.5	9
Diphenylide$^-$	Pyrene			5.	9
p-Terphenylide$^-$	Pyrene			3.6	9
m-Terphenylide$^-$	Pyrene			3.5	9
o-Terphenylide$^-$	Pyrene			4.0	9
$(CH_3)_2\dot{C}O^-$	Fluorenone	Ethanol	ALK	2.0	7
$\dot{C}H_2OH$	Nitrosobenzene	Water	7	3.2	10
$\dot{C}H_2O^-$	Nitrosobenzene		13	6.8	10
$(CH_3)_2\dot{C}OH$	Nitrosobenzene		7	5.0	10
$(CH_3)_2\dot{C}O^-$	Nitrosobenzene		13	7.0	10
$\dot{C}O_2^-$	Nitrosobenzene		7	4.0	10
$\dot{C}H_2OH$	Nitrobenzene		7	<0.01	14
$\dot{C}H_2O^-$	Nitrobenzene		13	2.7	14
$(CH_3)_2\dot{C}OH$	Nitrobenzene		7	1.6	14
$(CH_3)_2\dot{C}O^-$	Nitrobenzene		13	3.0	14
Acetophenone$^-$	Nitrobenzene		13	0.21	28
ϕ-$COCH_2CO$ ϕ^-	Nitrobenzene		13	1.2	28
$(CH_3)_2\dot{C}O^-$	Acetophenone		13	0.78	7
$\dot{C}O_2^-$	Acetophenone		12	0.01	8
Thymine$^-$	Acetophenone		12	2.7	8
Thymine$^-$	*p*-Chloracetophenone		12	2.5	8
$(CH_3)_2\dot{C}O^-$	Benzophenone		12	1.2	8
Acetophenone$^-$	Benzophenone		13	0.78	7
Thymine$^-$	Benzophenone		12	3.1	8
$CH_3NO_2^-$	$C(NO_2)_4$		7	1.1	11
CH_3NO_2H	$C(NO_2)_4$		3	0.11	11
Nitrobenzene	$C(NO_2)_4$		7	1.3	28

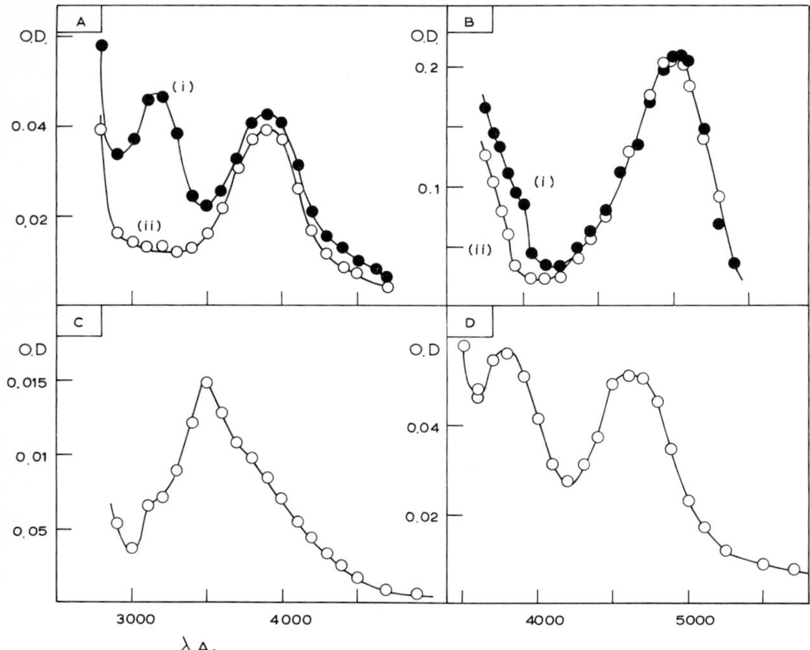

Figure 4. Electron transfer or attachment spectra

(A) *Transient spectra 1 μsec. after pulse, from 3.3 mM acetophenone in aqueous 10^{-1}N KOH*
(i) ●: *No acetone*
(ii) ○: *0.17M acetone*

(B) *Transient spectra from 0.2 mM benzophenone in aqueous 10^{-1}N KOH (1 μsec. after pulse)*
(i) ●: *No acetone*
(ii) ○: *41 mM acetone*

(C) *Electron attachment spectrum from 1 mM N-ethylmaleiimide, N_2 saturated, pH 11.2*

(D) *Electron attachment spectrum of chloracetophenone radical anion. 2 × 10^{-3}M chloracetophenone in N_2-saturated solution at pH 12.3 (peak at 3800° A. is that of the OH adduct)*

The radical produced by OH reaction with acetone $CH_3COCH_2\cdot$, is not oxidized by the phenone. When a solution containing high concentrations of both acetone and isopropyl alcohol is irradiated in the presence of benzophenone, the yield of ketyl anion is approximately twice that observed in isopropyl alcohol-free solutions (*8*). The concentrations of acetone and isopropyl alcohol can be adjusted so that all electrons react with acetone and OH radicals react exclusively with isopropyl alcohol. At high pH, the isopropyl radical ionizes, and electron transfer occurs,

$$\begin{array}{l} CH_3COCH_3 \xrightarrow{e^-_{aq}} CH_3\overset{O^-}{\overset{|}{C}}CH_3 \rightarrow \text{Electron transfer to benzophenone} \\ \qquad\qquad\qquad\qquad \uparrow OH \\ (CH_3)_2CHOH \xrightarrow{OH} CH_3\overset{OH}{\overset{|}{C}}CH_3 \end{array} \quad (21)$$

Solutions Containing N_2O

At high pH, high concentrations of nitrous oxide appeared ineffective in preventing the formation of the anion of nitromethane (*11*)

$$e^-_{aq} + CH_3NO_2 \rightarrow CH_3NO_2^- \quad (22)$$

It was suggested that the electron-scavenging reaction of N_2O involved the equilibrium

$$N_2O^- + H_2O \rightleftharpoons N_2OH + OH^- \quad (23)$$

and that the formation of OH was governed by the dissociation of N_2OH

$$N_2OH \rightarrow N_2 + OH \quad (24)$$

Thus, at high pH, the equilibrium would lie to the left, and it was postulated that N_2O^- was sufficiently long lived to permit electron transfer to nitromethane

$$N_2O^- + CH_3NO_2 \rightarrow N_2O + CH_3NO_2^- \quad (25)$$

Some similar experiments with fluorenone (*7*) and other phenones appeared to support this conclusion since in solutions containing low phenone concentrations at high pH, large concentrations of N_2O did not suppress the formation of ketyl anions. Again electron transfer from N_2O^- to fluorenone or other phenones was indicated.

$$N_2O^- + \text{phenone} \rightarrow N_2O + [\text{phenone}]^- \quad (26)$$

However, some recent experiments have shown that this interpretation is incorrect with respect to both the phenone system (*8*) and also the original nitromethane experiments (*28*).

Figure 5 shows the effect of pH on the transient absorption spectra present 1 μsec. after pulse radiolysis of 1-m*M* deaerated acetophenone solutions.

The two peaks at 3700 and 4400 A. arise from the OH and electron adducts, respectively. The positions of the two maxima are independent of pH, although the relative magnitudes are not. As the pH is changed from 10.4 to 13.5, the extinction of the OH adduct decreases while that of the ketyl anion increases. Although at high pH OH ionizes, the O^- radical anion will presumably add to the ring, like OH. Electron transfer from O^- to phenone is most unlikely. However, the anion of the OH adduct can be formed either by ionization, or by O^- addition to the ring (Reaction 27).

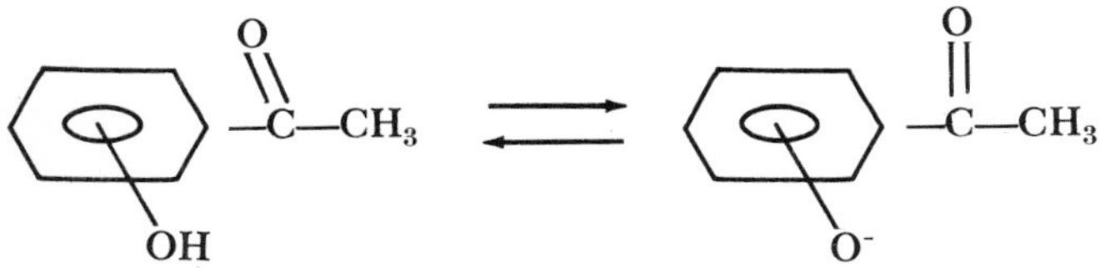

$$\text{(HO-substituted ring radical)}-C(=O)-CH_3 \rightleftharpoons \text{(}O^-\text{-substituted ring radical)}-C(=O)-CH_3 \qquad (27)$$

In such a structure there must be considerable resonance interaction between the carbonyl group and the electron associated with the ionized OH adduct. Under these conditions, therefore, an absorption spectrum similar to the normal ketyl anion would not be unlikely. If then, the absorption at 4400 A. at high pH includes a component caused by the species arising from oxidative attack by OH or O^- radicals as well as that caused by the ketyl anion, it is not surprising that adding N_2O has little effect, even if the conversion of e^-_{aq} to OH was complete during the pulse.

Absolute confirmation that electron transfer from N_2O^- to acetophenone does not take place was provided by the following experiments. In an aqueous, alkaline solution of acetophenone containing a large concentration of isopropyl alcohol and saturated with N_2O, the spectrum of ketyl is observed. However, when the experiment is repeated using a high concentration of *tert*-butyl alcohol instead of isopropyl alcohol, no ketyl spectrum is observed. If, therefore, in the former experiment the ketyl spectrum arises by electron transfer from N_2O^- to acetophenone, the presence of the alcohol would be irrelevant since isopropyl alcohol is a poor electron scavenger and thus a similar result should have been observed for *tert*-butyl alcohol.

Electron transfer to acetophenone from the isopropyl radical ion, an α-hydroxy radical, has been discussed above and is responsible for the ketyl spectrum in N_2O-saturated solutions of isopropyl alcohol. Hence, transfer from the *tert*-butyl radical ion, a β-hydroxy radical, either does not take place or is too slow to be observed under the given experimental conditions.

In the steady-state radiolysis of aqueous isopropyl alcohol containing N_2O, electron transfer from the isopropyl alcohol radical ion to N_2O has been suggested (*38*). Since electron transfer from this radical ion to benzophenone is efficient even in N_2O-saturated solution, transfer to N_2O, if it occurs, must be slow and unimportant under the conditions of the above pulse experiments.

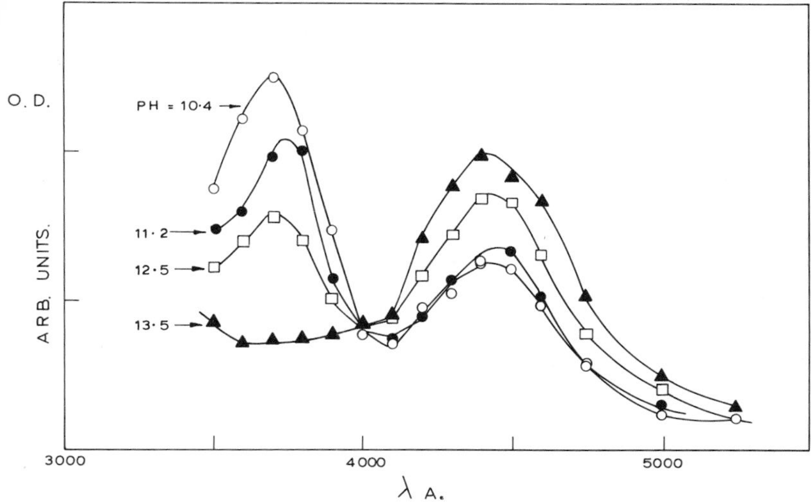

Figure 5. Effect of pH on the transient spectra 1 μsec. after the pulse, from 4.3 mM acetophenone in N_2-saturated water

Cascade Electron Transfer

Simple chain electron transfer has been observed in pulse radiolysis (*7*). One example was the irradiation of an alkaline solution (pH ~ 13) containing 6% acetone, 3.4 m*M* acetophenone, and 72 μ*M* benzophenone. The observed transient spectra are reproduced in Figure 6. Spectrum i which developed during the pulse, has a maximum at 4400 A. and is identical with that of the acetophenone ketyl anion shown in Figure 4. Within 50 μsec. of the pulse, this spectrum decayed and was replaced by that of benzophenone ketyl anion with a maximum at 6100 A. The oscillogram in Figure 7 illustrates the kinetic behavior. The exponential kinetics of the formation and decay curves are similar. All three ketones react efficiently with hydrated electrons, and therefore all hydrated electrons were scavenged by the acetone. The sequential formation of the ketyl spectra indicated the occurrence of a simple three-stage anionic electron transfer or "cascade" through the three molecular structures.

$$(-) \longrightarrow (-) \longrightarrow (-)$$

Acetone **Acetophenone** **Benzophenone** (28)

A similar result was obtained (*8*) using an N_2O-saturated solution containing the same phenones and 0.5*M* isopropyl alcohol in place of acetone. Spectra similar to those in Figure 6 were obtained, indicating chain transfer from the isopropyl radical ion. This system is interesting in that it illustrates an electron transfer process originating almost entirely from an OH radical-induced reaction. Other examples of this type of chain transfer are given in Table III.

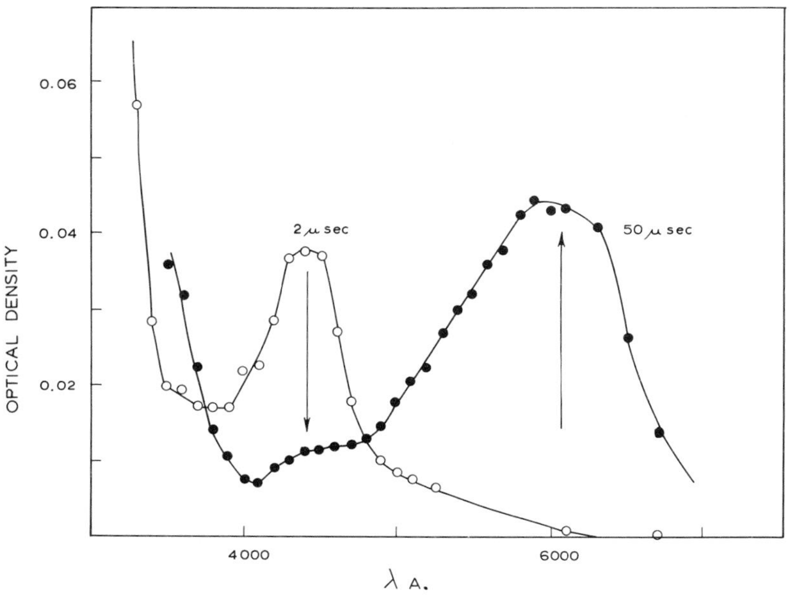

*Figure 6. Transient spectra from an aqueous solution containing 0.82*M *acetone, 3.34 m*M *acetophenone, 72* μM *benzophenone, and* 10^{-1} *KOH (*N_2*-saturated)*

○: *2 μsec. after pulse*
●: *50 μsec after pulse*

Model four-stage electron transfer chains have been observed (8) using either isopropyl alcohol radicals (or ethyl alcohol), aceto and benzophenone, and, in addition, a very low concentration of ferricyanide ion. One alkaline N_2O-saturated solution contained 0.5*M* isopropyl alcohol, $2.5 \times 10^{-3}M$ acetophenone, $10^{-4}M$ benzophenone, and 8 μ*M* ferricyanide ion. Electron transfer from the alcohol radical ion to acetophenone, followed by transfer to benzophenone, was observed, as expected. However, the benzophenone anion spectrum decayed exponentially. The transmission of the solution, over the spectral region of the ferricyanide absorption (4100 A. maximum) increased, indicating the consumption of this solute. The kinetics of ferricyanide decay were similar to those for decay of the benzophenone ketyl absorption. The final stage for the chain was the reduction of ferricyanide ion. The complete reaction sequence is as follows.

$$e^-_{aq} \xrightarrow{N_2O} OH$$

$$(CH_3)_2CHOH \xrightarrow{OH} (CH_3)_2\dot{C}OH \overset{OH-}{\rightleftharpoons} (CH_3)_2\overset{O^-}{\overset{|}{C}}\cdot$$

Acetophenone

$$C_6H_5\overset{O^-}{\overset{|}{C}}CH_3$$

Benzophenone

$$C_6H_5\overset{O^-}{\overset{|}{C}}C_6H_5$$

Ferricyanide

$$[Fe(CN)_6]^{4-}$$

In general, oxygen reacts rapidly with anion radicals of electron-affinic organic compounds (Table V). The anion spectra produced either directly by reaction of the solute with solvated electrons or by electron transfer, decay first order in oxygen when present.

$$A^- + O_2 \rightarrow A + O_2^- \text{ (or } AO_2^-) \quad (29)$$

At present, the alternative mechanisms of electron transfer to O_2 and of peroxy anion formation have not been resolved.

Kinetics of Electron Transfer

In principle, the direction of electron transfer between two organic molecules indicates, qualitatively, the relative order of electron affinities. In this respect, pulse radiolysis studies using electron acceptors whose formal reduction potential can be determined electrochemically and by other techniques, should be useful as reference standards. This would facilitate quantitative evaluation of relative electron affinities in solution.

It might be expected that where the reaction is thermodynamically favorable, electron transfer should proceed rapidly, with little activation energy. It is apparent from the collected data in Tables III and IV that anionic electron transfer involving organic molecules is indeed a rapid process. However, some of the reaction rate constants are significantly lower than that for a diffusion-controlled reaction. This question has

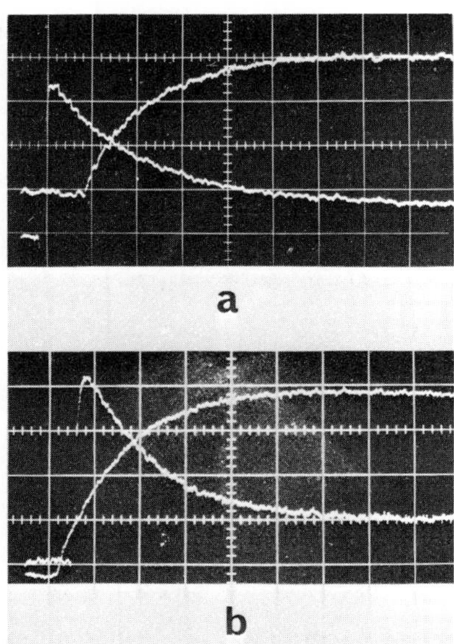

Figure 7. Oscillograms demonstrating electron transfer chains

(a) Data for Figure 6. Buildup, absorption at 6100 A.; decay, absorption at 4400 A.
Ordinate: Absorption, 2.1% per division
Abscissa: Time, 10 μsec. per division

(b) Data for N_2O-saturated solution containing 2×10^{-1}M isopropyl alcohol, 1 mM acetophenone, and 50 μM benzophenone; pH, 12.6; buildup, absorption at 6100 A.; decay, absorption at 4400 A.
Ordinate: Absorption, 1.66% per division (buildup); 1% per division (decay)
Abscissa: Time, 20 μsec. per division

been discussed by Dorfman and co-workers (9), who conclude from their data that although a simple encounter cross section, directly related to molecular size, is not necessarily an important parameter for the lower rate constants, the group of high rate constants may represent diffusion-controlled reactions. By making certain assumptions—*e.g.*, the neglect of any influence of the charge on the donor-anion including charge interaction with a permanent or induced dipole (this may be true for the examples given but may not be generally the case, particularly for some ketyls)—they calculate a collision frequency of about $4 \times 10^9 M^{-1}$ sec.$^{-1}$, which compares with the higher measured rate constants.

Table V. Rate Constants for Organic Radicals with Oxygen

Radical	*Solvent*	*pH*	*Rate Constant* $\times 10^{-9}$ M^{-1} *sec.*$^{-1}$	*Reference*
CH_2OH[a]	Water	7	9.6	8
$(CH_3)_2\dot{C}OH$[a]	Water	7	6.4	8
CO_2^-[a]	Water	7	4.5	8
Polyethylene oxide[a]	Water	7	3.7	8
Glycollate ion[a]	Water	7	2.3	8
Dimethylfumarate$^-$	Ethyl alcohol	$10^{-2}N$ NaOEt	1.5	7
	Water	11	5.3	7
Fluorenone$^-$	Ethyl alcohol	$10^{-2}N$ NaOEt	0.89	7
N-Ethylmaleiimide$^-$	Water	11.2	2.4	8

[a] Determined by ferricyanide competition.

Further, where the formal reduction potentials differences are small, the associated rate constants are somewhat lower (9). The data are, however, too limited to warrant further speculation at this stage.

Literature Cited

(1) Adams, G. E., "Current Topics in Radiation Research," p. 37, North Holland Publishing Co., 1967.
(2) Adams, G. E., Baxendale, J. H., Boag, J. W., *Proc. Chem. Soc.* **1963,** 241.
(3) *Ibid.,* **A277,** 549 (1964).
(4) Adams, G. E., Boag, J. W., Currant, J., Michael, B. D., "Pulse Radiolysis," M. Ebert *et al.,* Eds., p. 117, Academic Press, New York, 1965.
(5) Adams, G. E., Boag, J. W., Michael, B. D., *Trans. Faraday Soc.* **61,** 492 (1965).
(6) Adams, G. E., Dewey, D. L., *Biochem. Biophys. Res. Commun.* **12,** 473 (1963).
(7) Adams, G. E., Michael, B. D., Richards, J. T., *Nature* **215,** 1248 (1967).
(8) Adams, G. E., Michael, B. D., Richards, J. T., Willson, R. L., to be published.
(9) Arai, S., Grev, D. A., Dorfman, L. M., *J. Chem. Phys.* **46,** 2572 (1967).
(10) Asmus, K-D., Beck, G., Henglein, A., Wigger, A., *Ber. Bunsenges. Physik. Chem.* **70,** 869 (1966).
(11) Asmus, K-D., Henglein, A., Beck, G., *Ber. Bunsenges. Physik. Chem.* **70,** 459 (1966).
(12) Asmus, K-D., Henglein, A., Wigger, R., Beck, G., *Ber. Bunsenges. Physik. Chem.* **70,** 149 (1966).
(13) *Ibid.,* p. 756.
(14) Asmus, K-D., Wigger, A., Henglein, A., *Ber. Bunsenges. Physik. Chem.* **70,** 862 (1966).
(15) Baxendale, J. H., Dixon, R. S., *Proc. Chem. Soc.* ***1963,*** 148.

(16) Baxendale, J. H., Dixon, R. S., *Z. Physik. Chem.* **43,** 161 (1964).
(17) Baxendale, J. H., Fielden, E. M., Keene, J. P., *Proc. Roy. Soc. (London)* **A286,** 320 (1965).
(18) Baxendale, J. H., Hughes, G., *Z. Physik. Chem., Neue Folge* **14,** 306 (1958).
(19) Baxendale, J. H., Keene, J. P., Stott, D. A., "Pulse Radiolysis," Ebert *et al.,* eds., p. 107, Academic Press, New York, 1965.
(20) Baxendale, J. H., Keene, J. P., Stott, D. A., *Chem. Commun.* **1966,** 715.
(21) Beckett, A., Osborne, A. D., Porter, G., *Trans. Faraday Soc.* **60,** 873 (1964).
(22) Buxton, G. V., Dainton, F. S., Thielens, G., *Chem. Commun.* **1967,** 201.
(23) Czapski, G., Rabani, J., Stein, G., *Trans. Faraday Soc.* **58,** 2160 (1962).
(24) Dainton, F. E., "The Chemistry of Ionisation and Excitation," G. R. A. Johnson, G. Scholes, Eds., p. 3, Taylor and Francis, 1967.
(25) Dainton, F. S., Watt, W. S., *Nature* **195,** 1294 (1962).
(26) Fritsch, J. M., Layloff, T. P., Adams, R. N., *J. Am. Chem. Soc.* **87,** 1724 (1965).
(27) Gordon, S., Hart, E. J., Matheson, M. S., Rabani, J., Thomas, J. K., *J. Am. Chem. Soc.* **85,** 1375 (1963).
(28) Henglein, A., private communication.
(29) Holtslander, W. J., Freeman, G. R., *Abstr. 15th Ann. Meeting Rad. Res. Soc., Puerto Rico,* p. 95, 1967.
(30) Hughes, G., Wilils, C., *Discussions Faraday Soc.* **36,** 223 (1963).
(31) Logan, S. R., Wilmot, P. B., *Chem. Commun.* **1966,** 558.
(32) Meyerstein, D., Mulac, W. A., in press.
(33) Porter, G., Wilkinson, F., *Trans. Faraday Soc.* **57,** 1686 (1961).
(34) Rabani, J., Matheson, M. S., *J. Am. Chem. Soc.* **86,** 3175 (1964).
(35) Rabani, J., Stein, G., *Trans. Faraday Soc.* **58,** 2150 (1962).
(36) Rabani, J., Mulac, W. A., Matheson, M. S., *J. Phys. Chem.* **69,** 53 (1965).
(37) Russell, G. A., Janzen, E. G., Strom, E. T., *J. Am. Chem. Soc.* **86,** 1807 (1964).
(38) Scholes, G., Simic, M., Weiss, J. J., *Discussions Faraday Soc.* **36,** 214 (1963).

RECEIVED February 5, 1968.

21

The Application of Pulse Radiolysis to the Radiation Chemistry of Organic Dyes

LEONARD I. GROSSWEINER

Physics Department, Illinois Institute of Technology and Department of Radiation Therapy, Michael Reese Hospital and Medical Center, Chicago, Ill.

Pulse radiolysis studies have shown that many organic dyes are highly reactive toward the products of water radiolysis. Dyes with quinonoid structures are reduced by e^-_{aq} *to the semiquinone in encounter-limited reactions. Hydroxyl radicals react by oxidation and addition processes. In general, reductive bleaching takes place* via *semiquinone dismutation, while oxidative decoloration is a complex process involving several OH radicals. The complexing of dyes to high molecular weight substrates leads to a marked change of* e^-_{aq} *reactivity. Some oxidized dye intermediates and triplet states react with* e^-_{aq} *in chemiluminescent processes.*

The radiation chemistry of organic dyes has been studied for almost 40 years. In early work the emphasis was on the color changes induced by irradiation, motivated in part by the possibility that dye solutions might serve as convenient dosimeters (*25*). Although dyes are generally more complex than the other organic molecules whose radiation chemistry has been studied in detail, specific reasons can be cited for interest in this subject. From the viewpoint of radiation biology, dyes can act as well-defined models of biological redox systems. This aspect is particularly pertinent in connection with recent work on the radiolysis of dyes complexed to high molecular weight substrates. In addition, the strong visible coloration of dye derivatives facilitates the identification of the transient and permanent reaction products, which offsets to some extent the multiplicity of possible reactions. Some of the intermediates formed in radiolysis are photochemical products also, which has assisted considerably in elucidating reaction mechanisms in both cases. Despite the potential applications of pulse radiolysis to this subject, the actual amount of work reported since 1962 has not been large. The current status of the field appears to parallel dye photochemistry at approximately a decade ago, when flash photolytic methods were introduced to complement the usual procedures of continuous irradiation and permanent product characterization. Thus, the emphasis in the pulse radiolysis approach has been on identifying the transient species formed when the dye reacts with the products of water radiolysis and measuring their formation and decay rate constants. Typically, these intermediates can result from both oxidation and reduction processes, and they may exist in more than one ionic state with different spectra and reactivities. Relatively complete investigations have been attempted only for representatives of the thiazines and xanthenes. In addition to optical absorption spectra, new information on chemiluminescent reactions of dyes has been obtained by electron pulse-induced emission measurements. This paper comprises a summary of recent work, including a brief discussion of pertinent steady irradiation G values.

Research Results

Pulse Radiolysis of Aqueous Methylene Blue. The first pulse radiolysis study of an organic dye was carried out on the thiazine dye, methylene blue (*3, 12*). Considerable emphasis was given to the different ionic states of the dye, referred to as MBH_2^{3+} ($pK_a = -5.1$), MBH^{2+} ($pK_a = 0.0$), and MB^+. The transient spectra obtained by irradiating neutral and alkaline solutions with 2-μsec. pulses of 4 Mev. electrons in the presence of formate showed that the dye is bleached *via* a two-step process, with a concurrent absorption increase peaking at 420 mμ. The intermediate, designated as $MB\cdot$ corresponds with the methylene blue semiquinone first identified by flash photolysis in the presence of reducing agents (*11, 15, 17*). The faster step was attributed to the reduction of MB^+ by e^-_{aq} by comparing its rate with the decay of e^-_{aq} at 720 mμ, and the slower step was attributed to reduction by CO_2^- resulting from the scavenging of OH by formate. The semiquinone disappears by a second-order process accompanied by a partial return of the dye, which was explained by disproportionation leading to equal parts of MB^+ and the leuco base, MBH. The rate constants are summarized in Table I.

The methylene blue semiquinone protonation states assigned by Keene *et al.* (*12*) differ from the results of Matsumoto (*15*), who proposed the following four states: $MB\cdot$ (pH > 9), $M\dot{B}H^+$ (pH 3–8), $M\dot{B}H_2^{2+}$ (in 0.1N H_2SO_4) and $M\dot{B}H_3^{3+}$ (in conc. H_2SO_4). Recent measurements by J. Faure, R. Bonneau, and J. Joussot-Dubien [*J. Chim. Phys.* **65,** 369 (1968)] on the effect of the ionic strength on the dismutation rate constant support the conclusion of Matsumoto that the neutral semiquinone $MB\cdot$ is stable only above pH 9. Keene, Land, and Swallow

[*J. Chim. Phys.* **65**, 371 (1968)] now agree with the assignments suggested by Matsumota and Faure *et al.* and indicate that the reaction mechanisms given in Ref. *12* (which are summarized in Table I) must be modified accordingly.

Table I. Pulse Radiolysis Rate Constants for Methylene Blue

Reaction[a, b]	*pH*	*Rate Constant*[c]
$e^-_{aq} + MB^+ \rightarrow MB\cdot$	7.8	2.5×10^{10} (10%)
$CO_2^- + MB^+ \rightarrow MB\cdot + CO_2$	7.8	5.6×10^9 (10%)
$COOH\cdot + MB^+ \rightarrow M\dot{B}H^+ + CO_2$	1.8	$\sim 2 \times 10^9$
$COOH\cdot + MBH^{2+} \rightarrow M\dot{B}H^+ + CO_2 + H^+$	~ -0.8[d]	$\sim 10^9$
$COOH\cdot + MBH_2^{3+} \rightarrow M\dot{B}H_2^{2+} + H^+ + CO_2$	~ -5.7[d]	$\sim 7 \times 10^8$
$2\,MB\cdot + H_2O \rightarrow MBH + MB^+ + OH^-$	7.8	3.0×10^9 (10%)
$2\,M\dot{B}H^+ \rightarrow MBH^{2+} + MBH$	~ -0.8[d]	$\sim 1.6 \times 10^9$

[a] Data from Keene, Land, and Swallow (*12*).
[b] Ionic states of methylene blue MB^+, MBH^{2+}, MBH_2^{3+}, ionic states of the semiquinone: $MB\cdot$, MBH^+, MBH_2^{2+}; leuco base: MBH.
$M\dot{B}H^+$, $M\dot{B}H_2^{2+}$; leuco base: MBH.
[c] Units of liters/mole-sec.
[d] H_o.

The pulse radiolysis of MB^+ without formate led to the $MB\cdot$ absorption plus another transient peaking at 520 mμ. The latter corresponds with the spectrum of semioxidized dye obtained by flash photolysis (*11*, *15*) and was attributed to the attack of OH. However, the addition of OH to the dye was not ruled out. No evidence was found for triplet formation. The spectral changes obtained in more acidic solutions with formate show that the semiquinone occurs in two protonated states designated as $M\dot{B}H_2^{2+}$ (p$K_a \sim -3$) and MBH^+ (p$K_a \sim 2$). It was suggested that the first proton is attached to the central ring nitrogen atom and the second proton adds to the $-N(CH_3)_2$ group. The approximate formation and decay rate constants are given in Table I.

Pulse Radiolysis of Aqueous Fluorescein Dyes. The xanthene dyes of the fluorescein type were investigated using 1-μsec. pulses of 30 Mev. electrons (*4*, *5*, *8*). The transient spectra obtained with deaerated fluorescein solutions show three characteristic sets of bands. A prominent peak that shifts from 355 mμ in neutral solutions to 395 mμ in alkaline solutions corresponds with the semiquinone monoanion (p$K_a = 9.5$) (*13*). This band is quenched by e^-_{aq} scavengers, such as oxygen or H_2O_2, and was attributed to reduction of the dye by e^-_{aq}. A band at 415–420 mμ which does not change with pH was identified with the semioxidized radical monoanion, a phenoxyl derivative first observed in flash photolysis also (*13*). This band is quenched by formate and was attributed to the oxidative attack of OH. The remaining transient consists of a diffuse absorption to long wavelengths of the fluorescein dianion band (491 mμ) and was designated as the "red product." It was distinguished from the other two species by its considerably longer lifetime and first-order decay. The "red product" has at least two constituents with different buildup and decay rates. It is quenched entirely by H and OH scavengers such as formate or ethyl alcohol, while only one component was observed in air-saturated solutions. The longer-lived constituent was identified with OH adducts of the xanthene ring system, and the secondary components were assumed to be H-atom adducts. The initial yields of the semiquinone (R) and semioxidized dye (X) in deaerated solutions at pH 10.7 are $G(R) = 3.3 \pm 0.3$ and $G(X) = 1.4 \pm 0.2$ (*5*).

The results obtained with the eosin dianion are similar to fluorescein. In this case, the R absorptions at 369 mμ (monoanion) and 405 mμ (dianion) agree exactly with the flash photolysis assignments (*7, 10, 16*), while the X monoanion band at 450 mμ is reasonably close to the flash photolysis spectra reported at 462 (*10*) and 456 mμ (*16*). The eosin OH adduct maximum is located near 600 mμ compared with 570 ± 20 mμ for fluorescein (*4, 5*). The initial yields at pH 9.0 are $G(R) = 3.3 \pm 0.3$ and $G(X) = 2.0 \pm 0.3$ (*22*). The smaller contribution of the OH addition path in eosin compared with fluorescein is consistent with the occupation of four of the six xanthene ring sites by bromine atoms. The only information available on erythrosin from pulse radiolysis locates the R dianion at 450 mμ and the X monoanion at 470 mμ (*6*).

The rate constants for dye reduction by e^-_{aq} as calculated from the e^-_{aq} pseudo-first-order lifetime in the presence of formate (to suppress the overlapping "red product" absorption) are given in Table II. When both formate and an e^-_{aq} scavenger such as N_2O or H_2O_2 are present, the only significant reaction is the reduction of the dye by CO_2^-. The rate constants determined by analog computer fit to the growth rate of R are given in Table II. Although the broad "red product" absorption limits the use of competition methods for determining the OH reaction rates, estimates were made by analog computer solution to the kinetics of the [dye/e^-_{aq}/OH] system based on the dependence of $G(R)$ and $G(X)$ on initial dye concentration (Table II).

It was shown that R and X react together during the early stages of their decay in deaerated solutions, which accounts for the low dye bleaching yields under ^{60}Co irradiation unless an e^-_{aq} or OH scavenger is added. The decay of R in the absence of X is second order; however, the rate constant decreases markedly with increasing dye concentration. The proposed explanation is that the semiquinone forms a complex with unreacted dye, so that the actual decay rate is controlled by the equilibrium concentration of free semiquinone. The analysis led to the semiquinone disproportionation rate constant and a limiting value of the equilibrium constant. The "red product" decay is first order and parallels the return of coloration in the region of the dye absorption. The mechanism proposed is slow water (or OH^-) elimination from the OH adduct leading to the formation of X and eventually a colored permanent product (Table II).

Table II. Pulse Radiolysis Rate Constants for Fluorescein and Eosin

	Fluorescein			*Eosin*		
Reaction[a]	*Rate Constant*[b]	*pH*	*Ref.*	*Rate Constant*[b]	*pH*	*Ref.*
$e^-_{aq} + S + H^+ \rightarrow R$	1.4×10^{10} (15%)	10.7	5	2.2×10^{10} (20%)	9.0	[c]
	2.0×10^{10} (10%)	13	*20*			
$CO_2^- + S + H^+ \rightarrow R + CO_2$	2.6×10^7 (35%)	10.4	5	4.2×10^8 (20%)	8.8	4
$2R + H_2O \rightarrow L + S + OH^-$	2.0×10^7 (20%)	10.4	5	1.6×10^7 (20%)	9.0	[c]
$OH\cdot + S \rightarrow X + OH^-$	1.6×10^9 (20%)	10.7	5	1.7×10^9 (20%)	9.0	[c]
$OH\cdot + S \rightarrow SOH\cdot$	1.4×10^9 (15%)	10.7	5	0.6×10^9 (30%)	9.0	[c]
$R + X \rightarrow 2S$	4.7×10^8 (20%)	10.7	5	6.5×10^8 (20%)	8.5	4
$SOH\cdot \rightarrow X + OH^-$	100 $sec.^{-1}$ (20%)	10.7	5	70 $sec.^{-1}$ (10%)	9.0	[c]
$R + S \rightleftharpoons RS$	$K < 4 \times 10^6 M^{-1}$	10.4	5	$K < 5 \times 10^5 M^{-1}$	9.0	[c]

[a] Dye dianion(S); semiquinone dianion(R); semioxidized dye monoanion(X); OH adduct(SOH·); leuco base(L); complex(RS).
[b] In units of liters/mole-sec. unless indicated otherwise.
[c] Unpublished data.

Table III. Pulse Radiolysis Rate Constants for Other Dyes

Reaction	*Dye*	*Rate Constant*[a]	*Ref.*
Dye + e^-_{aq}	Acriflavine	3.3×10^{10} (10%)	*20*
	Rhodamine B	$\sim 3 \times 10^{10}$	*20*
	Acridine orange	3.2×10^{10}	2
	Methyl green	4.3×10^{10}	2
Dye + OH·	Rhodamine B	$\sim 9 \times 10^9$	*20*
Dye + CO_2^-	Rhodamine B	1.8×10^8 (25%)	*20*
Dye + D-glucose$_{ox}$	Methylene blue	2×10^9	2

[a] Units of liters/mole-sec.

Pulse Radiolysis of Other Dyes in Aqueous Solution. In connection with an investigation of electron pulse-induced luminescence (discussed below), Prütz and Land (*20*) reported rate constants for the reactions of rhodamine B and acriflavine (Table III). The rhodamine B reduction product (in the presence of formate) absorbs most strongly at 410 mμ, which corresponds with the semiquinone transient obtained by the flash photolysis of the dye in aqueous alcohol solutions (*24*). The species formed with N_2O present absorbs between 350 and 500 mμ. It was observed that both the semiquinone and the oxidation product are long lived in deaerated solutions, which suggests that the latter includes a substantial contribution from the OH adduct. In a study of dye–polyanion complexes by Balazs *et al.* (2) (discussed below) rate constants were reported for the reaction of e^-_{aq} with acridine orange (AO^+) and methyl green (MG^{2+}) (Table III). For AO^+ the disappearance of the dye is accompanied by the growth of a transient absorption at approximately 390 mμ, which was attributed to the one-electron addition product.

Pulse Radiolysis of Dye–Polymer Complexes. Pulse radiolysis studies of dye–polyanion complexes have yielded information on the reaction of reducible dyes with e^-_{aq} when the dye is bound to a high molecular weight substrate (2). The investigation of the methylene blue–heparin complex was based on the correlation of binding with the rate constant for dye reduction by e^-_{aq}, in the presence of D-glucose as OH- and H-atom scavenger. The occurrence of binding was deduced from the "metachromatic" spectral shift, in which the MB^+ absorption at 665 mμ is strongly quenched in the complex with the appearance of a new band at 580 mμ. Under such conditions the rate constant for the reaction of e^-_{aq} with MB^+ diminishes from the value in free solution (Table I) to as low as $1.1 \times 10^9 M^{-1}$ sec.$^{-1}$. The decay of the e^-_{aq} absorption was accompanied by the bleaching of the complex at the "metachromatic wavelength" and the growth of a transient species at 420 mμ. The latter was attributed to the semiquinone MB·, which was stable for a considerably longer period compared with the case of free dye. (A slower growth of MB· from the reaction of the dye with oxidized glucose was observed also). The direct relationship between complexing and the lower e^-_{aq} reactivity was shown by altering conditions to reverse the metachromatic wavelength shift, in which case the e^-_{aq} rate constant increases towards the free solution value. For example, adding NaCl or raising the temperature leads to an almost complete restoration of the high reactivity. A lower e^-_{aq} reactivity was observed also when MB^+ is complexed to other polymeric substrates (sodium hyaluronate, sodium polyethylene sulfonate, sodium polystyrene sulfonate, sodium carboxymethyl cellulose, and DNA) and with the metachromatic dye, acridine orange complexed to polyanions. Furthermore, the lowering of e^-_{aq} reactivity was found for the non-metachromatic dye, methyl green and several other cations (cetyl pyridinium chloride, protamine sulfate, and polylysine hydrobromide) when complexed to heparin or DNA. The last two cases are particularly interesting because they represent polycations bound to polyanions, in which the strong interactions can be demonstrated by pulse radiolysis in the absence of complicating precipitation effects which occur with turbidimetric methods.

Luminescence of Dyes Induced by Electron Pulse Irradiation. Prütz, Sommermeyer, and Land (*19*) made the remarkable discovery that the electron pulse irradiation of rhodamine B, fluorescein, or acriflavine in dilute aqueous solution leads to visible light emission that builds up and decays over tens of microseconds. The intensity is $\sim 10^3$ times higher than the emission induced by direct electron excitation and was attributed to a chemiluminescent process involving the water decomposition products. This light emission is quenched by either e^-_{aq} scavengers or formate, which led to a mechanism involving the reaction of e^-_{aq} with the oxidized dye intermediate. In a recent extension of this work utilizing sequential light flash and electron pulse irradiations, Grossweiner and Rodde (*9*) deduced that the form of oxidized fluorescein or eosin which reacts with e^-_{aq} is the OH adduct and not the semioxidized species X. Furthermore, the triplet states of these dyes also react with e^-_{aq}, leading to an intense chemiluminescence from the excited semiquinone. The latter work indicates that studies of metastable dye species are feasible with combined flash photolytic and pulse radiolytic methods.

Discussion

In a survey of dye radiation chemistry Swallow (*25*) noted that a number of dyes in aqueous solution react as follows:

(a) Irradiation of aerated solutions in the absence of organic substrates leads to irreversible oxidation, but oxygen-free solutions are bleached *via* irreversible oxidation and reversible reduction.

(b) When oxidizable substrates are present, aerated solutions are radiation resistant, while oxygen-free solutions are reversibly reduced.

These effects were explained by a general mechanism involving oxidation of the dye by OH and reduction of the dye by H atoms and the oxidized organic substrate. The pulse radiolysis results show that e^-_{aq} and not H atoms make the greater contribution to dye reduction in neutral and alkaline solutions and that H and OH addition must be considered as well as electron-transfer reactions. The following general radiolysis mechanism indicates the reactions likely to be significant in deaerated aqueous solutions of dyes possessing the quinonoid structure (*e.g.*, azines, thiazines, acridines, xanthenes).

$$H_2O \rightsquigarrow e^-_{aq}, H\cdot, OH\cdot, H_2O_2, H_2$$

$$D + e^-_{aq} \longrightarrow D_{red} \tag{1}$$

$$D + OH\cdot \rightarrow DOH\cdot \quad (2a)$$

$$D + OH\cdot \rightarrow D_{ox} + OH^- \quad (2b)$$

$$D + H\cdot \rightarrow DH\cdot \quad (3a)$$

$$D + H\cdot \rightarrow D_{red} \quad (3b)$$

$$D_{red} + D_{ox} \longrightarrow 2D \quad (4)$$

$$D_{red} + D_{red} \longrightarrow D + \text{leuco base} \quad (5)$$

$$D_{ox} + D_{ox} \longrightarrow \text{products} \quad (6)$$

For the fluoresceins it has been proposed that the OH adduct decays by slow water (or OH^-) elimination (*5*):

$$DOH\cdot \rightarrow D_{ox} + OH^- \quad (7)$$

and that the OH adduct is the species responsible for the chemiluminescence induced by electron-pulse irradiation (*9, 20*):

$$DOH\cdot + e^-_{aq} \rightarrow D^* + OH^- \quad (8)$$

[An intense luminescence has been observed also when I^- was present (*20, 21*), attributed to the reaction of iodine atoms with the reduced dye.] The reductive attack is suppressed by oxygen *via* Reactions 9 and 10.

$$e^-_{aq}(H\cdot) + O_2 \rightarrow O_2^- \quad (9)$$

$$D_{red} + O_2 \rightarrow D + O_2^- \quad (10)$$

Reaction 10 is the process responsible for restoring the dye in photochemical autoxidations. The reaction of O_2^- (or $HO_2\cdot$ in acidic solutions) with dyes is not expected to be fast. The oxidizable organic substrate scavenges H and OH.

$$AH_2 + OH\cdot\ (H\cdot) \rightarrow AH\cdot + H_2O\ (H_2) \quad (11)$$

In a number of cases it has been shown that the partially oxidized substrate can reduce the dye (*2, 4, 5, 12, 20*):

$$D + AH\cdot \rightarrow D_{red} + A \quad (12)$$

Table IV. Dye Bleaching G Values

Dye	*Conditions*	G(−D) *Oxidative*	G(−D) *Reductive*	*Ref.*
Methylene blue	Deaerated	0.6 ± 0.1[a]	1.6 ± 0.2[a]	25
	Aerated	0.68 ± 0.08[a]		25
	Deaerated with organic substances present		2.9 ± 0.1[a]	25
	Deaerated with formate		3.15 ± 0.15[a]	12
Fluorescein	Deaerated	0.59[b]		22
	Aerated	0.66[b]		18
	Deaerated with formate		2.32	22
Eosin	Deaerated	0.95[b, c]		22
	Aerated	0.85[c]		22
	Deaerated with formate		2.06	22
	Deaerated with H_2O_2	1.47[c]		22
	Deaerated with N_2O	1.71[c]		22
	Aerated with formate	0.00[b]		22
Safranine T	Aerated	0.65 ± 0.01		14

[a] Average of literature values cited in reference.
[b] Total of oxidative and reductive decoloration yields.
[c] G values corrected for absorption of permanent oxidation product.

It is interesting to compare the pulse radiolysis mechanism with dye bleaching yields reported for low intensity, steady irradiations (Table IV). If n OH radicals are needed to decolor one dye molecule, bleaching yields under ideal oxidizing conditions should be G_{OH}/n in air-saturated solutions, $(G_{OH} + G_e)/n$ in nitrous oxide-saturated solutions, and $\leqslant (G_{OH} + G_e + G_H)/n$ in the presence of moderate hydrogen peroxide concentrations (*i.e.*, when H and OH are not scavenged by H_2O_2). Taking 2.65, 2.8, and 0.55 for G_{OH}, G_e and G_H leads to $n \simeq 4$ for methylene blue, fluorescein, and safranine T and $n = 3\text{-}4$ for eosin. The possible intermediate steps include disproportionation of semioxidized dye and successive reactions of OH with the unstable radical and molecular products. The values of $G(-D)$ in the presence of oxidizable organic substrates should be $1/2(G_e + G_{OH} + G_H) \simeq 3.0$. This prediction is in excellent agreement with the average of many experiments on methylene blue with different substrates (*e.g.*, benzoate, ethyl alcohol, lactate, formate). However, there is an unexplained discrepancy of ~ 0.8 with the fluoresceins which may be caused by the oxidation of the semiquinone by primary H_2O_2. The extent of bleaching in deaerated solutions should be controlled by the competition between Reactions 5 and 6 with the back process, Reaction 4. The low values of $G(-D)$ for the fluoresceins are consistent with the measured rate constants of the radical decay reactions (*4*). The methylene blue results for deaerated solutions suggest that the back reaction is unimportant compared with the radical decay processes because the observed values of $G(-D)$ indicate that four OH radicals are required for permanent oxidation and that all H and e^-_{aq} lead to reversible reduction *via* Reactions 1, 3, and 5. (It is not known whether methylene blue forms OH- or H-atom adducts). The low bleaching yields obtained when aerated solutions of various dyes are irradiated in the presence of an oxidizable substrate (*24*) are explained by the scavenging of e^-_{aq} and H atoms by oxygen to give unreactive O_2^- (Reaction 9) and the reaction of OH (and possibly H) with the organic substance (Reaction 11). The extent of bleaching would still remain small even if the reacted scavenger reduces the dye (Reaction 12) because of Reaction 10.

Figure 1 shows a correlation of the reported e^-_{aq} rate constants with the values obtained from the Debye equation. (The calculations are based on Stokes' law for the dye diffusion constants, the experimental value of 4.7×10^{-5} sq. cm./sec. for the e^-_{aq} diffusion constant (*23*), dye radii from spheres of density 1.3 gram/cc. and the appropriate molecular weight, and an assumed e^-_{aq} radius of 2.7 A.). The agreement is reasonably good in view of the uncertainties in the choice of parameters and indicates that the nucleophilic attack of the electron on these dyes is controlled by the encounter rate. The available data show that reduction by CO_2^- is more selective, with rate constants ranging from 2.6×10^7 for fluorescein to 5.6×10^9 for methylene blue. It was suggested (*5*) that the rate constants obtained with the xanthenes correlate with the charge distribution of the quinonoid structure, while steric effects at the reducible central carbon atom and changes in the bridge structure may be involved in comparisons between the various dye types. Although it has been observed that the OH reaction products in the xanthenes build up more slowly than those of e^-_{aq} (*5, 20*), accurate determinations of the rate constants are complicated by the occurrence of both electron transfer and addition reactions. Furthermore, the strong visible coloration of these products limits the use of competition methods which have been applied to smaller aromatic molecules. Kinetic estimates have led to total OH rate constants of $3 \pm 1 \times 10^9$ for the fluoresceins (Table II) and $\sim 9 \times 10^9$ for rhodamine B (Table III). A comparison with the reaction rate of OH with hydroquinone (1.2×10^{10}) and benzoquinone (1.2×10^9) (*1*) suggests that the xanthene dye results are the correct magnitude.

The chemiluminescent reactions of e^-_{aq} with dyes represent a new process which may have broader implications. The formation of excited dye in Reaction 8 should lead to triplet formation *via* intersystem crossing, although the yield would be low because of competition from Reaction 1.

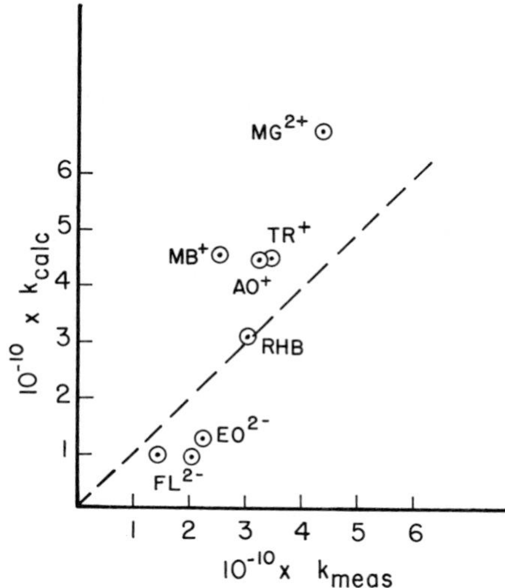

Figure 1. Rate constants for reaction of e^-_{aq} with dyes (liters/mole-sec.). Ordinate: calculated from Debye equation for encounter-limited reactions; abscissa: experimental results

The reaction of triplet dye with e^-_{aq} leading to the excited semiquinone has been observed only with fluorescein and eosin thus far (*9*):

$$^3\mathrm{D} + e^-_{\mathrm{aq}} \rightarrow \mathrm{D}^*_{\mathrm{red}} \tag{13}$$

Although Reaction 13 was identified by using light to excite the triplet dye and an electron pulse to generate e^-_{aq}, it is possible that both species can be formed photochemically in certain systems involving solvated or trapped electrons. This is equivalent to a two-quanta process, in which the reduction potential of the electron may be transferred to the dye species during the lifetime of the excited state. It would be interesting to learn whether Reaction 13 occurs with other aromatics in polar solvents that can solvate electrons including biological photosensitizers.

Acknowledgment

The author is pleased to acknowledge the support of the National Institutes of Health on Grants Nos. GM-10038 and GM-12716 during the preparation of this paper. In addition, he thanks G. O. Phillips of Salford University for preprints of work noted in the text and A. Husain and A. F. Rodde, Jr. of Michael Reese Hospital and Medical Center for making available unpublished results on eosin pulse radiolysis.

Literature Cited

(1) Adams, G. E., Michael, B. D., *Trans. Faraday Soc.* **63,** 1171 (1967).
(2) Balazs, E. A., Davies, J. W., Phillips, G. O., Scheufele, D. S., *J. Chem. Soc.*, in press.
(3) Baxendale, J. H., *et al., Nature* **201,** 468 (1964).
(4) Chrysochoos, J., Ovadia, J., Grossweiner, L. I., *J. Phys. Chem.* **71,** 1629 (1967).
(5) Cordier, P., Grossweiner, L. I., *J. Phys. Chem.* **72,** 2018 (1968).
(6) Cordier, P., Grossweiner, L. I., unpublished result.
(7) Grossweiner, L. I., Zwicker, E. F., *J. Chem. Phys.* **34,** 1411 (1961).
(8) Grossweiner, L. I., Rodde, A. F. Jr., Sandberg, G., Chrysochoos, J., *Nature* **210,** 1154 (1966).
(9) Grossweiner, L. I., Rodde, A. F. Jr., *J. Phys. Chem.* **72,** 756 (1968).
(10) Kasche, V., Lindqvist, L., *Photochem. Photobiol.* **4,** 923 (1965).
(11) Kato, S., Morita, M., Koizumi, M., *Bull. Chem. Soc. Japan* **37,** 117 (1964).
(12) Keene, J. P., Land, E. J., Swallow, A. J., "Pulse Radiolysis," M. Ebert, J. P. Keene, A. J. Swallow, J. H. Baxendale, eds., pp. 227-245, Academic Press, New York, 1965.
(13) Lindqvist, L., *Arkiv Kemi* **16,** 79 (1960).
(14) Marketos, D. G., Rakintzis, N. Th., *Z. Physik. Chem., N.F.* **44,** 270 (1965).
(15) Matsumoto, S., *Bull. Chem. Soc. Japan* **37,** 491 (1964).
(16) Ohno, T., Kato, S., Koizumi, M., *Bull. Chem. Soc. Japan* **39,** 232 (1966).
(17) Parker, C. A., *J. Phys. Chem.* **63,** 26 (1959).
(18) Patti, F., *J. Chim. Phys.* **52,** 38 (1955).
(19) Prütz, W., Sommermeyer, K., Land, E. J., *Nature* **212,** 1043 (1966).
(20) Prütz, W., Land, E. J., *Biophysik* **3,** 349 (1967).
(21) Prütz, W., Sommermeyer, K., *Biophysik* **4,** 48 (1967).
(22) Rodde, A. F., Jr., Grossweiner, L. I., *J. Phys. Chem.*, in press.
(23) Schmidt, K. H., Buck, W. L., *Science* **151,** 70 (1966).
(24) Stevens, B., Sharpe, R. R., Bingham, W. S. W., *Photochem. Photobiol.* **6,** 83 (1967).
(25) Swallow, A. J., "Radiation Chemistry of Organic Compounds," pp. 175-185, Pergamon Press, Oxford, 1960.

RECEIVED December 22, 1967.

22

Studies in the Radiation and Photochemistry of Aqueous *p*-Nitrosodimethylaniline

SHIRISH SHAH, CONRAD N. TRUMBORE, BERNARD GIESSNER, and WOO PARK

University of Delaware, Newark, Del. 19711

Yields for the radiolytic bleaching of aqueous solutions of p-*nitrosodimethylaniline (RNO) have been found to be sensitive functions of oxygen and RNO concentrations, pH, and added OH radical scavenger concentration. The bleaching yields were independent of temperature and radiation intensity over a limited region of the above variables. The nature of a "residual" bleaching yield in excess ethyl alcohol and an unusual kinetic dependence on oxygen in acidic RNO solutions were investigated and the evidence, while strongly in favor of an OH radical attack on RNO, does not preclude an acidic form of the OH radical. Preliminary reports of H_2O_2-RNO photolysis and H_2O_2-Fe^{2+} flow system electron spin resonance studies are also reported.*

In an earlier paper (*13*) *p*-nitrosodimethylaniline (RNO) was postulated to be an efficient scavenger of the OH radical at pH 9 in cobalt-60 gamma irradiated, air saturated, aqueous solutions. It was also postulated to be specific for the OH radical in these solutions since evidence was presented that neither $HO_2\cdot$ nor O_2^- destroyed the chromophoric group at 440 n.m., the absorption maximum of RNO in the visible region of the spectrum for neutral and basic solutions. Relative rate constants for the reaction of OH with RNO and other molecules were reported to be in good relative agreement with those reported by others who used both the pulse radiolysis method and indirect competition techniques.

Since $G(-\text{RNO})_{440}$ in alkaline solutions was equal to 1.1, it was assumed that secondary reactions regenerated RNO and that this yield of destruction was numerically equal to approximately half the yield of primary OH radicals escaping the "spur" region and reacting with RNO in a homogeneous fashion. (A subscript is used here to designate the

G value for the destruction of RNO molecules based solely upon the bleaching of either the 440 n.m. or 350 n.m. absorption, depending on the pH of the solution.) It was also assumed that since the spectral absorption maximum did not shift during the very early phases of the irradiation there was little absorbance by irradiation products at 440 n.m.

In these studies it was reported that the radiolytic behavior of the acid form of RNO (pK = 3.7) was quite different from that in neutral and pH 9 solutions. In the latter solutions simple competition kinetics for the OH radical were obeyed over wide concentrations of added competitor, S,

$$OH + RNO \rightarrow \text{product(s) which cause subsequent net bleaching of O.D. at 440 n.m.}$$

$$OH + S \rightarrow \text{no subsequent bleaching at 440 n.m.}$$

and in most cases S protected RNO completely from bleaching—*i.e.*, $G(-RNO)_{440}$ would approach zero at very high ratios of (S)/(RNO). In some cases this was not true and mechanistic complications prevented simple competition kinetics from being obeyed at high S concentration, but even in most of these cases the simple competition model applied at low relative S concentrations and gave relative rate constants which were in good agreement with other literature values. However, at pH 2 with the acid form of RNO a new phenomenon was noted, namely that at high S concentration RNO was not only not completely protected, but also that a plateau of $G(-RNO)_{440}$ was reached—*i.e.*, a constant value of this yield was attained with increasing S concentration. The nature of this yield has been investigated in the work reported here and efforts at mechanistic interpretation are made.

Kraljic (*11*) and Anbar *et al.* (*1*) have extended studies of relative OH rate constants using the RNO system to many different chemical compounds using cobalt-60 gamma rays as a source of ionizing radiation. More recently, several groups have independently investigated the pulse radiolysis of neutral aqueous RNO solutions (*3, 6*), as well as of nitrosobenzene (*2*). Briefly, the main conclusions of the pulsed electron RNO studies are: (1) RNO reacts with the OH radical and the hydrated electron with second order rate constants of $\sim 10^{10}$ liter moles^{-1} sec.$^{-1}$; (2) back reactions are noted—*i.e.*, the initial rapid bleaching of the 440 n.m. absorption is followed by a slow buildup of absorption at the same wavelength; and (3) the oxygenated systems were the simplest and in all cases there was no evidence that HO_2 or O_2^- reacted with RNO.

In this paper we wish to report further studies in the gamma radiolysis of the RNO system with special attention paid to solute concentration dependences and to unexpected effects found at low pH. In addition, preliminary results of photolysis and electron spin resonance studies of the aqueous RNO system are reported.

Experimental

Some of the techniques used in this study have been described previously (*13*). Solutions were saturated with Ar (99.99% pure, supplied by Linde), using a modification of the technique described by Swinnerton *et al.* (*17*). The normal dose rate of approximately 6×10^{16} e.v. gram^{-1} min.$^{-1}$ was delivered by a Gammacell-220 (AECL) cobalt-60 irradiation unit. Lower dose rates by a factor of nine were achieved by enclosing the irradiation vessels inside a lead container. Temperatures of irradiated samples were controlled to ± 1°C. in experiments where the effects of temperature were studied but in other experiments were 24 ± 2°C. Care was taken to minimize the effects of volume contraction and expansion at low temperatures in order to exclude air from Ar saturated solutions.

Products were separated either on ITLC glass fibre mats (Gelman) or on glass plates produced from a slurry of silica gel *G* (Brinkmann). After solution was applied to these plates ammonia was added to neutralize the acid and chromatograms were developed with a 50% (V:V) petroleum ether (30–60°C.) and benzene solvent. Bands or spots were extracted with ethyl alcohol or water.

All chemicals used were reagent grade. Acid solutions were prepared with $HClO_4$ unless otherwise noted. The Fricke ferrous sulfate dosimeter was employed in the usual manner.

Results

Figure 1 shows the effects at pH 9 of variable RNO concentration on $G(-RNO)_{440}$, calculated from linear portions only of dose-yield plots, for RNO solutions saturated with different gases. Measurements at high RNO concentration were difficult to obtain accurately since they involved small differences between large optical densities and at very low RNO concentrations curvature was noticeable in dose *vs.* bleaching curves at shorter irradiation times. Experiments at concentrations higher than $10^{-3}M$ RNO were conducted and $G(-RNO)_{440}$ was strongly dependent upon O_2 concentration but values were not very reproducible.

Competition studies of the type described in the introduction to this paper were carried out with oxygen saturated (1 atm.) solutions of RNO at pH 9 and compared with similar ones with air saturated solutions. Table I illustrates the differences in relative rate constants calculated from these studies, based upon linear plots of $1/G(-RNO)_{440}$ *vs.* (S)/(RNO).

Figure 2 illustrates the results of a study of the effects of RNO concentration on $G(-RNO)_{350}$ in pH 2 solutions. RNO in its acid form has been found in this study to have an extinction coefficient at its maximum

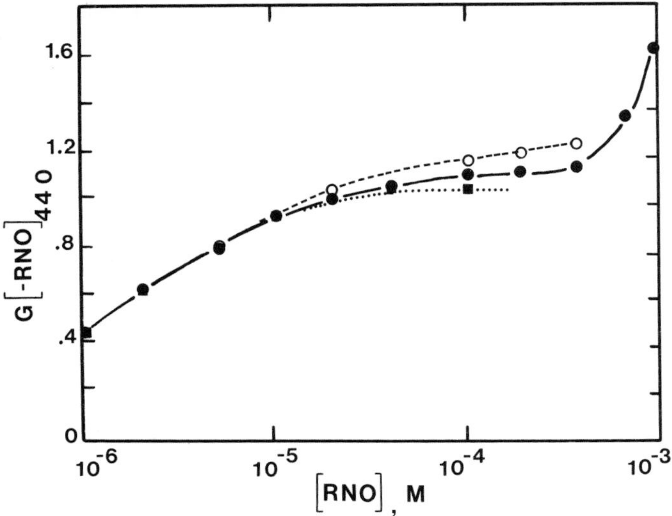

Figure 1. Effect of O_2 and p-nitrosodimethylaniline *(RNO) concentration on* G(−RNO)$_{440}$*, the initial cobalt-60 gamma radiolytic yield of bleaching at 440 n.m., in pH 9 ($Na_2B_4O_7$) aqueous solutions:* ○*, Ar saturated solution;* ●*, air saturated;* ■*, oxygen saturated. Dose rate is approximately 6 × 10^{16} e.v. gram^{-1} min.$^{-1}$ for this and all subsequent figures*

Table I. Effect of Variable Oxygen Concentration on Relative Bimolecular Rate Constants for Reaction with OH Calculated from $G(-RNO)_{440}$ for pH 9 Solutions

Scavenger	*(RNO)* × 10^5M	*Relative Rate Constant* air saturated	*Relative Rate Constant* oxygen saturated
RNO	4.0	100[a]	100[a]
I^-	4.0	90	103
NO_2^-	3.9	54	60
CH_3OH	3.8	7.7	8.2

[a] used as the basis for comparison with other rate constants.

(350 n.m.) of 21,000 as opposed to 34,200 at 440 n.m. for its neutral or basic form (*13*). Above $10^{-4}M$ RNO, $G(-RNO)_{350}$ increases with increasing RNO concentration regardless of the dissolved gas. Again $G(-RNO)_{350}$ is defined as the radiolytic yield for destruction of RNO calculated solely on the basis of bleaching of optical density at 350 n.m., assuming that only the destruction of the RNO is responsible for this loss and that the radiolysis products give no significant absorption. Experiments were performed in which the RNO was separated by TLC

from its radiolysis products at pH 2 and $G(-RNO)$ measured by extracting the RNO band, diluting, and taking optical density readings of the resulting solutions. Even though these semiquantitative experiments, carried out between $5 \times 10^{-5}M$ and $2.3 \times 10^{-4}M$ RNO, showed that within the relatively large experimental error $G(-RNO)$ calculated in this manner is the same as that calculated spectrophotometrically, other experiments showed that the absorption of products, some of which may be primary products, is not entirely negligible at 350 n.m. The difficulty lies in distinguishing between primary and secondary products, especially at low initial RNO concentrations.

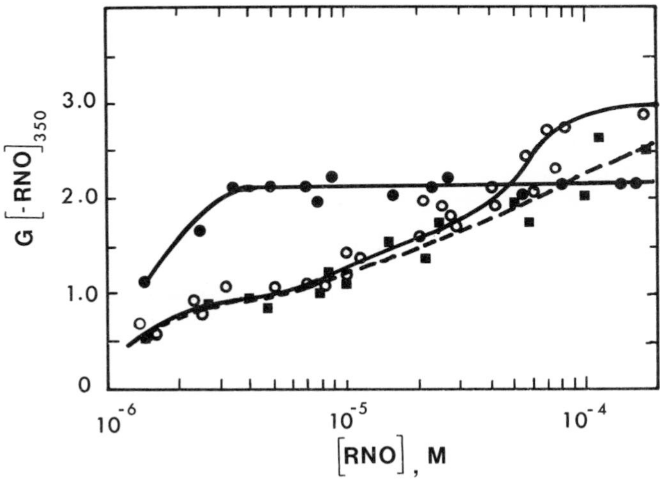

Figure 2. Effect of O_2 and RNO concentration on G(−RNO) yields calculated from spectroscopic changes at 350 n.m. in cobalt-60 gamma irradiated aqueous pH 2 ($HClO_4$) solutions of RNO: ●, oxygen saturated solutions; ○, air saturated; ■, Ar saturated

Table II. Effect of Variable Radiation Intensity on $G(-RNO)_{350}$

(RNO) M *(× 10⁵)*	*Soln. sat'd. with*	$G(-RNO)_{350}$ *normal dose rate*[a]	*low dose rate*[b]
8.4	O_2	2.26	2.24
8.4	Ar	1.20	1.21
11.2	Ar	1.39	1.38
49	Ar	1.87	1.84

[a] dose rate 6.0×10^{16} e.v. gram^{-1} min.$^{-1}$, pH 2 ($HClO_4$).
[b] dose rate 6.7×10^{15} e.v. gram^{-1} min.$^{-1}$, pH 2 ($HClO_4$).

Table III. Effect of Variable Temperature on Radiolytic Bleaching at 350 n.m.

Time of irrad.[a] *(min.)*	*(RNO)* M (× 10^5)	*Sol'n. sat'd with*	Δ*O.D. at 350 n.m.*						
			0°C.	*22°C.*	*23°C.*	*30°C.*	*40°C.*	*50°C.*	*60°C.*
3	20	Ar	—	.125	—	.125	.125	.125	.125
3	19.6	O_2	—	.142	—	.142	.149	.142	.138
1	0.98	Ar	.033	—	.031	.029	.032	.032	.033
1	0.98	O_2	—	—	.049	.049	.047	.049	.051

[a] dose rate 6 × 10^{16} e.v. gram^{-1} min.$^{-1}$.

Results of a somewhat limited study of the effects on $G(-RNO)_{350}$ of varying temperature and gamma ray radiation intensity are shown in Tables II and III. These show no observable effect on $G(-RNO)_{350}$ of changes of temperature or radiation intensity over the ranges studied, 0°–60° C. and a factor of nine, respectively.

The effects of adding ethyl alcohol to solutions of various RNO concentrations are shown in Figures 3 and 4. The "residual yield" is defined from these graphs as that limiting value of $G(-RNO)_{350}$ at

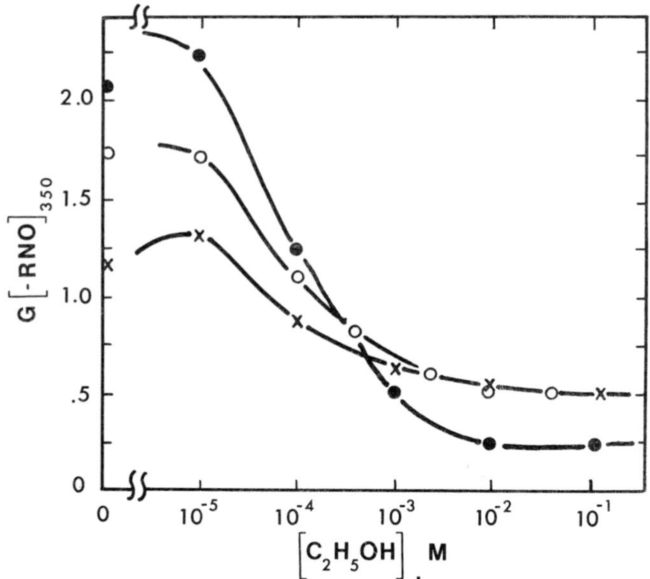

Figure 3. Effect of ethyl alcohol and RNO concentrations on G(−RNO)$_{350}$ in air saturated solutions of RNO at pH 2: ●, 4.3 × 10^{-5}M RNO; ○, 2.8 × 10^{-5}M RNO; ×, 8 × 10^{-6}M RNO. "Residual yields" for ○ and × would be 0.5 and 0.25 respectively

which further increases in ethyl alcohol concentration lead to no further substantial change in $G(-RNO)_{350}$—*e.g.*, 0.5 for $8 \times 10^{-6}M$ RNO in Figure 4. This yield is shown to be a sensitive function of RNO and O_2 concentration.

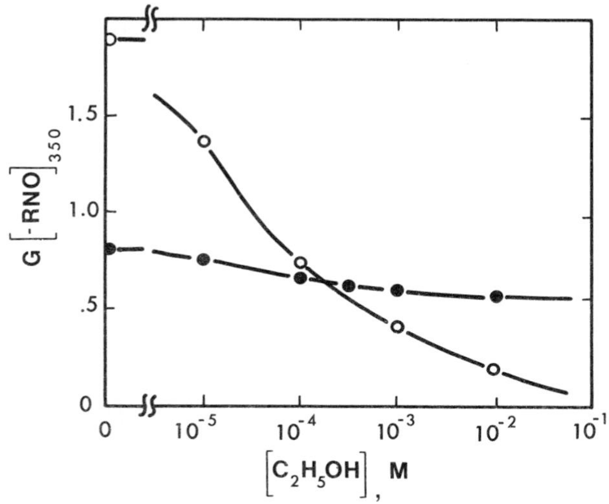

Figure 4. Effect of O_2 and ethyl alcohol concentration on $G(-RNO)_{350}$ *in pH 2 ($HClO_4$) RNO solutions:* ○, *O_2 saturated solutions of* 1.44×10^{-5}M *RNO;* ●, *Ar saturated solutions of* 8×10^{-6}M *RNO*

Similar competition studies in air saturated RNO solutions were also conducted using I^-, Br^-, and NO_2^- as competitive scavengers. Different residual yields of bleaching at 350 were found for NO_2^- and I^- (Figure 5) but none was apparent for Br^- in sulfuric acid solutions. Simple competition kinetics was only observed over a relatively small range of the (solute)/(RNO) variable.

The effect on $G(-RNO)_{350}$ of adding the suspected radiolysis product *p*-nitrodimethylaniline (RNO_2) in air saturated and oxygen saturated RNO solutions is shown in Figure 6. Differences between oxygen and air saturated solutions are again observed.

No effect of added KNO_3 or H_2O_2 on $G(-RNO)_{350}$ was observed in air saturated, pH 2, $HClO_4$ solutions as long as the concentrations of these additives remained below $10^{-3}M$. Above this concentration definite differences in this yield were noted but not studied quantitatively. Added $CuSO_4$ reduced the yield of $G(-RNO)_{350}$ to nearly zero in solutions of RNO at pH 2 and from concentrations $3\text{–}9 \times 10^{-6}M$ RNO.

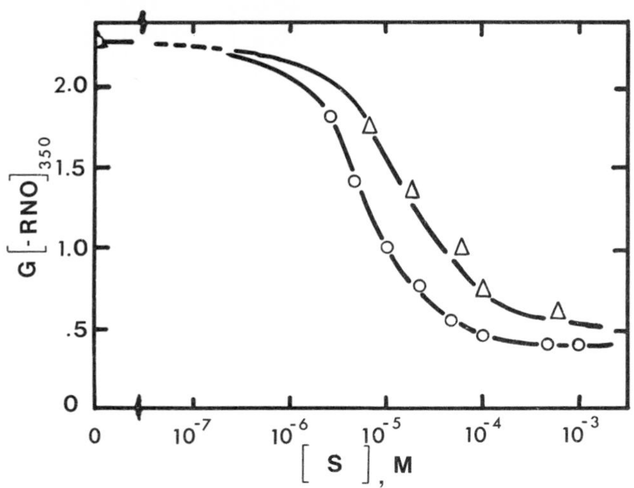

Figure 5. Effect of added OH scavengers, S, on $G(-RNO)_{350}$ in pH 2 solution (H_2SO_4), air saturated and containing RNO: △, KNO_2; ○, KI

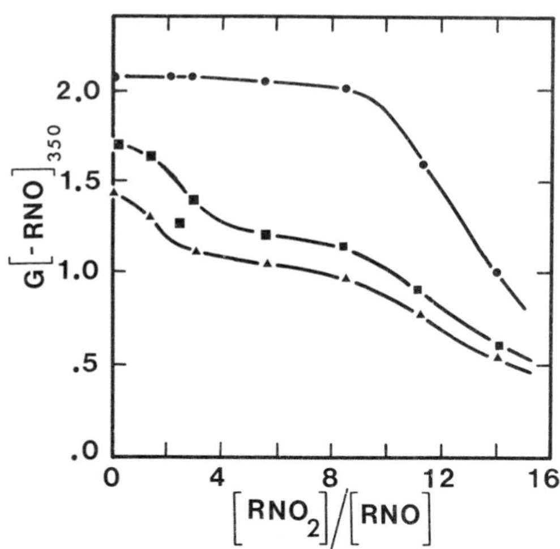

Figure 6. Effect of added p-nitrodimethylaniline *(RNO_2) on* $G(-RNO)_{350}$ *in pH 2 ($HClO_4$) solutions of RNO (2×10^{-5} to 10^{-4}M in RNO): ●, O_2 saturated solutions; ■, air saturated; ▲, Ar saturated*

Certain features of the thin layer chromatographic separation of the unidentified radiolysis products of pH 2 RNO solutions are reported here. There were about eight observed visible bands in these TLC separations. The addition of ethyl alcohol appeared qualitatively to eliminate one or possibly two products, leave a pink product undisturbed and reduce the yields of all other products. In oxygen saturated solutions, two products were completely eliminated.

It was noted qualitatively that the R_f values of the products of the Fenton Reagent ($H_2O_2 + Fe^{2+}$) reaction with RNO and the radiolysis products of acid RNO solutions were essentially the same. The spectral maxima of the extracted bands from the TLC plates of separated Fenton reaction and radiolysis products were also similar and many of these products absorb strongly in the 400–440 n.m. region of the spectrum but have minima around 350 n.m. Again it was difficult to distinguish between primary and secondary products.

Several runs were conducted at different RNO and O_2 concentrations at pH 2 with special pretreatment of the water used but no significant differences in $G(-\text{RNO})_{350}$ were observed. One water pretreatment consisted of gamma radiolysis followed by ultraviolet photolysis, the other, gamma radiolysis of H_2 saturated water.

Discussion

pH 9 Solutions. A falloff in G values with decreasing solute concentration has been noted before in many other radiolysis studies and is commonly attributed to either back reaction of primary or secondary radicals or reaction of these radicals with impurities with subsequent lowering in the yield of destruction of the solute in question. It would appear from Figure 1 that the falloff for RNO at pH 9 begins at slightly lower concentrations than with other solutes (*e.g.*, *5, 19*). The intensity of the cobalt-60 gamma radiation was too low to give competition between recombination of primary radicals and reaction of these radicals with RNO. The insensitivity of this falloff in $G(-\text{RNO})$ to oxygen concentration is unexpected. It would imply that none of the secondary radical reactions responsible for the final value of $G(-\text{RNO})_{350}$ are critically affected by oxygen concentration changes. The competition, therefore, would be between RNO and an impurity ($10^{-6}M$ or higher) for a primary radical (presumably OH), or possibly a competition between unimolecular decay of a precursor of the OH radical and reaction of that precursor with RNO. Estimates of impurity levels in the water used in these studies are less than micromolar amounts. Speculation on one possible reason for the high radiolytic sensitivity toward impurities has been given elsewhere (*9*) and involves the long range structure of liquid water.

The results of these pH 9 studies are consistent with some of the conclusions of the two pulse radiolysis studies reported earlier (*3, 6*). The $G(-RNO)_{440}$ of approximately 1.1 is slightly less than half the normally accepted values of G_{OH} (*14*), but this small difference could easily be because of primary product absorption at 440 n.m. The G values at around $5 \times 10^{-5}M$ RNO differ slightly with the results obtained by Dainton and Wiseall (*6*) who were working primarily at neutral pH rather than at pH 9. The rather steep rise in $G(-RNO)_{440}$ with increasing RNO concentration above $5 \times 10^{-4}M$ RNO may well represent a competition of the type represented by Equations 1 and 2.

$$O_2 + e_{aq}^- \rightarrow O_2^- \text{ (no subsequent net bleaching at 440 n.m.)} \quad (1)$$

$$RNO + e_{aq}^- \rightarrow RNO^- \text{ (subsequent net bleaching) } (3, 6) \quad (2)$$

The reasons for the almost negligible sensitivity of $G(-RNO)_{440}$ to O_2 at lower concentrations and the competitive falloff in $G(-RNO)_{440}$ at low (RNO) are not understood.

Studies at pH 2. Cobalt-60 gamma irradiations were carried out at pH 2 to investigate the unusual effects reported previously (*13*) on the "residual" yields of RNO destruction upon the addition of ethyl alcohol and to establish the sensitivity of $G(-RNO)_{350}$ to oxygen and RNO concentration so as to compare these results with those at pH 9.

INFLUENCE OF OXYGEN AND RNO CONCENTRATIONS ON $G(-RNO)_{350}$. The results shown in Figure 2 are difficult to understand on any simple competition scheme and appear to obey one of the possible combinations listed in the followed generalized kinetic scheme represented in the rate determining Equations 3a through 5, where X represents one or more primary or secondary intermediate radicals (or other radiolytic intermediates).

$$X + \text{impurity} \rightarrow \text{no subsequent net bleaching of 350 n.m. absorption} \quad (3a)$$

$$X \rightarrow \text{no subsequent bleaching of 350 n.m. absorption} \quad (3b)$$

$$X + X \rightarrow RNO + \text{bleaching at 350 n.m. (secondary reaction)} \quad (3c)$$

$$X + O_2 \rightarrow \text{more efficient bleaching at 350 n.m. per mole of X than in Equation 3c} \quad (4)$$

$$X + RNO \rightarrow \text{bleaching at 350 n.m. equal to or greater than that obtained from Equation 4} \quad (5)$$

This highly generalized scheme would seem to fit the results in Figure 2 in a semiquantitative fashion in the RNO concentration region from about $5 \times 10^{-6}M$ to about $5 \times 10^{-5}M$.

Below this region it will be noted that the G values for oxygen-saturated, air-saturated, and Ar-saturated solutions fall-off in a similar manner with approximately the same RNO concentration dependence. This could indicate that all of these G values depend upon one critical reaction of RNO possibly with an OH radical. If this were the case the different $G(-RNO)_{350}$ values for different O_2 concentrations in this RNO concentration region would result from more complex secondary reactions which were sensitive to O_2 concentration.

The increase in $G(-RNO)_{350}$ above concentrations of about $10^{-4}M$ RNO may be attributed to the scavenging of the hydrogen atom by the RNO in competition with the dissolved oxygen. Preliminary results of a pulse radiolysis study (*18*) of this system indicate a rapid attack by the hydrogen atom on RNO. The similarity between plateau values, such as in the case of oxygen-saturated solutions, and G_{OH} gives strong support in addition to the competition studies for an OH–RNO radical mechanism as the cause of the bleaching.

Studies of hydrogen peroxide yields (*15*) in irradiated RNO solutions show these yields to be higher than the usual "molecular" yields of approximately 0.7. This would appear as additional evidence that the HO_2 radical does not cause any net destruction of RNO.

The nature of X in the above reaction sequence is difficult to discern from the reported results. If X were a primary radiolytic intermediate it would almost have to be a precursor of the OH radical. Preliminary results (*4, 18*) from the pulse radiolysis study of these solutions indicate that the initial bleaching of the RNO in acidic as well as neutral solution is much larger than the final net bleaching. This would tend to imply a secondary reaction leading to regeneration of RNO, or at least to an eventual increase in optical density at 350 n.m.

Another less likely alternative, but one which cannot be ruled out from the evidence given, is that the apparent temperature independence reflects the presence of an electronically excited species X. Equation 3b represents a possible reaction of such a species, namely unimolecular decay in competition with a bimolecular reaction with RNO and O_2. This would explain the falloff of $G(RNO)$ at low solute concentrations.

The identification of X must await further studies in the cobalt-60 gamma radiolysis and pulse radiolysis of these systems.

EFFECTS OF OTHER ADDITIVES ON $G(-RNO)_{350}$. The results with added ethyl alcohol parallel those discussed in the previous section in their complexity. However, a relatively simple series of competitions illustrated in Equations 6 through 11 at least qualitatively serve as a model to explain the results of Figures 3 and 4.

$$OH + C_2H_5OH \rightarrow C_2H_4OH + H_2O \qquad (6)$$

$$OH + RNO \rightarrow RNO_2H \qquad (7)$$

$$RNO_2H + RNO \rightarrow \text{bleaching at 350 n.m.} \qquad (8)$$

$$RNO_2H + O_2 \rightarrow \text{bleaching at 350 n.m.} \quad (9)$$

$$\cdot C_2H_4OH + RNO \rightarrow \text{bleaching at 350 n.m.} \quad (10)$$

$$\cdot C_2H_4OH + O_2 \rightarrow \text{no bleaching at 350 n.m.} \quad (11)$$

In this reaction scheme the "residual yield" would be explained by the product $k_{10}(RNO)$ being a small but not negligible fraction of the sum of $k_{10}(RNO) + k_{11}(O_2)$. For each of the solutions investigated in Figures 3 and 4 the ratio $(O_2)/(RNO)$ is constant for all concentrations of ethyl alcohol. Thus, as the ethyl alcohol concentration is increased for each given RNO concentration, a certain fraction of the C_2H_4OH radicals would always back react to destroy the RNO molecule. In the oxygen saturated solutions the rate of reaction for Equation 11 would presumably be high enough to make the rate of reaction for Equation 10 negligible by comparison. A similar type secondary competition may be responsible for the different rate constant ratios at pH 9 in the air saturated *vs.* oxygen saturated RNO solutions.

At constant high (0.1*M*) ethyl alcohol concentration in air-saturated solutions, there appears to be a minimum in the residual yield *vs.* RNO concentration curve which is not easily explained by the above mechanism unless there is less efficient bleaching by Equation 8 than with Equation 9. The latter assumption is contrary to the mechanism presented earlier in this paper if X is taken as RNO_2H.

No noticeable residual yield was observed at pH 9 with the basic form of RNO. If a similar mechanism to the one proposed above is valid at pH 9, k_{10} must be greater for the acid form than for the basic form of RNO.

A less plausible, but nevertheless not entirely unreasonable mechanism, which could account for these results would invoke an acid form for the OH radical which is not scavenged by ethyl alcohol. There is evidence (*12*) that this residual yield increases with decreasing pH in both the H_2O_2 photolysis and gamma radiolysis of RNO solutions which is not compatible with the above mechanism unless there is some acid-base equilibrium involving either the RNO_2H or $\cdot C_2H_4OH$ radicals.

The RNO-RNO_2 system studies again reveal a simplification of the kinetics when excess O_2 is present. The results imply that in air saturated solutions two "species" bleach RNO and are "scavenged" by increasing RNO_2 concentration or that there is a change in mechanism upon oxygen saturation.

The lack of effect of added low concentrations of NO_3^- and H_2O_2 is expected since they are both electron scavengers. Thus, the molecular hydrogen peroxide is not participating in secondary reactions which increase or decrease $G(\text{-RNO})_{350}$ as the peroxide builds up with increasing dose.

The limited competition studies with air saturated pH 2 solutions of RNO demonstrate that because of the residual yields complex kinetics must be involved. Competition studies with the oxygen saturated system may show simpler kinetics but with systems such as bromide + RNO, care must be taken in the interpretation of even simple competition kinetics (*16*). However, the relative constancy of the residual yields for ethyl alcohol, NO_2^-, and I^- of approximately 0.5 is noteworthy unless this is merely because of a fortuitous similarity of rate constants for secondary competitive attack of the oxidized solute on RNO and O_2. The possibility that this residual yield is coming from another primary radiolytic intermediate has not been ruled out by the experimental evidence presented here.

Related RNO Studies. Several related studies on RNO have been carried out in this laboratory in connection with the OH radical reaction with RNO and some results of these studies are presented here for comparison with the gamma radiolysis results.

In a detailed study (*7*) of the ultraviolet photolysis of aqueous, air-saturated solutions of H_2O_2 containing the basic form of RNO, competition studies have been performed and within the limits of experimental error relative rate constants for several different solutes have been found to be the same as in the radiolysis results and the Fenton reagent studies reported by Kraljic (*11*). Aqueous solutions of RNO have been found to be stable—*i.e.*, no detectable net bleaching occurs—to both steady state ultraviolet irradiation and short, intense pulses of ultraviolet light from a flash photolysis lamp (*10*). When H_2O_2 is added to the RNO solutions and photolyzed there is a net bleaching of the RNO. In steady state low intensity ultraviolet photolysis of neutral solutions of H_2O_2 containing RNO and another OH radical scavenger the same calculated relative OH rate constants are found. In several competition studies where the simple competition kinetics relationship is not obeyed at high S concentrations, the same quantitative complexities and deviations are observed (*11*) in the results from gamma ray radiolysis and in the ultraviolet photolysis. This provides further evidence that the reducing species in the radiolysis is captured by oxygen, especially at low RNO concentrations, and is not effective in bleaching RNO. This is in agreement with the conclusions reached in the pulse radiolysis studies (*3, 6*).

Electron spin resonance studies have been carried out in a flow system in which ferrous sulfate, hydrogen peroxide, and RNO are rapidly mixed under acid conditions and a 13 line signal has been observed (*7*). The same signal has been observed (*7*) with the rapid mixing of titanium (III), hydrogen peroxide, and RNO. A tentative identification of the radical species has been made and indicates OH addition to the RNO ring *ortho* to the nitroso group. This ESR signal is quenched by adding oxygen and ethyl alcohol, but again in the presence of excess ethyl alcohol a "residual yield" for the radical production is observed (7) of the same order of magnitude as with the gamma irradiation and ultraviolet photolysis of RNO–H_2O_2 solutions. The reasons for these residual yields are not clear at present but it would appear that they are in some way associated with the OH radical or its acid form.

Conclusions

From the studies reported here and elsewhere it is clear that RNO in both its acidic and basic forms is a very effective radical scavenger not only for the primary radiolysis products of water, but also for other more complex secondary radicals. The chief difficulty in using this compound for scavenging studies is to sort out subsequent reactions of the free radicals resulting from the primary reactions. Pulse radiolysis studies appear to offer a way of surmounting this difficulty.

In the presence of excess oxygen many of these secondary radicals appear to form products which do not further attack the RNO molecule in either its acidic or basic form.

The reaction of the OH radical with the basic form of RNO appears to be slower than with the acidic form of RNO (*11*). The reason for this is not immediately apparent, but may be involved with a lower resonance stability of the protonated OH–RNO radical.

Under appropriate conditions, simple competition kinetics is obeyed when both the acidic and basic forms of RNO compete with another scavenger S for the OH radical generated by the radiolysis of water, photolysis of H_2O_2, or the Fenton reagent. It would appear that the oxygen saturated system offers the most simple kinetic system for such studies and presumably the most accurate values of the relative OH rate constants.

It must be emphasized that no claim is made that the relative rate constants obtained by the use of RNO are always valid for any compound, even if there is no spectral interference by the competitor with the RNO spectral absorption peaks in either its acid or basic form. Care must be taken to ensure that there are no back reactions of the oxidized solute with the RNO as pointed out by Dainton and Wiseall (*6*). However, it would appear that in very few cases of oxygen saturated RNO solutions containing OH competitors are there such reactions, especially with organic compounds.

The number of methods available for the generation of OH radicals combined with the various means for analysis of either the 350 n.m. or

440 n.m. peaks of RNO or the 325 n.m. and 550 to 575 n.m. bands of the radiolytic intermediates offer a wide range of possibilities for testing not only relative OH radical rate constants but also hypotheses of OH radical attack in more complex systems using either gamma ray or pulse radiolysis or both. The high extinction coefficient of RNO [and apparently its OH radical adducts (*3, 6*)] allows the use of RNO concentrations small enough to prevent rapid chemical reactions between RNO and the chemical system involved.

The question raised by Dainton and Wiseall (*6*) with respect to absolute values of the rate constant of OH radical reaction with the basic form of RNO must await clarification of product spectra and yields. These will resolve whether or not $G(-\text{RNO})_{440}$ is indeed numerically equal to $G(-\text{RNO})$. It is also not clear in acidic RNO solutions what kind of species are causing the "residual" yields with ethyl alcohol and the unusual kinetic behavior arising from changes in oxygen concentration. Clearly, more studies of these effects are called for and are underway at the present time.

Acknowledgments

This work was supported by the United States Atomic Energy Commission and this is AEC Document No. NYO-3380-10. The authors wish to acknowledge stimulating conversations about these results with I. Kraljic, H. A. Schwarz, J. A. Moore, E. J. Hart, J. W. Boag, and E. M. Fielden.

Literature Cited

(1) Anbar, M., Meyerstein, D., Neta, P., *J. Phys. Chem.* **70,** 2660 (1966).
(2) Asmus, V., Beck, G., Henglein, A., Wigger, A., *Ber. Bunsenges. Phys. Chem.* **70,** 869 (1966).
(3) Baxendale, J. H. (private communication).
(4) Dainton, F. S. (private communication).
(5) Dainton, F. S., Sutton, H., *Trans. Faraday Soc.* **49,** 1011 (1953).
(6) Dainton, F. S., Wiseall, B., *Trans. Faraday Soc.* **64,** 694 (1968).
(7) Hatada, M., Kraljic, I., and Trumbore, C. N. (submitted for publication).
(8) Hatada, M,. Trumbore, C. N. (unpublished work).
(9) Klein, N., Trumbore, C. N., Fanning, J. E., Warner, J. W., *J. Phys. Chem.* **72,** 880 (1968).
(10) Kobrin, R., Trumbore, C. N., Godfrey, T. (unpublished work).
(11) Kraljic, I., "The Chemistry of Ionization and Excitation," p. 303, G. R. A. Johnson, G. Scholes, eds., Taylor and Francis, Ltd., London, 1967.
(12) Kraljic, I., Hatada, M. (unpublished results).
(13) Kraljic, I., Trumbore, C. N., *J. Am. Chem. Soc.* **87,** 2547 (1965).
(14) *Proceedings of the 5th Informal Conf. on the Rad. Chem. of Water,* Notre Dame Univ., Radiation Laboratory, Notre Dame, Indiana, AEC Document **No. C00-38-519,** p. 27 (October, 1966).

(15) Shah, S. (unpublished results).
(16) Sutton, H. C., Adams, G. E., Boag, J. W., Michael, B. D., "Pulse Radiolysis," p. 77, M. Ebert, *et al.*, eds., Academic Press, N. Y., 1965.
(17) Swinnerton, J. W., Linnenbom, V. J., Cheek, C. H., *Radiation Res.* **19,** 636 (1963).
(18) Trumbore, C. N., Fielden, E. M., Boag, J. W. (unpublished results).
(19) Weeks, B. M., Cole, S. A., Garrison, W. M., *J. Phys. Chem.* **69,** 4131 (1965).

RECEIVED January 2, 1968.

23

^{60}Co-γ-Ray Induced Formation of Sulfur-Containing Amino Acids in Aqueous Solutions

N. GETOFF[1] and G. O. SCHENCK

Abteilung Strahlenchemie, Max-Planck-Institut für Kohlenforschung, D-433 Mülheim/Ruhr, Federal Republic of Germany

*Experimental results on the radiation induced formation of sulfur-containing amino acids in aqueous solutions are reported. By carboxylation of 0.01*M *ethylamine with simultaneous incorporation of sulfur the following substances are identified: cystine, cysteine, cysteic acid, α- and β-alanine and glycine. Cystine, alanine, and glycine are the main products. Different initial* G *values are obtained when either sodium sulfide, neutron irradiated sodium sulfide or hydrogen sulfide are used. In the first case,* G_i *(cystine)* = *0.2 and* G_i *(glycine + alanine)* = *1.05; in the second case,* G_i *(cystine)* = *0.5 and* G_i *(cystine + alanine)* = *0.3 and in the third case,* G_i *(cystine)* = *1.65 and* G_i *(glycine + alanine)* = *0.14. In order to explain the results a probable reaction mechanism is suggested.*

The study of the effect of ionizing radiation and ultraviolet light on amino acids, amines, and related substances in aqueous solutions is of biological interest. For a better understanding of the radiation induced reactions of these substances the knowledge of the primary products formed is necessary. In order to elucidate this problem their radiolysis is extensively investigated. The more important findings are summarized in review papers (*7, 11, 23, 24*). An additional approach to these very complicated reaction mechanisms is offered by the investigation of the radiation induced synthesis of amino acids and amines. This subject is

[1] On leave from the Institut für Radiumforschung und Kernphysik, A-1090 Wien, Austria.

studied by various research groups (*5, 6, 9, 17, 21, 26, 27, 28*). Recently we have reported results concerning the formation of amino acids by radiation induced carboxylation of several amines and also some data on the amination of carboxylic acids (*13*).

The photochemical carboxylation of amines in aqueous solutions has also been carried out (*8, 9, 10*). In addition we have communicated some data on the carboxylation and simultaneous incorporation of sulfur and phosphorus, respectively, in amines under the influence of ultraviolet light (*8, 9*) or gamma-rays (*9, 28*).

In the present paper new results are reported on the radiation-induced formation of sulfur-containing amino acids. Aqueous ethylamine served as a model substrate. It was carboxylated in the presence of sodium sulfide or hydrogen sulfide leading to the formation of cystine, cysteine, cysteic acid and other amino acids.

Experimental Procedure

For irradiation of the solutions a panorama ^{60}Co-source of 2.05×10^4 Ci (dose rate: 6.25×10^{18} e.v. ml.$^{-1}$ min.$^{-1}$) was used (*22*). A number of samples were irradiated with a second ^{60}Co-source (Gamma Cell 220; dose rate: 6.9×10^{17} e.v. ml.$^{-1}$ min.$^{-1}$). The dose rate was determined by means of the Fricke dosimeter using $G(Fe^{3+}) = 15.6$.

The samples were prepared with reagent-grade chemicals and triply distilled water in the same manner as previously described (*13*).

Three series of experiments have been carried out.

Series A: The solution (40–50 ml., pH 9.8) contained 0.01*M* ethylamine, 0.01*M* sodium bicarbonate and 0.01*M* sodium sulfide. To remove the oxygen, purified argon was bubbled through the solutions for about 40 minutes before irradiation.

Series B: In order to facilitate identification of the sulfur-containing amino acids 0.01*M* neutron irradiated sodium sulfide (integrated neutron dose: 2×10^{18} n/cm.^{2}) was used. The concentration of ethylamine and bicarbonate was the same as in Series A. The neutron irradiated sodium sulfide was first stored for about a week to allow the ^{24}Na to decay. The main activity was of ^{35}S which was found in eight different compounds (by high voltage electrophoresis, 70 volts/cm.; electrolyte: 0.8*M* α-hydroxy-isobutyric acid). Some of the ^{35}S-compounds could not be fully identified as yet. As above argon was bubbled before irradiation.

Series C: The solutions for irradiation consisted likewise of 0.01*M* ethylamine and 0.01*M* bicarbonate, were, however, saturated with purified hydrogen sulfide for 30 minutes.

The analysis of the amino acids formed was carried out by means of paper or thin-layer chromatography as previously reported (*13, 28*). Evaporation of the irradiated solutions before analysis, as described in References *13* and *28* to concentrate the amino acids, was not carried out in this case. It was established, that subsequent reactions can take place, during this procedure since the sulfur-containing compounds are very sensitive to oxygen. Therefore, to avoid any uncertainty, the original irradiated solutions were used directly for analysis.

The chromatograms were treated with ninhydrin and developed by heating at 70°C. for two hours. The spots of the individual amino acids were then cut out of the paper or scratched from the plate and extracted with methanol. The solutions were measured spectrophotometrically and the yields of the amino acids were calculated by means of calibration curves. Apart from this, special reagents were used for identification and detection of -SH and -SS- groups (*3*). The radioactivity measurements of the ^{35}S-compounds formed were either carried out on a 2π-proportional flow counter or on a liquid scintillation counter.

Results and Discussion

The organic sulfur compounds in aqueous solution are very sensitive to radiation. Cysteamine, $HSCH_2CH_2NH_2$—*e.g.*, is oxidized in air-free solution to the disulfide cystamine, $(SCH_2CH_2NH_2)_2$ (*30, 31*). Since the aqueous cysteamine undergoes spontaneous oxidation to cystamine, even by the air during the analysis, it is difficult to determine the G value for the oxidation process. The cystamine can be further oxidized by irradiation to the corresponding sulfinic acid, $HOOSCH_2CH_2NH_2$ and sulfonic acid (taurine) $HO_3SCH_2CH_2NH_2$.

In analogy to this, cysteine is also easily converted into cystine by mild oxidation. By irradiation of cysteine at low doses the formation of some H_2S, but no ammonia was observed (*2, 4, 33*). The reaction mechanism is complicated and depends also upon the pH of the solution. In the presence of oxygen, chain reactions were found to occur (*32*).

The carboxylation and incorporation of sulfur in $0.01M$ ethylamine leads to the formation of cystine, α- and β-alanine, glycine and small amounts of cysteine. When using hydrogen sulfide (Series C) also cysteic acid was found. Its yield increases with the radiation dose.

The formation of the amino acids was investigated as a function of the radiation dose. The yields are proportional to a dose up to about 2×10^{19} e.v./ml. and from there tend to have limiting values. The initial G values (G_i) calculated from the straight parts of the curves are presented in Table I.

The data for glycine (Gly) and alanine (Ala), not being very essential in this case are given as a sum.

By using neutron irradiated sodium sulfide (Series B) the yield of cystine is higher compared with Series A. The yield of glycine and alanine, however, decreases from 1.05 (Series A) to 0.3 (Series B). It seems that a very reactive sulfur compound, probably colloidal sulfur, is formed as a recoil product of the neutron capture. This sulfur compound acts as a good scavenger for the amine radicals. The highest yield of cystine G_i

Table I. Initial G Value (G_i) of Amino Acids Produced by Carboxylation of 0.01*M* Ethylamine with 0.01*M* Sodium Bicarbonate in the Presence of Sulfur Compounds

Series of Experiments	*G_i Values*		
	Cystine	*Glycine and Alanine*	*Cysteine*
Series A: 0.01*M* sodium sulfide	0.2	1.05	traces
Series B: 0.01*M* neutron irradiated sodium sulfide	0.5	0.3	<0.01
Series C: saturated with H_2S	1.6[a]	0.14	traces

[a] This value also includes the yield of cysteic acid.

(cystine) = 1.6, was obtained, however, by saturating the solution with H_2S gas (Series C).

For explanation of the results obtained in our experiments a probable reaction mechanism is suggested. The free radicals produced by the radiolysis of water can attack the ethylamine as well as the CO_2 and the sulfide. In consequence, amine radicals are formed by splitting off H atoms from the ethylamine molecule.

$$H_2O \leadsto H, e^-_{aq}, OH, H_3O^+, H_2, H_2O_2 \quad (1)$$

$$CH_3CH_2NH_2 + OH \rightarrow CH_3\dot{C}HNH_2 + H_2O \quad (2)$$

$$\text{or/and:} \quad \rightarrow \dot{C}H_2CH_2NH_2 + H_2O \quad (3)$$

The H atoms and the solvated electrons (e^-_{aq}) react in a similar way with ethylamine. The abstraction of hydrogen from the β-C-atom of ethylamine is possible. This was shown by carboxylation of ethylamine, where the main product was α-aminobutyric acid (G_i = 1.10) instead of the expected alanine (G_i = 0.51) (*13*).

In addition to this, a hydrogen could also be abstracted from the $-NH_2$ group of the ethylamine. This possibility has been studied in a previous paper (*13*).

Because of the equilibrium between CO_2 and bicarbonate in the solution, part of the free CO_2 can be reduced to CO_2^- or $\dot{C}OOH$ (*12, 13*).

$$CO_2 + e^-_{aq} \rightarrow CO_2^- + nH_2O \quad (4)$$

at pH 7, $k_4 = 0.77 \times 10^{10} M^{-1}$ sec.$^{-1}$ (*14*)

$$CO_2 + H \rightarrow \dot{C}OOH \quad (5)$$

at pH 4.5, $k_5 < 8 \times 10^{6} M^{-1}$ sec.$^{-1}$ (*15*)

Under our experimental conditions the $\dot{C}OOH$ radicals dissociate, since their pK = 2.8 (*16*). Furthermore, the H atoms are converted into e^-_{aq} in alkaline solutions:

$$H + OH^-_{aq} \rightarrow e^-_{aq} \quad (6)$$

at pH 7.5-12.5, $k_6 = 1.2 \times 10^7 M^{-1}$ sec.$^{-1}$ (*18*)

By combination of CO_2^- with the amine radicals, which are produced according to Reaction 2 and 3, alanine is formed (*13*):

$$CH_3\dot{C}HNH_2 + CO_2^- \rightarrow CH_3CH(NH_2)COO^- \quad (7)$$

(α-alanine)

$$\dot{C}H_2CH_2NH_2 + CO_2^- \rightarrow {}^-OOCCH_2CH_2NH_2 \quad (8)$$

(β-alanine)

Simultaneously, the sulfide ions or the hydrogen sulfide can react with the OH radicals:

$$S^{2-} + OH \rightarrow S^- + OH^- \quad (9)$$

$$HS^- + OH \rightarrow H\dot{S} + OH^- \quad (9a)$$

$k_{9a} = 5.4 \times 10^9 M^{-1}$ sec.$^{-1}$ (*20*)

$$H_2S + OH \rightarrow H\dot{S} + H_2O \quad (9b)$$

$k_{9b} = 1.1 \times 10^{10} M^{-1}$ sec.$^{-1}$ (*20*)

In this case the sulfide ions compete with ethylamine for reaction with the OH radicals. The solvated electrons react with H_2S but do not react with SH^-:

$$H_2S + e^-_{aq} \rightarrow HS^- + H \text{ (or: } S^- + H_2) \quad (10)$$

$k_{10} = 1.3 \times 10^{10} M^{-1}$ sec.$^{-1}$ (*25*)

Apart from this the H atoms can also attack the H_2S molecules:

$$H_2S + H \rightarrow \dot{S}H + H_2 \quad (11)$$

$k_{11} = 1 \times 10^9 M^{-1}$ sec.$^{-1}$ (*25*)

The very high reactivity of H_2S with e^-_{aq}, H and OH explains at least partly the formation of relatively high yield of cystine by carboxylation of ethylamine in the presence of hydrogen sulfide.

When alanine was irradiated in the presence of sulfide we observed the formation of cystine and cysteine. This suggests the following reactions:

$$CH_3CH(NH_2)COO^- + OH \rightarrow \dot{C}H_2CH(NH_2)COO^- + H_2O \quad (12)$$

at pH 10, $k_{12} = 3.4 \times 10^9 M^{-1}$ sec.$^{-1}$ (*29*)

H and e^-_{aq} can react with alanine in a similar manner.

$$\dot{C}H_2CH(NH_2)COO^- + S^- \text{ (or } H\dot{S}) \rightarrow {}^-SCH_2CH(NH_2)COO^-$$
$$\text{(or: } HSCH_2CH(NH_2)COO^-) \text{ (cysteine)} \quad (13)$$

As already discussed above, cysteine (RS^- or RSH) is oxidized to cystine under the influence of radiation, thus:

$$OH + RS^- \rightarrow R\dot{S} + OH^- \quad (14)$$

$$\text{or: } OH + RSH \rightarrow R\dot{S} + H_2O \quad (14a)$$

$$RS + RS^- \rightarrow RSSR^- \text{ (cystine)} \quad (15)$$

$$\text{or: } RS + RS \rightarrow RSSR \quad (15a)$$

Another path for the formation of cystine and cysteine is *via* the formation of cysteamine:

$$\dot{C}H_2CH_2NH_2 + S^- \rightarrow {}^-SCH_2CH_2NH_2 \text{ (cysteamine)} \quad (16)$$

$${}^-SCH_2CH_2NH_2 + OH \text{ (or H; } e^-_{aq}) \rightarrow$$
$${}^-SCH_2\dot{C}HNH_2 + H_2O \text{ (or } H_2\text{; } H_2 + OH^-) \quad (17)$$

$${}^-SCH_2\dot{C}HNH_2 + COO^- \rightarrow {}^-SCH_2CH(NH_2)COO^- \text{ (cysteine)} \quad (18)$$

In the sequel Reaction 14 and 15 lead to the production of cystine.

Because of the easy oxidation of cysteamine one has to assume that also cystamine is intermediately formed. Adams *et al.* (*1*) studied the conversion of cysteamine into cystamine by means of pulse radiolysis. They could observe the production of cystamine in the same way as shown by Reactions 14 and 15.

To explain the higher yields of cystine when neutron-irradiated sulfide is being used (compare Series A with B) we assume that among various products derivating from the sodium sulfide also colloidal sulfur is formed as a recoil product following the nuclear process. The colloidal sulfur could react rapidly with H atoms as well as with e^-_{aq}, forming SH radicals and S^- radical ions, respectively:

$$S + e^-_{aq} \rightarrow S^- + nH_2O \quad (19)$$

$$S + H \rightarrow \dot{S}H \quad (20)$$

Therefore, the OH radicals remain only for reaction with the ethylamine and the alanine (*see* Reactions 2, 3, and 12). Consequently, the yield of amine and alanine radicals is increased, leading to the formation of more cysteine, which is then converted into cystine.

Acknowledgment

We would like to express our thanks to O. E. Polansky for valuable discussions. We are also indebted to G. B. Cook, head of the IAEA Research Laboratory, Seibersdorf, Austria, for the permission to use the ^{60}Co-source . We wish to thank the crew of the ASTRA nuclear reactor at Seibersdorf, Austria, for neutron irradiation of the sodium sulfide sample.

Part of the experiments were carried out in the Institut für Radiumforschung und Kernphysik, Vienna, Austria.

Literature Cited

(1) Adams, G. E., Michael, B. D., McNaughton, G. M., "The Chemistry of Ionization and Excitation," p. 281, G. R. A. Johnson, G. Scholes, eds., Taylor & Francis, London, 1967.
(2) Allen, A. O., "The Radiation Chemistry of Water and Aqueous Solutions," D. van Nostrand Comp., Inc., Princeton, New Jersey, 1961.
(3) Bailey, J. T., "Techniques in Protein Chemistry," Elsevier Publ. Corp., Amsterdam, 1967.
(4) Dale, W. M., Davies, J. V., *Biochem. J.* **48,** 129 (1951).
(5) Dose, K., Ettre, K., *Z. Naturforsch.* **13b,** 784 (1958).
(6) Dose, K., Rajewsky, B., *Biochim. Biophys. Acta* **25,** 225 (1957).
(7) Garrison, W. M., *Radiation Res. Suppl.* **4,** 158 (1964).
(8) Getoff, N., *Abstr. Commun. II. Meeting European Biochem. Soc., Vienna, 1965,* pp. 55-56.
(9) Getoff, N., *Allg. Prakt. Chem.* **17,** 106 (1966).
(10) Getoff, N., *Intern. Congr. Radiation Res.* **Abstr. 339,** Cortina d'Ampezzo (1966).
(11) Getoff, N., "The Biological Effects of Transmutation and Decay of Incorporated Radioisotopes," IAEA-panel, Vienna, 9.-13. Oct. 1967 (in print).
(12) Getoff, N., *Z. Naturforsch.* **17b,** 751 (1962).
(13) Getoff, N., Schenck, G. O., *Radiation Res.* **31,** 486 (1967).
(14) Gordon, S., Hart, E. J., Matheson, M. S., Rabani, J., Thomas, J. K., *Discussions Faraday Soc.* **36,** 193 (1963).
(15) Gütlbauer, F., Getoff, N., *Z. Physik. Chem.* **47,** 299 (1965).
(16) *Ibid.,* **51,** 255 (1966).
(17) Hasselstrom, T., Henry, M. C., Murr, B., *Science* **125,** 350 (1957).
(18) Jortner, J., Rabani, J., *J. Phys. Chem.* **66,** 208 (1962).
(19) *Ibid.,* **66,** 2081 (1962).
(20) Karmann, W., Meissner, G., Henglein, A., *Z. Naturforsch.* **22b,** 273 (1967).
(21) Kopoldova, J., Liebster, J., Babicky, A., *Radiation Res.* **19,** 551 (1963).
(22) Krönert, H. Schenck, G. O., *Chem. Ing. Tech.* **35,** 641 (1963).
(23) Liebster, J., Kopoldova, J., *Advan. Radiation Biol.* **1,** 157 (1964).
(24) Luse, R. A., *Radiation Res. Suppl.* **4,** 192 (1964).
(25) Meissner, G., Henglein, A., *Ber. Bunsenges. Physik. Chem.* **69,** 3 (1965).
(26) Oró, J., *Nature* **197,** 971 (1963).
(27) Palm, Ch., Calvin, M., *J. Am. Chem. Soc.* **84,** 2115 (1962).

(28) De La Paz, L. R., Getoff, N., *Radiation Res.* **28**, 567 (1966).
(29) Rabani, J., Stein, G., *Trans. Faraday Soc.* **58**, 2150 (1962).
(30) Shapiro, B., Eldjarn, L., *Radiation Res.* **3**, 255 (1955).
(31) *Ibid.*, **3**, 393 (1955).
(32) Swallow, A. J., *J. Chem. Soc.* **1952**, 1334.
(33) Whitcher, S. L., Rotheram, M., Todd, N., *Nucleonics* **11**, (8), 30 (1953).

RECEIVED January 11, 1968.

Pulse Radiolysis of DNA and Related Pyrimidine Compounds: Reactions of the OH· Free Radical

L. S. MYERS, JR., MARY LYNN HOLLIS, and L. M. THEARD

Laboratory of Nuclear Medicine and Radiation Biology, Departments of Biophysics and of Radiology, University of California, Los Angeles, Calif. 90024 and Gulf General Atomic, Inc., San Diego, Calif.

Formation, decay, and absorption spectra of transient species produced by reaction of OH· free radicals with DNA and nucleic acid constituents have been investigated by pulse radiolysis. Dilute aqueous N_2O saturated solutions were exposed to 2–500 nsec. pulses (750–1700 rads/pulse) of 10 Mev. electrons, and changes in optical density were measured. The rate constant for formation of the DNA transient (nucleotide M.W. 350) is 6×10^8 M^{-1} sec.$^{-1}$. The transient persists for more than 1 msec. with no significant change in spectrum. Thymine, uracil, deoxyribose, and thymidine transients have complex decay patterns which vary with pH. Comparisons of transient spectra confirm that the sites of attack by OH· on thymine, 5-methylcytosine, and thymidine depend on pH. Abstraction from 5,6-dihydrothymine is slower than addition to thymine.

A pulse radiolysis study of the formation, decay, and absorption spectra of transients produced by reactions of DNA and of some of its constituents with the OH· free radical is presented in this paper. Solutions were saturated with N_2O so that the only significant reactive species produced by radiation was the OH· free radical. Rates of formation were determined by direct observation of the growth of transient absorption. Compounds and conditions were selected to permit investigation of (a) the sites of attack by OH· on pyrimidine bases, nucleosides, and DNA under various conditions; (b) charge effects on reaction rates; (c) comparative rates of addition to pyrimidine bases, and abstraction from saturated analogs; (d) comparative rates of reactions of bases, pentoses, nucleosides, and DNA; and (e) the reactivity of DNA, and stability of DNA radicals formed by OH· reactions. The results permit a number of significant conclusions to be drawn. The complexity of many of the reactions is such, however, that a major function of this paper is to outline areas where further work is needed.

An investigation of aerated solutions of DNA and nucleic acids constituents by pulse radiolysis has been published by Scholes, Shaw, and Willson (*12*), and a more extensive study has been reported by Willson in his Ph.D. thesis (*18*). Recent reviews of related stationary state studies have been published by Weiss (*17*) and by Scholes (*11*).

Experimental

The electron linear accelerator and associated apparatus for kinetic spectroscopy at Gulf General Atomic, Inc. have been described briefly (*14*). Details will be published elsewhere. In the present work 10 Mev. electron pulses of 2 to 500 nsec. duration were used. Radiation doses were measured for each pulse by a beam collector which was calibrated by electron absorption taking $g(e^-_{aq}) = 2.6$ and $\epsilon(e^-_{aq}) = 10,600$ at 578 n.m. They ranged from 750 to 1700 rads/pulse, and depended on machine configuration as well as pulse duration and current. Light for the spectrophotometric analyses was passed four times through the irradiation cell of 2 cm. path length. A xenon flash lamp was used for formation studies; mercury-xenon or xenon arc lamps were used for spectra and decay curves.

Solutions were prepared from triply distilled water with the purest chemicals usually available commercially. Measurements of pH were made with Beckman Zeromatic and Model G pH meters, and electrodes suitable for alkaline solutions. Solutions with pH greater than 11.4 were made immediately prior to the experiment. All solutions were saturated with Matheson N_2O (minimum purity 98%) by bubbling for at least 20 minutes. The N_2O was pre-saturated with water vapor to minimize concentration changes during bubbling.

Results and Discussion

NaOH Solutions. Spectra of transients observed in the radiolysis of NaOH solutions saturated with N_2O were obtained as controls for experiments with pyrimidine bases. The time required to reach maximum absorbance (rise time) was more than 35 μsec. Decay was much slower. Absorption is negligible at wavelengths between 350 and 450 n.m., at pH 9.9–12.4, but becomes appreciable at higher wavelengths (OD = 0.025 at λ 575 n.m., and light path 8 cm.).

The shape of the spectra suggests that the absorption is caused by CO_3^- (*1*). This can be formed by reaction of OH· with CO_3^{2-} present as an impurity in the NaOH. Its rate of formation is slow compared with other reactions reported in this paper (rise times < 15 μsec.), and its contribution to the absorption in the presence of these reactions must therefore be negligible. Accordingly, no corrections were made for it.

Spectra of transients observed on the ninth of a series of pulses delivered to the same NaOH sample at intervals of about one second resemble the spectrum of O_3^- (3), but have a broader peak at slightly longer wavelengths which could be caused by other radicals. The intensity of the absorption increases greatly above pH 11.9, possibly because of reactions of O^- or HO_2^-. To avoid this absorption fresh solution was used for each pulse in the experiments which follow.

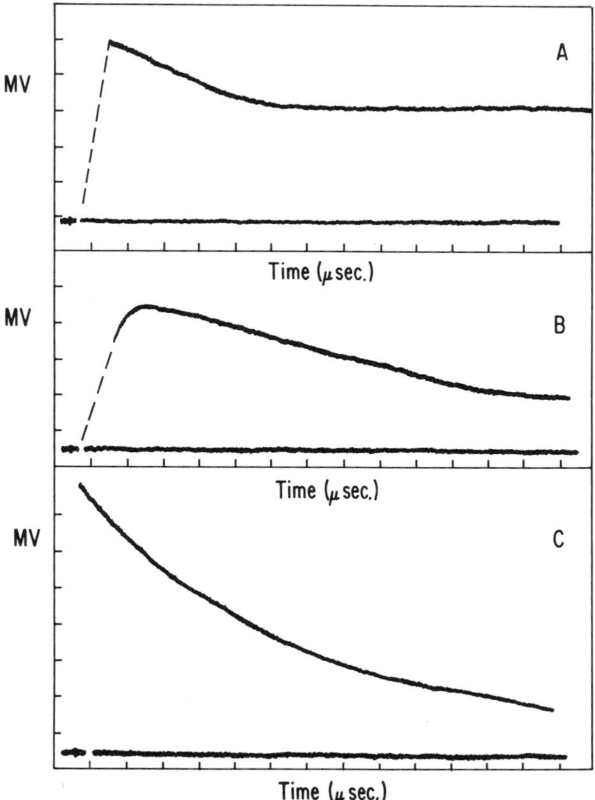

Figure 1. Typical oscillograms showing transient absorption in 5 × 10⁻⁴M N_2O saturated uracil solutions. Pulse width 500 nsec.

Transient Decay and Spectra: Thymine, Uracil, and 5-Methylcytosine. Typical oscillograms showing decay of transient absorption in N_2O saturated $5 \times 10^{-4}M$ solutions of uracil are shown in Figure 1. With thymine, curves similar to B were obtained at pH 9.0, 12.4, 13.0, and in 2*N* NaOH for all wavelengths, and at pH 10.6 and 11.4 for λ = 375–425 n.m. and 525–600 n.m.; and curves similar to A but with more rapid decay were obtained at pH 10.6 and 11.4 for λ = 325, 350, and 450–500 n.m. With uracil, type *C* curves were obtained at pH 8.6, 10.0, and 11.4 for λ = 350–500 n.m., and 12.4 for λ = 400–600 n.m.; type *B* curves at pH 11.4 for λ = 550–600 n.m., and type *A* curves at pH 12.4 for λ = 330–400 and pH 13 for all wavelengths except 350 n.m., where continued growth was observed.

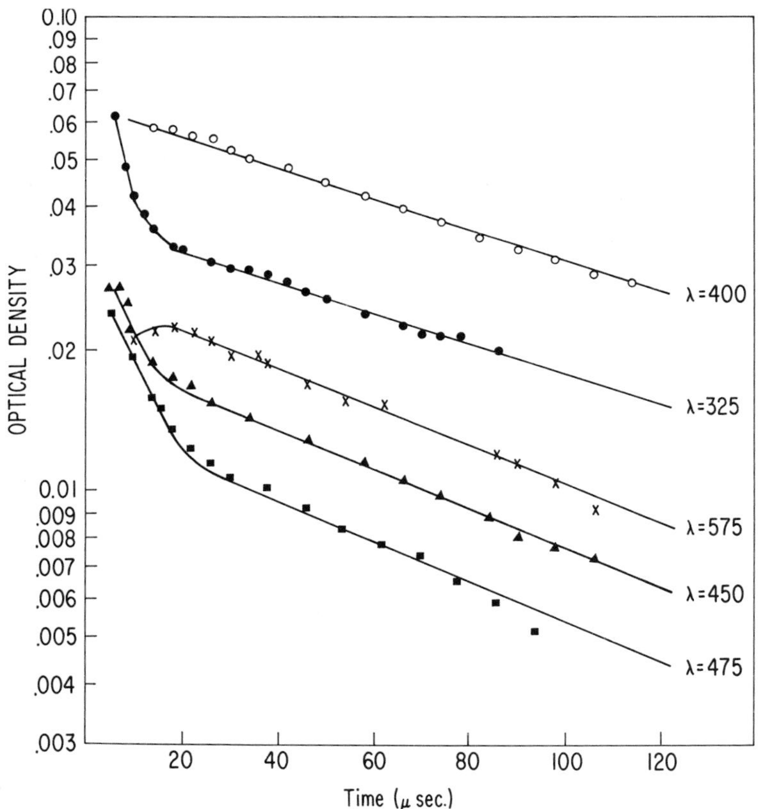

Figure 2. Decay of transient formed by 100 nsec. pulse in N_2O saturated solution of 5×10^{-4}M thymine, pH 10.6. Optical density adjusted to 1000 rads/pulse

Semilogarithmic plots of data taken from the oscillograms (Figures 2, 3, 4, and 5) illustrate four distinct patterns for change in absorbance of transient species with time. Most of the curves have at least two components, and the second usually follows first order kinetics fairly well. Transient absorptions at 400 n.m. in uracil solutions, pH 12.2 and 13.0 give good agreement with the requirements of second order kinetics, but graphs of 1/OD against time for the rest of the data deviate from linearity, usually in the direction expected for first order decay.

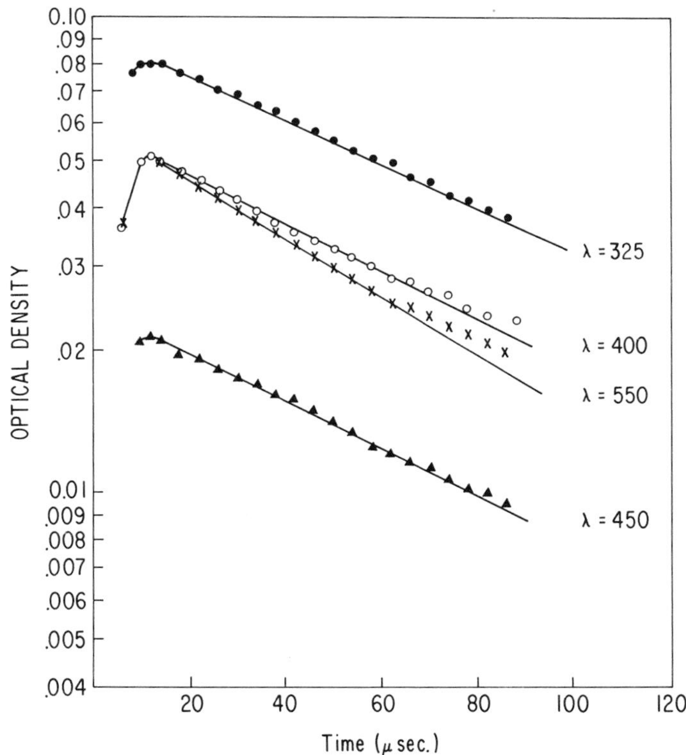

Figure 3. Decay of transient formed by 100 nsec. pulse in N_2O saturated solution of 5×10^{-4}M thymine, pH 13.0. Optical density adjusted to 1000 rads/pulse

First order decay constants for the longest lived species are given in Tables I and II. Rate constants for the first component of the two component curves cannot be calculated from available data.

In thymine, at pH 12.4 and below, the decay rates at 325 and 550 n.m. differ from one another and from the rates at 400 and 450, suggesting that three species contribute to the absorbance of the longest lived transient. At pH 10.6 and 11.4 at $\lambda = 325$ and 450, a slow decay is preceded by a rapid decay, while at $\lambda = 575$ n.m. the slow decay is preceded by a rapid growth. This may indicate a parent-daughter relationship. At pH 7 a similar relationship may hold: Scholes has observed a short lived transient absorption at $\lambda < 400$ n.m. (*10*) which has since been confirmed by us.

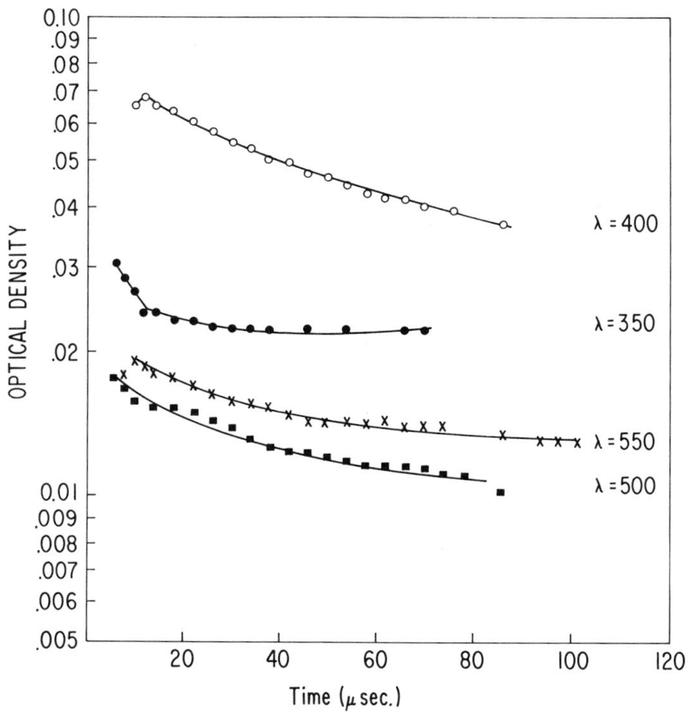

Figure 4. Decay of transient formed by 500 nsec. pulse in N_2O saturated solution of 5×10^{-4}M uracil, pH 12.2. Optical density adjusted to 1000 rads/pulse

With uracil at pH 8.6 uniform decay at all wavelengths indicates formation of one absorbing species and decay by one pathway. At pH 10.0, 11.1, and 11.4, at least two decay rates are seen, a fast decay observed at 350, 500, and 550 n.m. followed by a slower decay seen at all wavelengths. At higher pH values the rapid decay is followed by a very slow decay which results in the absorbance remaining almost constant, or in some cases increasing for as long as 200 μsec. At 400 n.m. the decay shows little change in rate over the entire pH range.

Spectra of transient absorptions at different pH values, obtained by plotting the maximum absorbance shown by the oscillograms, are given in Figure 6. These spectra are the sums of the spectra of transients

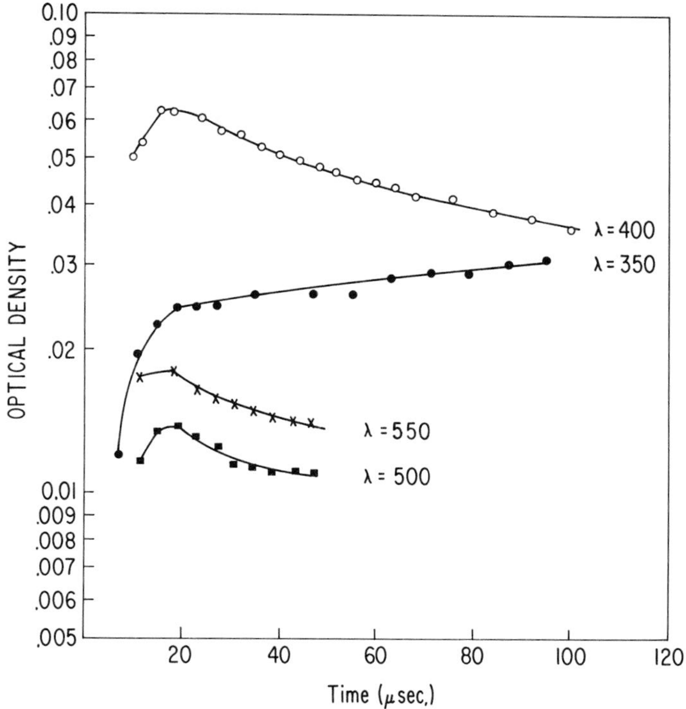

Figure 5. Decay of transient formed by 500 nsec. pulse in N_2O saturated solution of 5 × 10^{-4}M uracil, pH 13.0. Optical density adjusted to 1000 rads/pulse

Table I. First Order Rate Constants for the Decay of the Longest Lived Transient Species Formed in Radiolysis of N_2O Saturated Aqueous Thymine Solutions (10^{-4} k)

	λ (n.m.)			
pH	*325*	*400*	*450*	*550*
9.0	1.25	0.75	0.85	—
10.6	0.75[a]	0.75	0.95[a]	0.95 (575 n.m.)
11.4	0.65[a]	0.85	0.95[a]	1.10
12.4	0.75	0.95	0.95	1.25
13.0	1.05	1.15	1.15	1.45
2*N* NaOH	0.95 (350 n.m.)	1.45	0.95	0.95

[a] Short-lived component observed.

present between 2 and 12 μsec. following the pulse, and they change shape as the shorter lived transients decay. Figure 7 shows spectra of the transients persisting after short lived components have disappeared. They show the strong absorbance at 400 n.m. which is seen in the earlier spectra, and low absorbance at other wavelengths. The short lived component must therefore have a strong absorbance at 325–350 n.m.

Table II. First Order Rate Constants for the Decay of the Longest Lived Transient Species Formed in Radiolysis of N_2O Saturated Aqueous Uracil Solutions (10^{-4} k)

	λ (n.m.)			
pH	*350*	*400*	*500*	*550*
8.6	1.10	1.10	1.10	—
10.0	2.20	1.10	2.05	1.10
11.1	0.60[a]	0.85	1.35[a]	0.85
11.4	0.65[a]	0.95	Very Slow[a]	1.20
12.2	Very Slow[a]	1.10	Very Slow[a]	Very Slow[a]
13.0	Growth	0.55[a]	Very Slow	Very Slow

[a] Short-lived component observed (this component is much longer lived than the short-lived component of thymine).

In spite of the difficulties in the kinetic analyses, the changes in spectral shape with pH are so great that significant conclusions relative to the site of attack by OH· and its dependence on molecular structure can be based on them. Stationary state studies of pyrimidine bases have been interpreted by postulating that the site of attack by OH· on thymine and 5-methylcytosine shifts from the double bond to the methyl group as the pH is increased (*6, 7*). If this occurs the spectra of transients formed with 5-methylpyrimidines would be expected to change with changes in pH. An equivalent shift cannot occur with uracil, and its spectrum would be expected to change in a different way, or not at all. In Figures 6 A and 6 B three types of curves are seen for thymine: at pH 9 a broad flat assymetrical peak with a maximum at about 400 n.m., at pH 10.6 and 11.4 a sharp peak at 400 n.m., and at higher pHs an additional peak at 525–550 n.m. The changes correlate with the first stage of ionization of thymine and with the ionization of the OH· free radical, respectively.

Preliminary data obtained with 5-methylcytosine indicate that at pH 12.1 it gives a spectrum similar to that given by thymine. In contrast, Figures 6 C and 6 D show that the spectra resulting from reaction of OH· with uracil are not altered greatly by pH changes. Thus, the conclusions of stationary state studies that as the pH is increased the site of attack on pyrimidine bases shifts if a 5-methyl group is available are confirmed.

By combining these results with conclusions reached in other studies it is possible to identify tentatively the structures of some of the radicals contributing to the transient absorption. At pH 9.0 thymine ($pK_1 = 9.8$) is largely in the undissociated form. Analysis of products (*2, 13*) has

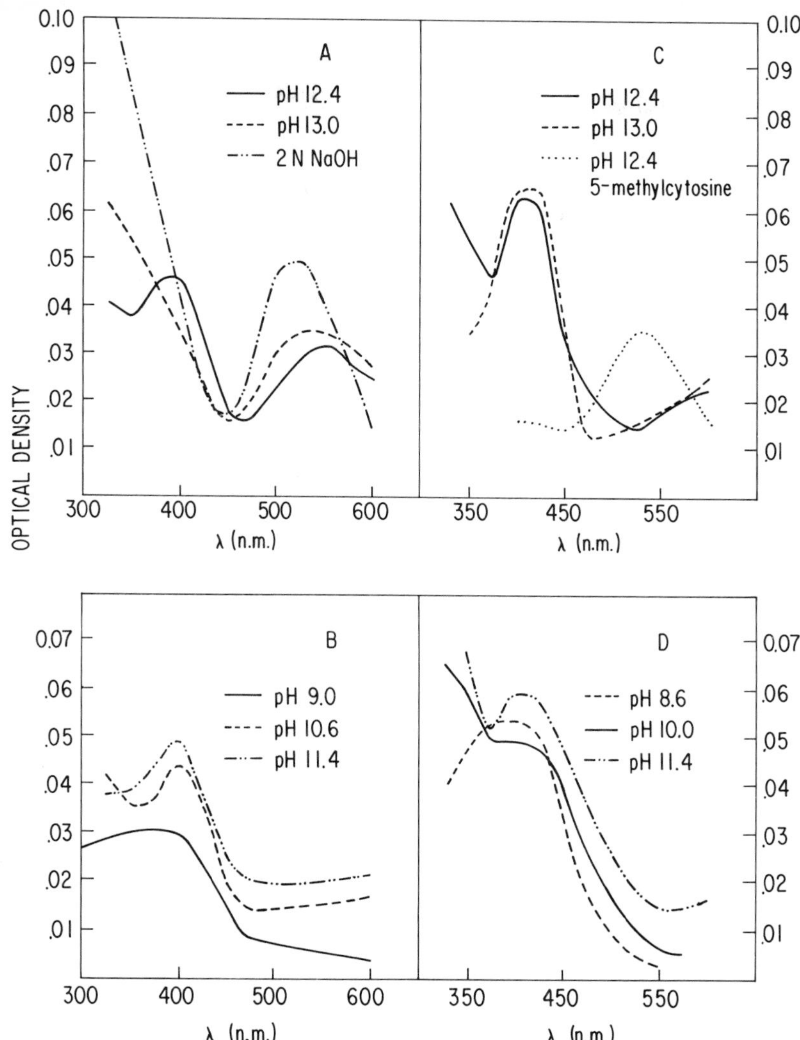

Figure 6. Absorption spectra of transient species formed on irradiation of N_2O saturated 5×10^{-4}M solutions of pyrimidine bases. The optical density is the maximum observed during formation and decay of the transient. Doses were 800 rads/pulse for thymine (A and B) and 5-methylcytosine (C), and 1070 rads/pulse for uracil (C and D)

shown that the principle products of thymine radiolysis in air-saturated solutions are the glycol and 6-hydroxy-5-hydroperoxide formed by addition to the 5,6 double bond of thymine. The mechanism proposed to account for these products postulates that OH· adds to the 6 position to give the radical

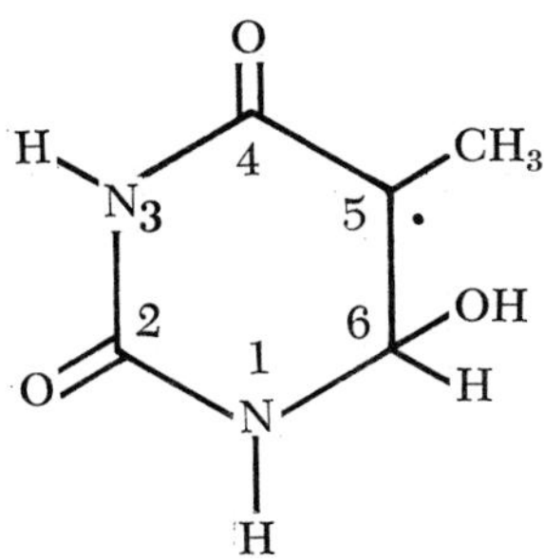

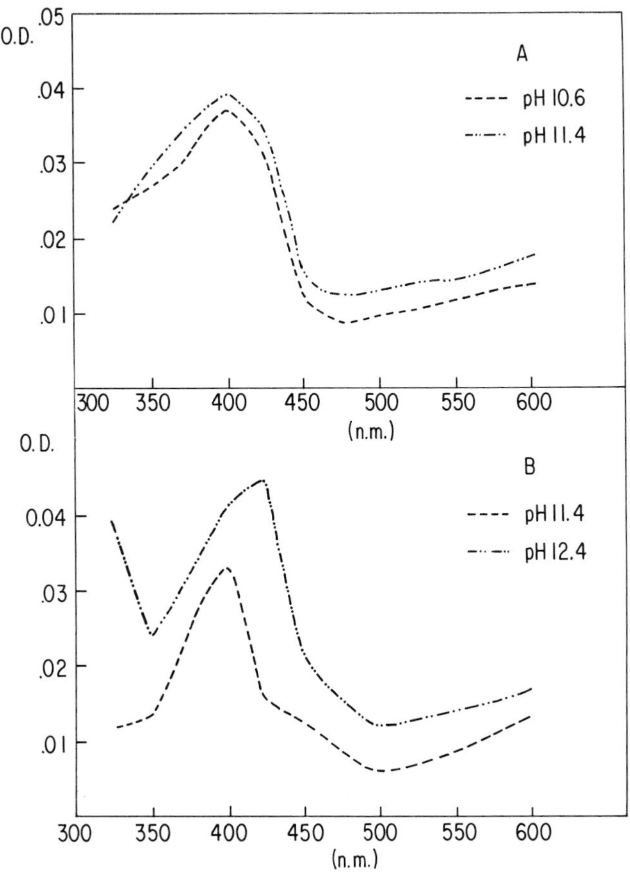

Figure 7. Absorption spectra of transient species present 80 μsec. after an 800 rad pulse to 5 × 10^{-4}M thymine solutions (A), and a 1070 rad pulse to 5 × 10^{-4}M uracil solutions (B)

EPR investigations designed to test this initial step suggest that OH· made by mixing Ti^{3+} and H_2O_2 with thymine also adds to the 5 position to give the radical (*8, 15*).

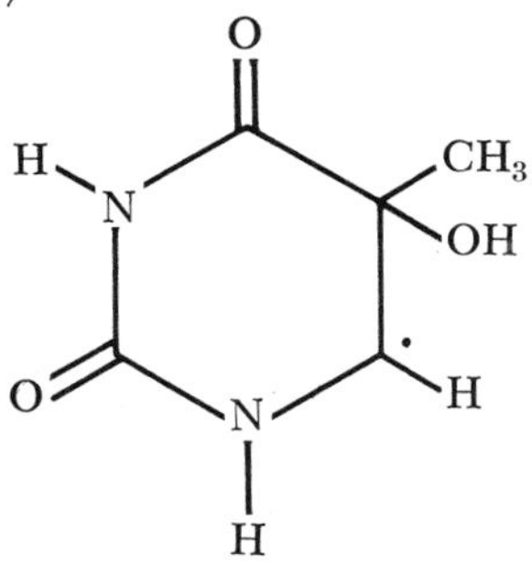

Determination of the proportions of the two reactions requires further product analyses and better understanding of the titanium-peroxide reaction, but addition of OH· to the double bond remains a reasonable proposal and it is likely that one or both of these structures contribute to the transient spectrum at pH 9.

At pH 10.6 and 11.4 thymine is mainly in the singly ionized form:

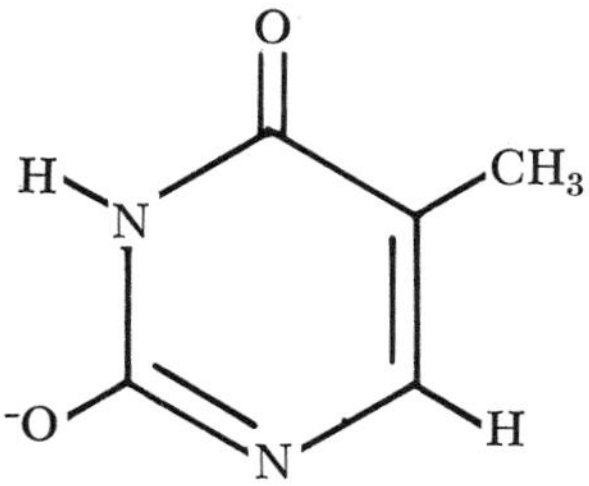

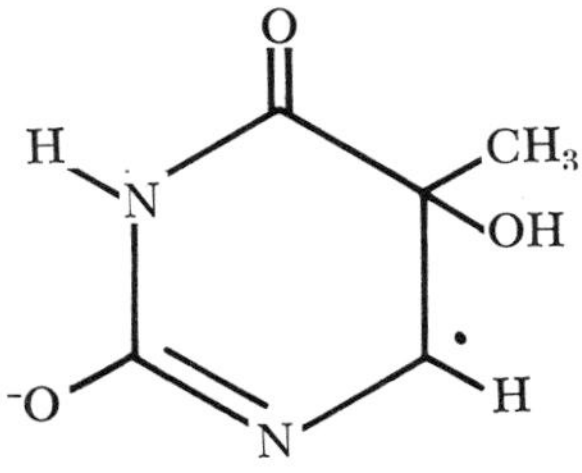

No product yields nor EPR studies have been reported for reactions of this ion with OH· free radical, but it is known that the *G*-value for disappearance of the unsaturated group is much less than in neutral or acid solutions (*6, 7*) and considerably less than *G*(OH). There must be two pathways, therefore, for removing OH· from the system, one which results in saturation of the double bond of thymine, and one which does not. By analogy with the radical believed to be formed at pH 9.0, the radical which leads to double bond disappearance might be although the radical, of course, may not have the same ionization constant as the initial compound. The structure of the other transient is unknown.

The appearance of a new absorption peak at 525–550 n.m. when the pH is increased to 12.4 correlates with ionization of OH· (*9*). Transient formation at this pH requires interaction of two negatively charged ions:

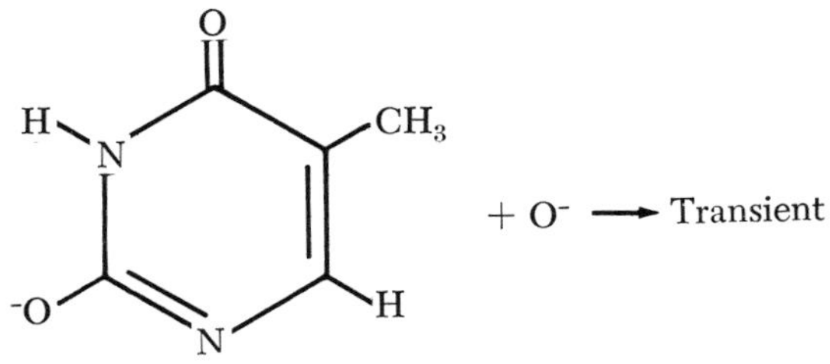

$+ O^- \longrightarrow$ Transient

A major product of radiolysis of strongly alkaline thymine solutions is believed to be hydroxymethyluracil (*6*).

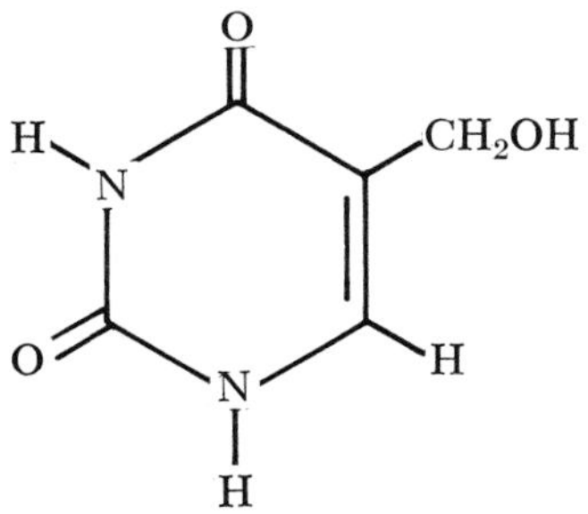

Although the mechanism for formation of this compound has not been established, the initial attack is most likely on the methyl group where the charge density is low. The spectrum obtained at pH $>$ 12 is therefore probably largely caused by radicals such as

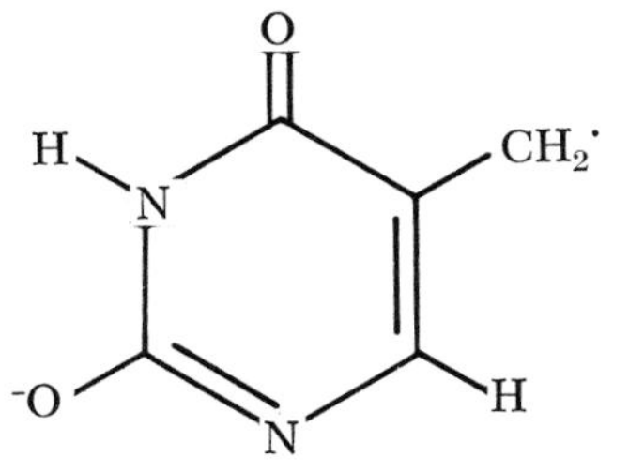

At the highest pH values the absorbance at 350 n.m. increases greatly. This is probably caused by the second ionization of thymine giving radicals such as

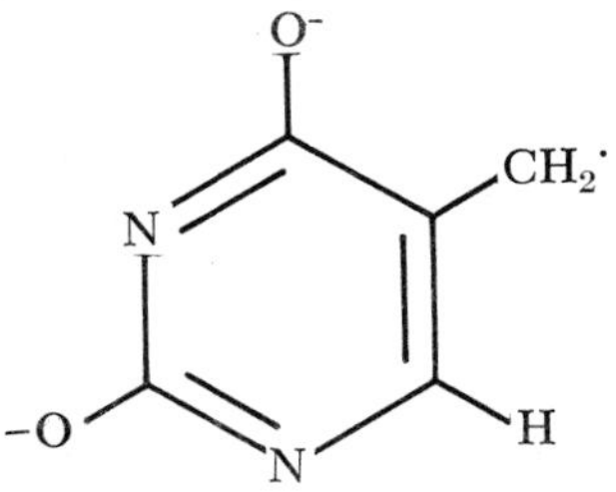

Spectra and Transient Decay: Deoxyribose, Thymidine and DNA. Spectra of the transients observed at neutral pH and at pH $\sim$ 12.4 shortly after the radiation pulse, and 400–500 μsec. later are shown in Figure 8. The decay of the transients is complex (Figures 9, 10, and 11), and each substance follows a different and pH dependent pattern.

The deoxyribose transient absorption, pH 6.7, decays to half its maximum intensity in about 350 μsec. The limited data available fit either first or second order kinetics about equally well. At pH 12.4 there appear to be at least three transients, including one with a very long lifetime observable at 300 n.m.

The thymidine transient absorption at pH 7.1 decays at almost exactly the same rate at 320 and 390 n.m. At pH 12.2 several decay rates can be seen. The data fall fairly well onto straight lines when 1/OD is plotted against time.

The decay of the DNA transient absorption pH 7 or 12.4 is negligible at 320 n.m. during the 700 μsec. observation period, but a rapid decay occurs at 550 n.m. at pH 12.4. The latter data give a linear 1/OD *vs.* time plot.

Superficial comparison of the thymidine transient spectra with the deoxyribose and thymine transient spectra, all at pH 7, suggests that both pentose and base transients may contribute to the observed spectra. The peak in the thymidine spectrum at 400 n.m. is at the same wavelength as the thymine transient peak, and the short wavelength absorption is similar to the deoxyribose transient absorption. However, thymine itself gives a transient spectrum at pH 10.6 which is similar to that of thymidine at pH 7 (*cf.* Figure 2), and the similarity in decay rates of the thymidine transient absorption at 320 to that at 390 n.m. indicates that both absorptions may be caused by the same transient species. If so, the transient probably involves the thymine moiety. At pH 12.2 the spectra and decay of the thymidine transient are consistent with formation of transients on both the pentose and base parts of the molecules.

Attack by OH· mainly on the base at pH 7, and to a large extent on the pentose at high pH is consistent with conclusions reached in steady state studies of nucleoside radiolysis (*7, 13*).

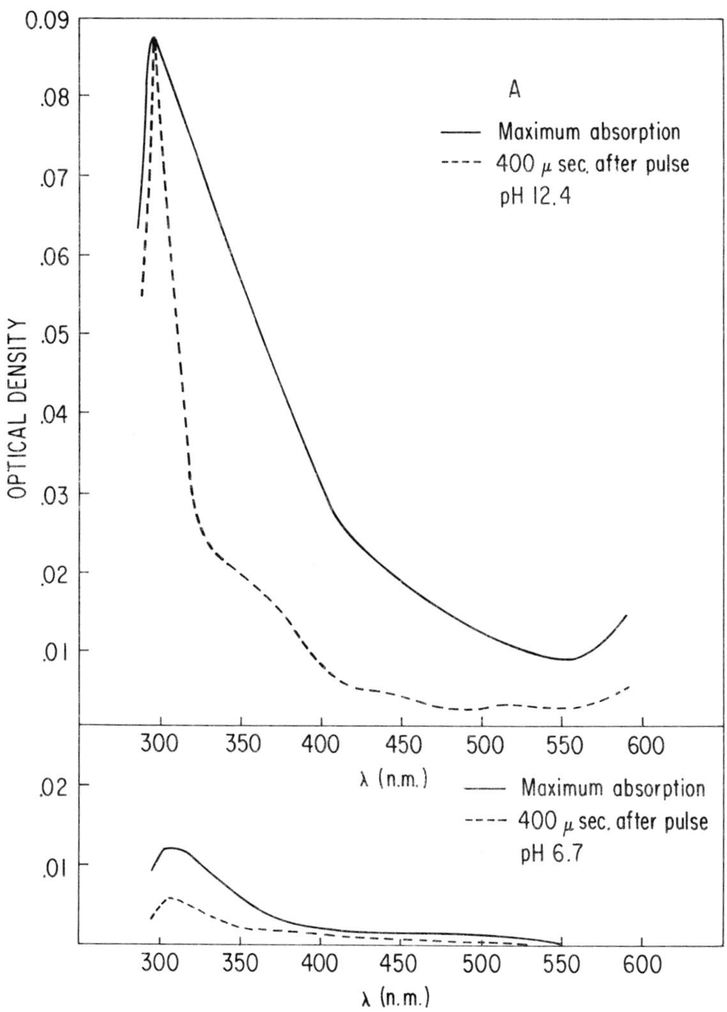

Figure 8a. Absorption spectra of transients produced by 10 nsec. pulses in N_2O saturated solutions of A) 5 × 10^{-4}M deoxyribose. Optical densities were adjusted to 1000 rads/pulse

The DNA transient at pH 6.9 has a spectrum which is generally similar to that of the deoxyribose transient. Shoulders at 375 and 425 n.m. and the suggestion of a peak at 475 n.m. may indicate the presence of transient species involving the bases, but the deoxyribose transient appears to make a major contribution to the absorption. (The DNA contains approximately 5% protein, and it is conceivable that this contributes to the transient absorption.) At pH 12.4 the spectrum appears to contain a long wavelength absorption caused by thymine or possibly other bases. The relatively low absorption at 400 n.m., however, is not consistent with a spectrum consisting simply of the weighted sum of base and deoxyribose transient spectra. More complex interactions appear to be occurring.

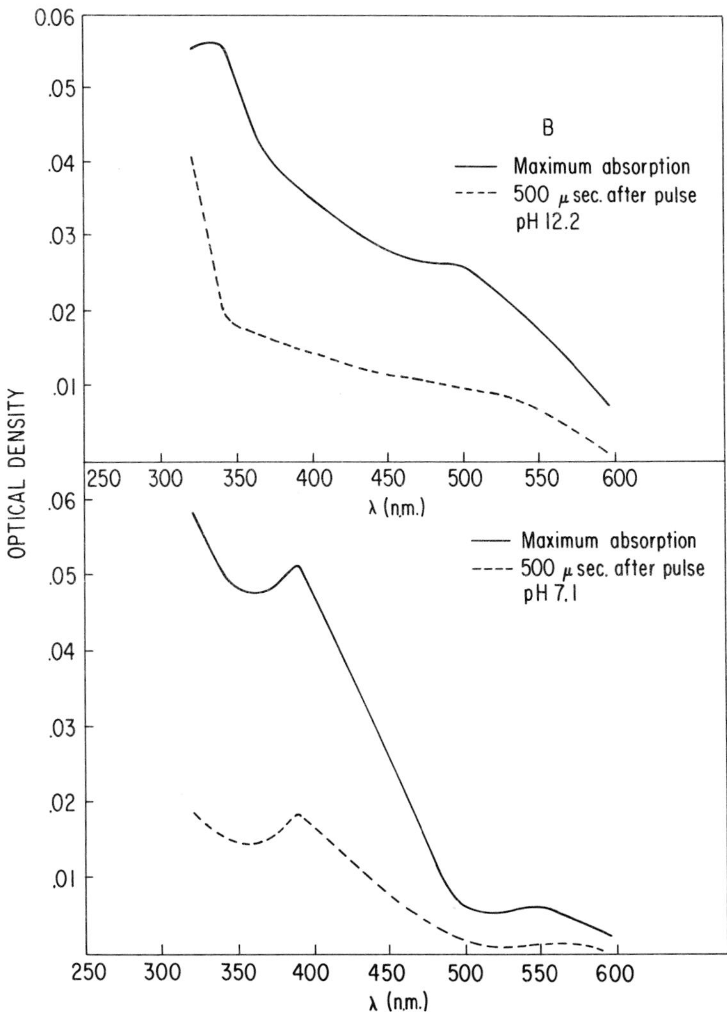

Figure 8b. Absorption spectra of transients produced by 10 nsec. pulses in N_2O saturated solutions of 5×10^{-4}M thymidine. Optical density was adjusted to 1000 rads/pulse

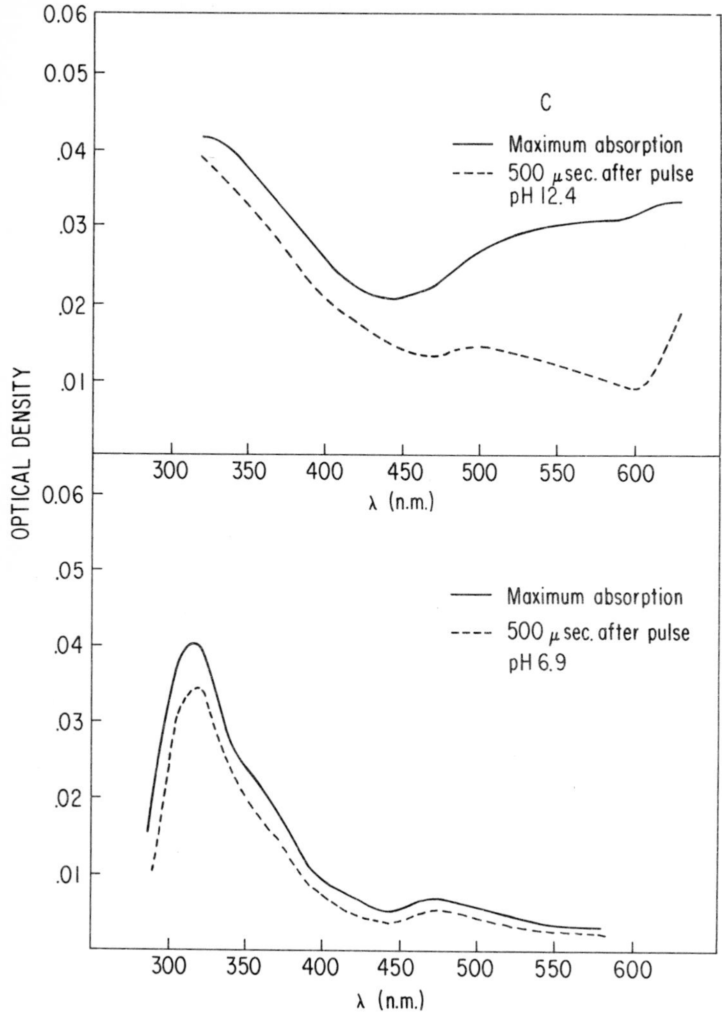

Figure 8c. Absorption spectra of transients produced by 10 nsec. pulses in N_2O saturated solutions 0.0075% DNA in 0.2M $NaClO_4$. Optical density was adjusted to 1000 rads/pulse

An increase in the contribution of transients involving the bases to the DNA transient spectrum as the pH is increased is consistent with chemical evidence that bases in the double helix of polynucleotides are protected from radiation to a degree which is related to helix stability. Radiation sensitivity of the pentose on the other hand, is unrelated to macromolecular structure (*16*).

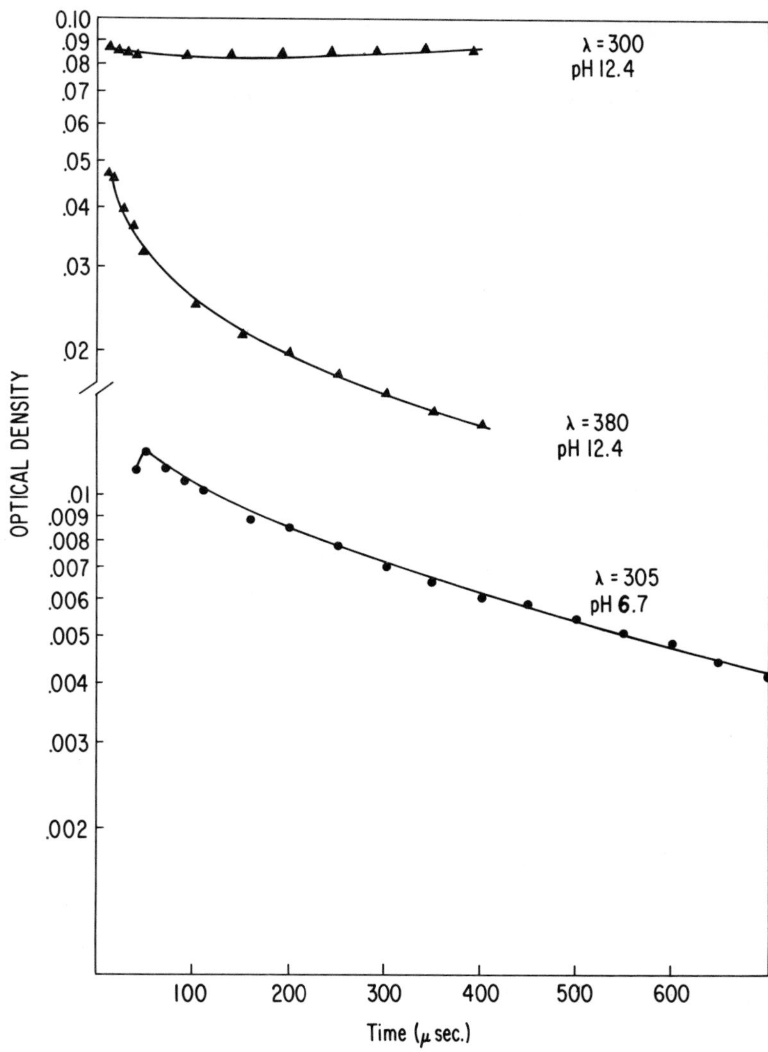

Figure 9. Decay of transient formed by 10 nsec. pulse in N_2O saturated 5×10^{-4}M deoxyribose. Optical densities were adjusted to 1000 rads/pulse

The slow decay of the DNA transient absorption at pH 7, and the absence of significant spectral changes during decay suggest that the radical is stable for periods greater than a millisecond to intramolecular changes or rearrangements affecting the chromophore. This provides ample time for reaction with a reducing agent, and indicates that repair of damage caused by OH· may be feasible provided that no irreversible reactions occur in times shorter than we observed.

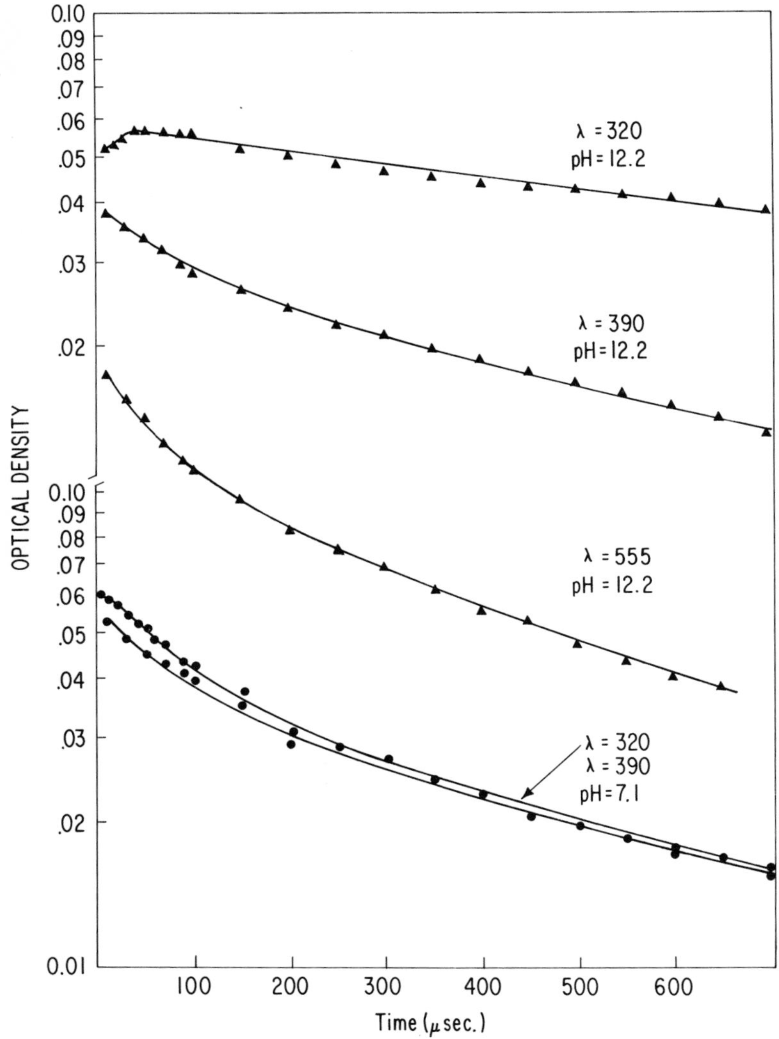

Figure 10. Decay of transient formed by 10 nsec. pulse in N_2O saturated solution of 5×10^{-4}M thymidine. Optical densities were adjusted to 1000 rads/pulse

Rates of Formation of Transient Species. Figure 14 shows the increase in transient absorption in N_2O saturated solutions of thymine and DNA following exposure to a 40 nsec. radiation pulse. Decay of electron absorption by reaction with N_2O can be seen in Figure 14b. It is complete by the time that the Cerenkov radiation has disappeared, and therefore does not interfere with observation of the transients formed by OH· free radical.

The formation reactions follow psuedo-first order kinetics. Apparent rate constants are given in Table III. Wavelengths at or near absorption

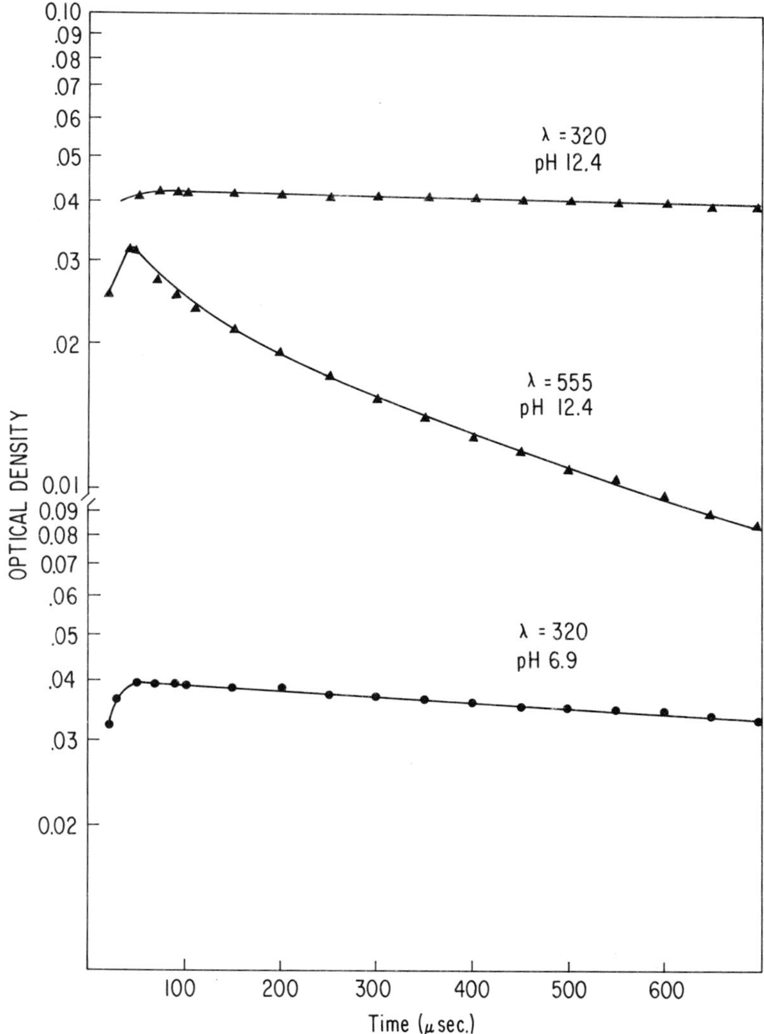

Figure 11. Decay of transient formed by 10 nsec. pulse in N_2O saturated 0.0075% DNA solutions 0.2M in $NaClO_4$. Optical densities adjusted to 1000 rads/pulse

maxima were used except with DNA at pH 7. In this case 400 n.m. instead of the peak at 320 n.m. gave a better signal to noise ratio.

The value for the reaction of OH· with thymine at pH 7, 7.4×10^9, is slightly more than twice the value previously obtained by the competition method using CNS^- (*12*). It seems likely that the mechanism of the CNS^- reaction is more complex than originally thought, and that it gave a low result with thymine.

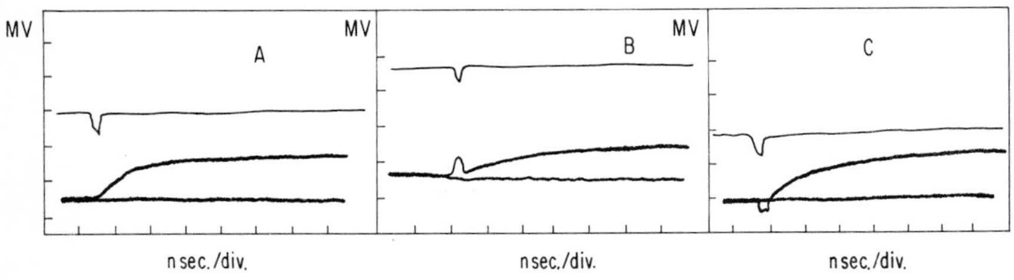

Figure 12. Oscillograms showing formation of transient absorption: A) 10^{-3}M thymine, pH 6.9, 400 n.m.; B) 10^{-3}M thymine, pH 11, 550 n.m.; C) 0.0042M (0.15%) calf thymus DNA, pH 6.6, 320 n.m. The top curve, showing the Cerenkov radiation, was obtained by pulsing with the analyzing light off. The bottom curve is the baseline (no radiation pulse, analyzing lamp on)

The values of the rate constants for thymine solutions of different pHs illustrate the effect of ionization on the rate of appearance of the transient absorption at 400 n.m. Ionization of thymine, pH 11, would not be expected to decrease the rate by the observed factor of nearly two. The earlier spectral and decay studies have shown that more than one transient may be formed at this pH, and possibly the apparent decrease in rate is caused by formation of some other species which is not observed at 400 n.m. A decrease in rate is expected at pH 12.4 because the attacking species is O^-. There also may be effects caused by formation of unobserved transients.

The experiments with 5,6-dihydrothymine are a preliminary attempt to compare rates of formation of transients by addition and by abstraction. Dihydrothymine is the saturated analog of thymine. The transient species which it forms by reaction with OH· have an absorption maximum at 400 n.m. at pH 7 and at 320 n.m. or lower at pH 12.4. The rate of formation of these transients appears to be slightly less than one-third of the rate of formation of transients by addition to thymine. At pH 7, OH· adds to the 5,6 double bond of thymine. The aqueous solution radiation chemistry of dihydrothymine has not been investigated, but electron paramagnetic resonance (EPR) studies in the solid phase show that H· atoms abstract

Table III. Rate Constants for the Formation of Transient Absorbing Species by Reaction of DNA and Related Compounds with OH· Free Radical (40 nsec. pulse, concentration $10^{-3}M$ except as noted, all solutions N_2O saturated, units 10^{-9} k (M^{-1} sec.$^{-1}$))

pH	~7		~11		~12.4	
	λ(n.m.)	$10^{-9}k$	*λ(n.m.)*	$10^{-9}k$	*λ(n.m.)*	$10^{-9}k$
Thymine	400	7.4	400	3.9	400, 550	1.1
Thymidine	375	4.7			400	2.1[a]
DNA	400	0.6[b]			320	0.6[c]
5,6-Dihydrothymine	400	2.2			320	0.4[a]

[a] $5 \times 10^{-3}M$.
[b] 0.15% or 0.0042*M* in nucleotides, 0.01*M* $NaClO_4$.
[c] 0.0039*M* in nucleotides, 0.01*M* $NaClO_4$.

hydrogen from the 5,6 bond to give the same radical as is obtained by the addition of H· to the double bond of thymine (*4, 5*). If OH· behaves similarly the reaction is

$$\text{5,6-dihydrothymine} + OH\cdot \longrightarrow \text{5-yl radical} + H_2O$$

Abstraction from position 6 is also a possibility. At pH 12.4 the site of attack by O^- on dihydrothymine is unknown. A more complete interpretation of these results requires further experimentation.

The effect of a pentose substituent on the rate of transient formation is illustrated by the results with thymidine. Earlier evidence has shown that the transient species observed with thymidine at 375 n.m., pH 7, probably involves the base part of the molecules, and that the spectrum is similar to the spectrum of thymine at pH 10.6. It may thus be more than a coincidence that the rate constant for formation of the thymidine transient absorption is closer to that of thymine at pH 11 than at pH 7. The effect on rate of increasing the pH to 12.4 is relatively small.

The rate constants for DNA are based on a mean nucleotide molecular weight of 350, and assume that nucleotides in DNA react independently with OH· free radical. Considered in this way the rate of formation of the transient in DNA at pH 7 is considerably lower than with the other compounds tested, and at pH 12.4 lower than all compounds tested except dihydrothymine.

Conclusions

(1) Decay of transients formed by reaction of OH· with any of the compounds studied is complex. More than one transient species is formed in nearly every system investigated. Parent-daughter relationships appear to occur in some cases.

(2) Uracil and thymine transients follow different patterns in their decay, particularly in alkaline solutions.

(3) Observation of the spectra of transient absorptions has confirmed the hypothesis of stationary state radiation chemistry that the site of attack by OH· free radical on thymine and 5-methylcytosine changes with pH.

(4) Similarly, observations on thymidine at pH 7 and 12.4 have confirmed that attack partially shifts from the base to the pentose as the pH is increased.

(5) Comparison of spectra of thymine, thymidine, deoxyribose, and DNA suggests that under physiological pH conditions OH· attack on the pentose part of DNA is a major reaction.

(6) The transient formed by reaction of OH· with DNA has been shown to have a long lifetime in comparison with speeds of other reactions studied and to survive without observable changes in radical structure. These observations suggest the feasibility of chemical reversal of the action of OH· radicals provided that irreversible changes do not occur in less time than we can observe.

(7) Preliminary studies have been made on the rates of formation of transient absorptions. These have given information on: (a) comparison of rates obtained by observation of transient formation with rates obtained by OH· disappearance (CSN^- method), (b) effects of ionization of thymine and OH· on rates, (c) direct comparison of rates of addition and abstraction to obtain a similar radical, (d) some effects of pentose substituents on rates, and (e) rate of reaction of OH· with DNA.

Acknowledgment

This work was supported in part by the Division of Biology and Medicine of the U.S. Atomic Energy Commission through contracts with the University of California and with Gulf General Atomic, Inc. The authors wish to acknowledge the many suggestions and help proffered by Robin Willson in setting up the pulse radiolysis equipment and in designing and carrying out the initial experiments. They also thank J. F. Ward and D. R. Howton for their assistance and many helpful discussions, W. T. Tsukamoto for assistance during the early stages of the work, F. C. Peterson for operating the equipment, and Irene Kuo and Aida Warnick for technical assistance.

Literature Cited

(1) Adams, G. E., Boag, J. W., Michael, B. D., *Proc. Roy. Soc.* **289,** 321 (1966).
(2) Ekert, B., Monier, R., *Nature 184,* (B.A.) 58 (1959).
(3) Felix, W. D., Gall, Bonnie L., Dorfman, Leon M., *J. Phys. Chem.* **71,** 384 (1967).
(4) Heller, H. C., Schlick, S., Cole, T., *J. Phys. Chem.* **71,** 97 (1967).
(5) Holmes, D. E., Ingalls, R. B., Myers, L. S., Jr., *Abstr. 3rd Intern. Congr. Radiation, Res.,* **Abstr. 436** (June-July 1966).
(6) Myers, L. S., Jr., Ward, J. F., Tsukamoto, W. T., Holmes, D. E., Julca, J. R., *Science* **148,** 1234 (1965).
(7) Myers, L. S., Jr., Ward, J. F., Tsukamoto, W. T., Holmes, D. E., *Nature* **208,** 1086 (1965).
(8) Ormerod, M. G., Singh, B. B., *Intern. J. Radiation Biol.* **10,** 533 (1966).
(9) Rabani, J., Matheson, M. S., *J. Am. Chem. Soc.* **86,** 3175 (1964)
(10) Scholes, G. (private communication).
(11) Scholes, G., "Progress in Biophysics and Biophysical Chemistry," John A. V. Butler, ed., Vol. 13, p. 59, Pergamon, London, England, 1963.
(12) Scholes, G., Shaw, Patricia, Willson, R. L., "Pulse Radiolysis," M. Ebert, J. P. Keene, A. J. Swallow, J. H. Baxendale, eds., p. 151, Academic Press, New York, 1965.
(13) Scholes, G., Ward, J. F., Weiss, J. J., *J. Mol. Biol.* **2,** 379 (1960).
(14) Theard, L. M., Peterson, F. C., Willson, R. L., Ward, J. F., Myers, L. S., Jr., Ingalls, R. B., *Radiation Res.* **31,** 581 (1967).
(15) Ward, J. F., Al-Thannon, A. A., Myers, L. S., Jr. (unpublished work).
(16) Ward, J. F., Urist, M. M., *Intern. J. Radiation Biol.* **12,** 209 (1967).
(17) Weiss, J. J., "Progress in Nucleic Acid Research and Molecular Biology," J. N. Davidson and W. E. Cohn, eds., Vol. 3, p. 103, Academic Press, New York, 1964.
(18) Willson, R. L., Ph.D. Thesis, University of Newcastle Upon Tyne (1966).

RECEIVED January 2, 1968.

25

Steady State and Pulse Radiolysis of Aqueous Chloride Solutions of Nucleic Acid Components

J. F. WARD and I. KUO

Laboratory of Nuclear Medicine and Radiation Biology of the Department of Biophysics and Nuclear Medicine, School of Medicine, University of California, Los Angeles, Calif.

The pulse radiolysis technique has been used to measure absolute rate constants for reactions of some nucleic acid constituents with Cl_2^- radicals (the species produced by reaction of OH radicals with chloride ions in acid aqueous solution). The rate of disappearance of the Cl_2^- absorption spectrum was measured in the absence and presence of the various solutes. Rate constants for the corresponding OH radical reactions are found to be 20 to 200 times greater than the rate constants for the Cl_2^- radical reactions. Steady state radiolysis showed that in some cases the radicals produced by reaction of these compounds with Cl_2^- radicals differ in their subsequent reaction from the corresponding OH radical adduct.

Hydroxyl free radicals formed in water radiolysis react with chloride ions in acid solution (*1*, *9*), to give a transient product which has been identified as the Cl_2^- ion radical (*1*). This species differs from the OH free radical in that it reacts rapidly with thymine but not with ethyl alcohol. Previous work (*9*) used this difference to determine a rate constant for the reaction of OH radicals with chloride ions (relative to the rate constant for the reaction of OH radicals with thymine). Subsequent work (*8*) has shown that the presence of chloride ions during irradiation of other pyrimidines in oxygenated, acid, aqueous solution leads to a marked departure from the results obtained in the absence of chloride—*i.e.*, chloride ions increase the extent of uracil and of cytosine destruction up to six-fold, but decrease G(-base) for purines, nucleosides, and nucleotides. These changes in yields show a pH dependence which closely follows that calculated for Cl_2^- formation. It seems that reaction of Cl_2^- with the pyrimidine or purine is important in determining the extent of base destruction. The present investigation was undertaken to determine the rates of reaction of some nucleic acid derivatives with Cl_2^- by pulse radiolysis and to attempt to correlate these with observed steady state radiolysis results.

Experimental

Pulse radiolysis experiments were carried out in cooperation with L. M. Theard at Gulf General Atomic, Inc., San Diego, Calif., using apparatus previously described (*7*).

Typically a 10-nsec. pulse giving a dose of 200–300 rads was used. The formation and decay of the Cl_2^- transient was followed at 360 n.m. The extinction coefficient of this species (*1*) at 360 n.m. is much higher than those quoted for pyrimidine and purine transients (*5*). Results obtained using other wavelengths of the Cl_2^- absorption spectrum, showed close agreement with those obtained at 360 n.m.

γ-Irradiations were carried out in a ^{60}Co source at a dose rate of 6×10^{16} e.v. ml.$^{-1}$ min.$^{-1}$ (calibrated by ferrous sulfate dosimetry). *G* values (G = number of molecules changed per 100 e.v. absorbed) were calculated from yield dose plots. Solutions for γ-irradiation were saturated with oxygen.

Materials. All nucleic acid chemicals were A grade (Calbiochem) irradiated dissolved in triply distilled water. Other chemicals were reagent grade. For pulse radiolysis, solutions were equilibrated with the required gas before introduction to the radiation cell, the same gas being used to drive the solution in the sample changing arrangement. Unless otherwise stated argon was used.

Results and Discussion

Previous work (*1*, *9*) has shown that the reaction of OH free radicals with chloride ions shows a first order dependence on hydrogen ion concentration and chloride ion concentration.

$$OH^{\cdot} + Cl^- + H_3O^+ \rightarrow Cl^{\cdot} + 2H_2O \qquad (1)$$

(The chlorine atom apparently reacts immediately with a chloride ion to give Cl_2^- in a reaction which is not rate limiting (*1*).) The third order reaction rate constant for Reaction 1 obtained in this laboratory using a steady state method is only half that found by Anbar and Thomas using pulse radiolysis (*1*). Using pulse radiolysis we obtain results close to those of the latter workers. The rate we obtained for Reaction 1 was $1.5 \pm 0.3 \times 10^{10} M^{-2}$ sec.$^{-1}$. We found no consistent variation of this value with changing pH (0.8 to 3.4) or changing chloride molarity (3×10^{-4} to 10^{-1}). The rate constant determined in the steady state work was obtained from a measured relative rate constant, using a published rate constant as a reference.

The method used in determining rate constants for Cl_2^- reactions is essentially the same as that used to determine hydrated electron rate constants: The rate of disappearance of the Cl_2^- absorption was measured in the presence of various concentrations of solute. The decay of Cl_2^- in the absence of reacting solute seemed to be second order. Increasing the dose to 850 rads and removing hydrated electrons by saturation of the solution with nitrous oxide at pH 3.1 gave a good second order plot for Cl_2^- decay. This suggests that Cl_2^- is decaying by Reaction 2:

$$Cl_2^- + Cl_2^- \rightarrow (2Cl^- + Cl_2) \qquad (2)$$

The rate constant for this reaction was found to be $1.4 \pm 0.3 \times 10^{10} M^{-1}$ sec.$^{-1}$ = $2k_2$ (The extinction coefficient used for Cl_2^- at 360 n.m. was 10,000 (*see* Reference 1). It was also shown that this decay rate was independent of pH from 0.9 to 3.2. Langmuir and Hayon (3) have recently measured rate constants of Cl_2^- reactions by a flash photolysis method. They measured the rate constant for Reaction 2 and found $2k_2 = 1.25 - 1.51 \times 10^{10} M^{-1}$ sec.$^{-1}$, which is in good agreement with the value obtained here.

All of the compounds examined for reaction with Cl_2^- react rapidly with OH free radicals (5). Thus, rate constants lower than $5 \times 10^6 M^{-1}$ sec.$^{-1}$ could not be detected: Increasing the solute concentration sufficiently to compete with Reaction 2 for the Cl_2^-, scavenges OH free radicals from reacting to form Cl^-_2.

Chloride ions are used in the Fricke dosimeter as hydroxyl radical scavengers (2). Since adding chloride ions does not decrease the yield of ferric ion (except in the presence of organic impurities), it can be argued that chlorine atoms and hence Cl_2^- radical ions react to oxidize ferrous ion. Using the present technique we have measured the effect of ferrous ions on the rate of decay of the Cl_2^- transient. Ferrous ions increased this rate, and a rate constant for Reaction 3 was determined $k_3 = 3.8 \pm 0.3 \times 10^7 M^{-1}$ sec.$^{-1}$ at pH 2.1

$$Fe^{2+} + Cl_2^- \rightarrow Fe^{3+} + 2Cl^- \qquad (3)$$

The effect of salt concentration (sodium perchlorate) on the decay rate of Cl_2^- transient in the presence of $10^{-3} M$ Fe^{2+} was examined. A marked salt effect was observed, the pseudo first order rate constant being reduced from 3.8×10^4 sec.$^{-1}$ at ionic strength 0.04, to 2.5×10^4 sec.$^{-1}$ at ionic strength 0.25. Reaction 3 would be expected to show a negative salt effect, but the observed decrease in rate constant with increasing ionic strength is somewhat less than expected.

Table I shows rate constants for reaction of some nucleic acid components with Cl_2^- and with OH radicals. The latter are the data determined by Scholes *et al.* (*5*). Also shown are our results from steady state work in which the *G*-value for base destruction, *G* (-base), was measured for irradiations carried out in the presence and in the absence of $10^{-1}M$ sodium chloride at pH 2.7.

Table I. Second Order Rate Constants for Reactions of Cl_2^- with Pyrimidines, Purines and Deoxynucleotides at pH 2.7 in $10^{-1}M$ Sodium Chloride Solution

	Rate Constant × $10^{-7}M^{-1}$ sec.$^{-1}$		*Steady State Value G(-Base)*	
	Cl_2^- + Base	*OH + Base*[a]	*With Cl^-*	*Without Cl^-*
PYRIMIDINES				
Thymine	12 ± 1.0	310	2.4	2.4
Uracil	4.1 ± 0.3	290	9.5	2.6
Cytosine	9.1 ± 0.7	185	5.6	2.7
PURINES				
Adenine	<0.5	53	0.5	1.3
Guanine[b]	8.1 ± 0.6		0.6	2.1
DEOXYNUCLEOTIDES				
Thymidylic Acid	4.4 ± 0.3	260	2.6	2.2
Deoxycytidylic Acid	<0.5	180	1.8	2.2
Deoxyadenylic Acid	<0.5	82	0.66	0.75
Deoxyguanylic Acid	12.0 ± 1.0	280	0.16	1.5

[a] from Reference 5.
[b] pH 2.3.

Pyrimidines. The pyrimidines react readily with hydroxyl radicals. Subsequent reactions of the pyrimidine-OH radical with oxygen lead to base destruction, thus *G*(-base) = *G*(OH) (*6*). Although the rate constants for pyrimidine reactions with Cl_2^- radicals are all one-twenty fifth or less of those of the OH radical rate constants (*see* Table I), they are still sufficiently high to ensure complete scavenging of Cl_2^- radicals by the pyrimidines at the concentrations used ($2 \times 10^{-4}M$) in steady state radiolysis.

G(-cytosine) is 5.6 and *G*(-uracil) is 9.5 at pH 2.7 in $10^{-1}M$ chloride solutions—*i.e.*, much larger than *G*(OH). The destruction increases even further as the pH is lowered, the maximum *G*(-uracil) being 13.0 at pH 2.2 in $10^{-1}M$ chloride solution. The high yields suggest that the pyrimidine -(Cl_2^-) radical can react with other pyrimidine molecules in a short chain reaction. Since reactions of free radicals with pyrimidine compounds takes place mainly at the 5.6 double bond (*6*), the presence of the 5-methyl group in thymine may restrict subsequent reactions of thymine radicals.

Purines. In the absence of chloride ions *G*(-base) for guanine and adenine is less than *G*(OH). Since both purines react rapidly with OH radicals the low yield of destruction is attributed to the existence of a back reaction of the purine -OH radical (*6*). The extent to which this back reaction occurs with purine -(Cl_2^-) radicals will determine the extent of destruction of purines when they are irradiated in acidic chloride solutions. Since guanine reacts readily with Cl_2^- radicals, the protective effect of chloride ions in the steady state radiolysis is conveniently explained by assuming an increase in the back reaction—*i.e.*, guanine -(Cl_2^-) radicals revert to guanine more readily than the guanine-OH radical. However, the protective effect of chloride in adenine radiolysis could be because of the inability of adenine to react with Cl_2^-.

Deoxynucleotides. In the Table the values for *G*(-base) are quoted, since radical attack on the deoxyribose moiety is not taken into consideration. We have shown that the presence of chloride in the radiolysis of deoxyribonucleotides in acid solution completely removes any radical attack on the sugar moiety. Attempts to measure reaction rates of the sugars ribose and deoxyribose with Cl_2^- radicals by the pulse radiolysis technique showed that the rate constants for these reactions must be below $5 \times 10^6 M^{-1}$ sec.$^{-1}$.

Using the same rationale as is used above in the purine section, it can be seen from the results in the Table that an extensive back reaction of the deoxyguanylic acid -(Cl_2^-) radical occurs. The slight radioprotective effect of chloride in acidic solutions of deoxycytidylic acid and deoxyadenylic acid may be caused by the inability of these compounds to react with Cl_2^-.

Conclusions

The rate constants for reaction of the Cl_2^- radical with the compounds investigated are much lower than the corresponding OH radical rate constants. The Cl_2^- rate constants for reaction with this series of compounds vary over a wider range than do their OH radical counterparts. The effect of this range of rate constants will be most evident in the radiolysis of mixtures of compounds. In the radiolysis of a mixture of equal concentrations of the deoxynucleotides, OH radicals cause approximately equal destruction of all four bases (*4*). Cl_2^- radicals, on the other hand, will react preferentially with deoxyguanylic acid and only a tenth of these reactions will cause base destruction. Thus, the net effect of conversion of OH radicals to Cl_2^- radicals, in this system, will be protection of all the bases but thymine and complete protection of the deoxyribose moieties.

Acknowledgments

We wish to thank the members of our pulse radiolysis group, L. S. Myers, Jr., R. L. Willson, and R. B. Ingalls for many useful discussions. Thanks are also due to L. M. Theard and F. C. Peterson of General Atomics, San Diego, for advice, and for operating the pulse radiolysis apparatus.

Literature Cited

(1) Anbar, M., Thomas, J. K., *J. Phys. Chem.* **68,** 3829 (1964).
(2) Dewhurst, H. A., *J. Phys. Chem.* **19,** 1329 (1951).
(3) Langmuir, M. E., Hayon, E., *J. Phys. Chem.* **71,** 3808 (1967).
(4) McCargo, M., Ph.D. Thesis, Univ. of Durham, England, 1961.
(5) Scholes, G., Shaw, P., Willson, R. L., Ebert, M., "Pulse Radiolysis," Academic Press, London, 1965.
(6) Scholes, G., Ward, J. F., Weiss, J. J., *J. Mol. Biol.* **2,** 379 (1960).
(7) Theard, L. M., Peterson, F. C., Willson, R. L., Ward, J. F., Myers, L. S., Jr., Ingalls, R. B., *Radiation Res.* **31,** 581 (1967).
(8) Ward, J. F., Kuo, I., *Radiation Res.* **31,** 651 (1967).
(9) Ward, J. F., Myers, L. S., Jr., *Radiation Res.* **26,** 483 (1964).

RECEIVED December 27, 1967. These studies were supported in part by the Division of Biology and Medicine of the U. S. Atomic Energy Commission through contracts with the University of California and Gulf General Atomic Inc.

26

The Radiation Chemistry of Anhydrous Solid State Glycine, Alanine, and Glycine Salts

W. CARL GOTTSCHALL, JR.[1] and BERT M. TOLBERT

University of Colorado, Boulder, Colo.

The radiation chemistry of glycine and alanine as well as the alkali metal salts of glycine has been investigated in the anhydrous solid state. Results of cesium-137 gamma irradiation indicate CO_2 is the chief gaseous product with larger amounts of NH_3 being released upon dissolution of the samples. Similarity of yields indicates little difference in decomposition mechanism and good agreement with the general mechanism postulated by Tolbert. $G(CO_2)$ *values were glycine, 1.02; alanine, 0.89; sodium glycinate, 0.43; potassium glycinate, 0.54; rubidium glycinate, 0.91. Other products and their* G *values were for glycine* $G(H_2) = 0.1$; $G(NH_3) = 4.3$, $G(CH_3NH_2) = 1$; $G(-M) = 6$ *and for alanine* $G(H_2) = 0.5$; $G(NH_3) = 3.3$; $G(CH_3CH_2NH_2) = 2$; $G(-M) = 5$.

Much work has been done on the irradiation of amino acids in solution (*8, 9, 10, 11, 16, 21*) but little information can be found on solid state work (*1, 18*) despite the advantage of avoiding indirect effects. EPR investigations of irradiated glycine (*4, 6, 12, 22*) and alanine (*17*) offer independent results of a physical nature which correlate with the chemical results of this investigation. The qualitative and quantitative effects of alkali metal cations in the crystalline matrix also are helpful in determining the mechanism of irradiation produced decomposition.

Experimental

Materials. The best grade commercial glycine and alanine from the California Corporation for Biochemical Research were recrystallized

[1] Present address: University of Denver, Denver, Colo. 80210.

twice—first from glacial acetic acid and then from ethyl alcohol water. An aliquot of labeled amino acid-1-^{14}C from Nuclear Chicago Corporation (calculated to yield amino acid of specific activity such that the acid or salts formed from it would have a specific activity of approximately one tenth of a microcurie per milligram) was pipetted into the solution immediately prior to the preparations. The amino acids were then precipitated or salts prepared by adding the appropriate alkali metal hydroxide or carbonate and subsequent crystallization. Crystals obtained were recrystallized and dried in a vacuum desiccator over $MgClO_4$. Specific activity of each compound was checked by combustion in a modified Pregl furnace followed by assay of the $^{14}CO_2$ with a Cary Vibrating Reed Electrometer.

Sodium and potassium hydroxides were Baker Analytical Reagent. Rubidium carbonate was Fisher Scientific Company "purified."

Apparatus. The irradiations were performed in the University of Colorado cesium-137 gamma source at 22°C. The source was calibrated at $2.78 \pm 0.02 \times 10^{19}$ e.v./gm./hr. by a Fricke dosimeter at 22°C. using $G(Fe^{3+}) = 15.6$.

Mass Spectra were run on a Consolidated Electrodynamics Corporation Mass Sepectrometer Type 21-103C to determine H_2 yields as well as yields from "dry" analyses for comparison with yields obtained after dissolution of the irradiated compound. Sample tubes were broken directly in the gas sampling system to yield "dry" analyses results.

The gas chromatograph also used to determine "dry" analysis yields was Perkin Elmer Fractometer Model 154. A simple device was constructed of Tygon tubing and brass connectors to permit breakage again of the irradiated capillaries directly in the carrier stream.

Procedure. Capillary tubing of $2 \pm 1/2$ mm. internal diameter and a thickness of 200 ± 100 micrometers was drawn out of borosilicate glass tubing. Segments of 10 ± 2 cm. length were sealed at one end and labeled. Funnels of similar tubing were used to load 15 ± 10 mg. of sample into each tube; in the case of hygroscopic salts loading was performed in a dry box. Samples reported in this paper were all evacuated to 10–20 microns of mercury before being sealed. Samples sealed in air were observed to give higher decomposition values.

Samples were irradiated at least in duplicate to total doses of 20, 40, 80, and 160 megarads. Hopefully to improve consistency of data, all samples were allowed to remain at least 2 days in a −15°C. freezer for dissipation of short lived free radicals before analyses were conducted. No data was obtained on radical content at time of analysis.

The apparatus used is shown in Figure 1. Twenty ml. of 1*N* NaOH was placed in crusher tube "a" and then a sample tube. The stopper was put in place and the bubbler tube "b" lowered to the bottom of the crusher tube. Nitrogen gas was used to purge the solution and then the sample tube was crushed under the NaOH with crushing rod "c." Oxygen containing 5% CO_2 was swept through the solution for several minutes and then into an evacuated ionization chamber. Ten ml. of 35% perchloric acid was added dropwise to the alkaline solution from the dropping funnel "e." $^{14}CO_2$ released was swept along with the O_2–CO_2 gas into the ionization chamber. After the chamber reached atmospheric pressure, the valve was closed and the voltage generated in the ionization chamber was measured with a Cary Vibrating Reed Electrometer (*14*).

The Conway microdiffusion method (*2*) was employed to determine the amounts of ammonia and amines resulting from irradiation of duplicate samples and subsequent dissolution in 0.006*N* H_2SO_4. The Russell procedure (*15*) for a quantitative colorimetric determination was employed with the readings made at 628 mμ on a Beckman Spectrophotometer.

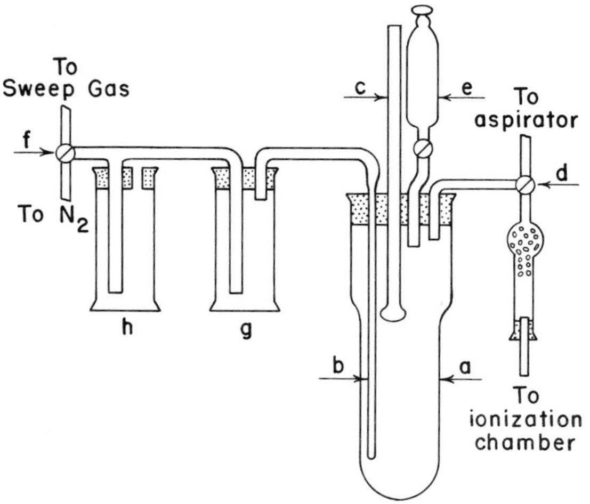

Figure 1. Generation apparatus for CO_2 "wet" analyses

(a)—*thickwall crushing tube,* (b)—*bubbler tube,* (c)—*crushing rod,* (d,f)—*3-way valve,* (e)—*dropping funnel,* (g)—*gas flow indicator apparatus, and* (h)—*pressure regulator*

High voltage electrophoresis at 50 volts/cm. has been shown to separate amines and ammonia from their parent amino acid (*13*) and was employed to permit colorimetric determination of ammonia and the amines. The excess of ammonia observed in every case coupled with factors of 10 and 100 higher sensitivity for ammonia than methylamine or ethylamine respectively in the procedure indicates that the microdiffusion results $G(NH_3 + \text{amines})$ to a good approximation are also the $G(NH_3)$ values.

$G(-M)$ values were determined by isotopic dilution using amino acids recrystallized as above, as well as with an automatic amino acid analyzer.

Results

Figure 2 shows the mole % of the original compound for CO_2 and NH_3 produced from duplicate radiolyses of glycine as a function of dose.

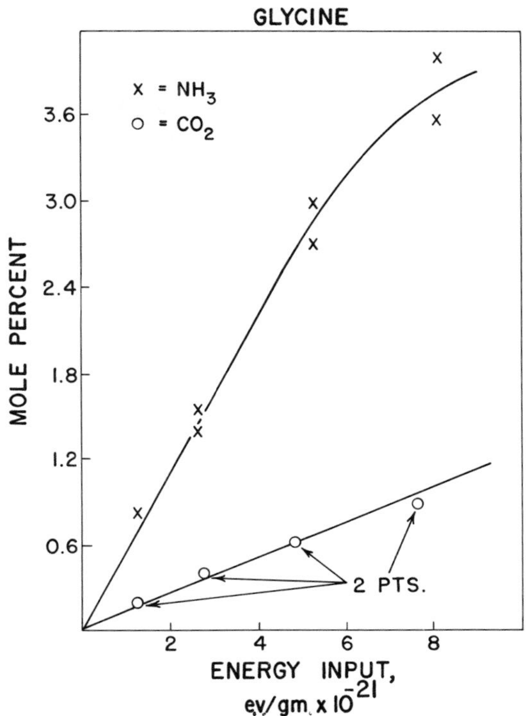

Figure 2. Yields of CO_2 and NH_3 for in vacuo *irradiated glycine*

Figure 3 is the same plot for alanine. The curves are all initially linear and the *G* values were calculated from this initial linear portion. Low deviations on the ammonia curves at the highest absorbed dose may reflect high decomposition of original amino acid. Amino acids with higher specific activities were used to determine $G(CO_2)$ at lower absorbed doses. These values are significantly lower as shown in Figure 4. The problem of impurity introduced by the radiation decomposition of the original material and its effect on measured *G* values confronts all workers in this area. For consistency and since these values have a much more reliable analytical basis, the high dose values will be used throughout. The results of interest are the relative *G* values in any case since absolute values are acknowledged to depend on dose.

It should be stressed that the $G(H_2)$ values in this paper arise from "dry" analyses of the gases released from the solid while the other represent "wet" analyses of product released upon dissolution. "Dry" results gave CO_2 in the largest yield though this corresponded to a $G(CO_2)$ of only 0.2 ± 0.1. When the mass spectral "dry" data are normalized to $G(CO_2) = 1$ the $G(H_2)$ value agrees approximately with Bregers and CO, CH_4, H_2O are also indicated as in Reference 1 but in less than 10% of the CO_2 yield. The NH_3 results from this "dry" study, however, are considerably lower with $G(NH_3) \leqslant 0.01$. Despite the large uncertainties it can be concluded that extensive trapping of gaseous products and or unstable products in chemical forms which could include radicals, imines, HCO_3^-, etc., exist. These products subsequently react when dissolved in water, to give the gaseous products. The magnitude of the quantitative uncertainties precludes a rational comparison of any significance based on these numbers and hence they will not be discussed. "Dry" hydrogen yields were, however, assumed to be quantitative.

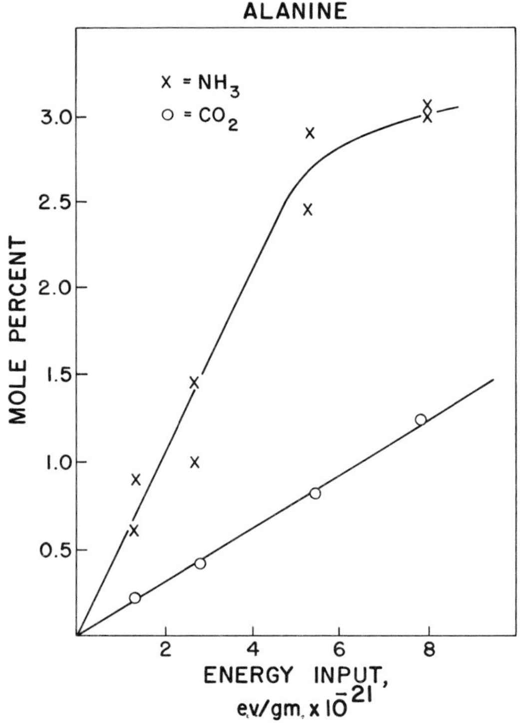

Figure 3. Yields of CO_2 and NH_3 for in vacuo *irradiated alanine*

Quantitative results for acetic and propionic acids and the appropriate α keto acids were not obtained in this study, but their presence was qualitatively indicated and material balance was used to approximate their G value sum as 5 for glycine and 4 for alanine.

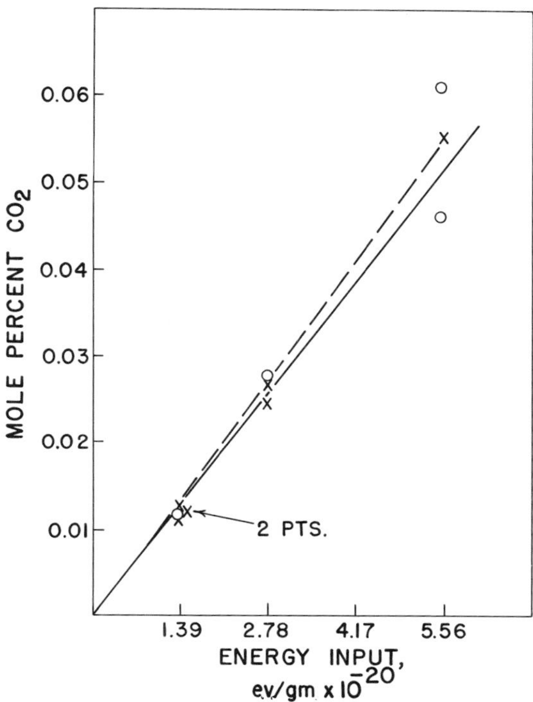

Figure 4. Yields of CO_2 for in vacuo *irradiated glycine and alanine*

×—*Alanine, $G(CO_2) = 0.63$*
○—*Glycine, $G(CO_2) = 0.75$*

Table I. Decomposition Products and G Values for *In Vacuo* Irradiated Glycine and Alanine

	Glycine				*Alanine*	
	Solid		*Aqueous*		*Solid*	*Aqueous*
	γ[a]	α[b]	γ[c]	α[d]	γ[a]	γ[e]
G(−M)	−6	—	—	—	−5	—
$G(H_2)$	0.1	0.3	2.0	—	0.5	1.1
$G(CO_2)$	1.02	1	0.90	—	0.89	0.59
$G(NH_3)$	4.3	0.2	4.0	1.7	3.3	4.5
$G(RNH_2)$	1	—	0.19	0.24	2	0.17
G(Σ acids)	5[c]	—	3.6	—	4[f]	3.0

[a] This work.
[b] Ref. 1 normalized to $G(CO_2) = 1$. Breger reported values as Volume% with CO_2 = 55.8%.
[c] Ref. 8
[d] Ref. 10.
[e] Ref. 16.
[f] Numbers deduced from material balance requirement.

A compilation of the results from this study for the various products of glycine and alanine gamma irradiated *in vacuo* are listed in Table I, along with corresponding α irradiated glycine values and aqueous solution yields as indicated. It is worth noting that the α irradiated glycine values tabulated result from conversion of Bregers reported volume % values and normalization to a $G(CO_2)$ value of 1. This data of course does not include gaseous products trapped, adsorbed, or resulting from dissolution of other species.

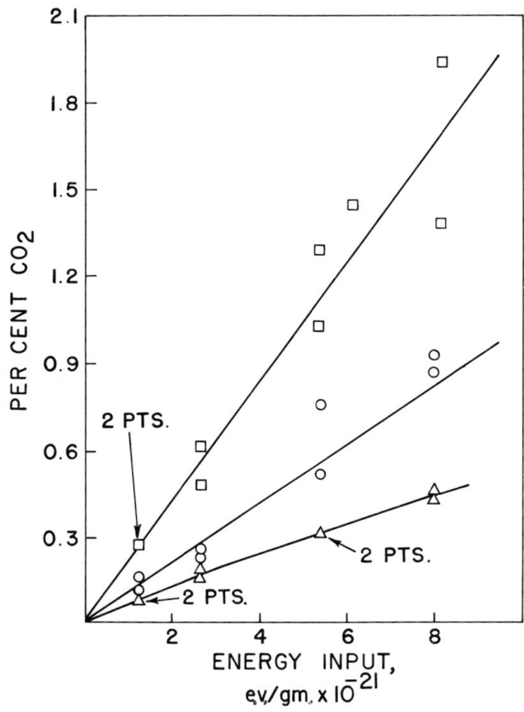

Figure 5. Yields of CO_2 for in vacuo *irradiated glycine salts*

□—*rubidium glycinate*
○—*potassium glycinate*
△—*sodium glycinate*

Figure V shows the amounts of CO_2 produced from the alkali metal salts as a function of dose. $G(CO_2)$ values obtained for these glycine salts and corrected for electron density are sodium glycinate, 0.43; potassium glycinate, 0.54; and rubidium glycinate, 0.91.

Discussion

Aqueous work (*8, 9, 10, 11, 16, 21*) has permitted deduction of principal stoichiometric relationships as well as a satisfactory reaction sequence for *in vacuo* irradiated amino acids. Comparison of the results from aqueous and solid state radiation chemistry is not a straightforward matter to be anticipated *a priori*, however, since in the aqueous work only amine and carbon dioxide were postulated to result from direct action whereas NH_3, H_2, acids, and additional CO_2 were products of secondary reactions involving aqueous species H°, OH°, and H_2O_2. It might be pointed out that effects observed in this study must represent a combination of radical degradations and pure direct radiation chemistry effects. Most solid amino acids saturate with free radicals at doses of $\sim 10^6$ rads (*7*) whereas the results discussed result from doses of 10^7–10^8 rads. Garrison (*3*) modified Maxwell's earlier scheme to include reactions of the hydrated electron; the reactions of an electron also can take place in the solid state. As is seen from Table I, gamma yields of NH_3 in the solid state are in fair agreement with aqueous values. As earlier noted, the solid state NH_3 values result from "wet" analyses and hence one concludes that regardless of pathway and possibly differing water unstable intermediates the final decomposition results are surprisingly close. Precautions were not taken to exclude oxygen from the "wet" analyses and the data of Maxwell *et al.* obtained by irradiation of oxygen saturated aqueous solutions (*10*) gave a $G(NH_3)$ of 4.3 also. The CO_2 yields are seen to be similar though amine yields differ significantly. Since amine yields *in aquo* are extremely small, the relative importance of primary effects, reflected by this yield, *vs.* secondary effects is obvious.

The following mechanistic scheme is therefore proposed based upon the ideas suggested by Garrison (*3*), modified and supplemented by Tolbert (*19*) to explain solid state complexities and consistent with the concepts introduced by Sinclair and Hanna (*17*).

$$RCHN^{+}H_3CO_2^{-} \rightsquigarrow (RCHN^{+}H_3CO_2^{-})^{\circ +} + e^{-} \qquad (1)$$

$$\rightsquigarrow R\overset{\circ}{C}N^{+}H_3CO_2^{-} + H^{\circ} \qquad (2)$$

$$(RCHN^{+}H_3CO_2^{-})^{\circ +} \xrightarrow{\text{fast}} R\overset{\circ}{C}HN^{+}H_3 + CO_2 \qquad (2)$$

$$e^{-} + RCHN^{+}H_3CO_2^{-} \rightarrow NH_3 + R\overset{\circ}{C}HCO_2^{-} \qquad (3a)$$

$$H^{\circ} + RCHN^{+}H_3CO_2^{-} \rightarrow NH_4^{+} + R\overset{\circ}{C}HCO_2^{-} \qquad (3b)$$

$$\rightarrow H_2 + R\overset{\circ}{C}N^{+}H_3CO_2^{-}$$

$$RCHN^{+}H_3 + RCHN^{+}H_3CO_2^{-} \rightarrow RCH_2N^{+}H_3 + R\overset{\circ}{C}N^{+}H_3CO_2^{-} \qquad (4)$$

$$\mathrm{R\dot{C}HCO_2^- + RCHN^+H_3CO_2^- \rightarrow RCH_2CO_2^- + R\mathring{C}N^+H_3CO_2^-} \quad (5)$$

plus radical combination and disproportionation reactions.

Without inclusion of radical combination and disproportionation reactions material balance can not be employed to verify or predict G values. Occurrence of radical reactions to regenerate amino acids is clearly implied, for example, since $G(-\mathrm{M})$ determined $= -6$ for glycine while summing appropriate preceding reactions would lead to a value of -14.1. Available data unfortunately cannot present a complete picture but this goal must await future results.

It has come to the authors' attention that data cited by Maxwell (*11*) indicate that Reaction 5 does not occur in aqueous solution. Disproportionation reactions

$$\mathrm{NH_2\dot{C}HCOOH + CH_2COOH \rightarrow NHCHCOOH + CH_3COOH} \quad (6)$$

and

$$\mathrm{2NH_2\dot{C}HCOOH \rightarrow NHCHCOOH + NH_2CH_2COOH} \quad (7)$$

have been suggested instead but these results may not disprove the possibility of Reaction 5 in the solid state.

The results for the alkali metal salts further indicate similarity in principal decomposition mechanisms for these examples. These results of course do not prove the mechanism. Note, however, the trend in the alkali metal salts toward greater decomposition descending the periodic column. This trend corresponds to a metallic ion decrease in electronegativity or charge density and suggests a correlation between radiation stability and electron density on the oxygen atom. Such a correlation and relationship to theory of the primary radiation event in solid state irradiations has been treated in a previous article (*5*).

The lower $G(CO_2)$ values at very low radiation levels (Figures 2, 3, and 4) are difficult to explain. Decarboxylation by radical–radical reactions suggested by comparison with saturation of EPR signals is a possibility. Recent work by Tolbert and Krinks (*20*) on the decarboxylation of phenylalanine *in vacuo* and in H_2S shows no change in G values and does not indicate such a mechanism. Another possible explanation for higher $G(CO_2)$ values at higher doses is radiation decarboxylation of intermediate species produced by the radiation decomposition process.

Acknowledgments

W. Carl Gottschall, Jr. would like to acknowledge support from a University of Colorado Fellowship, a Du Pont Teaching Fellowship, and an NIH Predoctoral Fellowship in successive years during which the research was performed.

Literature Cited

(1) Breger, I. A., *J. Phys. Chem.* **52,** 551 (1948).
(2) Conway, E., "Microdiffusion Analysis and Volumetric Error," Crosby Lockwood and Son, Ltd., London, 1957.
(3) Garrison, W. M., *Radiation Res. Suppl.* **4,** 158 (1964).
(4) Ghosh, D. K., Whiffen, D. H., *Mol. Phys.* **2,** 285 (1959).
(5) Gottschall, W. C., Tolbert, B. M., *J. Phys. Chem.* **72,** 922 (1968).
(6) Henricksen, T., *Radiation Res.* **17,** 158 (1963).
(7) Kohnlein, W., Muller, A., *Phys. Med. Biol.* **6,** 599 (1962).
(8) Maxwell, C. R., Peterson, D. C., Sharpless, N. E., *Radiation Res.* **1,** 530 (1954).
(9) Maxwell, C. R., Peterson, D. C., White, W. C., *Radiation Res.* **2,** 431 (1955).
(10) Maxwell, C. R., Peterson, D. C., *J. Phys. Chem.* **36,** 935 (1959).
(11) Maxwell, C. R., *Radiation Res. Suppl.* **4,** 175(1964).
(12) Patten, F., Gordy, W., *Radiation Res.* **14,** 573 (1961).
(13) Rajewsky, V., Dose, K., *Z. Naturforsch.* **12b,** 384 (1957).
(14) Rossi, B., Staub, H., "Ionization Chambers and Counters," McGraw-Hill, New York, 1949.
(15) Russell, J., *J. Biol. Chem.* **156,** 457 (1945).
(16) Sharpless, N. E., Blair, A., Maxwell, C. R., *Radiation Res.* **2,** 135 (1955).
(17) Sinclair, J. W., Hanna, M. W., *J. Phys. Chem.* **71,** 84 (1967).
(18) Tolbert, B. M., Lemmon, R. L., *Radiation Res.* **3,** 52 (1955).
(19) Tolbert, B. M., *Proc. Symp. Prep. Storage Marked Molecules* (1st), J. Sirchis, ed., Brussels, 1964.
(20) Tolbert, B. M., Krinks, M. H., *Tech. Progr. Rept., At. Energy Comm.* **AT(11-1)-690,** October 14, 1967.
(21) Weeks, B. M., Garrison, W. M., *Radiation Res.* **9,** 291 (1958).
(22) Weiner, R. F., Koski, W. S., *J. Am. Chem. Soc.* **85,** 873 (1963).

RECEIVED January 2, 1968. This work was supported in part by contract U. S. Atomic Energy Commission, Contract No. AT(11-1)-690.

27

Ionization and Excitation in Peptide Radiolysis

WARREN M. GARRISON, MICHAEL E. JAYKO, MICHAEL A. J. RODGERS, HARVEY A. SOKOL, and WINIFRED BENNETT-CORNIEA

Lawrence Radiation Laboratory, University of California, Berkeley, Calif. 94720

Major chemical effects of γ-rays on simple peptides in the polycrystalline state, in the glassy state and in concentrated aqueous solutions lead to degradation of the peptide chain. Several different reaction modes are involved and these all yield amide-like products that readily hydrolyze to give ammonia. Major concomitant products include fatty acid, ketoacid and aldehyde. Studies of N*-acetylalanine glass containing added electron scavengers provide a measurement of the ionization yield,* $G_{e^-} \simeq 3$*. Conventional radical scavengers have relatively little effect on* $G(NH_3) \simeq 3.5$*. However, certain aromatic compounds effectively quench a major fraction of the (amide) ammonia yield. The evidence is that keto acid and aldehyde are formed from positive-ion intermediates while fatty acid and amide are derived through reactions involving excited (triplet) states.*

A major chemical effect of γ-rays on simple peptides such as the *N*-acylamino acids under oxygen-free conditions, both in the solid state and in concentrated aqueous solution, leads to formation of labile amide-like compounds which are readily degraded on mild hydrolysis to yield ammonia as a characteristic product. Several classes of nitrogen-deficient products are formed concomitantly with the ammonia. Earlier communications have discussed certain limited aspects of the radiolytic lability of simple peptides in the solid state and in concentrated solutions (*9*, *10*, *18*). The radiation chemistry of these systems is more complex than that involved in the radiolysis of simple peptides in dilute oxygen-free aqueous solution under which conditions main-chain degradation is of minor importance (*10*). In this paper we report detailed experimental evidence and specific formulations for a number of degradation modes that have been found to be induced directly through ionization and excitation of peptides in the polycrystalline state, in the glassy state, and in concentrated aqueous solution.

Experimental

Materials. The *N*-acetylamino acids were of reagent grade or of the highest purity available commercially (Cyclo Chemicals, K and K Laboratories, Mann Research Laboratories, Nutritional Biochemicals) and were recrystallized at least once from distilled water. Polyalanine (Yeda, M. W. 1700) was dialyzed against distilled water and lyophilized. Chloracetic acid (Eastman) was redistilled *in vacuo*. Other chemicals were of C.P. grade. Water from a Barnstead still was redistilled first from alkaline permanganate and then from phosphoric acid. The pH adjustments were made with NaOH or H_2SO_4.

SAMPLE PREPARATION AND IRRADIATION. To obtain acetylalanine glass, the polycrystalline free acid was dissolved to $\sim 2M$ in redistilled water and the solution was adjusted to pH 6.5 with NaOH. Ten-ml. aliquots were transferred to flat-bottomed cylindrical irradiation cells (2.5 cm. diam.) and water was slowly removed on the vacuum line. The solutions were kept at 0°C. during the dehydration. Under these conditions the water content gradually decreases over a period of 24 hours until a clear glass of composition $CH_3CONHCH(CH_3)COONa \cdot 2H_2O$ is obtained. Additional four to six hours pumping does not change the water mole-fraction appreciably. The samples were irradiated at 0°C. More dilute solutions were prepared in the ordinary way. The polycrystalline *N*-acetylamino acid RCONHCH(R)COOH, and the polyalanine were degassed by evacuation on the vacuum line for at least 24 hours prior to irradiation.

All samples were irradiated with ^{60}Co γ-rays at a dose-rate of 1.2×10^{18} e.v./gram/min. as determined by the Fricke dosimeter [$G(Fe^{3+}) = 15.5$, $\epsilon_{305} = 2180$ at 24°C.]. All yields are expressed as G values (molecules per 100 e.v. of absorbed energy). Energy deposition in the solids and concentrated solutions was taken to be proportional to electron density.

ANALYTICAL METHODS. Gaseous products were pumped off following complete dissolution of the irradiated solid in degassed water on the vacuum line; analysis was by mass spectrometry (Consolidated 120) and by gas-chromatography (Aerograph A90-P3).

For other analyses, the irradiated solids were dissolved in water under nitrogen in a glove box.

Free ammonia and amide ammonia were determined by modifying the micro-diffusion method of Conway (*6*); the diffusates were assayed by means of Nessler reagent. In the measurement of free ammonia, the samples were diluted three times with saturated K_2CO_3 solution in the outer compartment of the diffusion cell; recovery of ammonia in the acid compartment ($0.1N$ H_2SO_4) is complete in three hours. For total ammonia (free plus amide) the sample was made $2N$ in NaOH; the amide hydrolysis and ammonia transfer is complete in 24 hours. The necessary blank and standard runs were made in parallel.

The fatty acids were separated through lyophilization of the sample solution after acidification to 2*N* with H_2SO_4. Assay was by vapor-phase chromatography (Aerograph, 600 C). The polyalanine was dissolved in 2*N* H_2SO_4 (under N_2) and hydrolyzed 18 hours prior to lyophilization.

Carbonyl products were identified by paper chromatography of the 2,4-dinitrophenylhydrazones (*20*). The irradiated *N*-acetylalanine showed only pyruvic acid and acetaldehyde. These were determined quantitatively by the method of Johnson and Scholes (*13*) with minor modifications. Chloride ion was determined by the method of Luce *et al.* (*15*) after Hayon and Allen (*12*).

A colorimetric method (*8*) was used to set a limit on the yield of lactic acid.

Results and Discussion

The 100 e.v. yield for the radiolytic degradation of the peptide bond, as measured in terms of $G(NH_3)$ after mild hydrolysis, has been determined for a variety of aliphatic, aromatic and sulfur-containing amino acids in the *N*-acetyl form. These data are summarized in Table I. In the case of the aliphatic series, we note that the length of the side-chain has relatively little effect on the yield of main-chain degradation. The effect of the aromatic groups of acetylphenylalanine and of acetyltyrosine is to quench in part the yields of those reactions that lead to formation of amide ammonia. The sulfur moiety of methionine on the other hand appears to be relatively ineffective in quenching such reactions.

Table I. γ-ray Induced Degradation of Solid *N*-acetylamino Acids, $CH_3CONHCH(R)COOH$

N-acetyl Derivative[a]	*(R)*	$G(NH_3)$[b]
glycine	—H	2.68
alanine	$—CH_3$	3.4
α-aminobutyric acid	$—CH_2CH_3$	2.7
leucine	$—CH_2CH(CH_3)_2$	3.2
glutamic acid	$—CH_2CH_2COOH$	2.3
phenylalanine	$—CH_2(C_6H_5)$	0.8
tyrosine	$—CH_2(C_6H_4OH)$	1.6
methionine	$—CH_2CH_2SCH_3$	2.3

[a] *N*-acetyl-DL-amino acids were used with the exception of *N*-acetyl-L-glutamic acid.
[b] After hydrolysis.

As a preliminary step in this inquiry into the nature of the radiolytic processes that lead to degradation of the peptide chain, we have completed a detailed study of the reaction products formed in the γ-radiolysis of simple peptide derivatives of alanine, *viz* poly-DL-alanine and acetyl-DL-alanine polycrystalline. These data are summarized in Table II. We find that the major organic products in the order of decreasing yield are propionic acid, acetaldehyde, pyruvic acid, and lactic acid. The labile ammonia from acetylalanine, $G = 3.4$, is derived primarily from acetamide, $G = 2.8$, plus a small amount of free ammonia, $G = 0.6$.

Table II. Product Yields in the γ-Radiolysis of *N*-acetyl-DL-alanine and Poly-DL-alanine

	G	
Product	N-*acetylalanine*	*Polyalanine*
ammonia (total)	3.4	3.6
amide	2.8	3.1
free	0.6	0.5
propionic acid	1.4	1.8
pyruvic acid	0.4	~1
acetaldehyde	0.8	~0.4
lactic acid	≤0.2	—
acrylic acid	trace	—
hydrogen	0.40	0.45

Table III. Ammonia and Fatty Acid Yields in the γ-Radiolysis of Aliphatic N-Acetylamino Acid

	G	
N-acetylderivative	(NH_3)	(RCH_2COOH)
glycine	2.6	1.2
alanine	3.3	1.5
α-aminobutyric	2.7	1.9

The presently available data on product yields from other *N*-acetylamino acids is less complete although the limited data of Table III are consistent in showing for the aliphatic *N*-acetyl amino acids that the corresponding fatty acid represents the major nitrogen-deficient product.

From these studies of the concomitant organic products it is clear that the observed $G(NH_3)$ values represent the combined yield of a number of different modes of degradation of the peptide chain. And, before proceeding to detailed considerations of elementary processes, it is useful here to formulate working hypotheses as to the stoichiometry of these reactions. First of all we note that the maximal yields of lactic acid and of the carbonyl products, acetaldehyde and pyruvic acid from acetylalanine are obtained only after mild hydrolysis of the irradiated solid (2*N* HCl, 95°C., 90 minutes). The present chemical requirements are met by the stoichiometric relationships

$$RCONHCHR_2 \rightarrow \overset{\displaystyle NH}{\overset{\|}{R}}COCHR_2 \quad (1)$$

$$RCONHCHR_2 \rightarrow RCON{=}CR_2 + H_2(2H) \quad (2)$$

$$RCONHCHR_2 \rightarrow RCON{=}CHR + RH \quad (3)$$

The radiation-induced N–O shift represented by Equation 1 leads to formation of a labile imino ester which species is readily hydrolyzed to yield ammonia and the hydroxyacid, lactic acid

$$\overset{\displaystyle NH}{\overset{\|}{R}}COCHR_2 + H_2O \rightarrow RCOOH + NH_3 + R_2CHOH \quad (4)$$

The unsaturated products (dehydropeptides) of Equations 2 and 3 are labile and readily hydrolyze to yield amide plus pyruvic acid and acetaldehyde respectively (*11*)

$$RCON{=}CR_2 + H_2O \rightarrow RCONH_2 + R_2CO \quad (5)$$

$$RCON{=}CHR + H_2O \rightarrow RCONH_2 + RCHO \quad (6)$$

Acetyl α-aminobutyric acid yields α-ketobutyric acid and propionaldehyde in accord with the above formulation.

The formation of propionic acid as the principal organic product of the radiolysis of acetylalanine implies that direct main-chain cleavage is involved as the major decomposition mode. We tentatively define the stoichiometry of this cleavage in terms of

$$RCONHCHR_2 \rightarrow RCO\dot{N}H + \dot{C}HR_2 \quad (7)$$

$$RCO\dot{N}H + RCONHCHR_2 \rightarrow RCONH_2 + RCONH\dot{C}R_2 \quad (8)$$

$$\dot{C}HR_2 + RCONHCHR_2 \rightarrow CH_2R_2 + RCONH\dot{C}R_2 \quad (9)$$

where the radicals $RCONH\dot{C}R_2$ are long-lived and correspond to the radical species observed at room temperature by ESR measurements (*4*). On dissolution in water (oxygen-free) the α-carbon radicals $RCONH\dot{C}R_2$ undergo dimerization to yield α,α′-diaminosuccinic acid derivatives which are stable end-products (*10*). The formulation of Equations 7, 8, and 9 is intended only to convey the nature of the overall stoichiometry. Ionic and/or excited species are presumably involved as actual intermediates since caging effects in the solid phase would lead to preferential recombination of the radical pair of Equation 7. It is this question of the nature of the intermediates involved in the formation of amide and fatty acid that we now consider.

The initial radiation-induced step we represented in terms of the ionization

$$RCONHCHR_2 \xrightarrow{\sim} (RCONHCHR_2)^+ + e^- \quad (10)$$

Simple charge recombination may be envisaged as leading to dissociation of the N–C bond

$$e^- + (RCONHCHR_2)^+ \rightarrow RCO\dot{N}H^* + \dot{C}HR_2 \quad (11)$$

to give radicals with excess energy which would tend to favor the abstraction Reactions 8 and 9 in competition with radical recombination. Alternatively, the ion-molecule reaction

$$(RCONHCHR_2)^+ + RCONHCHR_2 \rightarrow (RCONH_2CH_2CHR_2)^+ + RCONH\dot{C}R_2 \quad (12)$$

which is of the type observed in other polar organic systems (*16*, *21*) may occur prior to the neutralization

$$e^- + (RCONH_2CHR_2) \rightarrow RCONH_2 + \dot{C}HR_2 \quad (13)$$

The other possibility of course is that the electron escapes the positive charge and reacts at a distance—*e.g.*,

$$e^- + (RCONH_2CH_2CHR_2)^+ \rightarrow RCONH^- + \dot{C}HR_2 \quad (14)$$

We note that the radiation-induced Step 10 followed by electron removal *via* any of Reactions 11, 13, and 14 leads to stoichiometry of Equations 7–9.

It is of interest to consider at this point the effects of added electron scavengers on the yield of main-chain rupture. Fortunately, for this purpose we have been able to prepare *N*-acetylalanine in the form of a clear glassy solid at room temperature. The glass has the composition $CH_3CONHCH(CH_3)COONa \cdot 2H_2O$, and gives product yields that are essentially the same as those obtained with the polycrystalline solid—*e.g.*, $G(NH_3) \simeq 3.4$, $G(\text{propionic}) = 1.6$, $G(\text{acetaldehyde}) = 0.8$ Chloracetate ion which has been shown to be an effective electron scavenger

$$e^- + RCl \rightarrow R + Cl^- \quad (15)$$

in other polar glasses (*3*) is soluble (as the sodium salt) in acetylalanine glass when prepared as described in the experimental part of this paper. We find that $G(Cl^-)$ increases with chloracetate concentration in the concentration range 1 to 10 mole percent as shown in Figure 1; the reciprocal-yield plot of Figure 2 gives a limiting value of $G(Cl^-) \simeq 3$ which value provides a measure of the yield for ion-pair production *via* Reaction 10 in the present system. At the same time there is but a small effect of added chloracetate on $G(NH_3)$ even under the condition in which $G(Cl^-)$ is maximal. The evidence is then that the electron-capture reactions of type 11, 13, and 14 do not represent major paths for cleavage of the N–C bond.

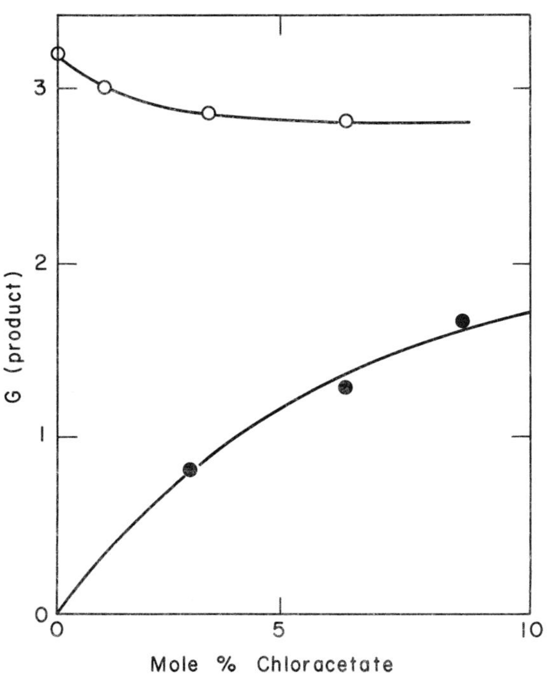

Figure 1. Ammonia (○) and chloride-ion (●) yields as a function of chloracetate concentration in acetylalanine glass, RCONHCH(R)COONa $2H_2O$

There would appear to be two remaining possibilities; (a) the positive ions formed in Reaction 10 undergo fragmentation, for example

$$(RCONHCHR_2)^+ \rightarrow RCONH^+ + \dot{C}HR_2 \quad (16)$$

$$RCONHCHR_2 + (RCONHCHR_2)^+ \rightarrow RCONH_2^+ + \dot{C}HR_2 + RCONH\dot{C}R_2 \quad (16a)$$

and/or (b) neutral excited species are formed through a process other than that of charge recombination and subsequently undergo unspecified chemistry to yield amide and propionic acid. To obtain information on the possible importance of these reaction modes, we have taken advantage of the fact that the acetylalanine glass $CH_3CONHCH(CH_3)COON_a$ ·

$2H_2O$ is miscible with water in all proportions. If direct energy-absorption in the peptide *via* Reaction 10 followed by the dissociation Reaction 16 is of importance, we could expect that the degradation yields would decrease with increasing water content of the system. The possibility that ionization in water

$$H_2O \rightsquigarrow H_2O^+ + e^- \qquad (17)$$

is followed by charge transfer—*e.g.*,

$$H_2O^+ + RCONHCHR_2 \rightarrow RCONH^+ + \dot{C}HR_2 + H_2O \qquad (18)$$

or

$$H_2O^+ + RCONHCHR_2 \rightarrow RCONH_2^+ + \dot{C}HR_2 + OH \qquad (18a)$$

would also be excluded at the higher water concentrations by virtue of the fast competing Reaction 14

$$H_2O^+ + H_2O \rightarrow H_3O^+ + OH. \qquad (19)$$

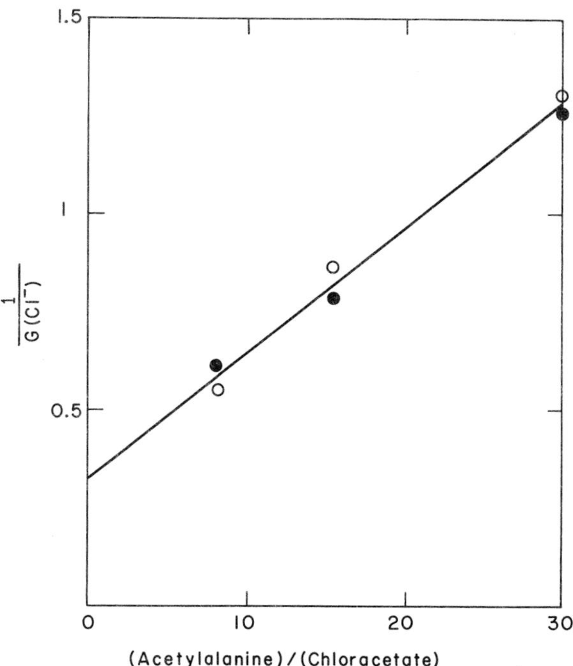

Figure 2. Reciprocal chloride-ion as a function of (acetylalanine)/(chloracetate) concentration ratio in the systems RCONHCH(R)COONa · $2H_2O$, (○); RCONHCH(R)COONa · $8H_2O$, (●)

The effects of added water on $G(NH_3)$ and G(propionic) from the sodium salt of acetylalanine are summarized in Figure 3. The ammonia yield which as we have noted is derived from a number of reaction modes shows but a small decrease, $\Delta G(NH_3) \sim 1$, as the acetylalanine concentration is decreased to $1M$. And, even more striking is the fact that the yield of the major organic product, propionic acid, is essentially independent of acetylalanine concentration over the entire range of Figure 3. Our tentative conclusion is then that cleavage of the N–C bond to yield propionic acid does not arise in the main from the positive-ion chemistry of Reactions 16, 16a, 18, and 18a.

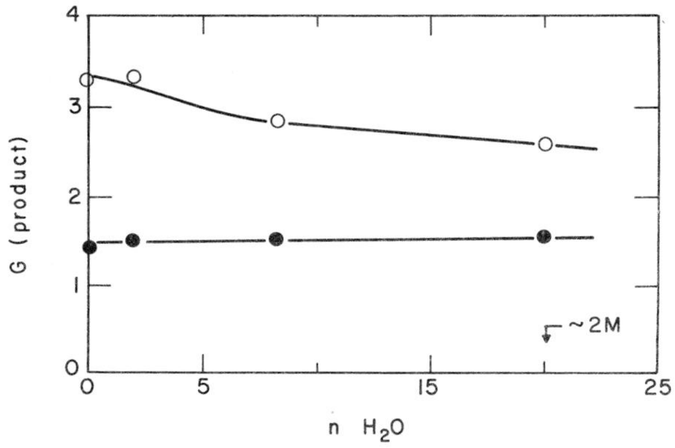

Figure 3. Effect of increasing water content on ammonia (○) and propionic acid (●) yields from acetylalanine in the system RCONHCH(R)COONa · nH₂O. Values at n = o are for polycrystalline acetylalanine, RCONHCH(R)COOH

On lowering the acetylalanine concentration from $1M$ to $0.1M$, G(propionic) drops to zero and $G(NH_3)$ decreases to 0.5; the chemistry of these dilute solutions is of a different nature as we have described elsewhere (*2, 10*).

Now, we have already noted on the basis of the chloracetate data of Figure 1, that electron capture *via* Reactions 11, 13, and 14 does not represent a major path for cleavage of the N–C bond in the case of the acetylalanine glass, $CH_3CONHCH(CH_3)$ $COON_a \cdot 2H_2O$. Similarly, we find that the quantitative scavenging of e^-_{aq} by chloracetate ion in $2M$ acetylalanine solution has relatively little effect on $G(NH_3)$ as shown by the data of Figure 4. And, we also observe from Figure 4 that the preferential removal of OH radicals by formate ion has essentially no effect on $G(NH_3)$ from the $2M$ solution.

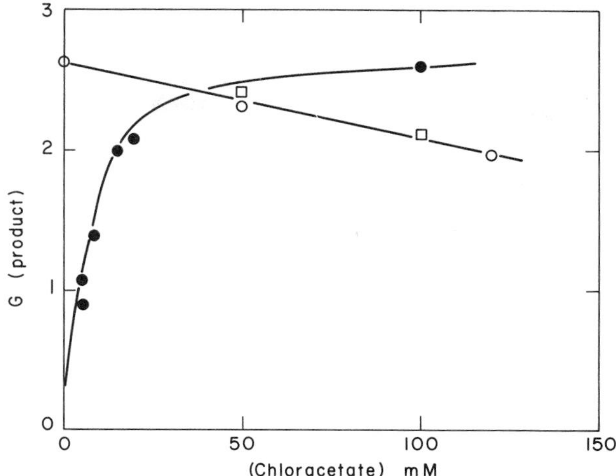

Figure 4. Ammonia (○) and chloride-ion (●) yields as a function of chloracetate concentration in 2M acetylalanine, pH 7. The points (□) represent ammonia yields in the presence of 0.5M and 1.0M formate ion [e^-_{aq} + chloracetate, k = 1.2 × $10^9 M^{-1}$ sec.$^{-1}$; e^-_{aq} + acetylamine (pH 7), k = 1.1 × $10^7 M^{-1}$ sec.$^{-1}$; OH + formate, k = $10^9 M^{-1}$ sec.$^{-1}$; OH + acetylalanine (pH 7), k = 2.5 × $10^8 M^{-1}$ sec.$^{-1}$ (Refs. 1, 18, 23)]

By a process of elimination, then, we come to the possibility that amide formation in these concentrated peptide solutions involves reactions of neutral excited species. Now, aromatic compounds are, of course, known to be effective scavengers of excited states providing the energy levels of the excited species are higher than those of the quencher (*22*). We do find that certain aromatic solutes such as naphthalenesulfonic acid, benzaldehyde, and benzoic acid at millimolar concentrations are remarkably effective in quenching the formation of amide ammonia in 2*M* acetylalanine. Typical data for naphthalenesulfonic acid are shown in Figure 5. We also find that phenol and benzenesulfonic acid are essentially without effect even at the higher concentrations. There is, of course, the possibility that the quenching of $G(NH_3)$ by naphthalenesulfonic acid, benzaldehyde, and benzoic acid involves simply the scavenging of an amide precursor *via* radical-addition to the benzene ring, for example

$$CH_3CO\dot{N}H + OH \rightarrow CH_3CONH\dot{O}H \qquad (20)$$

However, if this were the case both phenol and benzenesulfonic acid should also be effective. In fact, rates for radical addition to phenol are even faster than those for addition to benzaldehyde and benzoic acid (*1*).

We can only conclude from the present observations *in toto* that (a) a major fraction of the N–C fragmentation in these concentrated solutions does indeed arise from reactions of excited species and that (b) such reactions can be effectively quenched through excitation transfer to solutes such as naphthalenesulfonic acid benzaldehyde and benzoic acid. That benzenesulfonic acid and phenol are ineffective quenchers in the present system is not inconsistent with the fact that the energy levels (singlet *and* triplet) of these two benzene derivatives are somewhat higher than those of the effective quenchers. We note that the singlet-state levels of all the aromatics studied here (*5*) are well below the singlet-state level of the peptide bond (*19*). Hence, the fact that naphthalenesulfonic acid quenches while phenol does not would suggest we are dealing with a triplet-state of the peptide configuration. The reciprocal-yield plot of Figure 5 gives $G(NH_3) = G(\text{propionic}) = 1.6$ as the excitation yield in 2*M* acetylalanine.

Excitation of the peptide bond by low-energy electrons *via*

$$e^- + RCONHCHR_2 \rightarrow RCONHCHR_2^* + e^- \tag{21}$$

would be consistent with the present experimental requirements. A theoretical treatment of this mode of excitation for the general case has been given by Platzman (*17*). We envisage the chemistry of the excited state both in concentrated solution and in the solid systems to be of the form:

$$\begin{array}{ccc} R{-}\overset{\overset{\displaystyle O}{\|}}{C}{-}\underset{\underset{\displaystyle \vdots}{\underset{\displaystyle H}{|}}}{N}{-}CHR_2 & & R{-}\overset{\overset{\displaystyle O}{\|}}{C}{-}\dot{N}{-}CHR_2 \\ & \rightarrow & \\ R{-}\overset{\overset{\displaystyle O}{\|}}{C}{-}\underset{\underset{\displaystyle H}{|}}{N}{-}CHR_2^* & & R{-}\overset{\overset{\displaystyle HO}{|}}{C}{=}\underset{\underset{\displaystyle H}{|}}{N} + \cdot CHR_2 \end{array} \tag{22}$$

where $RCO\dot{N}CHR_2$ rearranges instantaneously to give the long-lived radical $RCONH\dot{C}R_2$. Since the radical products of Reaction 22 are formed at a distance, the effects of caging will be minimal. The over-all energy requirement for Reaction 22 is essentially that required for dissociation of the aliphatic N–C bond—*i.e.*, ~3 e.v. (*7*). We note that benzoic acid which is an effective quencher of $RCONHCHR_2^*$ has a triplet level at 3.4 e.v. (*22*).

If solid acetylalanine is irradiated at the temperature of liquid nitrogen, then the propionic acid is almost wholly quenched from

$G(\text{propionic})_{290°\text{K.}} = 1.6$ to $G(\text{propionic})_{77°\text{K.}} \leqslant 0.1$. The ammonia yield shows a corresponding drop from $G(NH_3)_{290°\text{K.}} = 3.2$ to $G(NH_3)_{77°\text{K.}} = 1.3$. We interpret this as evidence that an energy of activation is involved in Reaction 22. The yields of carbonyl products are unchanged at the lower temperature with $G(\text{carbonyl})_{77°\text{K.}} = G(NH_3)_{77°\text{K.}} = 1.3$. We suggest that the carbonyl products arise from positive ion precursors

$$RCONHCHR_2 \xrightarrow{\wedge\!\wedge} (RCONHCHR)^+ + R + e^- \quad (23)$$

$$RCONHCHR_2 \xrightarrow{\wedge\!\wedge} (RCONHCR_2)^+ + H + e^- \quad (24)$$

which species undergo proton stripping to yield the dehydropeptide derivatives referred to in Equations 2 and 3.

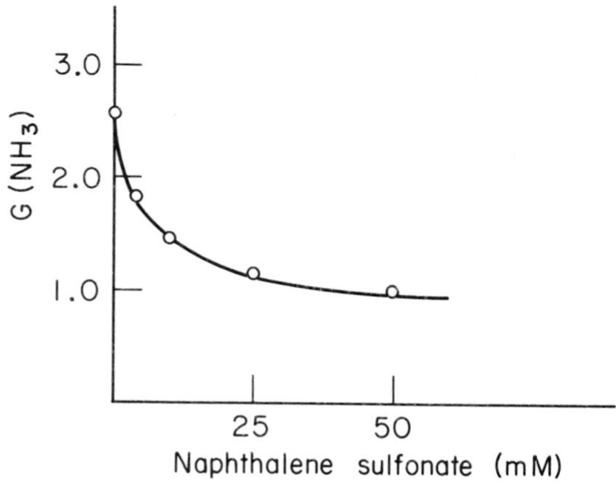

Figure 5. Effect of naphthalenesulfonic acid on ammonia yields from 2M acetylalanine, pH 7

We conclude, then, from these studies of elementary processes in peptide radiolysis that (a) a number of reaction modes are of importance in the radiolytic degradation of the peptide chain, (b) charge recombination does not appear to be involved as a step in any of the major reaction sequences that lead to main-chain degradation, (c) the electron escapes the positive ion and can be chemically trapped by appropriate electron scavengers, (d) positive-ion chemistry leads to the formation of carbonyl products, (e) neutral excited species appear to be major intermediates in the radiation-induced cleavage of the N–C bond to yield amide and fatty acid. Although this is not the place to speculate on the radiation-biological implications of particulars (a) to (e), we would, nevertheless, point out that finding (e) suggests that excitation scavengers as well as radical scavengers can be of importance in mitigating the biological effects of ionizing radiations.

Literature Cited

(1) Anbar, M., Neta, P., *Intern. J. Appl. Radiation Isotopes* **17,** 493 (1967).
(2) Atkins, H. L., Bennett-Corniea, W., Garrison, W. M., *J. Phys. Chem.* **71,** 772 (1967).
(3) Ayscough, P. B., Collins, R. G., Dainton, F. S., *Nature* **205,** 965 (1965).
(4) Box, N. C., Freund, H. G., Lilga, K., "Free Radicals in Biological Systems," M. Blois *et al.*, ed., Academic Press, New York, N. Y., 1961.
(5) Calvert, J. G., Pitts Jr., J. N., "Photochemistry," John Wiley and Sons, New York, N. Y., 1967.
(6) Conway, E. J., "Microdiffusion Analysis," Crosby Lockwood and Sons, Ltd., London, 1962.
(7) Cottrell, T. L., "The Strengths of Chemical Bonds," Butterworths Scientific Publications, London, 1954.
(8) Feigel, F., "Spot Tests in Organic Analysis," Elsevier Publishing Co., New York, N. Y., 1956.
(9) Garrison, W. M., Jayko, M. E., Weeks, B. M., Sokol, H. A., Bennett-Corniea, W., *J. Phys. Chem.* **71,** 1546 (1967).
(10) Garrison, W. M., Weeks, B. M., *Radiation Res. Suppl.* **4,** 148 (1964).
(11) Greenstein, J. P., Winitz, M., "Chemistry of Amino Acids," John Wiley and Sons, Inc., New York, N. Y., 1961.
(12) Hayon, E., Allen, A. O., *J. Phys. Chem.* **65,** 2181 (1961).
(13) Johnson, G. R. A., Scholes, G., *Ind. Eng. Chem.* **79,** 217 (1954).
(14) Lampe, F. W., Field, F. H., Franklin, J. L., *J. Am. Chem. Soc.* **79,** 6132 (1957).
(15) Luce, N. E., Denice, E. C., Akerlund, F. E., *Ind. Eng. Chem.* **15,** 365 (1943).
(16) Myron, J. J., Freeman, G. R., *Can. J. Chem.* **43,** 381 (1965).
(17) Platzman, R. L., *Radiation Res.* **21** (1955).
(18) Rogers, M. A. J., Garrison, W. M., *U. S. At. Energy Commission* **UCRL 17886,** October 1967 (*J. Phys. Chem.* **72,** 758 (1968)).
(19) Saidel, L. J., *Arch. Biochem. Biophys.* **54,** 184 (1955).
(20) Weeks, B. M., Garrison, W. M., *Radiation Res.* **9,** 291 (1958).
(21) Ward, J. A., Harrill, W. H., *J. Am. Chem. Soc.* **87,** 1853 (1965).
(22) Wilkinson, F., *Adv. Photochem.* **3,** 241 (1964).
(23) Willix, R. L. S., Garrison, W. M., *U. S. At. Energy Commission* **UCRL-17285,** November 1966 (*Radiation Res.* **32,** 452 (1967)).

RECEIVED December 26, 1967. This work was performed under the auspices of the U. S. Atomic Energy Commission.

28

Pulse Radiolysis Studies of Reactions of Primary Species in Water with Nucleic Acid Derivatives

C. L. GREENSTOCK, M. NG, and J. W. HUNT

Department of Medical Biophysics, University of Toronto, Toronto, Canada

Bimolecular rate constants have been measured for the reactions of the solvated electron (e^-_{aq}) and the hydroxyl free radical (·OH) with a variety of nucleic acid derivatives. In neutral solution, the e^-_{aq} reaction rates are diffusion controlled and the ·OH reaction rates are only slightly lower. For uracil, the e^-_{aq} reactivity is reduced as the pH is increased partly because of the electrostatic repulsion from the negatively charged molecule and partly because of a tautomeric structural change. The ·OH reactivity shows no distinct changes around the pK_a value. The sites of attack of e^-_{aq} are probably the carbonyl groups in pyrimidines and the imidazole ring in purines. The primary site of attack of ·OH is the 5,6 double bond in pyrimidines. The reactivity per nucleotide is considerably reduced in long-chain polynucleotides, the effect increasing with chain length.

When a beam of ionizing radiation hits living cells, important cell functions may be altered or destroyed. In particular, the replication mechanisms of the cell which are associated with their genetic material, deoxyribonucleic acid (DNA), are particularly radiosensitive. In order to appreciate fully the biological implications of this damage, further understanding at the chemical level is needed. For these reasons, we are undertaking a detailed study of the reactions of the primary reactive species in water (e^-_{aq}, ·OH) with nucleic acid derivatives.

A large number of papers have been published in which the reactivity of e^-_{aq} and ·OH radicals with organic compounds of biological interest have been studied in an attempt to determine the controlling factors in such reactions (*2, 7, 10, 11, 17, 21, 23*). In most cases, e^-_{aq} acts like a nucleophile, attacking positions of low electron density. For example, electron withdrawing groups such as $>C=O$, $-C(=O)OH$ and $-C\equiv N$ increase the reactivity, while H, OH, CH_3, and NH_2 groups reduce it. While unsubstituted heterocyclic compounds are fairly unreactive, the introduction of carbonyl or imidazole groups greatly increases the reactivity. Another factor affecting the e^-_{aq} reactivity, the charge on the solute molecule, has been investigated by Gordon *et al.* (*14*) and Dainton *et al.* (*12*) and in organic molecules by Braams (*10, 11*).

The observations of Hart *et al.* (*17, 18*) and Scholes *et al.* (*23*) have shown that both the purine and pyrimidine bases of nucleic acids react rapidly with both e^-_{aq} and $\cdot OH$. In this paper, the reaction rates of these primary species with a variety of nucleic acid derivatives have been measured under different chemical conditions in an attempt to understand the factors responsible for variations in their reactivities.

Experimental

A 30 Mev. linear accelerator producing 0.25-2μsec. electron pulses delivering a dose per pulse of 50–500 rads was used as the radiation source. A Sylvania DXM 250 watt quartz iodide lamp or a Philips SP 1000, 1000 watt high pressure mercury arc was used as the analyzing light source. The light was passed four times through a 6 cm. long detection cell and was beamed by 8-inch diameter mirrors to an adjacent room where the desired signal was detected by a Bausch and Lomb 50 cm. focal length monochromator and Dumont 7664Q photomultiplier. The output was displayed on a Hewlett Packard 180A oscilloscope and photographed. Upon opening the camera shutter, the oscilloscope was triggered four times to record on the same photograph the zero level, the transmitted light level, and also another base line and the absorption signal at higher sensitivity (*15*).

The linac pulse intensity was monitored with a secondary emission monitor (*19, 26*) which has the same aperture size as the irradiation cell.

Each rate constant determination represents the average of three decay curves which were read from the photographs and converted into digital form by an Oscar K77 curve reader. The rate constants and confidence limits were calculated from these data by making a regression fit to an exponential decay with the assistance of a General Electric Data Net computer.

The compounds, cytosine, thymine, uracil, uridine, uridylic acid (UMP), uridylyl-(3′ → 5′)-uridine (UpU), oligouridylic acid (oligo U), adenine, and adenosine (Calbiochem. Inc.) were chromatographically pure. The substituted pyrimidines and purines, 1,3-dimethyl uracil, 2,4-diethoxypyrimidine, dihydrouracil, and imidazole were obtained from Sigma Chemical Corp. and Cyclochemical Corp. The CH_3OH (Fisher) was spectroscopic grade and KCNS, H_2O_2, $HClO_4$, K_2HPO_4, KH_2PO_4,

Na_2CO_3, $NaHCO_3$, NaOH, and Na_2SO_4 were "AnalaR" grade (British Drug Houses). All these compounds were used without further purification.

The solutions were prepared using triply distilled water obtained from a quartz still based upon a design by K. Schmidt (*22*). Since the reaction rates of the compounds studied were very dependent on pH, the pH was stabilized by comparatively low concentrations ($0.5 \times 10^{-3}M$) of unreactive inorganic buffers. A list of the buffers used to control the pH are shown in Table I, together with typical e^-_{aq} lifetimes of the deoxygenated matrices (blank solutions missing only the reactive solutes). To eliminate changes in reactivity as a function of the ionic environment, the e^-_{aq} studies were done with solutions maintained at 0.1 ionic strength with the unreactive salt, Na_2SO_4. Methanol ($10^{-2}M$) was added as an ·OH scavenger, and the solutions were deoxygenated by bubbling for 15 minutes with extra high purity nitrogen (Ohio Chemical Corporation), using Hart's syringe technique (*16*).

When the e^-_{aq} reaction rates were being measured, the concentration of solute was chosen to give an e^-_{aq} half-life of approximately 1 μsec. Hence, at low pH values, the correction to the absolute rate constant because of the finite e^-_{aq} lifetime in the matrix is as large as 20%, but this falls to below 1% at the highest pH (*see* Table I).

Table I. Buffers Used to Stabilize pH for e^-_{aq} Measurements and Typical Half-Lives ($\tau 1/2$) Observed in These Deoxygenated Matrices Containing $10^{-2}M$ Methanol, $5 \times 10^{-4}M$ Buffer and Na_2SO_4 to 0.1 Ionic Strength

Buffer	*pH Range*	$e_{aq}\tau 1/2$ (*μsec.*) *of Matrix*
KH_2PO_4	5–6	5–10
K_2HPO_4	6–8	10–20
Na_2CO_3	8–9	20–30
$NaHCO_3$	9–11	30–50
NaOH	11–13	50–150

Because the ·OH absorption spectrum is in the ultraviolet region of the spectrum (*28*), where all nucleic acid derivatives absorb strongly, ·OH reaction rates in these experiments were measured using a modification of the competition method of Adams *et al.* (*1, 2, 3, 4, 5*). In this method, the competitive solute (CNS^-) forms a long lived species (*P*) absorbing at 500 mμ following its reaction with ·OH at a rate k_2. The solute (*S*) competes with CNS^- for ·OH at a rate $k_{\cdot OH}$ reducing the yield of P (Reactions 1 and 2).

$$\cdot OH + S \xrightarrow{k_{\cdot OH}} \text{non-absorbing product} \quad (1)$$

$$\cdot OH + CNS^- \xrightarrow{k_2} \text{absorbing product } (P) \quad (2)$$

In the absence of solute, for a given dose, the optical density of the absorbing species is OD_o. When solute is added, the final optical density

(OD) of the absorbing species is reduced by the fraction of ·OH radicals which now react with the solute. This change in absorption is given by:

$$OD_o/OD = 1 + \frac{k_{\cdot OH}[S]}{k_2[CNS^-]} \quad (3)$$

If k_2 is known, the value of $k_{\cdot OH}$ may be determined from the optical density change.

In studying reactions with ·OH an e^-_{aq} scavenger must be added to eliminate interference from e^-_{aq} addition products. Nitrous oxide is often used for this purpose, but at the high concentrations of CNS^- used in these experiments, unusual scavenging kinetics were observed, suggesting that the intermediates N_2O^- or O^- might be interfering with the reaction. In these experiments, an alternative electron scavenger, H_2O_2, was used. The H_2O_2 concentration must be low enough to prevent the reaction of ·OH with H_2O_2 from competing with Reactions 1 and 2. Alternatively, it must be high enough to ensure efficient e^-_{aq} scavenging. The important reactions which must be considered in the CNS^- competition are:

$$\cdot OH + S \xrightarrow{k_{\cdot OH}} \text{products} \quad (4)$$

$$\cdot OH + CNS^- \xrightarrow{k_2} CNS\cdot + OH^- \quad (5)$$

$$CNS\cdot + CNS^- \underset{k_4}{\overset{k_3}{\rightleftarrows}} (CNS)^-_2 \quad (6)$$

$$e^-_{aq} + H_2O_2 \xrightarrow{1.4 \times 10^{10}} \cdot OH + OH^- \quad (7)$$

$$e^-_{aq} + S \xrightarrow{\sim 10^{10}} \text{products} \quad (8)$$

$$e^-_{aq} + O_2 \xrightarrow{1.9 \times 10^{10}} O_2^- \quad (9)$$

$$\cdot OH + H_2O_2 \xrightarrow{2.2 \times 10^{7}} HO_2\cdot + H_2O \quad (10)$$

For ·OH reaction studies, aerated solutions containing $2 \times 10^{-3}M$ KCNS and $10^{-2}M$ H_2O_2 were used. At the highest concentrations ($4 \times 10^{-3}M$) of a typical solute, uracil, 30% of the e^-_{aq} react with uracil, 70% with H_2O_2, and only 1% with the oxygen present in aerated solutions (Reactions 7, 8, and 9). The theoretically expected ·OH yield should consist of almost equal contributions from the primary yield and the component arising from the conversion of e^-_{aq} to ·OH through Reaction 7. However, in the presence of $4 \times 10^{-3}M$ uracil, the ·OH yield is reduced to 85% of the expected yield by Reaction 8. For all uracil concentrations, the reaction of ·OH with H_2O_2 (Reaction 10) only reduces the ·OH yield by 1–2% and is, therefore in significant in the competition for ·OH compared with uracil and CNS^-.

A correction was applied for this reduction in ·OH yield to each point in the competition plot. If this correction were not applied, it would lead at the worst to a 17% overestimation in the absolute rate constant for ·OH attack on uracil.

The transient absorption spectra obtained immediately after the pulse from aerated KCNS solutions at pH 2, 7 and 13.5 respectively, are shown in Figure 1. These spectra are in good agreement with those reported by Adams *et al.* (*3, 4, 5*). Both H_2O_2 and N_2O are found to double the yield of the absorbing species (*3, 4, 5*) as would be expected from Reaction 7. This spectrum was originally thought to be caused by the CNS· radical (Reaction 5), but recently Baxendale *et al.* (*9*) have suggested that the spectra are in fact caused by $(CNS)_2^-$ formed by Reaction 6.

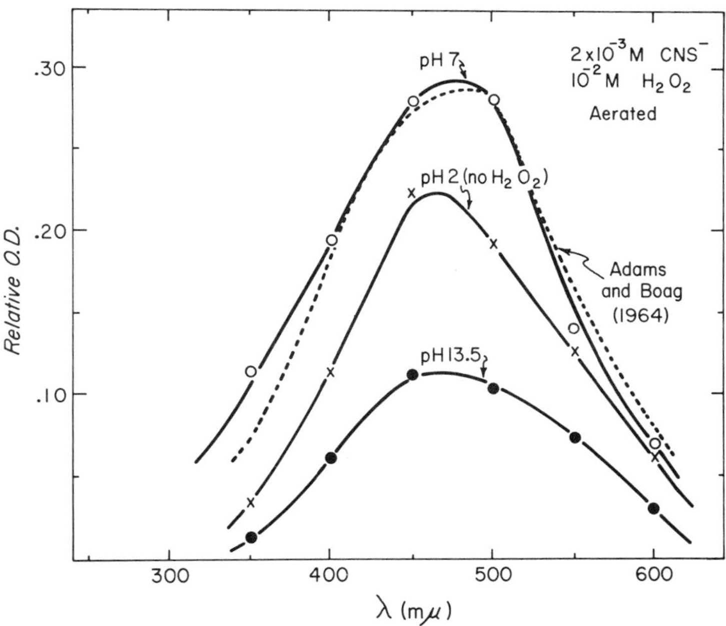

*Figure 1. Transient absorptions in aerated 2 × 10^{-3}*M *CNS^- solutions containing 10^{-2}*M *H_2O_2 at pH values of 2, 7, and 13.5. The dotted curve shows the absorption spectrum obtained by Adams* et al. (3) *normalized to the curve obtained at pH 7. Dose per pulse approximately 500 rads*

The direct observation of ·OH reaction rates by the disappearance of the 5, 6 double bond in uracil was also used in these experiments. This method has many advantages since it is not subject to the uncertainties which plague the competition experiments. However, such a direct method is complicated by the necessity to use a relatively high concentration of uracil (about $10^{-4}M$) so that the reaction is fast, while obtaining a reasonable light transmission in the region of the 5, 6 double bond absorption ($\epsilon_{259} = 8.20 \times 10^3 M^{-1}$ cm.$^{-1}$). To accomplish this, two light passes through a 5 mm. detection cell were used. Scattered light corrections under these conditions were less than 10%. In addition, a large radiation pulse (1–4 Krad) was used to change a measurable fraction (about 10%) of the uracil in each pulse. Dark current from the linac, which might have reduced the concentration of unreacted uracil, was eliminated by adding a pneumatically operated block in the beam line which moved out of the way 1/2 second before the pulse. The samples were changed after each pulse by a remotely-controlled flow system.

Several matrices were tried for the direct ·OH reaction technique, but oxygenated, deoxygenated, and N_2O bubbled solutions showed absorbing species in the 250 to 270 mμ region, so no clear-cut measurements of the 5,6 double bond disappearance could be made. Fortunately, however, no interfering species were present at 270 mμ in solutions of H_2O_2 and uracil ($\epsilon_{270} = 5.6 \times 10^3 M^{-1}$ cm.$^{-1}$). At a concentration of $0.5 \times 10^{-3}M$ H_2O_2, e^-_{aq} are rapidly scavenged and converted to ·OH, and well defined traces may be obtained showing increases in light transmission caused by ·OH attack of the 5,6 double bond.

Results and Discussion

Solvated Electron Reaction Rates. Purines and Pyrimidines. The reaction rates of e^-_{aq} with purines and pyrimidines at neutral pH are shown in Table II. All are very reactive, the reaction rates being close to diffusion controlled. However, the pyrimidine cytosine, which has an amino group at the C–4 position, is somewhat less reactive than thymine and uracil which have carbonyl groups at this position. Adenine, which also has an amino group in this position, has a very high reactivity, but this is probably because of the presence of the positively charged imidazole ring.

Also in Table II are listed the reaction rates of e^-_{aq} with a series of compounds having similar substituents or structural groups to the purines and pyrimidines. Benzene ($ke^-_{aq} = 1.4 \times 10^7 M^{-1}$ sec.$^{-1}$) is very unreactive, but the introduction of a heterocyclic nitrogen into the benzene ring increases the reactivity to $10^9 M^{-1}$ sec.$^{-1}$.

Introduction of carbonyl groups onto carbons 2 and 4, brings the reactivity of the resultant compound, uracil, up to that of a diffusion controlled reaction ($1.5 \times 10^{10} M^{-1}$ sec.$^{-1}$). In benzene derivatives, it has been shown (7) that adding ·OH groups to benzene does not increase the reactivity, but adding two carbonyl groups to form benzoquinone increases the reactivity appreciably to $1.3 \times 10^9 M^{-1}$ sec.$^{-1}$. When the 5,6 double bond in uracil is saturated to form dihydrouracil, a three-fold decrease in reactivity occurs. This suggests that the presence of the 5,6 double bond is at least partly necessary for the uracil to show high reactivity. However, the high reactivity of cyclohexanone (0.8×10^{10})

suggests that other changes in the dihydrouracil molecule may be more important. All these observations point to the carbonyl groups of the pyrimidine molecule as the most reactive sites.

In purines, such as adenine (*see* Table II), an imidazole ring is attached to a pyrimidine ring. Imidazole itself is reactive, but less reactive than the purine molecule. This suggests that the high reactivity of purines is caused by e^-_{aq} attack on the imidazole ring, or by the inductive effect of the imidazole group on the pyrimidine ring.

More detailed studies with substituted purines and pyrimidines at different pH values confirm the above findings. Figure 2 shows the rate constants as a function of pH as well as the ionizable groups in uracil and uridine and their pK_a values. As the pH is raised above each pK_a and the molecules become negatively charged, the e^-_{aq} reaction rates fall. This is to be expected because of the electrostatic repulsion between the negatively charged molecule and the negatively charged e^-_{aq}.

From the slope of the curve at pH 12.5, it can be seen that the reactivity is not so drastically changed by ionization of the ribose sugar in uridine as it is by the ionization of the pyrimidine ring.

The Debye equation (*13*) for a diffusion controlled reaction predicts approximately a twofold decrease in reactivity of e^-_{aq} upon ionization of the molecule being attacked. (In the Debye equation:

$$k = 4\pi \frac{(r_1 + r_2)}{1000} (D_1 + D_2)\, N \left\{ \frac{Z_1 Z_2 e^2}{(r_1 + r_2)} \epsilon kT \Bigg/ \left(\exp\left[\frac{Z_1 Z_2 e^2}{(r_1 + r_2)} \epsilon kT \right] - 1 \right) \right\}$$

The values of $r_1 = 3A.$ and $r_2 = 3A.$ were used as the encounter radii of e^-_{aq} and uracil respectively, and the values of $D_1 = 4.7 \times 10^{-5}$ cm.^{2} sec.$^{-1}$ and $D_2 << D_1$ were used as their diffusion constants. A dielectric constant (ϵ) of 78 was used for H_2O. Using these values, the change in reactivity predicted in going from a neutral to a singly charged molecule is 1.9. The Debye equation only applies for zero ionic strength and should be modified for an ionic strength of 0.1. It has been observed that the rate constant for e^-_{aq} attack of ionized uracil is almost independent of ionic strength so no correction was applied.) The decrease in reactivity on ionizing the ribose sugar is close to this twofold value but the decrease upon ionizing the pyrimidine ring is much larger (a factor of 5). In order to explain this large change in reactivity occurring when one carbonyl group on the pyrimidine ring is ionized, a series of substituted pyrimidines were investigated. It was reasoned that if the negative charge produced only a twofold decrease in reactivity, the further two and a half-fold decrease observed must be because of some structural change. From Figure 2, it can be seen that the ionization of the carbonyl group at a pK_a of 9.8 involves a partial keto-enol tautomerism of the pyrimidine ring. In order to study the effects of such a tau-

Table II. Rate Constants for e^-_{aq} Reactions

Molecule	*Structure*	*pH*	$k_{e^-_{aq}}$ (M^{-1} $sec.^{-1}$)	*Reference*
Cytosine	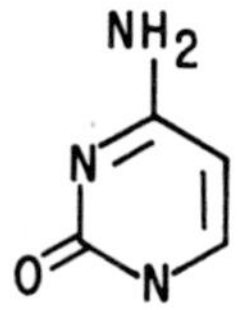	7	0.7×10^{10}	*17*
Thymine	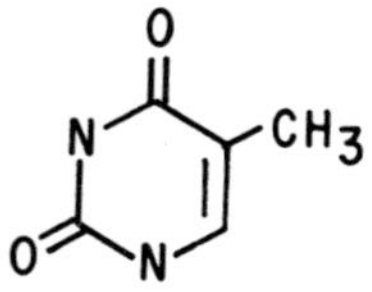	7	1.7×10^{10}	*18*
Uracil	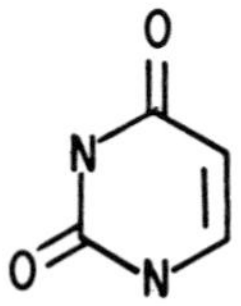	7	1.5×10^{10}	This work
Benzene		11	1.4×10^{7}	*6*
Pyridine	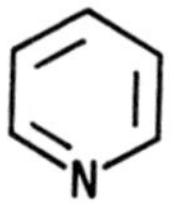	7	1.0×10^{9}	*17*
Hydroquinone		13	$< 10^{7}$	*17*
Benzoquinone		7	1.3×10^{9}	*17*

Table II. (Continued)

Molecule	*Structure*	*pH*	ke^-_{aq} (M^{-1} *sec.*$^{-1}$)	*Reference*
Cyclohexanone	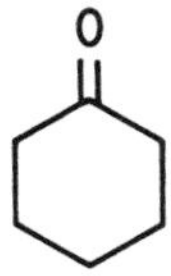	6	8×10^9	*8*
Acetone	$(CH_3)_2C{=}O$	7	6×10^9	*17*
Dihydrouracil	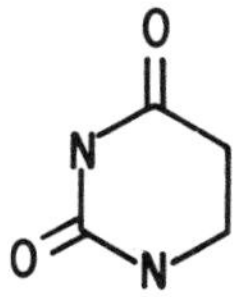	7	4.5×10^9	This work
Adenine	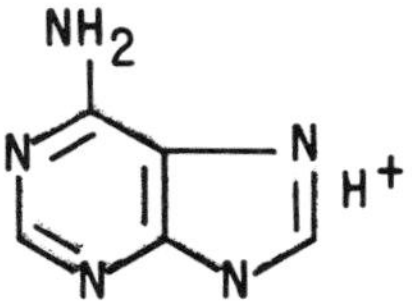 H^+	6	3×10^{10}	This work
Pyrrole		10	6×10^5	*25*
Imidazole	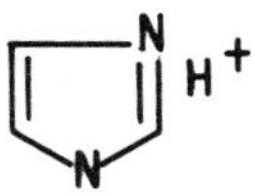 H^+	6	3.4×10^9	This work
Purine	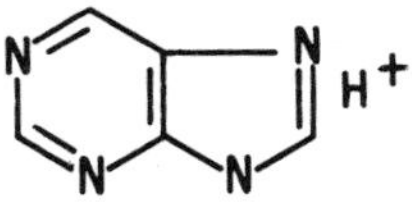 H^+	7	1.7×10^{10}	*17*

tomerism at neutral pH, the reactivities of e^-_{aq} with 1,3-dimethyluracil and 2,4-diethoxypyrimidine were measured.

The results shown in Table III indicate that the exclusive enol form of the 2 and 4 carbonyl groups in 2,4-diethoxypyrimidine leads to a five-fold decrease in reactivity. Alternatively, 1,3-dimethyluracil, which is in the diketo form similar to uracil, has the same reactivity as uncharged uracil, the methyl groups apparently having little influence on the reactivity. In 1,3-dimethyluracil and 2,4-diethoxypyrimidine, the measured rate constants are the same at pH 7 and pH 11 because the potentially ionizable groups have been blocked.

From these observations, it would be predicted that a partial keto-enol tautomerism of the carbonyl groups (last entry in Table III) such as is found in the singly ionized uracil molecule, would lead to a two and a half-fold decrease in reactivity. Hence, the fivefold decrease in e^-_{aq} reactivity upon ionization of the pyrimidine ring may be accounted for by a twofold decrease because of the negative charge and a two and a half-fold decrease because of the partial tautomerization.

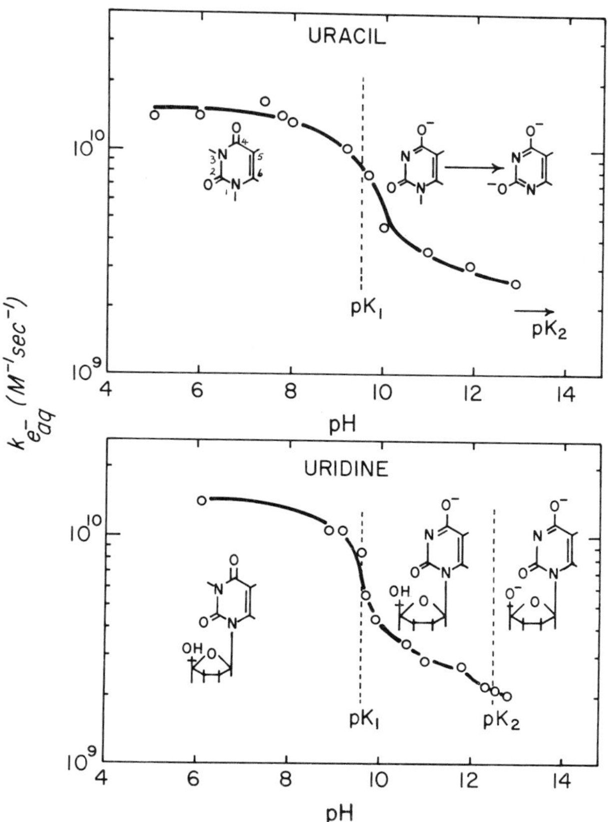

Figure 2. The effect of pH on the rate constants for the reactions of e^-_{aq} *with uracil and uridine. Also shown are the ionizable groups of uracil and uridine and their* pK_a *values. The unionizable ·OH groups on the ribose molecules are not shown*

Table III. Effect of Keto-enol Tautomerism on e^-_{aq} Reactivity of Uracil

Molecule	*pH*	*Structure*	ke^-_{aq} (M^{-1} *sec.*$^{-1}$)
Uracil	7	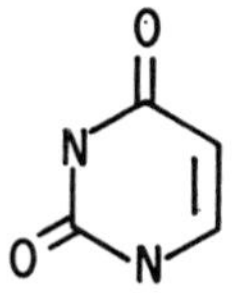	1.5×10^{10}
	11	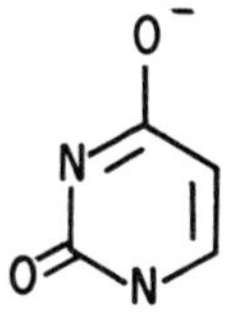	3×10^{9}
1,3-Dimethyluracil	7	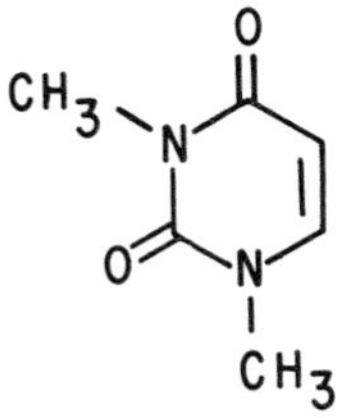	1.65×10^{10}
	11	No change	1.45×10^{10}
2,4-Diethoxypyrimidine	7	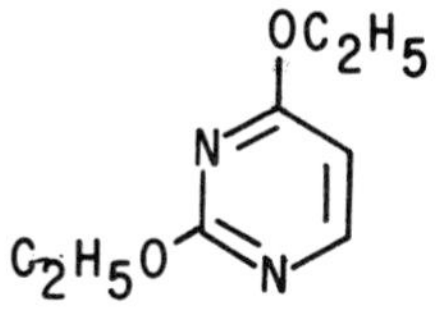	2.8×10^{9}
	11	No change	3.2×10^{9}
Hypothetical tautomer (2 keto, 4-enoluracil)	7	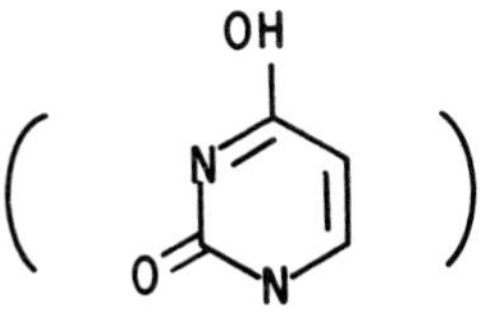	(6×10^{9}) (predicted)

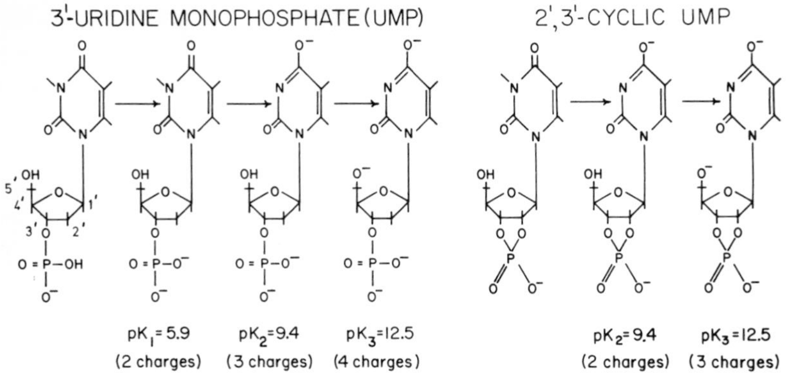

3'-URIDINE MONOPHOSPHATE (UMP) 2',3'-CYCLIC UMP

$pK_1 = 5.9$ (2 charges) $pK_2 = 9.4$ (3 charges) $pK_3 = 12.5$ (4 charges)

$pK_2 = 9.4$ (2 charges) $pK_3 = 12.5$ (3 charges)

Figure 3. Ionizable groups and pK_a values in 3'-UMP and 2',3'-cyclic UMP. Note that the second ionization which occurs in 3'-UMP at pH 5.9 is absent in 2',3'-cyclic UMP. The unionizable ·OH groups on the ribose molecule are not shown

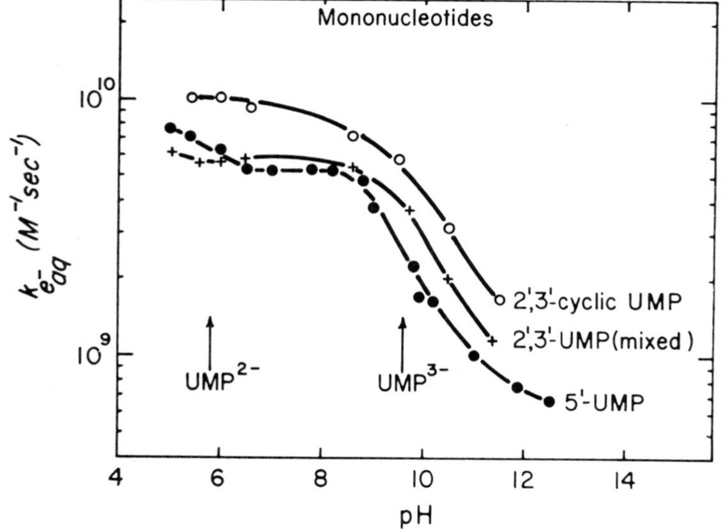

Figure 4. The effect of pH on the rate constants for the reactions of e^-_{aq} with the mononucleotides of uracil. Note that 2',3'-cyclic UMP does not show a change in reactivity around pH6 as do 2',3'-UMP (mixed) and 5'-UMP which become doubly ionized (UMP^{2-}) above this pH

NUCLEOTIDES. Phosphate groups may be attached to the ribose group of uridine at the 2', 3', or 5' positions to give 2', 3', or 5'-uridylic acid (UMP). The ionizable groups in 3'-UMP are shown in Figure 3. These groups are negatively charged at pH 5 causing a 1.5 fold decrease in the e^-_{aq} reactivity compared with uracil or uridine (Figure 4). The phosphate group becomes doubly ionized at a pK_a of 5.9 which results in a further decrease in the e^-_{aq} rate constant. This decrease is larger for 5′-UMP (twofold) than for 2′, 3′-UMP (mixed) (one and a half-fold) as expected if the e^-_{aq} attacks principally the pyrimidine ring, since a negative phosphate group on the 5′ position is much closer to the site of e^-_{aq} attack than when it is on the 2′ or 3′ position, and should have a greater influence. The 2′, 3′-cyclic UMP (Figure 3) does not have a second ionizable group on the phosphate as this is taken up forming the 2′, 3′ bond. As expected, the decrease in reactivity at pH 5.9 is absent for 2′, 3′-cyclic UMP. The three mononucleotides, like uracil and uridine, all show a large decrease in reactivity at the pK_a for the ionization of the carbonyl group.

For uridylic acid dinucleotides (UpU) and short chain polynucleotides (oligo U), a marked protective effect against e^-_{aq} attack is observed. The reactivity per nucleotide has been measured as a function of pH for UpU and for an oligo U molecule which contains about 20 nucleotides. The results are compared with those for uracil in Figure 5. In the absence

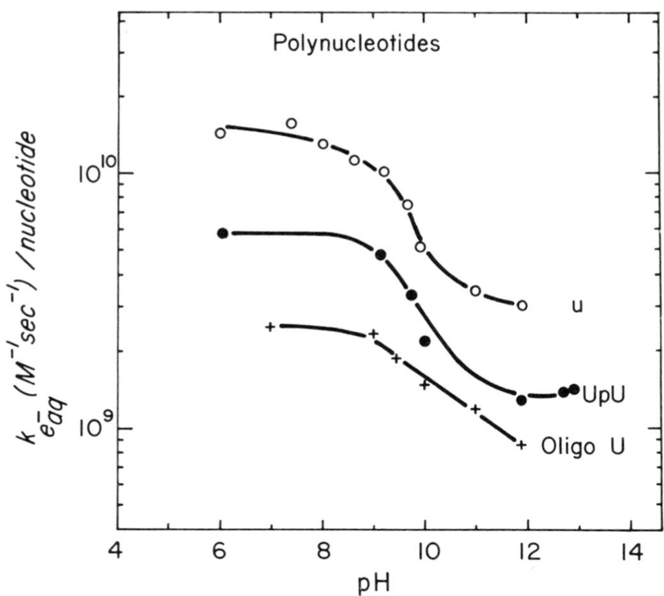

Figure 5. The effect of pH on the rate constants for the reactions of e^-_{aq} with the dinucleotide (UpU) and oligonucleotide (oligo U, about 20 bases) of uracil. Note that these are plotted as the absolute rate constant per nucleotide. The reactivity of uracil (u) is shown for comparison

of any shielding effect, the rate constant per nucleotide will be unchanged. However, in these results, the reactivity per nucleotide decreases as the number of nucleotides in the chain increases.

Hydroxyl Radical Reaction Rates. COMPETITION METHOD. Values of $k._{OH}$, the ·OH reaction rate with uracil, have been measured as a function of pH by utilizing competition with CNS^- (Equations 1 and 2), and also more directly by following the rate of disappearance of the chromophore for the 5,6 double bond. In the competition technique, the value of $k._{OH}$ depends upon using the correct value of k_2, the ·OH reaction rate with CNS . Because this rate is still somewhat in doubt (9) new measurements were made of the rate of buildup of the absorbing species in $10^{-4}M$ solutions of KCNS (Figure 6). If one assumes that the rate limiting step in the formation of the absorbing species is k_2 and not k_3 (Reactions 5 and 6), then a value for k_2 of $7.5 \pm 0.5 \times 10^9 M^{-1}$ sec.$^{-1}$ is obtained which is independent of pH within our experimental errors ($\pm 7\%$). This value is slightly higher than the value of $6.6 \times 10^9 M^{-1}$ sec.$^{-1}$ reported by Adams *et al.* (*3, 4, 5*). Since there is evidence that the absorbing species is not CNS· but instead an ion-radical complex $(CNS)_2^-$ (9), the formation of this complex by Reaction 6 may actually be the rate limiting step in this process. If this were true, the values of

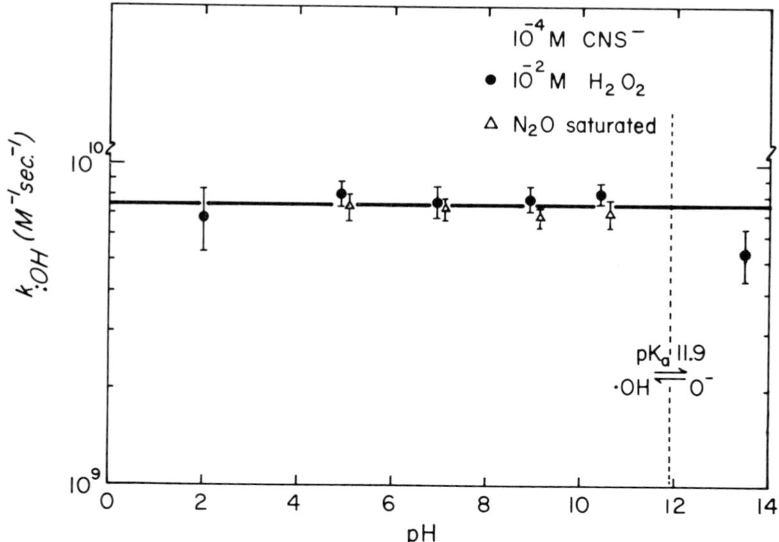

Figure 6. The rate constant for the reaction of ·OH with the thiocyanate ion (CNS^-) as a function of pH, using 10^{-2}M H_2O_2 or N_2O as the e^-_{aq} scavenger. Note the sharp drop in reactivity above the pK_a for dissociation of ·OH to O^-. Observations made in a 10^{-4}M KCNS solution at a wavelength of 500 mμ

k_2 reported here would be low, and all values for $k_{\cdot OH}$ would have to be corrected accordingly.

As a check on the validity of the competition kinetic method under the conditions of these experiments, the rate of ·OH reaction with isopropyl alcohol was determined using the above value of k_2 and compared with the values reported by other workers. Table IV shows the results obtained using the different methods mentioned. The value obtained for

Table IV. Comparison of ·OH Reaction Rates with Isopropyl Alcohol by Different Methods

$k_{\cdot OH}$	*Competitive Solute*	*Reference*
1.25×10^9	$2 \times 10^{-3}M$ CNS^- in $10^{-2}M$ H_2O_2 (aerated)	This work ($k_{\cdot OH} = 7.5 \times 10^9 M^{-1}$ sec.$^{-1}$)
1.2×10^9	$8\text{-}20 \times 10^{-5}M$ thymine (pH2, aerated)	*23*
1.7×10^9	$5 \times 10^{-5}M$ PNDA (pH9)	*20*
1.74×10^9	$3\text{-}20 \times 10^{-5}M$ KI	*27*

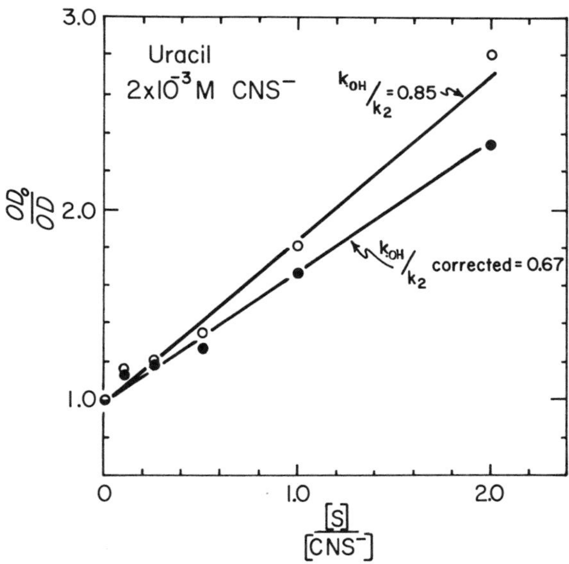

Figure 7. Competition for ·OH between uracil and thiocyanate. The ratio of the optical density at 500 mμ without solute (OD_0), to that with solute (OD) has been plotted as a function of the ratio of solute (S) to CNS^- concentration. The lower curve is corrected for the theoretical decrease in absorbance arising from the failure of H_2O_2 to completely scavenge e^-_{aq}

$k._{OH}$ falls within the spread of values reported in the other experiments, but both the CNS^- and thymine competition methods give values 50% lower than obtained by using I^- or *p*-nitrosodimethylaniline (PNDA) as the competitive solute.

Figure 7 shows the result of a typical competition plot for uracil at pH 6.5. From the slope of the upper straight line ($k._{OH}/k_2$), a value for the ·OH reaction rate with uracil of $6.4 \pm 0.8 \times 10^9 M^{-1}$ sec.$^{-1}$ is obtained using the measured value of k_2. When the slope is corrected for the theoretical loss of e^-_{aq} to uracil (lower line in Figure 7) as described earlier, a lower value ($k._{OH}$ corr.) for the ·OH reaction rate with uracil of $5.0 \pm 0.6 \times 10^9 M^{-1}$ sec.$^{-1}$ is obtained. This corrected value for the ·OH reaction rate with uracil at neutral pH has been verified using a higher concentration of H_2O_2 ($5 \times 10^{-2} M$). In this solution the correction is less than 5% and gives a value of $5.7 \pm 0.6 \times 10^9 M^{-1}$ sec.$^{-1}$.

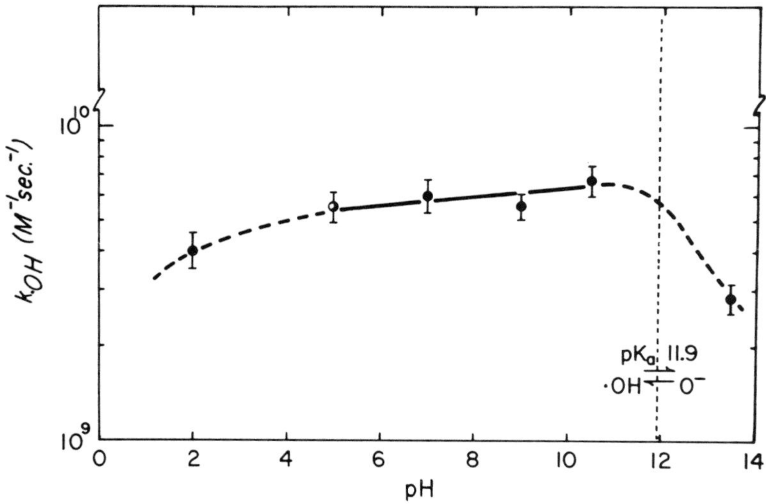

Figure 8. The effect of pH on the rate constant for the reactions of ·OH with uracil obtained using the CNS^- competition technique

There appears to be a gradual increase in ·OH reactivity with uracil as the pH is varied from 5 to 10.5 (Figure 8). There is no abrupt change in reactivity at the pK_a indicating that the changes in charge and tautomeric form which occur at the pK_a have no effect on the ·OH reaction. The lower values for the ·OH reactivity obtained at pH 2 and 13.5 are both considerably in doubt. The value at pH 2 is doubtful because of the possibility that H· may be entering into the reaction in some way, and the pH 13.5 value because this is above the pK_a for the dissociation of ·OH to O^-. The non-equilibrium conditions existing following the electron pulse make it uncertain whether the ·OH or O^- radical is reacting. The ·OH reactivity with dihydrouracil, in which the 5,6 bond is saturated, is less than one-fifth of that of uracil ($\leqslant 1 \times 10^9 M^{-1}$ sec.$^{-1}$). This is evidence that ·OH attacks the 5,6 double bond as suggested by the radiolysis product analysis studies in which the total loss in pyrimidine is the same as the yield calculated from the loss of 5,6 double bond (*24*).

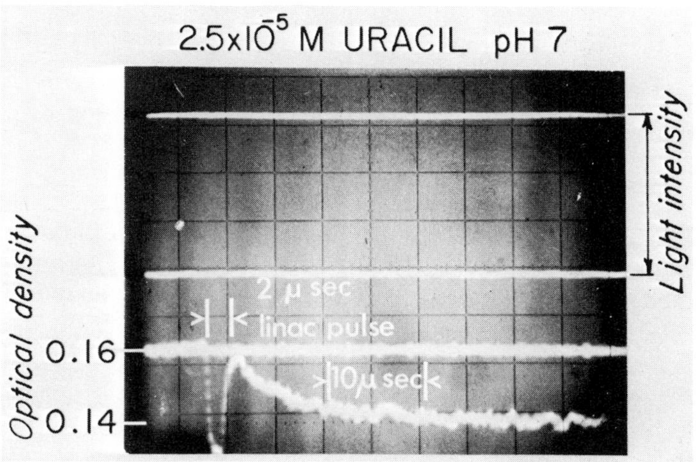

Figure 9. The disappearance of the 5,6 double bond absorption in an aerated 0.25 × 10^{-4}M uracil solution containing 0.5 × 10^{-3}M H_2O_2 as an e^-_{aq} scavenger. The wavelength of observation was 270 mμ and dose about 3 Krads. The two upper traces correspond to the signal levels with analyzing light off (upper) and on (central trace) at a gain of 0.05 volts/cm. The lower traces were obtained at a gain of 0.005 volts/cm., the increase in light transmission corresponding to loss of 5,6 double bond absorption for approximately 12% of the uracil. The sweep rate was 5μ sec./cm. graticule division

DIRECT OBSERVATION OF ·OH REACTION RATES. The reactivity of the 5,6 double bond of pyrimidines with ·OH radicals suggested that the disappearance of this chromophore might be used for a more direct measurement of the absolute rate constant for their reactivities. The increase in transmission at 270 mμ because of the ·OH attack on uracil is shown in Figure 9. The ·OH reaction rates with uracil obtained using this technique are compared with values obtained using competition methods and different values of k_2 (*see* Table V). The rate constants measured

Table V. Comparison of Rate Constants Measured

	Method	k_2 *(M^{-1} sec.$^{-1}$)*	*[C.S.] (M)*
1.	Loss of 5,6 double bond		
	Dose rate reduced 50%		
2.	CNS^- Competition	$7.5 \pm 0.5 \times 10^9$	2×10^{-3}
3.	(corrected)	$7.5 \pm 0.5 \times 10^9$	2×10^{-3}
4.	CNS^- (corrected)	2×10^{10} (9)	2×10^{-3}
5.	CNS^-	6.6×10^9	10^{-4}
6.	PNDA competition		5×10^{-5}

using three different uracil concentrations agree within experimental error, the value of $7.4 \pm 1.0 \times 10^9$ being quite close to the uncorrected value obtained by CNS^- competition. A reduction in the dose by a factor of two did not change the decay rate, indicating that radical-radical reactions were not entering into the reaction scheme. Since the direct measurement of 5,6 double bond disappearance does not suffer from the uncertainties of the CNS^- measurement, it should yield a reliable value. It should be noted, however, that if the value of k_2 reported by Baxendale *et al.* (9) is used in these calculations (Table V, No. 4), a much higher value of 1.3×10^{10} is obtained for $k_{\cdot OH}$ corr. Using a competition reaction with PNDA, Kraljic and Trumbore (*20*) have also calculated a value of $5.4 \times 10^9 M^{-1}$ sec.$^{-1}$ for $k_{\cdot OH}$, at pH 9 which is in reasonable agreement with the values reported in this paper. From the results in Table V it appears that the CNS^- competition technique of Adams *et al.* (3, 4, 5) gives a slightly lower value for the ·OH reaction rate with uracil but a much larger rate constant for the reaction, $CNS^- + \cdot OH \xrightarrow{k_2} CNS\cdot + \cdot OH^-$ (9) would not be in keeping with the direct observations. A true value for k_2 of $1.0 \times 10^{10} M^{-1}$ sec.$^{-1}$ is suggested by these measurements:

Rates with Other Nucleic Acid Derivatives. The ·OH reaction rates with uridine, UMP, and adenine are compared in Table VI with those for uracil obtained using the same CNS^- competition method. Uridine and 2′,3′-UMP (mixed) at neutral pH show lower corrected ·OH reaction rates of $2.9 \times 10^9 M^{-1}$ sec.$^{-1}$ and $3.5 \times 10^9 M^{-1}$ sec.$^{-1}$ respectively, indicating that the ribose sugar and phosphate groups are not highly reactive sites for ·OH attack. Adenine, the complementary purine base to uracil in RNA has a much lower ·OH reactivity than uracil of 1.9 ×

for the Reaction of ·OH Radicals with Uracil ($k_{\cdot OH}$)

[u] (M)	pH	$k_{\cdot OH}$ (M^{-1} sec.$^{-1}$)	Reference
0.25×10^{-4}		$7.9 \pm 1.1 \times 10^9$	This work
0.5×10^{-4}	7.0	$6.9 \pm 0.9 \times 10^9$	This work
1.0×10^{-4}		$8.6 \pm 1.2 \times 10^9$	This work
0.25×10^{-4}		$6.2 \pm 0.6 \times 10^9$	This work
	Mean value	$7.4 \pm 1.0 \times 10^9$	
$\leqslant 4 \times 10^{-3}$	6.5	$6.4 \pm 0.8 \times 10^9$	This work
$\leqslant 4 \times 10^{-3}$	6.5	$5.0 \pm 0.6 \times 10^9$	This work
$\leqslant 4 \times 10^{-3}$	6.5	$(1.3 \pm 0.2 \times 10^{10})$	*9* and this work
$\leqslant 3 \times 10^{-4}$	5–7	$3.1 \pm 0.4 \times 10^9$	*23*
	9	5.4×10^9	*20*

$10^9 M^{-1}$ sec.$^{-1}$. This would be in agreement with the lower *G*-value for loss of the adenine base in irradiated DNA solutions (*24*).

Conclusion, Summary and Discussion

The reaction rates of uracil and its derivatives with solvated electrons have been studied in detail. On the basis of variations of the e^-_{aq} reaction rate as a function of pH, and also with the tautomeric form of the molecule, it is concluded that the changes in reactivity are too great to be accounted for by charge alone, and that the keto-enol prototrophy which occurs during ionization is responsible for the large fraction of the change in the reaction rate. These results also show that the carbonyl groups of uracil are responsible for the high reactivity of these molecules.

Table VI. ·OH Reaction Rates with Other Nucleic Acid Derivatives

Molecule	$k_{\cdot OH}$(*corrected*) (M^{-1} sec.$^{-1}$)
Uracil	$5.0 \pm 0.6 \times 10^9$
Uridine	$2.9 \pm 0.4 \times 10^9$
3′,5′-UMP (mixed)	$3.5 \pm 0.5 \times 10^9$
Adenine	$1.9 \pm 0.3 \times 10^9$

Studies of the e^-_{aq} reaction rates with uridine, UMP, and oligo-U show that the sugar and phosphate groups are unreactive, and as one would predict, slightly reduced changes occur in the reaction rates at the pH values where ionization takes place in the phosphate and sugar groups. In the larger chain oligo U molecules studied (about 20 bases), the reactivity per nucleotide is considerably reduced, suggesting that steric effects are important.

The values here for $\cdot OH$ radical reaction rates with uracil measured using the CNS^- competition method, whether corrected or not, are appreciably higher than those obtained by Scholes *et al.* (*23*) using a similar method (6.4 or $5.0 \times 10^9 M^{-1}$ sec.$^{-1}$, as against $3.1 \times 10^9 M^{-1}$ sec.$^{-1}$ at pH 5-7). This can only partially be explained by the slightly higher value for $k_{\cdot OH + CNS^-}$ obtained in our measurements. However, the values obtained by Scholes were made using such a low concentration of CNS^- that these ions would have been unable completely to scavenge the $\cdot OH$ radicals (*1, 2*) and might lead to this discrepancy. The $\cdot OH$ reactivity with uracil measured directly by the disappearance of the uracil 5,6 double bond is slightly higher than that obtained by CNS^- competition. This may indicate that the value of k_2 of $7.5 \times 10^9 M^{-1}$ sec.$^{-1}$ should be increased a maximum of about 50%. At present, there is no evidence that even higher values of k_2 (*9*) would be compatible with the more direct observations.

The lower reactivity of the hydroxyl radical with the partially saturated uracil derivative, dihydrouracil, is in agreement with the reaction schemes proposed on the basis of radiolysis measurements which indicate that damage to uracil is always accompanied by saturation of the 5,6 double bond. However, when one compares the radiolysis yields in the absence of the electron scavenger oxygen, many pieces appear to be missing in the puzzle. Although solvated electrons react more rapidly with uracil than do $\cdot OH$ radicals, the product yield under conditions where both species react is greatly reduced—*i.e.*, the yield for loss of uracil in oxygen is 2.1 as against 0.4 in a deoxygenated solution (*29*) instead of being doubled by the attack of both $\cdot OH$ and e^-_{aq}. This suggests some type of a back reaction, and experiments are being carried out at present in an attempt to study this.

Acknowledgments

We are pleased to acknowledge the use of the linear accelerator facilities in the Physics Department of the University of Toronto. In particular we wish to thank K. G. McNeil, E. Horrigan, T. Elder, and the linac operators for their assistance in getting the linac operating for pulse radiolysis work. The experiments were carried out with financial assistance from the Medical Research Council of Canada, the National Cancer Institute, and the Ontario Cancer Institute. Two of us (C. L. G., and M. N.) wish to acknowledge the financial support of the National Cancer Institute. The authors wish to thank their fellow colleagues Kim Umemoto, M. J. Bronskill, and M. Duke for their assistance in this work and to H. E. Johns for his keen interest in reading the manuscript and offering valuable suggestions.

Literature Cited

(1) Adams, G. E., Boag, J. W., Currant, J., Michael, B. D., "Pulse Radiolysis," p. 117, Academic Press, New York, N. Y., 1965.
(2) *Ibid.*, p. 131.
(3) Adams, G. E., Boag, J. W., Michael, B. D., *Proc. Chem. Soc.* **1964,** 411.
(4) Adams, G. E., Boag, J. W., Michael, B. D., *Trans. Faraday Soc.* **61,** 1417 (1965).
(5) *Ibid.*, **61,** 1674 (1965).
(6) Anbar, M., Hart, E. J., *J. Am. Chem. Soc.* **86,** 5633 (1964).
(7) Anbar, M., Meyerstein, D., Neta, P., *J. Phys. Chem.* **70,** 2660 (1966).
(8) Anbar, M., Alfassi, Z. B., Reissler, H. (unpublished results).
(9) Baxendale, J. H., Stott, D. A., *Chem. Comm.* **1967,** 699.
(10) Braams, R., *Rad. Res.* **27,** 319 (1966).
(11) *Ibid.*, **31,** 8 (1967).
(12) Dainton, F. S., Watt, W. S., *Proc. Roy. Soc.* **275A,** 447 (1963).
(13) Debye, P., *Trans. Electrochem. Soc.* **82,** 265 (1942).
(14) Gordon, S., Hart, E. J., Matheson, M. S., Rabani, J., Thomas, J. K., *J. Am. Chem. Soc.* **85,** 1375 (1963).
(15) Greenstock, C. L., Bronskill, M. J., Hunt, J. W. (in preparation).
(16) Hart, E. J., Fielden, E. M., ADVAN. CHEM. SER. **50,** 253 (1965).
(17) Hart, E. J., Gordon, S., Thomas, J. K., *J. Phys. Chem.* **68,** 127 (1964)
(18) Hart, E. J., Thomas, J. K., Gordon, S., *Radiation Res. Suppl.* **4,** 74 (1964).
(19) Karzmarck, J., *Rev. Sci. Inst.* **35,** 1646 (1964).
(20) Kraljic, I., Trumbore, C. N., *J. Am. Chem. Soc.* **87,** 2547 (1965).
(21) Rabani, J. Matheson, M. S., *J. Am. Chem. Soc.* **86,** 3175 (964)
(22) Schmidt, K., personal communication (1966).
(23) Scholes, G., Shaw, P., Willson, R. L., Ebert, M., "Pulse Radiolysis," p. 151, Academic Press, New York, N. Y., 1965.
(24) Scholes, G., Ward, J. F., Weiss, J., *J. Mol. Biol.* **2,** 379 (1960).
(25) Szutka, A., Thomas, J. K., Gordon, S., Hart, E. J., *J. Phys. Chem.* **69,** 289 (1965).
(26) Taimuty, S. I., Deaver, B. S., Jr., *Rev. Sci. Inst.* **32,** 1098 (1961).
(27) Thomas, J. K., *Trans. Faraday Soc.* **61,** 702 (1965).
(28) Thomas, J. K., Rabani, J., Matheson, M. S., Hart, E. J., Gordon, S., *J. Phys. Chem.* **70,** 2409 (1966).
(29) Umemoto, K. (unpublished results).

RECEIVED February 2, 1968.

29

Photochemical Genetics. I. The Ionic Nature of Uracil Photohydration

J. G. BURR, B. R. GORDON, and E. H. PARK

Science Center/Aerospace and Systems Group, North American Rockwell Corporation, Thousand Oaks, Calif. 91360

The rates of photohydration at 265 n.m. of uracil, 1-ethyluracil (EU), 1-cyclohexyluracil (CU), and 1-ribosyluracil (uridine) in oxygen-saturated water are found to be sigmoid functions of the pH over a pH range of 1.5 to 10. The rates of uracil photohydration (10^{-4}M solutions) are independent of the concentration of UH^+ and are unaffected by added NaCl. A mechanism is postulated which includes an equilibrium between singlet excited uracil molecules and hydrogen ions. The main product forming reaction in the pH range 1.5 to 7 is that between an excited $(UH^+)^*$ and a water molecule. At higher pH values, the reactive species seem to be excited uracil and a water molecule. It is inferred from these data that the pK of the four excited (UH^+)-type species are approximately 3.5 for $(UH^+)^*$, 6.5 for $(EUH^+)^*$, and 7.5 for $(CUH^+)^*$.*

Ultraviolet irradiation of aqueous solutions of uracil, cytosine, and thymine derivatives has been shown to lead to the formation of two kinds of photoproducts (*4, 13*). One type is a dimer of the pyrimidine; several such products seem to be formed but the best known are those containing a cyclobutane ring system (shown in I for uracil).

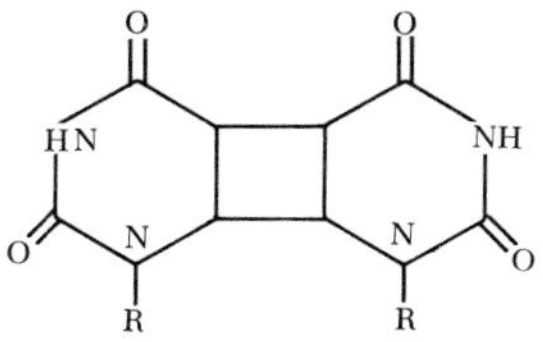

O O H HN NH HN H H N N N O O O OH R R R

I 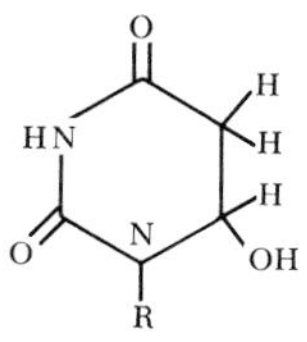 II

Formation of such dimers in the nucleic acids of an organism or virus has been shown to be a probable cause for the inactivation of the organism (*17*) or virus. The intermediate responsible for formation of such dimers, at least in simple pyrimidines, is probably the triplet excited state of the pyrimidine, on the basis of the effects of known triplet sensitizers and quenchers (*8, 10, 18*).

The other photoproduct which is formed is one resulting from the light-induced addition of water across the 5,6-double bond of the pyrimidine, shown in II for uracil. This product will be denoted in this paper by the term "photohydrate." Little has been reported about the mechanism of this reaction, or about the nature of the responsible intermediate (*4*). It is the purpose of this paper to report some observations about the variation with pH and salt concentration of the rate of the photohydration process in four uracil derivatives—(1) uracil (R = H), (2) 1-ethyluracil (EU, R = ethyl), (3) 1-cyclohexyluracil (CU, R = cyclohexyl), and (4) uridine (R = ribosyl).

Experimental

Materials. Uracil (U), 1-ethyluracil (EU), 1-cyclohexyluracil (CU), and 1,3-dimethyluracil (DMU) were obtained from Cyclo Chemical Corporation; uridine was from Calbiochem. They were used as obtained; in working with them, no impurities were apparent, spectroscopically or chromatographically. Solutions for photolysis at a particular pH were prepared by diluting a $10^{-3}M$ triple-distilled water stock solution of the uracil derivative tenfold with the appropriate phosphate buffer. Concentrations were determined by absorbance measurement, using a Perkin-Elmer Model 202 Spectrophotometer. The values of λ_{max}, in n.m., and ϵ measured for the four substances were: uracil: 259, 8.6×10^3; 1-ethyluracil: 267, 9×10^3; 1-cyclohexyluracil: 270, 9×10^3; uridine: 265, 10×10^3.

Optics. The light source used was a 1000 watt GE BH6 or FH6, aircooled mercury arc supported vertically in a modified Orion Optics lamp holder. The light was passed through a B&L High Intensity monochromator. Examination with a 500 mm. B&L monochromator and photocell of the light emitted from the High Intensity monochromator showed that scattered light was negligible and that at a monochromator setting of 270 n.m. the transmitted light actually peaked at 265 n.m., with a width at half-height of 9 n.m. The half-widths of the absorption peaks were wider—*e.g.*, $10^{-4}M$ uracil (A = 1) had a peak centered at 259 n.m. with a half-width of 33 n.m. Two different lamp-monochromator assemblies were used; it was found, by methods discussed below, that the fraction of light absorbed by the same dimethyluracil solution was different for each assembly.

Actinometry. The light output (I_o) of each lamp-monochromator assembly was monitored (at least daily) by measuring the ΔA_{15} (ΔA_{15} = absorbance change for 15 minutes irradiation) of a standard dimethyluracil solution ($A_o = 0.925$, $C = 1.075 \times 10^{-4}M$). These ΔA_{15} values were converted to numerical estimates of I_0 in quanta liter^{-1} min.$^{-1}$, by use of a remeasured value for the quantum yield for photohydration of dimethyluracil. Remeasurement of this value resolved an existing anomaly in the literature of pyrimidine photochemistry. It has been reported (*4, 13*) that the quantum yields for photolysis of several uracil derivatives, including that of dimethyluracil, which is known at these values of total dose to form only the photohydrate, varied with concentration to such an extent that the apparent quantum yield for dimethyluracil varied during the course of a photolysis. These apparent variations in the order of a supposedly first order process have elicited attempts at mechanistic interpretation (*13*).

Accordingly, we determined the quantum yield of the photohydrate of 1,3-dimethyluracil (DMU) for initial DMU concentrations of $1 \times 10^{-3}M$, and $1 \times 10^{-4}M$ in unbuffered triple-distilled water. The measurements were made according to the conventional double cell technique (*12*), using uranyl oxalate as the actinometer. In this method, the total number of incident and transmitted quanta are measured by chemical actinometry. The quantum yield for DMU disappearance was found to be 3.93×10^{-3} at $1 \times 10^{-4}M$ DMU and 3.79×10^{-3} at $1 \times 10^{-3}M$ DMU (single determinations), and is thus independent of concentration in this range.

The absorbance change during photolysis of the $10^{-4}M$ solution was from 1.0 to 0.5. The quantum yield calculated from this concentration change, using the conventional expression, $I_a = I_0\ (1 - 10^{-A})$, to estimate the number of quanta absorbed was indeed found to vary during the course of a run, and thus to vary with concentration. However, the actual fraction of I_0 absorbed in the solution during the run was measured by chemical actinometry to be 0.31; that estimated by the exponential expression was about 0.8. This discrepancy is caused, of course, by the fact that the simple exponential expression is valid only if I_0 is monochromatic; the actual half-height beam width was about 9 n.m. The amount of light absorbed is thus expressed by the integral equation

$$I_a t = \int_{\lambda_1}^{\lambda_2} \int_{t_1}^{t_2} I_0(\lambda)\,[1 - 10^{-\varepsilon(\lambda)C(t)\text{liter}}]\,d\lambda dt$$

where t = time, and the limits of λ are arbitrarily set to the band width of the base of the DMU absorption peak.

Inspection of the earlier literature (*4, 13*) reveals that many of the data which suggested a variation of quantum yield with concentration were obtained with solutions whose initial absorbances were about 1.0, and with light beams of equal or greater band width than the one used here. It is possible that some of the reported quantum yield variations may be artifacts of the method of estimating light absorption rather than real phenomena.

Calculation of Rates and Rate Constants. The raw data reported in this paper consist of measurements of the absorbance, *A*, of a solution as a function of time, *t*, and of various changes in the solution variables, such as pH and solute concentrations. It is desired to express these data as rates, or as rate constants, which could be discussed validly as functions of the solution variables.

For a process whose overall rate genuinely depends only on the absorption of light by the reactant, this rate is the product of a cross section $\sigma_p C$, and a light flux, L; this is usually expressed (Equation 1) as a quantum yield, Φ_p, and the rate of absorption of light quanta, I_a.

$$-dC/dt = \sigma_p CL = \Phi_p I_a \tag{1}$$

$$= \Phi I_o[1 - \exp(-2.3\,\epsilon C)]. \tag{2}$$

This rate is often expressed in terms of an incident light flux, I_o, and a fraction of light absorbed, estimated by use of the ordinary molar extinction coefficient, Equation 2 (*7, 13*). This expression actually simply normalizes the rates at different concentrations to the limiting rate for a solution which absorbs all the incident light.

It would be preferable to express the rates as simple first order functions of the solute concentration, but with the actual extinction coefficients of the four solutes, 9×10^3, and the concentrations used, $10^{-4}M$, the limiting first order approximation to Equation 2, $dC/dt = 2.3\,\epsilon\Phi I_o C$, would be valid only at concentrations of C less than $10^{-5}M$. However, it was found that in nearly all of the photolyses, the rates actually obeyed a first order relationship over the whole range of concentrations—ordinarily about $1.0 \times 10^{-4}M$ to $0.1 \times 10^{-4}M$—*i.e.*, plots of log (C_o/C) *vs.* time were straight lines. The data have in all cases, therefore, been expressed as the rate constants, $K'_f = (1/t) \log (C_o/C)$. This anomolous behavior results from the beam width of the photolyzing light beam (*see* Actinometry Section).

The values of K'_f thus obtained depended upon the rate of light absorption according to the Expression 3, where $F(C)$ was the experimental fraction of I_o absorbed at a particular concentration, C, of solute.

$$K'_f = \Phi I_o[F(C)/C] \tag{3}$$

All runs were made with nearly the same initial concentration of solute (the first order behavior of the rates, however, infers that F is a linear function of C), and the values of K'_f so measured have been normalized to those, K_f, at a standard value of I_o^s ($= 5.36 \times 10^{20}$ quanta liter^{-1} min.$^{-1}$) by the expression in Equation 4.

$$K_f = K'_f(I_o^s/I_o) \tag{4}$$

Product Analysis and Control. It was the intent of this study to examine the mechanism of photohydrate formation in uracil and substituted uracils. The primary measurement of absorbance change which measured solute disappearance was thus supplemented by measurements of photohydrate content in the products. At the doses employed in this investigation, the only products which were formed in appreciable amounts were the photohydrates and photoproducts of a dimeric nature. The photohydrate content of irradiated solutions at pH 5.5–7 were estimated by adjusting the irradiated solution (1.50 ml. in all cases) to pH 1.5 with 25 λ of 6*N* HCl, heating at 75°C. for 30 minutes, and measuring the initial absorbance, the absorbance after irradiation, and the absorbance after acidification and heating. Both photodimers and photohydrate were determined in irradiated uracil solutions by paper and thin layer

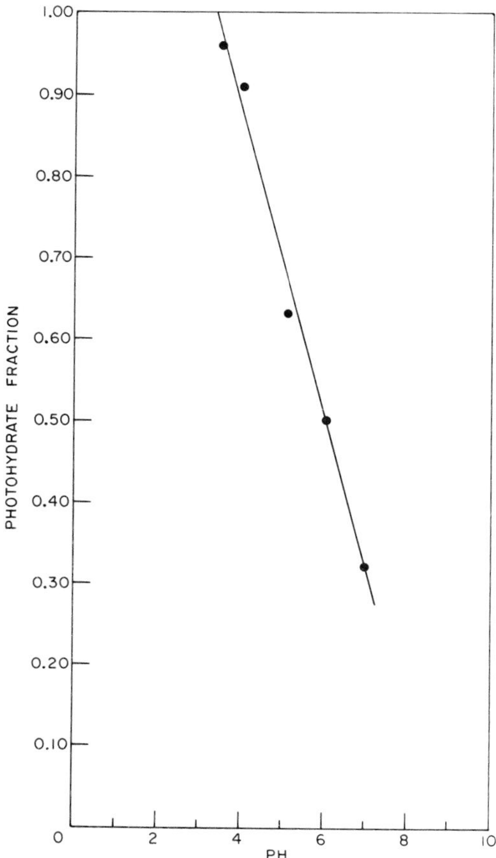

Figure 1. The fraction of photohydrate formed in the photolysis of 10^{-4}M solutions of uracil in phosphate buffers as a function of the pH of the solution

chromatography, using ^{14}C-labelled or tritium-labelled uracil (Calbiochem). Radioactivity in the spots was assayed by liquid scintillation counting of strips from the chromatograms. Relative amounts of dimer and hydrate determined both thermally and chromatographically were in agreement. Three products were found in the dimer region of the chromatograms.

A serious loss ($\sim$ 50%) of tritium from uracil-5-t was observed to be one result of these photolyses. This loss of isotope was probably not caused by cycles of photohydrate formation and decomposition because the photohydrate should have been quite stable under the conditions of the photolyses. We think that this is likely the result of rapid isotope exchange in the protonated excited uracil molecule, by a mechanism similar to that postulated by Wechter (*19*) for deuterium exchange in aqueous uracil solutions.

The photoproducts of 1,3-dimethyluracil, 1-ethyluracil, 1-cyclohexyluracil and uridine were thus determined to be 95–100% photohydrate for solutions air-saturated or oxygen-saturated during irradiation. The photohydrate of EU was isolated as white crystalline solid, m.p. 85°–86°C., 98% pure by thermal analysis: elemental analysis; found: C, 45.40; H, 6.40; N, 17.69; calc. for $C_6H_{10}N_2O_3$: C, 45.5; H, 6.3; N, 17.7. The photohydrate of CU was isolated as white crystals; purification of this is still in progress. The photohydrate of uridine has been reported as a pale yellow amorphous solid, m.p. 95°C. (*4*); we have repeated the preparation and confirm this observation. The properties and characterization of these substances is in progress and will be discussed at more length in a future publication.

The composition of the product mixture observed in irradiated uracil solutions depended upon the total dose (and probably the dose rate) (*4*), the oxygen concentration in the solution (*4, 8, 10, 13*) and upon the pH. In our hands, and with our equipment, the fraction of photohydrate in irradiated, air-saturated, neutral uracil solutions ranged from 0.32 to 0.61 for various irradiations. For a particular set of conditions, the fractional content of photohydrate in the photoproducts was found to be a linear function of the pH, Figure 1, becoming 1.00 at a pH around 3. The photodimers comprise the other fraction of the products. The results of individual runs were often difficult to reproduce, but it was our observation that the photohydrate content of uracil irradiated in degassed or nitrogen-saturated solutions ranged from 0 to 0.20, and that the overall rate was fastest for the experiments in which least hydrate was produced. The limiting result, obtained in three or four runs, is shown in Figure 2; no photohydrate was found in the degassed irradiated solution and the photolysis was not first order in uracil. On the other hand, the product produced in the oxygen-saturated solution was always entirely photohydrate, as measured both by thermal analysis and by chromatographic analysis; a typical chromatogram is shown in Figure 3.

All subsequent studies on uracil photolysis reported here were, therefore, carried out in oxygen-saturated solution; for reasons of uniformity, photolysis of the substituted uracils was also done in oxygen-saturated solution.

Plots of $\log_{10}(C_o/C)$ *vs.* time for the photolyses of uracil are shown as an example of the data in Figure 4. Two sorts of deviation from linearity are seen in some of the log plots. The line at pH 1.5 for uracil (Figure 4); at 1.5, 10, and 11 for EU; at 1.5, 2.5, and 9 for CU; and at 9, 10, and 11 for uridine bend over and in several cases reach or nearly reach a photoequilibrium. These are cases in which the rate of the thermal back reaction became equal or nearly equal to the rate of the forward reaction, according to Equation 5.

$$dC/dt = K_f C - K_b(C_o - C). \tag{5}$$

At the equilibrium concentration, C_e, the value of K_f could be

$$K_f = K_b \frac{(C_o - C_e)}{C_e} \tag{6}$$

calculated by the relationship in Equation 6, using values of K_b chosen from those in Figure 6, discussed below. When the curvature was slight, K_f was calculated from the initial slope. Values of K_f were difficult to obtain from plots which showed much curvature but where the reaction did not reach the photoequilibrium.

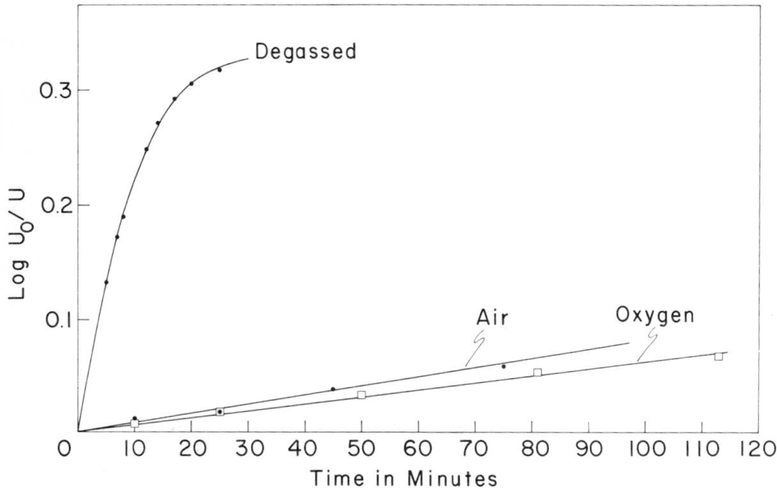

Figure 2. The rates of uracil photolysis (uracil loss) in 10^{-4}M unbuffered aqueous solution at different partial pressures of oxygen

A few of the plots for photolyses of CU showed a different behavior; several of the log (C_0/C) plots show an initial curvature (lower slope at the higher concentrations of CU) becoming linear at longer times (lower concentrations). This behavior is caused by deviation at the higher concentrations of CU from the empirical first order rate law. In the case of these particular runs, the initial concentrations apparently lay in the region between first order and the zero order reaction of optically black solutions. K_f was calculated from the slopes of the linear portions of the plots.

Measurement of Back Reaction. The photohydrates formed in these photolyses can be dehydrated back to the uracil. This elimination reaction is catalyzed by both H_3O^+ and OH^- (*4, 13, 15, 16*), and at extreme values of the pH the back reaction competes visibly with the forward photolytic reaction. It was thus necessary to measure the rate constant for the back reactions under photolytic conditions. This was accomplished by photolyzing a solution in a 1 cm. cuvette in a normal manner, placing the photolyzed solution in the spectrophotometer and measuring the time variation of absorbance change, using the time drum accessory of the spectrophotometer. The temperature in the solution during photolysis and in the sample chamber of the spectrophotometer was the same,

32°C. The solution was finally brought to pH 1.5 with 6*N* HCl and heated to 100°C. for 15 minutes to complete the dehydration. H_o, the initial hydrate concentration was calculated from the *A* value measured after acidification and heating, and the *A* value at the end of the photolysis. The rate constant, K_b, was calculated from the slope of the (usually) linear plots of log (H_o/H) *vs.* time. For the 1-alkyluracils, a curvature was sometimes observed at large values of log (H_o/H); for 1-cyclohexyluracil photolyzed at pH = 1.5 a sharp break in the dehydration plot was observed, Figure 5. This break, and the other curvatures, signal the formation of more than one dehydratable photoproduct. The second one dehydrates more slowly than the first one. It is possible that the second product is 1-alkyl-5,6-dihydro-5-hydroxyuracil since such products are known (*14*) to be more stable than the more common photohydrate, 1-alkyl-5,6-dihydro-6-hydroxy-uracil.

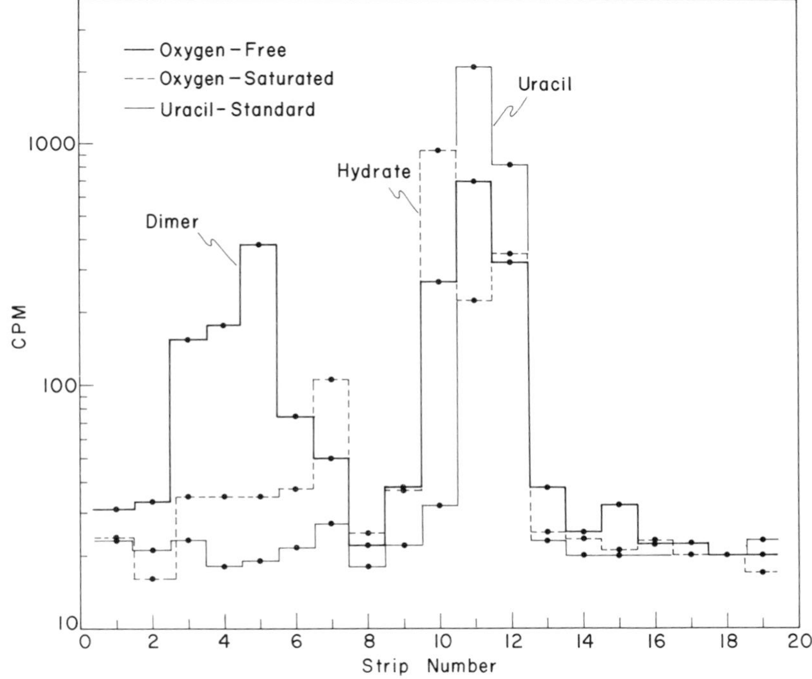

Figure 3. A typical chromatogram of photolyzed solutions of uracil-5-t (*10^{-4}*M) *in unbuffered water (86:14 Bu:H_2O, on Whatman No. 1). The amount of dimer formed in the oxygen-saturated solution is about 4% of that formed in degassed solution*

The rate constants for this back reaction, as functions of pH, are shown in Figure 6 for the photohydrates of uracil, EU, CU, and uridine; all at 32°C. The shape of these curves, exhibiting catalysis by both H_3O^+

and OH^-, is similar to those reported previously for uracil and 1,3-dimethyl uracil (*15, 16*) at 20°C., but there appear to be quantitative differences in the rate constants.

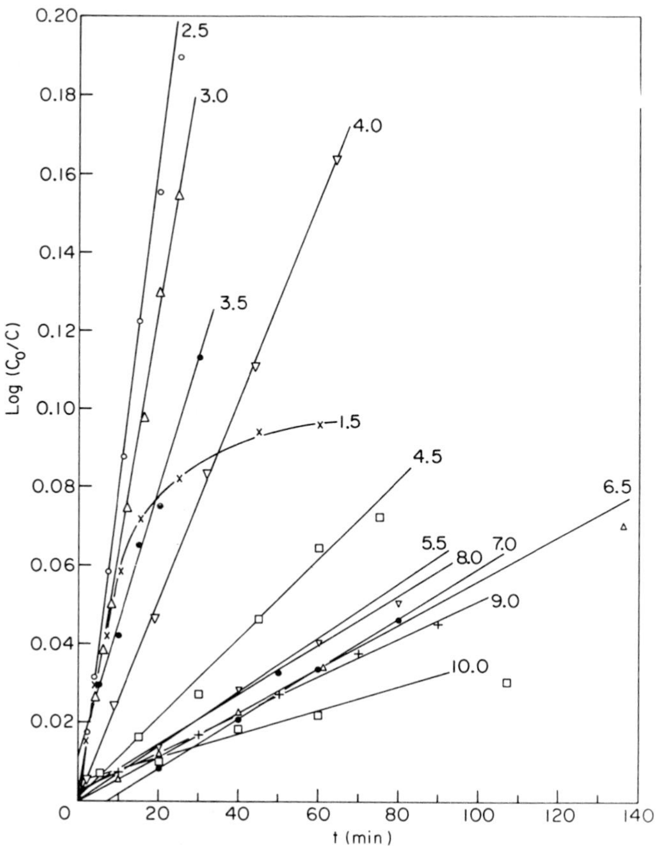

Figure 4. Rates of formation of uracil photohydrate as functions of pH

Results and Discussion

The values for the rate constants for photohydration of uracil, EU, CU, and uridine, calculated as described in the Experimental section, have been plotted as functions of the pH, and the plots are shown in Figure 7. The photohydration rates for all four compounds are sensitive to the pH; the effect is most pronounced for uracil and least apparent for uridine. The photohydration of dimethyluracil is independent of the pH in the range of 2 to 7[1].

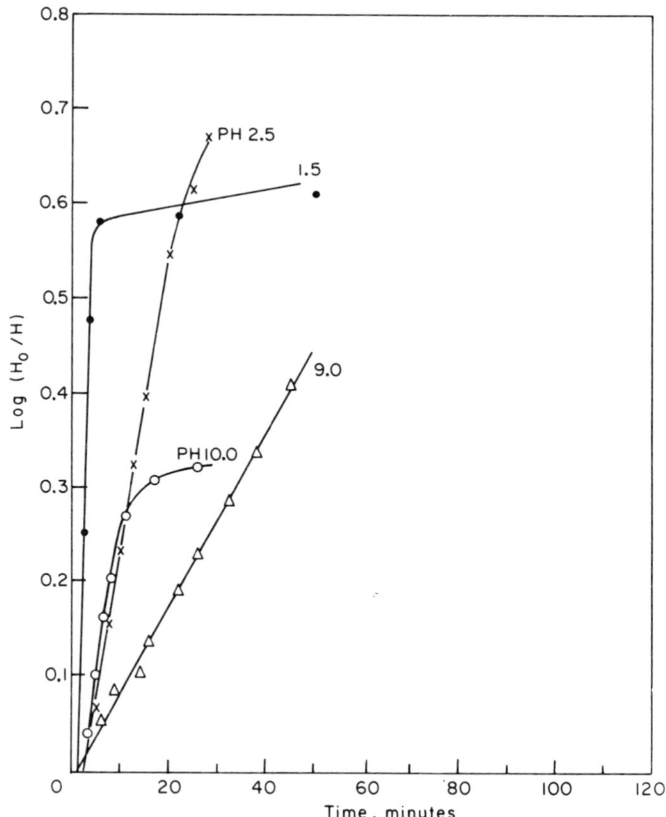

Figure 5. Rates of dehydration of 1-cyclohexyluracil photohydrate as functions of pH

The shapes of three of these curves—for uracil, EU and CU—resemble those of titrations curves. It can be thus inferred that the photohydration rates are determined by the concentration of a species in equilibrium with hydronium ion—*i.e.*, a species whose mole fraction can be represented by Equation 7, where K_e is the equilibrium constant.

$$f_{UH^+} = \frac{(H^+)}{K_e + (H^+)} \quad (7)$$

Three such equilibria can be considered for the photolysis of uracil (and the substituted uracils), Equations 8a, 8b, and 8c. Equation 8c represents protonation of an excited uracil molecule. The excited species involved

$$UH^+ \rightleftarrows U + H^+ \; pK_a \cong 0.5 \quad (8a)$$

$$U \rightleftarrows U^- + H^+ \; pK_b = 9.5 \quad (8b)$$

$$(UH^+)^* \rightleftarrows U^* + H^+ \tag{8c}$$

in photohydrate formation must result from excitation of UH^+, U, or U^-, or by protonation of U^*, as in Reaction 8c.

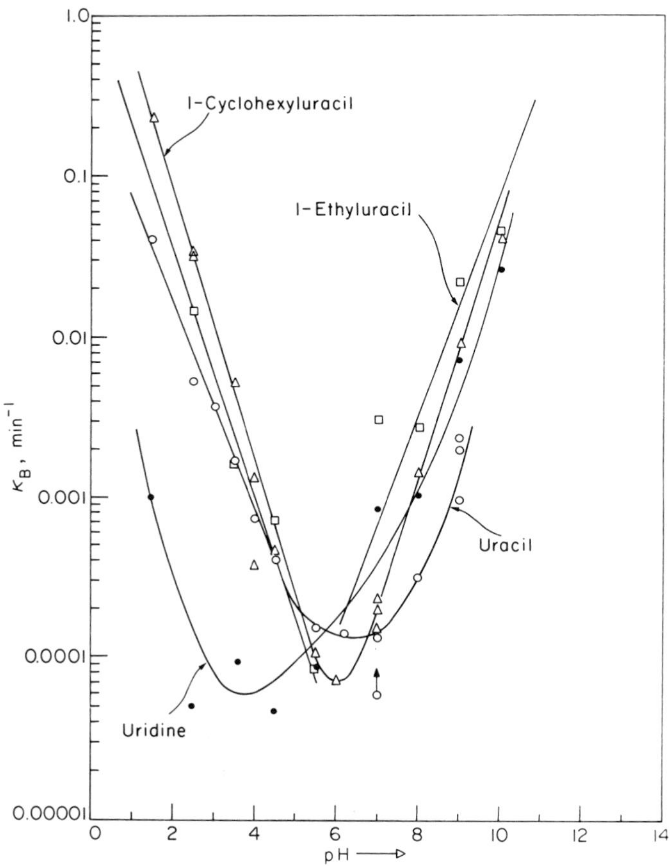

Figure 6. Rate constants for the dehydration of the 1-substituted uracils as functions of the pH. ⊙—uridine; ○—uracil; □—1-ethyluracil; △—1-cyclohexyluracil

Excitation of a ground state UH^+ or U^- can be easily eliminated as the responsible process for uracil photohydration. In the first place, the midpoint of the uracil curve in Figure 7, at about 4.5 does not agree with either of the known pK values of uracil, Reactions 8a and 8b.

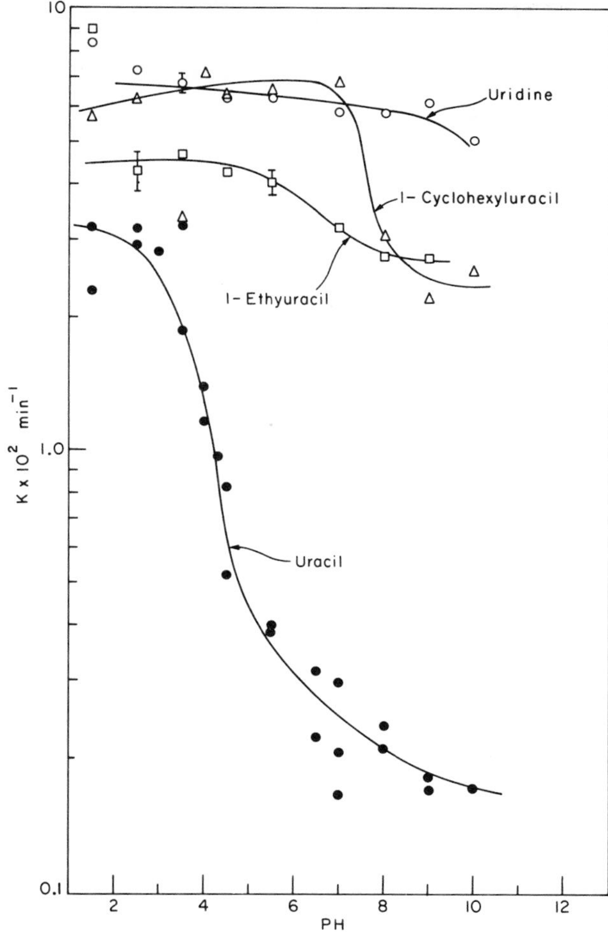

Figure 7. Rates constants for photohydrate formation in the 1-substituted uracils

Energy transfer from excited U* to UH^+ or U^- can also be eliminated as the responsible process by the same observations.

Secondly, the quantum yields required to explain the observed rates when estimated from the calculated concentrations of UH^+ or U^- (assuming these to be the absorbing species responsible for reaction) turn out to range from 0.1 at pH 2 to 3 at pH 4, and even higher at higher pH values for UH^+. The required quantum yields for excitation of U^- would be even higher, since the fraction of light absorbed at 265 n.m. by these species is negligible in the pH range 2 to 7. The reactive intermediate for photohydration is thus not likely to have been formed by excitation of ground state UH^+ or U because the concentration of these is simply too low in the pH range of 2 to 7 to account for the observed rates of photolysis.

The effect of the ground state UH^+ concentration upon the rate of the reaction can also be considered specifically. The data of Figure 7 reflect the rates of the reaction at constant (initial) U concentration, and varying H^+ and UH^+ concentrations. It is possible to study the rate of the reaction at constant UH^+ concentration, and different values of pH, by varying the U concentration. Table I gives the results of such a study.

Table I. Uracil Photohydration Rate Constant, K_f, at Constant (UH^+)

pH	*10^4U*	*10^8UH^+*	*10^2K_f*
5	1.74	0.55	0.293
4	0.18	0.55	1.40

The rate of the reaction is independent of the ground state $[UH^+]$ in this pH range. At lower pH values, where the fraction of UH^+ becomes equal or greater than the fraction of U, excitation of ground state UH^+ may become the important process in photohydration but it looks as if the rate of the reaction saturates at such low pH values—*i.e.*, all of the uracil possible is reacting, regardless of the source of the excited UH^+. Over the pH range of 3 to 9, however, it is most likely protonation (or proton loss) of an excited state which is providing the reactive species.

The observed sigmoidal dependence of rate constant upon pH is consistent with an ordinary photochemical reaction mechanism which includes an equilibrium between an excited uracil molecule and hydrogen ion. Consider the following set of reactions, a–f

$$U \xrightarrow{hv} {}^1U^* \quad (a)$$

$${}^1U^* \rightarrow U\ (+{}^3U^* \xrightarrow{O_2} U) \quad (b)$$

$${}^1U^* + H^+\ (\text{or } H_3O^+) \rightarrow {}^1(UH^+)^* \quad (c)$$

$${}^1(UH^+)^* \rightarrow U^* + H^+ \quad (d)$$

$${}^1(UH^+)^* \rightarrow U + H^+ \quad (e)$$

$${}^1(UH^+)^* + W \rightarrow U_{H_2O} + H^+ \quad (f)$$

in which ${}^1U^*$ and ${}^3U^*$ stand for singlet and triplet excited uracil molecules, W stands for water (without commitment to the molecularity of the species; the role of water in this reaction will be discussed in a subsequent paper), and U_{H_2O} stands for the photohydrate. The excited uracil species involved in photohydrate formation have been specified as the singlet because of our own observations (*4*) that the rate of photolyses of dimethyluracil was unaffected by equimolar concentrations of isoprene ($E_t = 55$ kcal.) or acetophenone ($E_t = 73$ kcal.), and by the insensitivity of uracil photohydrate formation to known triplet donors of higher or lower triplet energy than uracil (*8, 10*). The product forming step of the sequence will be considered to be Reaction f; and the rate of photohydrate formation is

$$dU_{H_2O}/dt = K_f{}^1[UH^+]^*[W].$$

The steady state concentrations of $^1U^*$ and $^1(UH^+)^*$ are then:

$$[^1U^*] = (\Phi I_a + k_d[UH^+]^*)/(k_b + k_cH^+)$$

$$^1[UH^+]^* = (k_c[^1U^*][H^+])/(k_d + k_e + k_fW)$$

and the overall rate of the reaction, in terms of the steady state concentration of $^1[UH^+]^*$ is:

$$dU_{H_2O}/dt = \left\{\frac{k_f W \Phi I_a}{k_e + k_f W}\right\} \left\{\frac{[H^+]}{\dfrac{AB}{A - C} + [H^+]}\right\} \qquad (9)$$

where $A = k_c(k_d + k_e + k_fW)$

$B = k_b/k_dK^*$ $\qquad K^* = k_c/k_d$

$C = k_d{}^2K^*$ $\qquad W = (H_2O)_n$

ΦI_a = Rate of formation of $^1U^*$.

Equation 9 predicts the proper sigmoidal variation of rate with pH, analogous to that shown in Equation 7. This agreement depends upon the insertion into a conventional mechanism of the equilibrium between U^* and H^+ (Reactions c and d).

The water species involved in this reaction must be neutral (and not OH^-) because of the fact that the rate of uracil photohydrate formation is independent of NaCl concentration up to 1*M*, and is the same in unbuffered water as in 0.1*M* phosphate buffer. The rate constant for photohydrate formation in CU was also observed, in a series of runs all made in the same day with the same initial CU concentration, to be 0.0418 ± 0.010 at NaCl concentrations of 0, 0.001*M*, 0.01*M*, 0.1*M*, and 1*M*. The lack of salt effect is consonant, according to Debye-Huckel theory (*3*) with the reaction of a charged species $(UH^+)^*$ with an uncharged species, as written in Reaction f, and eliminates reaction between two charged species in the product-forming process.

The constant, $AB/(A\text{-}C)$ contains the equilibrium constant, K^*, as a function of the listed rate constants. The relationship between K^* and $AB/(A\text{-}C)$ can be estimated if some simplifying assumptions are made. Since the validity of the mechanism depends upon the assumption that equilibrium is established between $^1U^*$ and $^1(UH^+)^*$, k_d must be much greater than k_e or k_fW; since the quantum yield for the overall conversion is very low, either $k_b >> k_c$ or $k_d + k_e >> k_fW$. Assuming the latter, then:

$$pK^* = pH - \log (k_b/k_e).$$

If the ratio k_b/k_e is anywhere between 0.1 and 10 (not unlikely, since in each case the decay of a singlet excited state is the process), then the pH at the midpoint of the uracil line in Figure 7 is within a unit of equaling the pK of the excited state.

The relationship of $AB/(A\text{-}C)$ to K^* could be evaluated more certainly, if the pK* values of the excited states of uracil were known by independent measurement—*e.g.*, by the pH dependence of fluorescent intensity (*20*). This information is not available for any of the substances studied in this investigation. A weak fluorescence at 77°K. is reported for 1-methyluracil and 1,3-dimethyluracil (*11*), but no observations of the pH dependence. The fluorescence maximum for 1-methyluracil shifts from 328 n.m. at pH 7 to 338 n.m. at pH 13[11]. The pK* of the uridine phosphorescent state appears to be about 10, an upward shift from basic pK_b of 9.12 for ground state uridine[13]. Borrensen (*5*) reports a shift of the acid pK_a (dissociation of protonated pyrimidine) of primidine to about 2.0 in the singlet excited state from 1.4 in the ground state, and Krishna and Goodman (*9*) state that the singlet excited pyrimidine forms much weaker hydrogen bonds than does the ground state. Both of these results are consistent with the notion that the protonated pyrimidines are weaker acids in the singlet excited states—*i.e.*, the pK_a values would be expected to shift to larger values upon excitation. (It is not unreasonable to ask whether there is time for a proton to diffuse in to the excited uracil during the lifetime of the excited state ($\sim 10^{-9} s$). It can be estimated that, assuming $D = 10^{-5}$ cm.^{2}/sec., that a proton can move about 10A. in 10^{-9} sec., and that at pH 1, every excited molecule would have a proton within 10A. The change in pK values of the pyrimidines mentioned here with excitation is empirical proof that the protons do move fast enough; Calden (*6*) comments that protonation of excited molecules in the fluorescent state is not diffusion limited.)

The point of inflection of the uracil rate curve in Figure 7 indicates a pK* for the reactive state of about 4.0. This reflects an increase in the acid dissociation constant (from $\sim$ 0.5). The inference from this is that the reactive species is likely $^1(UH^+)^*$, as represented in the Equations a–f; and not $(U^-)^*$, for which a completely analogous mechanism could be written, although not easily related to the very low rates of photolysis at high values of pH.

The corresponding pK* value for EU is then about 6.4, and that for CU is about 7.5; the ground state pK_a values are not known but are probably about 0. The data for uridine are more difficult to understand.

(It was thought at first that the uridine photoproduct might be one resulting from addition of the 5′-CH_2OH across the 5,6-double bond, but NMR measurements by W. J. Wechter (*19*) indicate that the product is actually one resulting from addition of water, presumably in the normal manner. Photolysis rates of uridine—2′(3′)-phosphate, and of uridine-5′-phosphate are also faster at low pH values than at neutral pH values; that of the 5′-phosphate is inflected at pH values of about 1.5 and also at about 6.5. This behavior is unlike that reported for cytidylic acid (*2*), and will be discussed more fully in a separate publication.) The break in the rate curve, Figure 7, comes at a pH of about 10, similar to the pK reported for the fluorescent state (*11*), and which is the pK for proton loss from the N_3 position.

It is evident from the non-zero rate for uracil photohydrate formation at high values of pH that the fast reaction of $^1(UH^+)^*$ with water is accompanied by a slower reaction which is presumably the reaction of $^1U^*$ with water. This type of reaction is apparently quite fast for EU and CU, although still slower than the reaction of the protonated excited state. It is possible that both protonated and neutral excited uridine species react at the same rate.

Several useful conclusions can be drawn from these observations. The large increase in the acid pK of these pyrimidines upon excitation, and the consequent marked weakening of hydrogen-bond forming ability may be a process contributing to the ultraviolet-induced denaturation of double helix nucleic acids (*1*), along with the possibly weaker hydrogen bonding of the photoproducts. The dependence of photohydration rate upon the concentration of $(PyH^+)^*$ helps to understand why photohydration and photodimerization can compete in uracil photolysis, and why photohydration is the sole process in cytidine and cytosine (*13*). It is possible that the failure of thymine to form a photohydrate may be because of an instability of the photohydrate and not to an abnormally slow rate of photohydrate formation (*4*).

Equation f is formally an electrophilic attack of a charged species on neutral water, and is naturally faster for a species with a formal positive charge. However, the appreciable rate of photohydration observed for excited uracil suggests that there may be an appreciable charge separation in this singlet excited molecule, as suggested by others (*see* Reference 4 for a review).

However, on the other hand the mechanism proposed here may be specific only for photohydration of uracil and the 1-alkyluracils examined. The lack of pH dependence in photohydration of dimethyluracil, the failure of thymine to form a photohydrate even at low pH values (*4*), and the recent observation that cytidine-3′-phosphate hydrates faster at neutral pH values than at acid pH values (*2*), suggest that the fastest hydrate-forming reaction path of the singlet excited pyrimidine molecules may be specifically different for each particular pyrimidine derivative.

Acknowledgment

One of us (J. G. B.) would like to acknowledge gratefully the support of the John Simon Guggenheim Memorial Foundation for a sabbatical year in which the work described here was begun, and to thank the staff of the University Chemical Laboratory, Cambridge, England, in general, and Professor Lord Todd, in particular, for much assistance during that year. We would also like to thank M. Cher (this laboratory) and J. Y. Yang (Western Nuclear Research Center, Buffalo, New York) for many helpful conversations during the course of this work.

Literature Cited

(1) Alexander, P., Moroson, H., *Nature* **185,** 678 (1960).
(2) Becker, H., LeBlanc, J. C., Johns, H. E., *Photochem. Photobiol.* **6,** 733 (1967).
(3) Benson, S. W., "The Foundations of Chemical Kinetics," p. 525, McGraw-Hill, New York, 1960.
(4) Burr, J. G., in "Advances in Photochemistry," Vol. 5, J. N. Pitts, G. W. Hammond, A. A. Noyes, Jr., eds., Interscience Publishers, New York (*in press*).
(5) Borrensen, H. C., *Acta. Chem. Scand.* **17,** 921 (1963).
(6) Calden, E. F., "Fast Reactions in Solution," p. 160, John Wiley, New York, 1964.
(7) Calvert, J. G., Pitts, Jr., J. N., "Photochemistry," pp. 21-22, John Wiley, New York, 1966.
(8) Greenstock, C. L., Brown, I. H., Hunt, J. W., Johns, H. E., *Biochem. Biophys. Res. Comm.* **27,** 431 (1967).
(9) Krishna, V. G., Goodman, L., *J. Am. Chem. Soc.* **83,** 2042 (1961).
(10) Lamola, A. A., Mittal, J. P., *Science* **154,** 1560 (1967).
(11) Longworth, J. K., Rahn, R. O., Shulman, R. G., *J. Chem. Phys.* **45,** 2930 (1966).
(12) Masson, C. R., Boekelheide, V., Noyes, W. A., "Technique of Organic Chemistry," Vol. II, 2nd ed., p. 295, Interscience, New York, 1956.
(13) McLaren, A. D., Shugar, D., "Photochemistry of Proteins and Nucleic Acids," Chap. VI, Pergamon, London, 1964.
(14) Moore, A. M., *Can. J. Chem.* **36,** 281 (1958).
(15) Moore, A. M., Thompson, C. H., *Prog. in Radiobiol.* **4,** 75 (1956).
(16) Moore, A. M., Thompson, C. H., "Photochemistry of Proteins and Nucleic Acids," p. 177, Pergamon, London, 1964.
(17) Setlow, R. B., *Science* **153,** 379 (1966).
(18) Sztumpf-Kulikowska, E., Shugar, D., Boag, J. W., *Photochem. Photobiol.* **6,** 41 (1967).
(19) Wechter, W. J., Upjohn Co. (personal communication).
(20) Weller, A., *Progr. in Reaction Kinetics* **1,** 189 (1961).

RECEIVED December 28, 1967. A preliminary account of this work has been published in *Photochemistry and Photobiology* **8,** 23 (1968).

30

Photochemical Genetics. II. The Kinetic Role of Water in the Photohydration of Uracil and 1,3-Dimethyluracil

J. G. BURR and E. H. PARK

Science Center/Aerospace and Systems Group, North American Rockwell Corporation, Thousand Oaks, Calif. 91360

The rate of photohydration of uracil with light of 265 n.m. in mixtures of acetonitrile and water is a linear function of the water content of the mixture; the deuterium isotope effect, R_{H_2O}/R_{D_2O}, *is 1.18. These observations are shown to be consistent with the mechanism for uracil photohydrate formation proposed to explain the pH dependence of the rates. The rate of photohydrate formation for 1,3-dimethyuracil is approximately proportional to the square of the water concentration in acetonitrile-*H_2O *mixtures, acetonitrile-*D_2O*, and in dioxane-water mixtures,* R_{H_2O}/R_{D_2O} = *2.84. These data are also interpretable in terms of a common photohydration mechanism.*

The effect of pH changes and neutral salt concentration upon the rate of uracil photohydration has been reported (together with similar data for some 1-alkyluracils and uridine) in the first paper of the series (*3*). It was concluded from those observations that the product-forming reaction was one between an excited $(UH^+)^*$, formed by equilibrium protonation of singlet excited uracil, and a neutral water species. The molecularity of this neutral water species has now been examined by measuring the rate of uracil photohydration in mixtures of acetonitrile and water, and acetonitrile and D_2O. Photohydrate formation in 1,3-dimethyluracil (DMU) in similar mixtures, as well as in mixtures of dioxane and water has also been studied. The results of these studies are reported in this paper.

Materials and Sample Preparation

Dioxane from a variety of manufacturers and of various degrees of purity were all unsatisfactory without extensive purification; the measure of quality was a sharp ultraviolet cutoff at 203 n.m. and a low and reproducible rate of DMU photolysis in the neat solvent. This could only be achieved in dioxane fractionated in a nitrogen atmosphere five times from sodium through a ten plate packed column and distilled immediately into flask containing the pyrimidine. Dioxane was not considered a satisfactory solvent.

Acetonitrile (Eastman Spectrograde) was used without further purification, since fractional distillation had little effect on the spectrum of the solvent or upon the rate of pyrimidine photolysis in the neat solvent.

Some photolyses were attempted with bis(dimethoxyethyl) ether and with tetrahydrofuran, but these were even more unsatisfactory than dioxane and no reliable quantitative measurements of pyrimidine photolysis rates were obtained.

Uracil and 1,3-dimethyluracil were Cyclo Chemical Company stock. Solutions were prepared in the neat solvents at $10^{-3}M$, and diluted with additional solvent to make $10^{-4}M$ solutions; these were then diluted with the appropriate amount of water.

The densities of both dioxane-water and acetonitrile-water show slight (4%) deviations from ideality (*12, 13*), so that minor corrections were necessary in calculating pyrimidine concentrations. Both dioxane and acetonitrile are weaker bases than water (acetonitrile is much weaker) (*8*); acetonitrile has a high dielectric constant (*10*) of 37.5 and dioxane a low one of 2.209. If dilution were simply the only factor the pH of 5.6*M* water in acetonitrile should be 8; actually the pH of unbuffered oxygen-bubbled water was 6.3 and that of oxygen-bubbled 5.6*M* (10 Vol.%) water in acetonitrile was 5 (Beckman pH Meter). This admittedly crude measurement is taken only to indicate that large changes in hydrogen ion availability do not occur when water is diluted to this extent by acetonitrile. The proper value would be pa_H, as defined by R. G. Bates (*2*), but the necessary data are not available for mixtures of acetonitrile and water. We shall assume that the pH changes in the acetonitrile-water and in the dioxane-water system are insufficient to affect photohydration rates (*3*).

Irradiations. The source of light was a 1000 watt GE BH6 high pressure mercury arc, filtered through a Bausch and Lomb High Intensity Monochromator. Details of this apparatus and irradiation procedures are described in the previous paper (*3*).

Product Analysis. Analysis of the photolyzed solutions for photohydrate content was carried out by acidification and heating, as described previously (*3*). The fraction of photohydrate formed in photolysis of DMU and uracil in air-saturated acetonitrile-water and acetonitrile-D_2O solutions thus determined is shown in Figure 1. Substantial amounts of products, reported as dimers (*9*), are formed from uracil and thymine in acetonitrile—that from thymine differing from the thymine dimer produced in DNA or frozen thymine solutions (*9*). However, the rates of photolysis of uracil, thymine and DMU in neat acetonitrile follow first

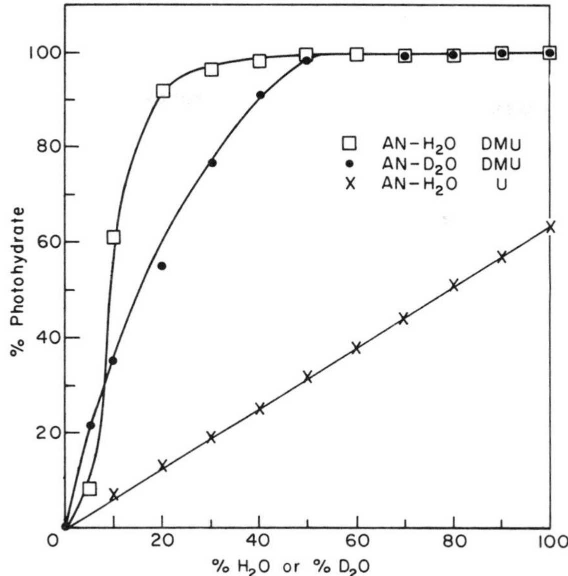

Figure 1. The fraction of photohydrate formed in mixtures of acetonitrile and H_2O or D_2O; initial pyrimidine concentrations 10^{-4}M

order kinetics, Figure 2, agreeing with the observations of Lamola and Mittal (9). First order kinetics for dimer formation in acetonitrile are difficult to understand since in our photolysis system photohydrate formation in uracil followed similiar first order kinetics; dimer formation thus should be initially at least second order in pyrimidine concentration as observed by Sztumpf-Kulikowska *et al.*, (*11*) for orotic acid dimerization, and by us for uracil dimerization in well degassed aqueous solution (*3*). Greenstock *et al.*, indicate that products other than dimers are formed in acetonitrile (*7*); we have some indication that acetonitrile may be reacting with the excited pyrimidine molecules under certain conditions. We are continuing our investigation of the nature of these products, with the thought that they may not be the photodimer.

The nature of the products formed from DMU in dioxane with less than 40% water were complicated. Products were formed in pure dioxane which on acidification and heating reverted to DMU but which did not have the same R_f as DMU on paper chromatograms. These products persisted up to about 30 to 40% water; above this water concentration, the photoproduct was entirely the known photohydrate. It is probable that carbinols and peroxides present in the dioxane were reacting with the excited DMU molecules, since carbinols and other neutral nucleophiles are known to be capable of such reactions (*4*).

Calculation of Rates. The relative rates of pyrimidine photolysis in these solvent mixtures given in Figures 3 and 4 were obtained by observing the absorbance changes for a standard photolysis time (usually 20 minutes), after it was determined that the reactions were first order in pyrimidine—*i.e.*, plots of log A_0/A were linear with time. These values of ΔA_{20} were converted to rates, using known values of the extinction coefficient. The rates were normalized to a standard value of $I_0 = 5.36 \times 10^{20}$ quanta liter^{-1} min.$^{-1}$, as in the previous study (*3*). Normalized standard rates of photohydrate formation were then obtained by multiplying the photolysis rate at each solvent composition by the fraction of photohydrate formed in a mixture of that composition, taken from Figure 1. Rates of DMU photohydrate formation in the region 0 to 40% water could only be estimated from the paper chromatograms; the variation of photohydrate formation rate was approximately linear with water concentration in this range. As can be seen from Figure 4, some product yield uncertainty in this region of water concentration did not have much effect on the final result.

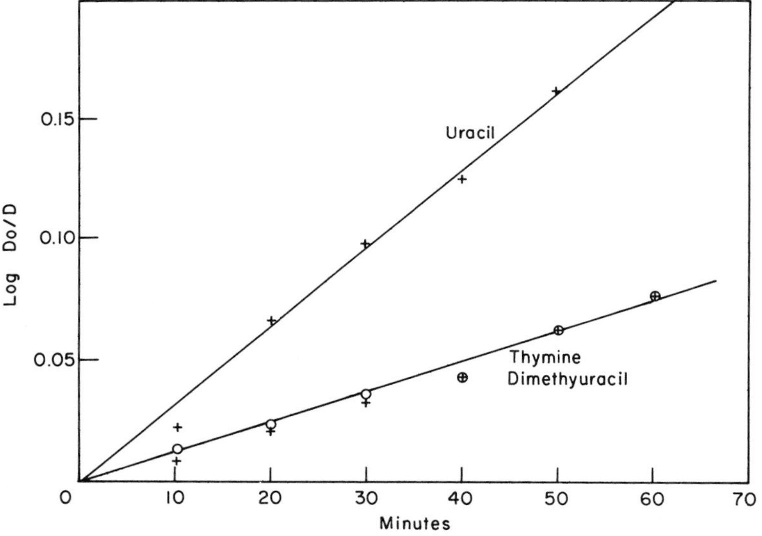

*Figure 2. Rates of photolysis of several pyrimidines in neat acetonitrile; initial pyrimidine concentrations about 10^{-4}*M

Results and Discussion

The rate of uracil photohydrate formation is a linear function of the H_2O or the D_2O concentration in acetonitrile, Figure 3. This variation in rate is not caused by a variation in hydrogen ion—*i.e.*, solvated hydrogen ion—because the estimated variation in pH over this solvent range (1

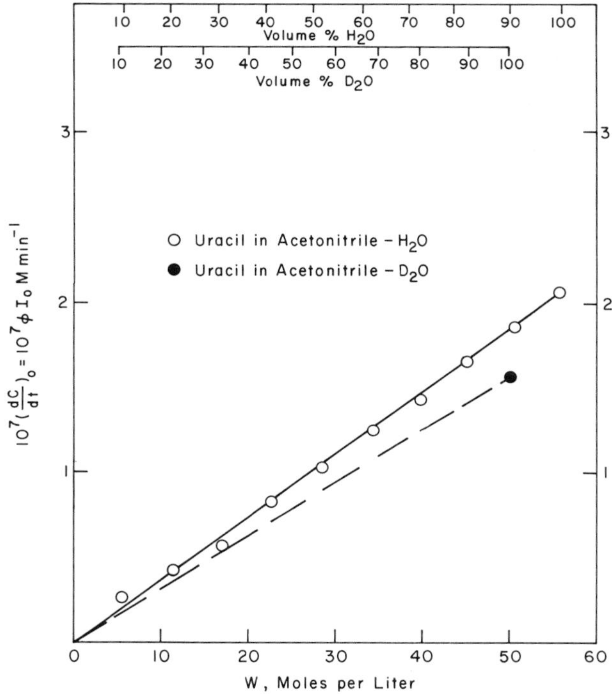

Figure 3. Rates of photohydration of uracil (10^{-4}M) in mixtures of acetonitrile and H_2O or D_2O. The rates are all normalized to $I_0 = 5.36 \times 10^{20}$ *quanta liter^{-1} min.$^{-1}$*

unit) is insufficient to cause such a rate variation (*3*); furthermore, the trend is opposite to that which would be predicted by the pH variation. The linearity and direction of the trend in rate is not in conformity with trends predicted for variations of cation-dipole reaction rates or dipole-dipole reaction rates with variation of dielectric strength. The fastest product-forming step in uracil photohydration was shown in the first paper of this series (*3*) to be proportional to the concentration of excited protonated uracil $(UH^+)^*$ and a neutral water species. The rate constants of reactions between cations and neutral dipolar molecules should increase as the dielectric constant of the medium decreases (*1*). The effects of dielectric constant on reactions between two neutral dipolar molecules—i.e., between excited uracil, U*, and a neutral water species—are difficult to distinguish from other solvent and structural effects, but if this can be done, then the log of the rate constant should be inversely proportional to the dielectric constant of the medium (*1*). However, the variation of the photohydration rate of DMU with water concentration (Figure 4) is the same in mixtures of dioxane-water, D = 2.21–78.54, as it is in mixtures of acetonitrile and water, D = 37.5–78.54. This coincidence also excludes many other properties of the mixed solvents as sources of the rate variations.

The rate trends indicated in Figures 3 and 4 may be used with good assurance, therefore, to determine the molecularity of the neutral water species concerned in the photohydration reactions. The linear variation of uracil photohydration rate with water concentration indicates that this reaction is first order in water concentration. The product forming step in this reaction can now be written with assurance, employing the notation from our first paper (3), as Equation 1.

$$(dU_{H_2O})/dt = k_f(UH^+)^*(H_2O) \qquad (1)$$

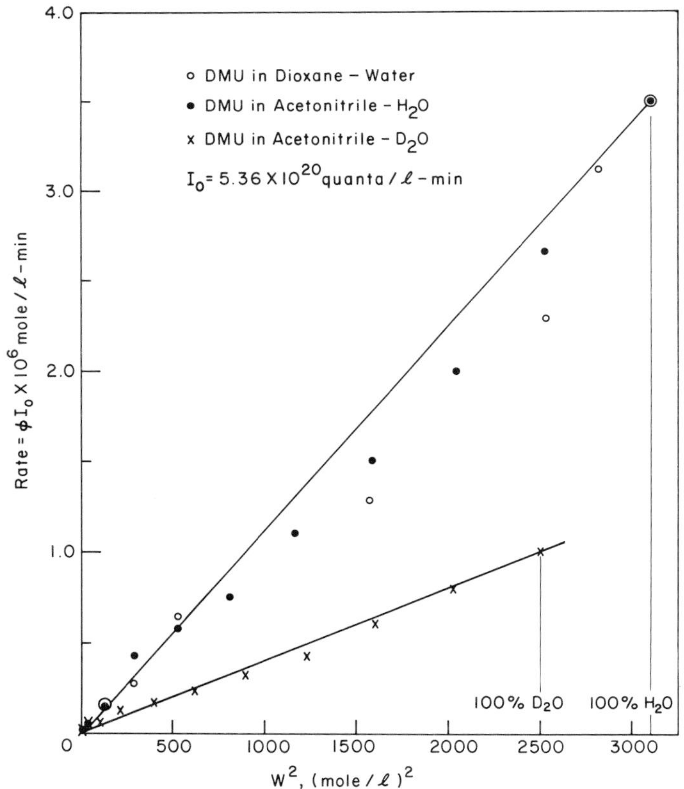

Figure 4. Rates of photohydration of DMU (10^{-4}M) in mixtures of water with dioxane or acetonitrile and in mixtures of acetonitrile and D_2O; $I_o = 5.36 \times 10^{20}$ quanta liter^{-1} min.$^{-1}$

This conclusion is reinforced by the direction of the deuterium isotope effects for photohydrate formation in both uracil and DMU: k_H/k_D is 1.18 for uracil photohydration and 2.8 for DMU photohydration (Figures 3 and 4). The fact that k_H/k_D is greater than 1.0 for uracil photohydration is significant because in that photolysis the principal product forming reaction mechanism was shown (2) to include a equilibrium between excited uracil and hydrogen ion. This is now shown

$$U^* + H^+ \rightleftharpoons (UH^+)^*$$

$$(UH^+)^* + H_2O \rightarrow U_{H_2O} + H^+$$

to be followed by reaction between the excited protonated uracil and H_2O. Ionic reactions such as this in which the water is involved only in equilibrium protonation of a base, and in which the product formation from the protonated base is relatively slower than the protonation —*i.e.*, acid-catalyzed reactions with a "pre-equilibrium," generally are faster in D_2O than in H_2O because D_2O is a better proton donor than H_2O ($pK_{D_2O} = 14.955$, $pK_{H_2O} = 13.997$ at 25°C.) (*6*); the concentration of protonated base is thus higher in D_2O than in H_2O, and the rate is faster (5)—*i.e.*, k_H/k_D is less than 1.0. The magnitude of the isotope effects in these photolyses is, however, characteristic of a kinetic isotope effect in which molecular water would be involved in the product-forming step. The magnitude of the value for uracil is that of a secondary isotope effect, and magnitude for DMU is that normally found in a primary isotope effect.

The rate of photohydration of DMU in either dioxane-water or acetonitrile-water is, however, not linear in the water concentration but more nearly proportional to the square of the water concentration. It should be said at once that the reasons for the differences between the kinetic behavior of uracil and DMU in these solvent mixtures is not completely understood, and may eventually be found to reflect simply undiscovered features of photolyses in such mixed solvent systems. It is nevertheless instructive to examine these differences in the light of the

$$U \xrightarrow{a} {}^1U^*$$

$${}^1U^* \xrightarrow{b} U(+{}^3U^* \xrightarrow{O_2} U)$$

$${}^1U^* + H^+ \underset{d}{\overset{c}{\rightleftharpoons}} (UH^+)^*$$

$$(UH^+)^* \xrightarrow{e} U + H^+$$

$$(UH^+)^* + H_2O \xrightarrow{f} U_{H_2O} + H^+$$

reaction mechanism which has been proposed for uracil photohydration (3), consisting of reaction steps (a)–(f). The overall rate of photohydration, written as Equation 2 in the earlier paper, can be rewritten as Equation 3.

$$dU_{H_2O}/dt = \frac{k_f W \varphi I_a}{(k_e + k_f W)} \left[\frac{(H^+)}{\frac{AB}{A - C} + (H^+)} \right] \quad (2)$$

where $A = k_c(k_d + k_e + k_f W)$, $B = k_b/k_d K_e^*$, $C = k_d^2 K_e^*$, $K_e^* = k_c/k_d$, $W = H_2O$ and φI_a is the rate of formation of $^1U^*$.

$$dU_{H_2O}/dt = \frac{K_w' \varphi I_a k_f W^2}{[k_e + k_f W] \left[\frac{AB}{A - C} + H^+ \right]} \quad \text{where } K_w' = K_w/(OH^-)(55.5) \quad (3)$$

The second order water dependence and large isotope effect follow if in DMU photohydrate formation, $k_e >> k_f W$, whereas the first order water dependence and small isotope effect observed for uracil photolyses, are consistent with $k_f W >> k_e$. The differences in isotope effect (although not the differences in the order of water dependence) can also be understood if the product-forming reaction for DMU is that between a neutral excited molecule and neutral water. The isotope effect then is the primary one in the attack on the water molecules. In the case of uracil, this primary isotope effect is partly offset by the smaller "pre-equilibrium" isotope effect of opposite sign (observed values (5) for this isotope effect range up to about $k_D/k_H = 2.1$).

This correlation of second-order water dependence with large primary isotope effect and first order water dependence with the small isotope effect is of course quite tentative, but it is interesting that it can be fitted so neatly into a reaction mechanism which was proposed to explain the variation of uracil photohydration rate with hydrogen ion concentration. This scheme, provisional as it is, seems to provide a framework which includes all of the known kinetic factors in these photolyses.

Acknowledgment

One of us (J. G. Burr) wishes to acknowledge gratefully the support of John Simon Guggenheim Memorial Foundation for a sabbatical year in which the work described here was begun, and to thank the staff of the University Chemical Laboratory, Cambridge, England, in general, and Lord Todd, in particular, for much assistance during that year.

Literature Cited

(1) Amis, E. S., "Solvent Effects on Reaction Rates and Mechanisms," Academic Press, New York, 1966.
(2) Bates, R. G., "Determination of pH, Theory and Practice," p. 228, John Wiley, New York, 1963.
(3) Burr, J. G., Gordon, B. R., Park, E. H., ADVANCES IN CHEMISTRY **81,** 418 (1968).
(4) Burr, J. G., "Advances in Photochemistry," J. N. Pitts, G. W. Hammond, W. A. Noyes, Jr., eds., Interscience Publishers, New York, *in press.*
(5) Burr, J. G., "Tracer Applications for the Study of Organic Reaction Mechanisms," Chap. III, Interscience Publishers, New York, 1957.
(6) Covington, A. K., Robinson, R. A., Bates, R. G., *J. Phys. Chem.* **70,** 3820 (1966).
(7) Greenstock, C. L., Brown, I. H., Hunt, J. W., Johns, H. E., *Biochem. Biophys. Acta* **27,** 431 (1967).
(8) King, E. J., "Acid-Base Equilibria," Chap. 11, McMillan Co., New York, 1965.
(9) Lamola, A. A., Mittal, J. P., *Science* **154,** 1560 (1967).
(10) Robinson, R. A., Stokes, R. H., "Electrolytic Solutions," Appendix 1.2., 2nd ed., Butterworth Publishers, London, 1959.
(11) Sztumpf-Kulikowska, E., Shugar, D., Boag, J. W., *Photochem. Photobiol.* **6,** 41 (1967).
(12) Timmermans, J., "Physico-chemical Constants of Binary Systems in Concentrated Solution," p. 12, Interscience Pub., New York, 1960.
(13) *Ibid.*, p. 64.

RECEIVED December 28, 1967.

31

Luminescence Kinetics of Microcrystalline Adenine Following Pulse Irradiation

E. M. FIELDEN and S. C. LILLICRAP

Physics Department, Institute of Cancer Research, Clifton Avenue, Sutton, Surrey, England

The spectra and decay kinetics of the luminescence of microcrystalline adenine following irradiation by 4.3 Mev. electrons are reported over a temperature range from 93° to 540°K. At the lowest temperatures the emission is followed from 5 μsec. to 5 min. after a 1.6 μsec. electron pulse, and over this time scale the emission intensity decreases by a factor of 10^7. A first order phosphorescence decay component is observed below 130°K. between 5 msec. and 8 sec. The residual non-exponential decay components can be explained by a trapping model possessing a uniform distribution of traps from 0–0.22 e.v. deep with frequency factors $\sim 10^9$ sec.$^{-1}$. An alternative explanation of the initial decay in terms of a cluster ("spur" type) model that is consistent with the data is also discussed.

Absorption of energy from ionizing radiation leads to direct excitation as well as ionization of the absorbing medium. Additional excited states may be produced by ion recombination following the initial ionization events. The resultant excited molecules may lose their excess energy by collisional deactivation or by fission of the molecule to give radicals either spontaneously or by interactions with other molecules, or by emission of a photon. The fission processes will be rapid, occurring over a time scale of the order of the molecular relaxation time, although it may require crossover from the original to a dissociative excited state. In addition to the excitation of single molecules Fano (9) has proposed a collective excitation effect to explain the energy loss spectra of electrons in solid films. This process involves the deposition of 10 to 20 e.v. in a volume of about (100 A.)^3. This energy may be subsequently localized by rupture of a chemical bond or may be delocalized by diffusion or transfer of excitation energy.

The radiative lifetime of an excited state depends on the spin selection rules and is typically of the order of 10^{-8} sec. for a spin allowed transition and up to 10^9 times longer for a spin forbidden transition. Optical excitation generally produces excited singlet states followed by extremely rapid radiationless energy loss, leaving the excited molecules in the first singlet state S_1. The rapid fluorescence process $S_1 \rightarrow S_0$ is in competition with the intersystem crossing process giving triplets $S_1 \rightarrow T_1$. Excitation by slow electrons, however, does not obey all the optical spin selection rules and normally forbidden transitions such as $S_0 \rightarrow T_1$ have a higher probability of occurring directly (*8, 14, 17*). Thus, the absorption of ionizing radiation may lead to the production of triplets as a primary step giving a higher yield of triplets than would have been produced if the primary excitation was to singlet states only. It has been suggested (*20*) with some experimental evidence (*2*) that excitation to high singlet levels by the faster electrons leads to enhanced intersystem crossing to triplet states.

Emission spectroscopy is a convenient method of following the behavior of excited states, possessing many advantages over absorption spectroscopy, especially in the solid state.

The low temperature thermoluminescence spectra of organic materials have also been investigated (*3, 15, 22, 25*), and it is found that most of the glow peaks lie between 100° and 170°K. Lehman and Wallace (*15*) have listed thermoluminescence spectra, glow curves, and emission spectra for a large number of biologically important molecules. The luminescence was recorded during, and several minutes after, irradiation by sources of a wide range of linear energy transfer (LET). These authors also reported an effect of gas pressure on the luminescence yield at low temperatures that was interpreted as the effect of gas penetration into the crystal lattice. Other workers (*7*), however, have demonstrated similar gas effects and shown them to be owing to the temperature differences caused by restricted convection cooling of the powders by the surrounding gas.

The kinetics of the radioluminescence of organic compounds have not been widely published. Bollinger and Thomas (*6*) reported the room temperature decay kinetics of the long-lived scintillation component of trans-stilbene. The decay profile was non-exponential over the 100 μsec. time scale covered and, apart from intensity differences, the decay profile was identical for γ-rays, neutrons and α-particles. However, the decay kinetics of several inorganic phosphors excited by low energy electrons—*e.g.*, cathode ray tube phosphors—have been investigated (*21*). The theoretical treatment of the kinetics of the emission from these ionic lattices has been on the basis of electron trapping, and one of the earlier papers (*18*) points out how apparently simple decay kinetics can arise from various distributions of trap depths. The existence of trapping in organic crystals is confirmed by their thermoluminescent behavior, and it is likely that some of the spontaneous emission involves trapping processes.

Several kinetic schemes have been put forward (*4, 13, 24*) to explain the kinetics of excited states in solid solutions and pure and mixed crystals following optical and ionizing-particle excitation. These schemes, as well as the direct quenching reactions for singlets and triplets, include triplet-triplet annihilation reactions

$$T_1 + T_1 \rightarrow S_1 + S_0$$

and bimolecular triplet quenching reactions

$$T_1 + T_1 \rightarrow T_1 + S_0$$

The first reaction, by producing a singlet state, can lead to a singlet-ground state emission and is responsible for "delayed fluorescence."

The present program is aimed at filling the gap between the emission during radiation and the emission found several minutes after irradiation. By a study of the kinetics and spectra of the emission it is hoped to gain more knowledge of the processes involved.

Experimental

Radiation Source. The source of radiation is a Mullard 4.3 Mev. electron accelerator, Model SL 46, which produces 1.6 μsec. duration pulses at up to 250 mA, with repetition rates varying from a single pulse to 400 pulses per second.

Irradiation Assembly. The irradiation assembly is shown in Figure 1. It consists of a rectangular Perspex (Lucite, Plexiglas) box with two compartments. The rear section contains a phosphorus pentoxide tray to prevent condensation on the cooled sample. The front section contains the sample and is lined with black PVC tape to obscure the luminescence from the irradiated Perspex. At the front end of the box, in line with the sample, is a 1 mm. thick Perspex window through which the electron irradiation beam enters horizontally. Directly above the sample is a Spectrosil quartz window 0.25 mm. thick through which the luminescence is observed. Light emitted from the sample passes through the window and is then reflected horizontally by a front surfaced mirror inclined at 45° (*see* Figure 1). The powdered sample is held in a 6 mm. diameter cup turned in the end of a short aluminum rod. A thermocouple is fixed in this rod just below the sample cup. This cup assembly makes good thermal contact with a 9 mm. diameter copper rod which passes horizontally into the rear compartment. A small heating coil is wound on the copper rod close to the aluminum cup. In the rear compartment the copper rod is soldered to a copper tube of the same external diameter which protrudes from the back of the Perspex box and is bent upwards. A cylindrical brass cup, 5 cm. diameter, is soldered vertically onto the copper tube. The brass cup and the copper tube outside the box are insulated with 4 cm. of expanded polystyrene. The sample is cooled by filling the brass cup with liquid nitrogen. After 10 minutes the sample has cooled to 93°K. and, by controlled use of the heating coil, intermediate temperatures can be obtained. Above 200°K., solid CO_2-acetone is a more suitable coolant. The interior of the box can be flushed with any available gas by means of an entrance tube in the rear section of the box and an exit tube in the front section.

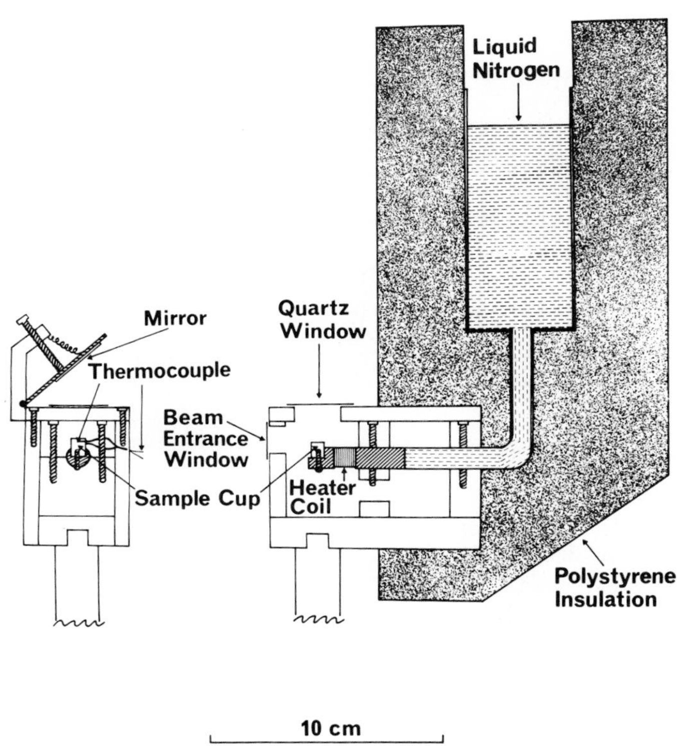

Figure 1. Schematic diagrams of the irradiation assembly. For clarity the liquid nitrogen reservoir has been omitted from the front view and the inclined mirror from the side view

Iradiations above room temperature are carried out by pressing the powder into a 6 × 1 mm. slot milled in a 5 mm. diameter aluminum rod. The rod replaces the normal bit in a 25W soldering iron which acts as a heat source. The assembly is mounted vertically with a thermocouple fixed in the sample holder. Temperatures can be controlled to within 5°C. by regulating the current through the heating element with a Variac transformer.

The light emitted by the irradiated powders is relayed by means of two quartz lenses and two mirrors to the detecting system in the accelerator control room. The optical and photometer system are to be described in detail elsewhere (*10*). Briefly, the optical system imaged the powder sample on the monochromator slits with a 1:1 object-to-image ratio and a light acceptance angle of f 3.5. The monochromator is a Bausch and Lomb High Intensity type with two gratings covering the range 180 to 400 n.m. and 350 to 800 n.m. The light emerging from the monochromator is monitored by a photomultiplier, EMI type 9558BQ, whose output was fed directly to an oscilloscope (Tektronix type 547 or 555). The resultant display of light intensity *vs.* time was photographed. Figure 2 gives an example of two such photographs; the photographs are enlarged

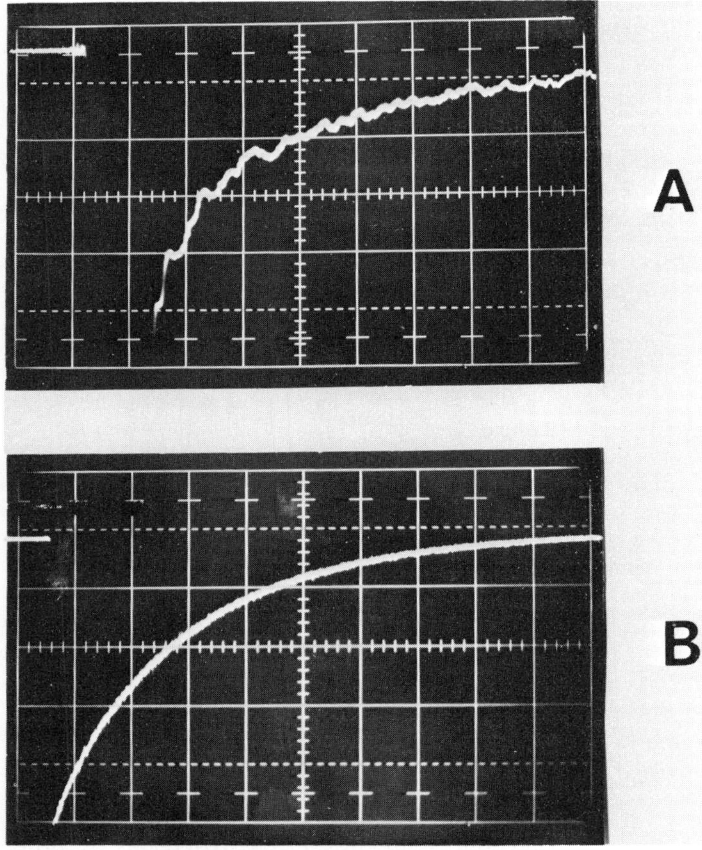

Figure 2. Oscilloscope traces of luminescent decays from adenine following a 10 Krad pulse of 4.3 Mev. electrons of 1.6 μsec. duration. Curve A, 2 μsec./large horizontal division, measured at 295°K. Curve B, 0.5 sec./large horizontal division, measured at 93°K. The vertical sensitivity of Curve B is a factor of 400 greater than that of Curve A

to twice the original size for the purpose of analysis. The optical system is aligned by illuminating the powder with a tungsten lamp and then focussing the light scattered from the powder surface onto the entrance slit of the monochromator.

Calibration of the Photometer System. In order to produce meaningful emission spectra the relative responses at different wavelengths of the entire optical and detecting system had to be known. The overall response is a function of the response of the photo-multiplier, the monochromator efficiency and transmission factors, the reflectivity of mirrors and the transmission and dispersion of the lenses. The relative response of the total system was obtained by comparison with a known emission spectrum; that of Cerenkov radiation. The spectrum of the Cerenkov light emitted when high energy particles pass through a medium has been calculated and measured experimentally (*11, 19*). The spectral intensity $I_{(\lambda)}$ is given by:

$$I_{(\lambda)} = \frac{\text{Const}}{\lambda^2} \cdot \left(1 - \frac{1}{\beta^2 n^2}\right)$$

where β is the electron velocity relative to light in vacuo and n is the refractive index of the medium.

For the purpose of calibration the sample cup was filled with finely powdered Spectrosil high purity quartz, which was assumed to exhibit negligible fluorescence compared with the intensity of the Cerenkov light. With the photomultiplier operating at a fixed voltage the intensity of Cerenkov light produced by a single pulse of 4.3 Mev. electrons was recorded at various wavelengths. As the ultraviolet grating has half the dispersion of the visible range grating, the entrance and exit slits were doubled when the former was in use to maintain a constant band-width. Supplementary Chance-Pilkington color filters were used over some wavelength ranges to remove scattered light from the monochromator. The resultant spectrum consisted of the Cerenkov spectrum modified by the system response. From a comparison of the measured spectrum with the known spectrum the relative system response was deduced. Figure 3 shows the response of the apparatus together with the quartz Cerenkov spectrum calculated from the expression above.

Care was taken to operate the photomultiplier only in the linear region of its characteristics. Unfortunately the luminescence intensity of irradiated adenine immediately after the electron pulse was less than 2% of the Cerenkov plus fluorescence emission during the pulse. Thus, in order to fill the oscilloscope display with the luminescence signal, the oscilloscope amplifiers were necessarily overloaded during the radiation pulse. The time taken for the system to recover was measured by observing the overload recovery of the amplifiers following a similar pulse of Cerenkov light from irradiated quartz powder (which has no long-lived luminescence). Under these conditions it was found that there was no spurious signal 3.4 μsec. after the end of the pulse. Similar tests were made for all working conditions of the photomultiplier.

Temperature Measurements. A Chromel/Alumel thermocouple made from 0.25 mm. diameter wires was used for all temperature measurements. Above 0°C. the temperature/EMF curve followed the published values (*12*) but below 0°C. there was an approximately linear deviation with temperature amounting to an increased EMF of 5% at liquid nitrogen temperature. This low temperature deviation is caused by impurities in the wires and is common to several thermocouple systems. The thermocouple EMF was measured by a Solartron digital voltmeter, model LM1420.

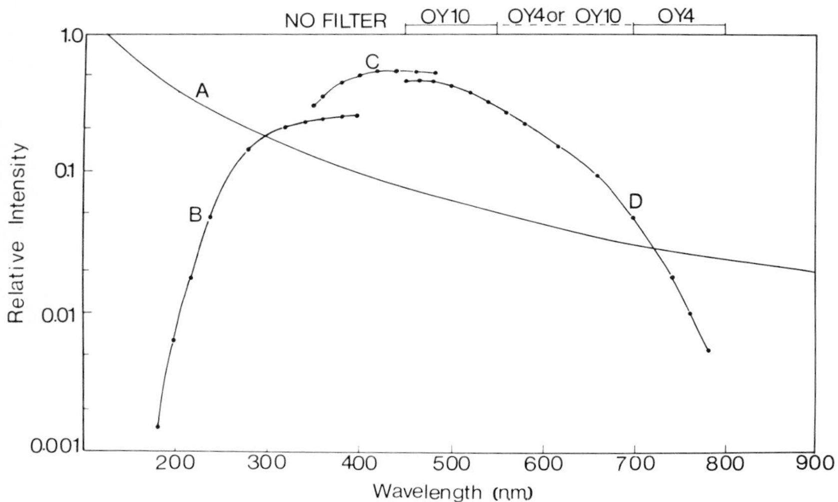

Figure 3. Spectral response of photometer system. Curve A is the emission spectrum of Cerenkov light from irradiated quartz. Curves B, C, and D show the photometer response using Bausch and Lomb gratings. Curve B, ultraviolet grating type 33-86-01, no filter. Curve C, visible grating type 33-86-02, no filter. Curve D, visible grating type 33-86-02, using the Chance filters indicated above the curve

Materials. The adenine was obtained from Calbiochem as A grade microcrystalline powder and was used without further purification. This is a synthetic product, free from contamination with related natural products. It showed only one spot when checked by thin layer chromatography. Most of the powder passed through a 90μ sieve. A sample was also recrystallized from triply-distilled water.

Dosimetry. For dose measurements the adenine powder in the sample cup was replaced by a similar quantity of LiF powder (TLD 100). The thermoluminescence of the LiF was measured 24 hours after a single pulse irradiation on a commercial reader, the Madison Research S-2L. A typical dose was 10 to 15 Krad in water from a 1.6 μsec. pulse.

Experimental Results

Emission Spectra. Spectra of the light emission from adenine powder, after receiving a 15 Krad pulse of 4.3 Mev. electrons, were measured at both room temperature and 93°K. Figure 4 shows the emission spectra of adenine at 5 μsec. and 500 μsec. after irradiation at room temperature, and at 5 μsec., 500 μsec., 600 msec., and 15 sec. after irradiation at 93°K. The bandpass of the monochromator for these measurements was 8.5 n.m., and the spectra were corrected for the spectral response of the whole system. The room temperature spectra are similar in position and shape to the corresponding low temperature spectra, although there are differences at the longer wavelengths. There is also a progressive narrowing of the spectrum and a slight shift to shorter wavelengths with increase in time. The low temperature spectra measured at 600 msec. and 15 sec. after irradiation are the same, within experimental error, as the ultraviolet excited low temperature phosphorescence spectrum of solid adenine described by Singh and Charlesby (*22*) and agree well with that found for the integrated emission at low temperatures following .01 rad x-ray pulses (*16*). It is not unlikely, therefore, that a common process is responsible for the four similar spectra and possibly also for the broader 5 μsec. and 500 μsec. spectra. The 15 sec. low temperature spectrum is in agreement with the limited spectral data published by Lehman and Wallace (*15*) for irradiated adenine powder.

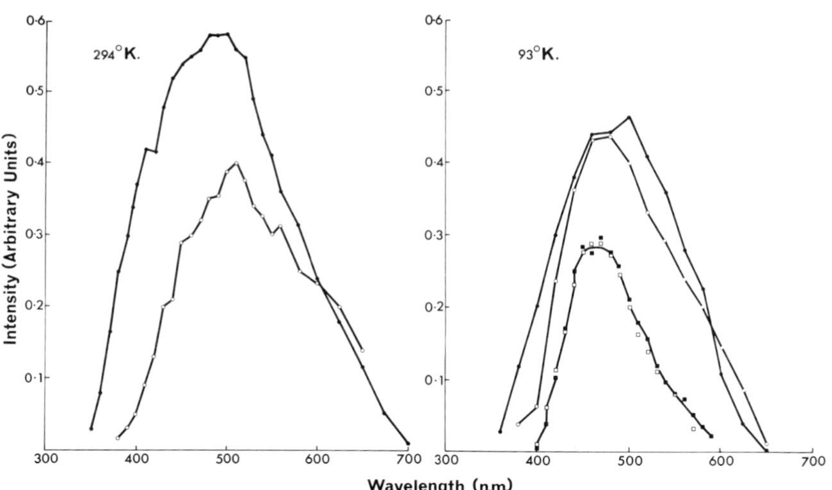

Figure 4. Emission spectra from adenine at 294°K. and 93°K., at different times after irradiation. —●—●— 5 μsec., —○—○— 500 μsec., —■—■— 600 msec., —□—□— 15 sec. The intensity scales have been expanded by different factors to allow comparison. At 294°K., expansion factors are × 1 (5 μsec. spectra), × 100 (500 μsec. spectra). At 93°K. expansion factors are × 2 (5 μsec. spectra), × 100 (500 μsec. spectra), × 200 (600 msec. spectra), × 4.10^5 (15 sec. spectra)

Decay Profiles. The decay of adenine emission was recorded over a range of temperatures. Figure 5 shows the decay profiles at 475 n.m. plotted from 5 μsec. to 1 msec. after irradiation by an 11 Krad electron pulse at 296°K. and 93°K. In all experiments zero time is taken to be the beginning of the pulse. The interesting features of this plot are that the room temperature decay is initially slower than the low temperature decay and that the decay curves cross at 230 μsec. The luminescence is weaker for about 200 μsec. at 93°K. than at room temperature, whereas the integrated emission was found to increase on lowering the temperature. Neither curve is exponential over this range. In addition to the measurements at 475 n.m., decay profiles were also recorded at 400 n.m. and 520 n.m. If the 5 μsec. spectra of Figure 4 are the sum of component spectra, then the decay at 400 n.m. in particular might be expected to be caused by a single component and hence have simpler kinetics than in an overlap region. However, neither of the decay curves at 400 n.m. or 520 n.m. could be fitted to a simple decay scheme. Above room temperature the decays are all similar and no new features appear.

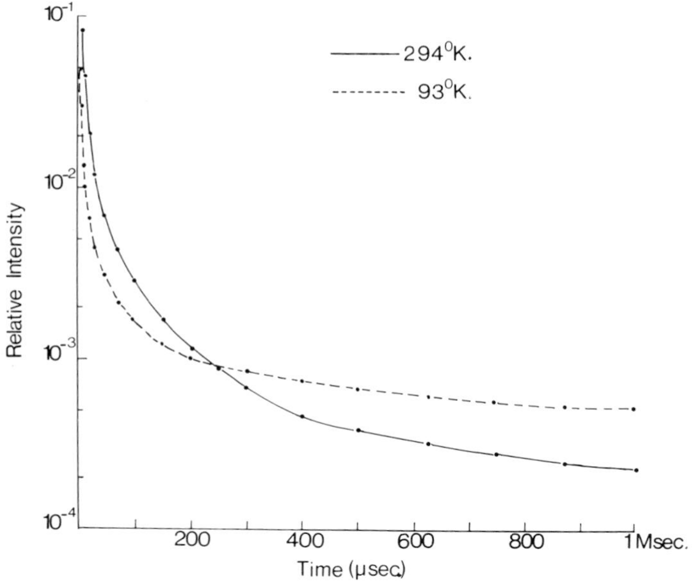

Figure 5. Decay curves of adenine luminescence from 5 μsec. to 1 msec. after irradiation by an 11 Krad. electron pulse at 93°K. and 296°K.

The decay of adenine luminescence at 93°K. is plotted in Figure 6 from 5 μsec. to 5 min. after irradiation. The decay curves out to 30 sec. were recorded following single pulses of electrons and those from 10 sec.

to 5 min. following 140 electron pulses given in 1.4 sec. The two curves were identical in shape in the region of overlap from 10 sec. to 30 sec., and the part of the curve taken with 140 pulses was therefore matched to the rest of the curve in the region of overlap since absolute calibration of dose was not accurate in the multiple pulse run.

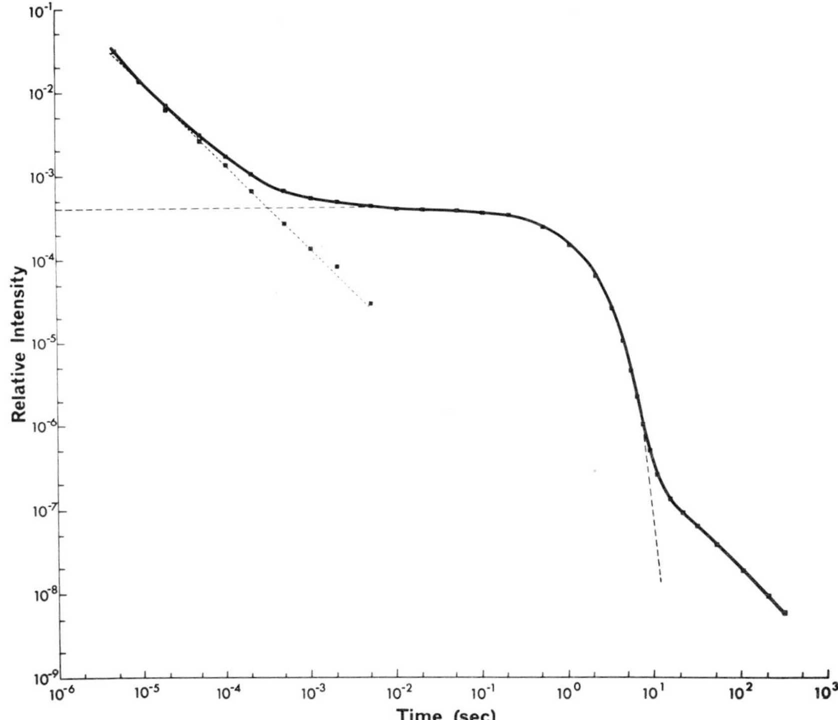

Figure 6. Decay curves of adenine luminescence at 93°K. From 5 μsec. to 30 sec. the decay was recorded following a single electron pulse of 11 Krad, and from 10 sec. to 5 min. following 140 electron pulses in 1.4 sec. The broken line is the continuation of the exponential portion of the curve (5 msec.–8 sec.). The dotted line is the result when the exponential portion is subtracted from the total decay curve

Between 5 msec. and 8 sec. after irradiation the decay curve is exponential with a half-life of 800 msec. Beyond 10 sec. the emission obeys the simple law $I \propto t^{-1}$ in agreement with Lehman and Wallace (*15*). If it is assumed that the exponential decay can be extrapolated back to 5 μsec. after irradiation, then the exponential portion may be subtracted from the total decay profile. The decay curve derived in this way is shown in Figure 6 by the dotted line. This curve also follows a reciprocal power law decay although it does not extrapolate to meet the portion of the curve beyond 10 sec. after irradiation.

Dose Dependence. In order to investigate the effect of dose on the light emission from adenine the intensity of the electron beam was reduced by scattering and the complete decay curves were re-recorded. The thickest scattering plate used reduced the dose to the powder by a factor of 4.6. Over this limited dose range it was found that the emission intensity at any time after irradiation was proportional to the dose at both room temperature and at 93°K., except at post-irradiation times less than 50 μsec. at room temperature. At these short times the light emission per rad slightly increased with increasing dose. The deviation from a linear dose dependence was greater at the shortest time and could be approximated to a $(\text{Dose})^{1.2}$ dependence at 5 μsec. There is an indication of a similar smaller dose dependence at short times at 93°K., but this departure is at present within the experimental error of a linear dependence.

Temperature Dependence. The temperature dependence of the intensity at 475 n.m. at various times after irradiation out to 4 msec. are presented in Figure 7. At temperatures above 300°K. there is a decrease in the residual luminescence with increasing temperature. Below 300°K., however, the residual emission at a given time after irradiation has a maximum value at a particular temperature. This maximum occurs at lower temperatures as the observation time after irradiation is increased. All the decay curves, whether directly observed at constant temperature, or plotted at intermediate temperatures from the smoothed curves of Figure 7, are non-exponential in form and change gradually from the shape at high temperature to that at 93°K.

Because of the low intensity of the emission at temperatures above 160°K. for times greater than 100 msec., it was not possible to follow the variation of luminescence efficiency with temperature over the complete temperature range shown in Figure 7. It was, however, possible to investigate the effect of temperature on the exponential portion of the low temperature decay curve over a limited range near liquid nitrogen temperature. An Arrhenius plot of the exponential decay at temperatures between 93° and 130°K. yielded an activation energy of 0.007 e.v./molecule. This value is in agreement with the activation energy found previously (*16*) for the effect of temperature over the same range on the integrated emission following 0.01 rad x-ray pulses. As the dominant part of the long-lived emission at the low temperature is the exponential, this is further evidence, in agreement with the spectral results, that the same process is responsible for emission at these extremes of dose.

Radiation Damage. It was found that after delivering about 1 Mrad to the powder at 93°K., the slope of the exponential portion of the decay decreased from a half-life of 800 msec. to 600 msec., and also the intensity of emission at 1 sec. after irradiation dropped by a factor of two. After warming the powder to room temperature and recooling, the decay curve returned to normal.

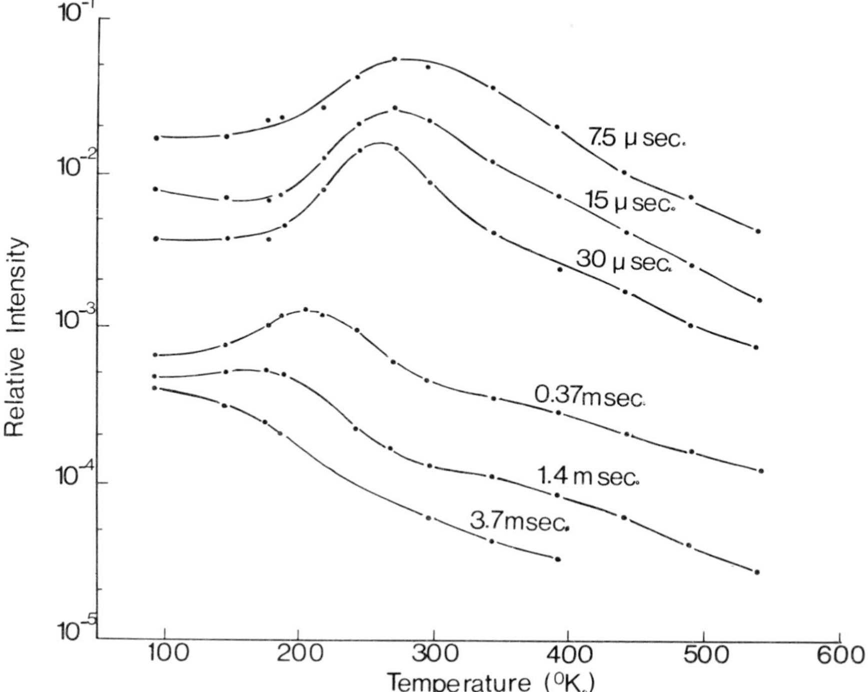

Figure 7. A composite plot of the temperature dependence of the luminescence intensity at various times after irradiation out to 4 msec. The data on this plot are taken from decay curves measured at various temperatures between 93°K. and 540°K.

Physical Effects. To investigate the effect of a different atmosphere on the light emission from adenine, dry argon was introduced into the sample compartment and the decay curves at room temperature and 93°K. measured. No difference exceeding experimental error could be detected between these curves and those recorded in an atmosphere of air. Wet samples also gave the same decay curve at room temperature.

Finally, to test whether the emission depended on the size of the crystals, as it might do if the emission were limited by diffusion of some entities to the crystal surface but not if it arose from physical defects throughout the crystal, an attempt was made to reduce the crystal size by grinding it with an agate pestle and mortar and to increase the size by recrystallization. Neither of these processes caused any significant change, but it is not certain that they succeeded in changing the size of the crystals.

Discussion

The main features of this experiment which require an explanation are the complex shape of the luminescence decay curves, especially at 93°K., and the temperature dependence of the emission. On a simple excitation theory which will be considered initially, only triplet states remain 1 μsec. or longer after irradiation as all the singlets produced will have returned to the ground state or undergone intersystem crossing to triplet states. In addition to the direct phosphorescence, $T_1 \rightarrow S_o$, a number of different pathways are available for the removal of the remaining triplets. A complete decay scheme must include the following processes.

$T_1 \rightarrow S_o$	k_1	Non-radiative quenching	(I)
$T_1 \rightarrow S_o + h\nu$	k_2	Phosphorescence	(II)
$T_1 + T_1 \rightarrow T_1 + S_o$	k_3	Bimolecular triplet quenching	(III)
$T_1 + T_1 \rightarrow S_1 + S_o$	k_4	Triplet-triplet annihilation	(IV)

The singlet produced in Process IV may lead to delayed fluorescence by the radiative process $S_1 \rightarrow S_o + h\nu$, or to the production of a further triplet by intersystem crossing. As the singlet S_1 has a very short lifetime, Process IV is normally the rate determining step in delayed fluorescence.

From these reactions the rate of disappearance of triplets is given by:

$$\frac{-d[T]}{dt} = (k_1 + k_2)[T_1] + (k_3 + \overline{2 - \alpha}k_4)[T_1]^2 \qquad (1)$$

where α = probability of intersystem crossing, $S_1 \rightarrow T_1$

The luminescence intensity (I) of all quanta is given by the equation:

$$I = \frac{dh\nu}{dt} = k_2[T_1] + k_4[T_1]^2 f \qquad (2)$$

where f = probability that S_1 will fluoresce.

The initial concentration of triplets following irradiation may be assumed to be proportional to the dose as no second or higher order process has been proposed for their production (*5, 24*). The relative importance of the first and second order decay processes depends on the initial concentration of triplets and also on the time of observation after irradiation. This is because, in general, the rate of formation of products (photons in this experiment) at any time after irradiation is directly proportional to dose in first order reactions, whereas in a second order reaction the dependence of the product formation rate on dose varies from (dose)^2 at zero time to (dose)^0 at infinite time. As the present apparatus only allows observation from 5 μsec. after irradiation, it was not possible to make measurements at zero time.

Decay Curve at 93°K. The decay curve at 93°K. (Figure 6) is readily resolved into three components which may be considered separately. The time intervals after irradiation in which these components occur are 5 μsec. to 1 msec., 5 msec. to 8 sec., and 10 sec. to 300 sec.

5 MSEC. TO 8 SEC. AFTER IRRADIATION. From 5 msec. to 8 sec. after irradiation the curve is exponential over nine half-lives and the intensity is directly proportional to dose. This behavior is that expected from phosphorescence (Process II) with negligible competition from bimolecular Processes III and IV. As further evidence that this is the process observed, the spectrum taken at 600 msec. is identical with the ultraviolet-induced phosphorescence of adenine (22). However, as the exponent of the exponential varies with temperature it would appear that the triplets are also being quenched by a radiationless process with rate k_1. If the phosphorescence decay (Process II) has a true rate constant much smaller than would give the observed 800 msec. half-life, then the quenching Process I must be the rate determining step in the observed decay. If this is so then the activation energy of 0.007 e.v. (0.16 kcal.) obtained earlier from the temperature dependence of the exponential decay relates to the quenching process. However, if k_1 and k_2 are approximately equal, the use of a simple Arrhenius plot is not justified even if phosphorescence is assumed to have zero activation energy. The half-life of the exponential gives the sum $k_1 + k_2 = 0.875$ sec.$^{-1}$ at 93°K. with the possibility that this is the value of k_1 only.

5 μSEC. TO 1 MSEC. AFTER IRRADIATION. The sections of the decay curves at times less than 1 msec. and greater than 10 sec. after irradiation both show an intensity dependence which is inversely proportional to the time after irradiation—*i.e.*, $I \propto t^{-1}$. In a decay scheme applicable to short times after irradiation, Processes I and II have to be ruled out as being rate determining since the sum of their first order rate constants cannot give a time constant shorter than 0.875 sec.$^{-1}$ at 93°K. As bimolecular processes have a greater relative importance at short times when the concentration of species is highest, Processes III and IV may be mainly contributing to the early part of the decay. Triplet-triplet annihilation leading to delayed fluorescence has been shown by a number of authors to follow ultraviolet- and ionizing-irradiation and has been

suggested as an explanation of the delayed component in scintillation counting (5).

If bimolecular Processes III and IV are the only ones of importance at short times, then Equations 1 and 2 may be reduced to:

$$\frac{-d[T]}{dt} = (k_3 + \overline{2 - \alpha} k_4)[T_1]^2 \tag{3}$$

$$I = k_4[T_1]^2 f \tag{4}$$

Solving Equations 3 and 4 for the time dependence of I gives:

$$I = \frac{I_0}{(KT_0 t + 1)^2} \tag{5}$$

where $K = (k_3 + \overline{2 - \alpha}\, k_4)$, $I_0 = [T_0]^2 k_4 f$ and T_0 = initial concentration of triplets. A plot of log I *vs.* log t with these kinetics would show a negative slope whose magnitude would increase with time and approach a value of −2 after several half-lives. As the experimental data are a very close fit to a reciprocal plot, delayed fluorescence cannot be contributing much to the initial decay.

Alternatively, although Process II cannot be the rate determining process it may still be the emission process provided that the quenching of emission determines the rate of decay. If the bimolecular processes (Processes III and IV) are the important quenching processes, Equation 3 remains applicable. Also, as delayed fluorescence has been shown to be unimportant, then either k_4 or the factor f is small and Equation 2 reduces to:

$$I = k_2[T_1] \tag{6}$$

Solving Equations 3 and 6 for the time dependence of I gives:

$$I = \frac{I_0}{(KT_0 t + 1)} \tag{7}$$

where $I_0 = k_2[T_0]$. This expression describes bimolecular quenching of phosphorescence and approximates to $I \propto t^{-1}$ after I_0 has decreased by a few half-lives. It thus fits the data of Figure 6 from about 5 μsec. after irradiation.

In the region where the reciprocal approximation holds, Equation 7 also predicts that the intensity is independent of dose. It is found, however, that the intensity is proportional to dose. This dose dependence could arise in this kinetic scheme if the species causing luminescence are in non-overlapping clusters or "spurs" and an increase in dose simply results in a proportionate increase in the number of such clusters. However, this "cluster model" would imply that virtually all triplets must be formed in the clusters, and there is as yet no other evidence for this.

10 SEC. TO 300 SEC. AFTER IRRADIATION. The reciprocal decay at times longer than 10 sec. cannot be caused by bimolecular triplet reactions since, if present, these became negligible compared with the simple first order triplet decay from 10 msec. onwards. Processes I to IV alone are therefore not sufficient to account for this long-lived emission and an alternative explanation must be considered.

The property of thermoluminescence demonstrates the existence of trapping sites in adenine powder (*15, 16, 22*). The luminescence decay at times greater than 10 sec. after irradiation can be adequately explained by the existence of such traps. As the emission spectrum at 15 sec. is identical with that of the phosphorescence (Figure 4), it is reasonable to assume, in such a trapping model, that the emission after 10 sec. is from the same energy transition as the phosphorescence but that the release of energy from the traps is the rate determining step.

The kinetics of delayed emission arising from electron trapping in inorganic phosphors has been considered by Randall and Wilkins (*18*) who showed how the form of the decay and its dependence on temperature depended on the distribution of trap depths. For a uniform distribution of trap levels they showed that the intensity is inversely proportional to time after irradiation for times greater than one microsecond. Provided there is no saturation the intensity will be proportional to dose. This relation and predicted dose dependence agree with the experimental data from 10 sec. after irradiation. If the frequency factors (*18*) of the traps in adenine are all of the same magnitude, then traps responsible for the long term decay will be shallower than the $\sim$0.2 e.v. trap responsible for the 120°K. glow peak (*15, 16*). Thus, a trapping model with an approximately uniform distribution of trap depths will adequately account for the decay at times greater than 10 sec. Such a model will also explain the reciprocal decay from 5 μsec. to 1 msec. and its dose dependence, provided the liberation of energy from the traps is also the rate determining process in this region.

Temperature Dependence. At room temperature the exponential phosphorescence decay is absent, presumably because of the removal of triplet states by the temperature sensitive quenching process found at low temperatures. The decay from 5 μsec. to 5 msec. did not fit any simple decay scheme although the mean slope of the decay on a log-log plot was -1. In the first 200 μsec. after irradiation the room temperature emission is more intense than at 93°K. A similar temperature dependence of the luminescence of anthracene crystals has been observed following ultraviolet excitation (*1, 23*). This behavior was interpreted as being caused by the enhanced intersystem crossing to the triplet states at the higher temperatures. This model, however, would not explain why the luminescence intensity of hot adenine powder in Figure 7 was lower than that at room temperature. In the trapping model, however, the higher luminescence intensity at room temperature would result if the time spent in traps decreased with increasing temperature so that the energy normally trapped at low temperature was immediately available for re-emission at the higher temperatures. This would also account for the peaks in the luminescence intensity *vs.* temperature plots of Figure 7 if the subsequent decrease in intensity at temperatures above the peak temperature was the result of a competing temperature-sensitive quenching process which dominated after the deepest traps were emptied. The temperature at the peaks of Figure 7 changes with observation time, and this time can be taken as a representative value of the lifetime, τ, of the trapped species. The relationship between τ and the energy of the trap, E, is given by:

$$\frac{1}{\tau} = se^{-E/kT} \tag{8}$$

A plot of log τ *vs.* $1/T$ *should,* therefore, be linear with a slope of $-E/k$. Figure 8 shows the result of this plot for observation times between 7.5 μsec. and 375 μsec., and temperatures between 200° and 300°K. At lower temperatures the peak is not seen because of the appearance of the $T_1 \rightarrow S_0$ phosphorescence. The slope of this plot gives a trap depth of 0.22 e.v. Substituting this trap depth into Equation 8 yields a frequency factor, s, of 9×10^8 sec.$^{-1}$. This value may be compared with a lower limit of 10^8 sec.$^{-1}$ estimated by Lehman and Wallace (*15*) from which they derived a minimum value of 0.17 e.v. for the trap depth responsible for thermoluminescence. Using the higher value of s derived above together with the glow peak data of Lehman and Wallace (*15*) yields a "thermoluminescence" trap depth of 0.19 e.v. in closer agreement with the present value of 0.22 e.v.

Above the peak temperatures the emission quenching curves are approximately parallel and an Arrhenius plot of these portions of the curves gives an activation energy for the quenching of luminescence of about 0.15 e.v./molecule. This value is much larger than 0.007 e.v./molecule obtained for quenching of the phosphorescence at low temperatures. However, it does agree approximately with the low-dose x-ray data (*16*) where it was found that there are two temperature sensitive quenching processes, one dominating above and one below a transition temperature of 130°K. The activation energies in Reference 16 for these two processes were found to be 0.07 e.v./molecule and 0.007 e.v./molecule for the high and low temperature regions, respectively.

Differences in Emission Spectra. The cluster model, which arose from a consideration of triplet state Processes I to IV only, does not suggest an obvious explanation for the broader spectra at short times (*see*

Figure 4), unless impurities are responsible, as the transition $T_1 \rightarrow S_0 + h\nu$ gives the observed luminescence at all times after irradiation. On the trapping model, where the liberation of energy from traps is the rate determining process, the emission spectrum at short times is expected to be different from the phosphorescence spectrum as this transition, $T_1 \rightarrow S_0 + h\nu$, is much slower than the initial decay. Hence, a faster transition must be responsible for this early emission. One possible transition which may be contributing here is the fluorescence transition $S_1 \rightarrow S_0 + h\nu$ if the initial release of energy from traps leads to excited singlet states. As all immediate fluorescence is masked in this experiment by the accompanying Cerenkov light, it would be necessary to operate below the Cerenkov energy limit to test this point.

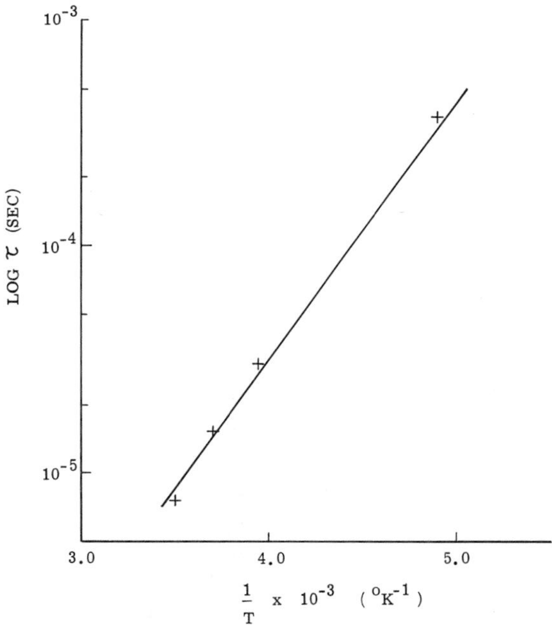

Figure 8. Dependence of the lifetime, τ, of the trapped species on temperature. The lifetimes and corresponding temperatures are derived from Figure 7 (see *text)*

Conclusions

The evidence reviewed above suggests that although a cluster-model for the initial formation of triplet states with subsequent bimolecular triplet quenching cannot be ruled out, a more probable explanation of the early reciprocal decay curve at both room temperature and 93°K. is the proposed trapping model, which has an approximately uniform distribution of trap depths in a range 0 to 0.22 e.v. This trapping model is also the most likely explanation of the low temperature emission at times longer than 10 sec. after irradiation. At these longer times, emission is the result of a triplet to singlet ground state transition which is also responsible for the low temperature phosphorescence from 5 msec. to 8 sec. after irradiation.

Acknowledgments

The authors would like to thank J. W. Boag for his encouragement and for many helpful discussions and L. T. Loverock for his technical assistance. We also wish to thank J. Currant and R. Hale for their operation of the linear accelerator for these studies.

Literature Cited

(1) Adolph, J., Williams, D. F., *J. Chem. Phys.* **46,** 4248 (1967).
(2) Augenstein, L., Carter, J., Nag-Chaudhuri, Y., Nelson, D., Yeargers, E., "Symposium on Physical Mechanisms in Radiation Biology," L. Augenstein, R. Mason, B. Rosenberg, eds., p. 73, Academic Press, New York, 1964.
(3) Augenstein, L. G., Carter, J. G., Nelson, D. R., Yockey, H. P., *Radiation Res. Suppl.* **2,** 19 (1960).
(4) Azumi, T., McGlynn, S. P., *J. Chem. Phys.* **39,** 1186 (1963).
(5) Birks, J. B., "The Theory and Practice of Scintillation Counting," Chapter 6, Pergamon Press, London, England, 1964.
(6) Bollinger, L. M., Thomas, G. E., *Rev. Sci. Instrum.* **32,** 1044 (1961).
(7) Carter, J. G., Birkhoff, R. D., Nelson, D. R., *Health Physics* **10,** 539 (1964).
(8) Collinson, E., Swallow, A. J., *Chem. Rev.* **56,** 471 (1956).
(9) Fano, U., "Comparative Effects of Radiation," M. Burton, J. S. Kirby-Smith, J. L. Magee, eds., p. 14, J. Wiley and Sons, New York, N. Y., 1960.
(10) Fielden, E. M. (to be published).
(11) Frank, I. M., Tamm, I., *Dokl. Akad. Nauk, S.S.S.R.* **14,** 109 (1937).
(12) Hodgman, C. D., Weast, R. C., Selby, S. M., eds., "Handbook of Chemistry and Physics," 45th ed., Chemical Rubber Publishing Co., 1964.
(13) King, T. A., Voltz, R., *Proc. Roy. Soc.* **A289,** 424 (1966).
(14) Kupperman, A., Raff, L. M., "Symposium on Physical Mechanisms in Radiation Biology," L. Augenstein, R. Mason, B. Rosenberg, eds., p. 161, Academic Press, New York, 1964.
(15) Lehman, R. L., Wallace, R., "Electronic Aspects of Biochemistry," B. Pullman, ed., p. 43, Academic Press, New York, 1964.
(16) Lillicrap, S. C., "Radiation Effects on Subcellular Systems and Model Compounds," p. 175, K. Lohs, A. Rakow, eds., Studia Biophysica **7,** East Berlin, 1968.
(17) Massey, H. S. W., Burhop, E. H. S., "Electronic and Ionic Impact Phenomena," 1st ed., p. 141, Oxford University Press, London, 1952.
(18) Randall, J. T., Wilkins, M. H. F., *Proc. Roy. Soc.* **A184,** 390 (1945).

(19) Rich, J. A., Slovacek, R. E., Studer, F. J., *J. Opt. Soc. Am.* **43**, 750 (1953).
(20) Robinson, G. W., Frosch, R. P., *Duke Univ. Symp. Reversible Photochem. Processes,* Durham, North Carolina, 1962.
(21) Seitz, F., Fonda, G. R., eds., "Solid Luminescent Materials," J. Wiley and Sons, New York, 1948.
(22) Singh, B. B., Charlesby, A., Intern. J. Radiation Biol. **9**, 157 (1965).
(23) Singh, S., Jones, W. J., Siebrand, W., Stoicheff, B. P., Schneider, W. G., *J. Chem. Phys.* **42**, 330 (1965).
(24) Sternlicht, H., Nieman, G. C., Robinson, G. W., *J. Chem. Phys.* **38**, 1326 (1963).
(25) Weinberg, C. J., Nelson, D. R., Carter, J. G., Augenstein, L. G., *J. Chem.* Phys. **36**, 2869 (1962).

RECEIVED December 26, 1967.

32

The Influence of Changes in Conformation of a Macromolecule on Reaction Rates

REINIER BRAAMS

Physics Laboratory, Utrecht University, Bijlhouwerstraat 6, Utrecht, the Netherlands

MICHAEL EBERT

Radiation Chemistry Department, Paterson Laboratories, Christie Hospital and Holt Radium Institute, Manchester 20, England

The change in the rate constants with temperature for the reactions of ribonuclease (RNase) with hydrated electrons and OH radicals was measured. The RNase molecule unfolds reversibly at elevated temperatures exposing sites particularly reactive towards hydrated electrons. The theoretical treatment leads to an estimate of the encounter frequencies for differently shaped macromolecules with small radiolytically produced solvent radicals. The derived encounter frequencies are compared with experimentally determined rate constants. Values as high as 10^{13} M^{-1} *sec.*$^{-1}$ *are understandable.*

In recent experiments (3) we have found that the value of rate constants for reactions between e^-_{aq} and certain protein molecules such as ribonuclease (RNase) depends on the conformation of the molecule. For ribonuclease it was found that the rate constant increases upon unfolding of the molecule. This increase can partly be ascribed to exposure of the hidden disulfide bridges but could also partly be caused by an increase in encounter frequency of the hydrated electron with the unfolded molecule.

The expression derived by Debye for the encounter frequency in reactions between spherical reactants can not be applied to molecules that differ markedly from spherical shape, such as the rodshaped collagen. In this paper the theory applied by Debye has been extended to reactions between a small spherical molecule and a cylindrical macromolecule.

The results obtained with the extended Debye theory have been compared with reported data for reactions between small reactants and biomacromolecules and good agreement has been found. The extended theory has then been used to analyze the data on ribonuclease. It is concluded that the exposure of disulfide bridges contributes substantially to the increase of the rate constant upon unfolding.

Material

Ribonuclease (RNase) is a compactly folded protein molecule of approximately spherical shape. It consists of one peptide chain with four intramolecular disulfide cross-links.

In RNase the protonated histidyl residues and the cystyl residues are apparently the most reactive sites in reactions with the hydrated electron. This was concluded from measurements of the absolute reaction rates of amino acids, peptides, and proteins (*1, 2*) and from an analysis of the reactivity of proteins in terms of the reactivities of the individual amino acids. At a pH of about 9 the histidyl residues are dissociated and have a low reactivity. The absolute reaction rate constant of RNase at this pH is 5×10^9 M^{-1} sec.$^{-1}$ (*2*) and can only be explained on the assumption that the four disulfide bridges inside the protein molecule contribute to its reactivity. This contribution, however, is less than would be expected for cystyl residues which show a rate constant of about $K_{e^-_{aq}} = 2 \times 10^{10}$ M^{-1} sec.$^{-1}$. The lack of a full contribution from the disulfide bonds was ascribed to the shielding of these reactive groups by the unreactive peptide chains.

At elevated temperatures the RNase molecule undergoes a transition from a folded to an unfolded state (*5*). This can be shown by optical and viscosity measurements. The transition temperature depends on pH and ionic strength. Above this temperature the tertiary structure is destroyed but the covalent disulfide bonds remain intact. The unfolding is reversible since on lowering the temperature the native conformation is regained.

Experimental

The properties of the RNase molecule are useful for investigating the shielding of reactive groups by the tertiary structure. Pulse-radiolysis techniques (*6*) were used for measurements of the reaction rate of RNase with the hydrated electron in buffered solutions below and above the transition temperature. An $11\mu M$ solution of RNase in $0.67 mM$ phosphate buffer (pH 6.8) and $0.01M$ KCl was continuously bubbled with argon gas to remove oxygen, heated slowly from 20°C. to 70°C. and allowed to cool again. At different temperatures some solution was flushed into a temperature controlled spiral radiation cell and pulse-radiolyzed. The rate constant for the disappearance of the optical absorption of the hydrated electron was measured and thus the rate constant for the reaction RNase + e^-_{aq} derived.

In Figure 1 the rate constants obtained in a typical experiment are plotted against temperature, after correction for reactions of the hydrated electron with the buffer solution at the different temperatures. Between 20°C. and 40°C. the reaction rate increases slowly, but at temperatures at which the molecular transition from the folded to the unfolded form occurred the reaction rate rises sharply. In other experiments at still higher temperatures it was found that after the transition is completed the reaction rate rises only slightly with temperature. Upon cooling, the reaction rate decreases sharply again and attains values lower but close to those observed on heating. This difference is an experimental artifact and can be ascribed to a partial denaturation of the protein in solution at the highest temperatures caused by the gas bubbles and is difficult to avoid.

Experiments to establish the rate constant of the OH radical with the RNase molecule at different temperatures were also carried out. $32\mu M$ RNase and $100\mu M$ KCNS were allowed to compete for the OH radicals. Within the experimental error no sudden increase of the rate constant for the reaction of OH with RNase was observed at the transition temperature. The rate constant increased from $2.6 \times 10^{10}\ M^{-1}$ sec.$^{-1}$ at 20°C. to $5.2 \times 10^{10}\ M^{-1}$sec.$^{-1}$ at 60°C.

Discussion

An explanation of these results will be attempted by first dealing with the problem of encounter frequency of reactants in general and then discussing the special case of RNase.

The frequency of encounters between spherical particles of different size has been treated by Debye (*4*), following a method first used by Smoluchowski (*10*). The number of collisions is obtained from the diffusion equation for particles diffusing steadily into a hole surrounding the particle in question. For spherical particles the equation can be solved and the well known Expression 1 is found.

$$\nu = 4\pi (R_1 + R_2)(D_1 + D_2) N \cdot 10^{-3} \text{ liter mole}^{-1} \text{ sec.}^{-1} \qquad (1)$$

Here ν is the encounter frequency, R_1 and R_2 are the radii of the two different reacting particles in cm., D_1 and D_2 are the diffusion constants for the two different molecules in cm.^{2} sec.$^{-1}$ and N is Avogadro's number. This expression cannot be applied to macromolecules which are not spherical in shape.

The equation can also be solved for spherical particles diffusing into a hole which has the shape of an ellipsoid of rotation but for most other shapes no exact solution is available. The differential equation for spheres of radius R diffusing into a hole of any given shape is the same as for the electrical capacity C of a closed surface enclosing the hole at a distance R.

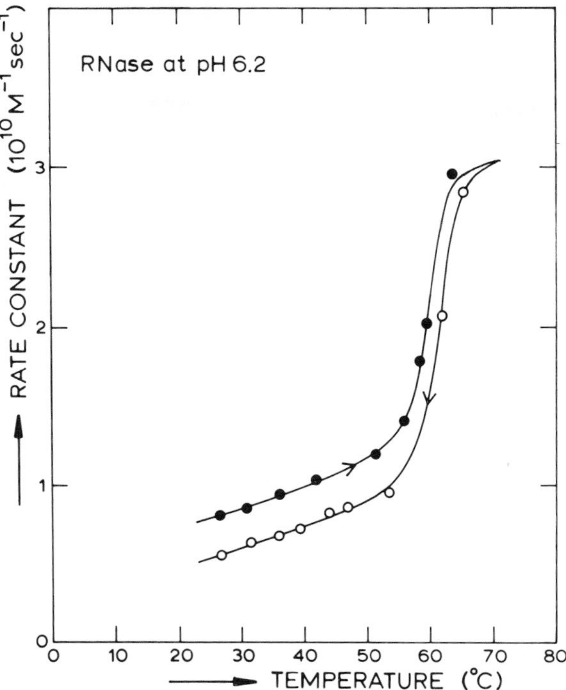

Figure 1. Rate constants for the reaction between the hydrated electron and RNase at different temperatures. The upper curve (●) is for increasing temperatures. The lower curve (○) is obtained after cooling the heated solution

In order to obtain the collision frequency the term $(R_1 + R_2)$ in Expression 1 has to be replaced by the capacity C of the closed surface. Expressions for the capacity of some simple surfaces can be found in textbooks on electricity. For other and more complex shapes the value can be obtained from a measurement of the electrical capacity of a model surface.

The encounter frequency can now be expressed as:

$$\nu = 4\pi C(D_1 + D_2)N \cdot 10^{-3}\ M^{-1}\ \text{sec.}^{-1} \tag{2}$$

For a prolate ellipsoid of rotation with the axis a $\neq$ b $=$ c the electrical capacity C is:

$$C = \frac{\sqrt{a^2 - b^2}}{\ln \dfrac{\text{a} + \sqrt{a^2 - b^2}}{b}}\ \text{cm.} \tag{3}$$

For a long cylinder the capacity can be derived from Expression 3 by extrapolation:

$$C = \frac{L}{2 \ln \frac{L}{r}} \text{ cm.} \tag{4}$$

in which L is the length of the cylinder in cm. and r is the radius of rotation of the cylinder in cm.

For macromolecules of cylindrical shape, C can be derived from Expression 4 using the dimensions of the molecule. With the aid of Expression 2 the encounter frequency and therefore the maximum rate constant for reactions between spherical reactants and spherical or cylindrical macromolecules can be estimated.

In Tables I and II data for the hydrated electron and OH radicals respectively are given.

Table I. Calculated Encounter Frequencies and Experimentally Determined Rate Constants for Reactions of Hydrated Electrons with Macromolecules of Different Size and Shape, Using $D_{e^-_{aq}} = 4.75 \times 10^{-5}$ cm.^{2} sec.$^{-1}$ (*8*) and $R_{e^-_{aq}} = 3$A. for the Hydrated Electron[a]

Substance	*Molecular Weight*	*Conformation*	*Capacity C in 10^{-8} cm.*	*Encounter Frequency in 10^{10} M^{-1} sec.$^{-1}$*	*Rate Constant in 10^{10} M^{-1} sec.$^{-1}$*
RNase	13,683	compact sphere	19	7	0.5 [b]
RNase	13,683	linear extended chain	81	29	
collagen	360,000	rigid rod	266	94	
spherical protein	360,000	compact sphere	51	18	
gelatin	120,000	extended	360	130	
gelatin	120,000	helix	322	117	
gelatin	120,000	random coil	55	20	5 [b]
gelatin	120,000	compact sphere	36	13	
DNA	5×10^6	double helix	5550	2000	$\simeq 10^3$ [c]
amino acid	90	sphere	6.2	2	max. 2 [d]
nucleotide	350	sphere	11	4	$\simeq 1$ [c]

[a] The diffusion constant of RNase was taken as 10^{-6} cm.^{2} sec.$^{-1}$, for larger macromolecules the diffusion constant is so small that their diffusion can be neglected.
[b] Ref. 2.
[c] Ref. 9.
[d] Ref. 1.

From the data presented in Table I it can be seen that the collision frequency depends on the shape of the macromolecule and is lowest when the molecule is folded into a compact sphere. Molecules such as collagen and DNA are known to deviate strongly from the compact folded form. The collagen molecule is a rigid rod about 3000 A. long composed of three intertwined single peptide chains. DNA consists of two single polymeric chains that form a double helix. It was treated as an extended molecule. For the calculation of the encounter frequency it has been assumed that they have a cylindrical shape. The calculated diffusion controlled reaction rates for collagen and DNA considerably exceed the values usually found for small reactants (approx. 10^{10} M^{-1} sec.$^{-1}$). For a double stranded DNA molecule of MW 5×10^6 the absolute rate constant for reaction with a small species could be as high as 2×10^{13} M^{-1} sec.$^{-1}$. Such high values have been reported by Scholes (9) for the hydrated electron and by Kraljic (7) for the hydroxyl radical.

Since the value of the diffusion constant of OH is less than half the value for e^-_{aq} the encounter frequencies tabulated in Table II for OH are lower than those given in Table I. The measured rate constants in the last column of Table II agree well with the calculated encounter frequencies. For proteins this must be ascribed to the high reactivity of OH for several amino acid side chains and for the peptide group, linking the amino acid residues together. For DNA this can be ascribed to the reactivity of nucleotides.

Table II. Calculated Encounter Frequencies and Experimentally Determined Rate Constants for Reactions of Hydroxyl Radicals with a Few of the Molecules Listed in Table I, Assuming $D_{OH} = 2 \times 10^{-5}$ cm.^{2} sec.$^{-1}$ and $R_{OH} = 2.2$ A.

Substance	*Molecular Weight*	*Conformation*	*Capacity* C *in* 10^{-8} *cm.*	*Encounter Frequency in* 10^{10} M^{-1} *sec.*$^{-1}$	*Rate Constant in* 10^{10} M^{-1} *sec.*$^{-1}$
RNase	13,683	compact sphere	18.2	3.0	2.6
collagen	360,000	rigid rod	260	39	40 [a]
gelatin	100,000	random coil	52	8.4	9.1 [a]
DNA	5×10^6	double helix	5500	830	$\simeq$ 1000 [b]

[a] Ref. 11.
[b] Ref. 7.

Since the hydrated electron is reactive with only a few amino acid residues the measured rate constant for proteins is less than the calculated diffusion controlled reaction rate.

In the special case of the RNase molecule, some geometric information is available from viscosity data in solution. It has to be kept in mind that the temperature induced reversible unfolding of RNase is incomplete, since the four disulfide bridges remain intact. The relation between the intrinsic viscosity η and the radius of gyration R_g is given by $\eta = \frac{10\pi N}{3M} R_g^3$ where N is Avogadro's number and M the molecular weight of the molecule (*12*). For the folded RNase η = 3.3 ml./g. and R_g = 19 A. For the unfolded RNase η = 7 ml./g. (*13*) and R_g = 25 A.

Since it is difficult to calculate the encounter frequency of the hydrated electron with the unfolded molecule it is helpful to consider it as a random coil located in a sphere with the radius R_g. The increase in R_g from 19 A. to 25 A. with increasing temperature can only account for an increase of the encounter frequency of less than 50%. We, however, find a factor of four in rate constants.

Therefore, the increase in absolute rate constant for the reaction of the hydrated electron with the molecule upon unfolding is either because of an increase in reactivity of the reactive sites or to a better exposure of available reactive sites. There is no evidence for a substantial increase in reactivity of amino acid residues with a change in conformation of the protein. The exposure of reactive sites must be the main reason for the increased reactivity. This confirms our previous conclusions (*3*).

Another important point in the above argument is that the dramatic increase in the rate for the reaction of the hydrated electron is not paralleled for the OH radical reaction. This demonstrates clearly a specific increase for the reactivity towards the electron in contrast to the behavior towards the OH radical.

We would like to conclude that the reactivity of a macromolecule is certainly not a linear function of the number of monomer units, and that it depends critically on the size and the shape of the molecule. The misleading custom of quoting rate constants of macromolecules on the basis of the concentration of monomer units should be discontinued.

Acknowledgments

It is a pleasure to acknowledge gratefully the interest B. U. Felderhof of Utrecht University has taken in the problem and to thank him for the theoretical foundation of this paper. This collaboration was supported by a travel grant from NATO.

Literature Cited

(1) Braams, R., *Radiation Res.* **27**, 319 (1966).
(2) *Ibid.*, **31**, 8 (1967).
(3) Braams, R., Ebert, M., *Intern. J. Radiation Biol.* **13**, 195 (1967).
(4) Debye, P., *Trans. Electrochem. Soc.* **82**, 265 (1942).
(5) Hermans, J., Scherega, H. A., *J. Am. Chem. Soc.* **83**, 3283 (1961).
(6) Keene, J., "Pulse Radiolysis," Ebert *et al.*, eds., p. 1, Academic Press, London and New York, 1965.

(7) Kraljic, I., "The Chemistry of Ionization and Excitation," G. R. A. Johnson, G. Scholes, eds., p. 303-309, Taylor and Francis Ltd., London, England, 1967.
(8) Schmidt, K. H., Buck, W. L., *Science* **151**, 70 (1966).
(9) Scholes, G., Shaw, P., Willson, R. L., Ebert M., "Pulse Radiolysis," Ebert *et al.*, eds., p. 151, Academic Press, London and New York, 1965.
(10) Smoluchowski, M. S., *Z. Physik. Chem.* **92**, 129 (1918).
(11) Southern, E. M., Davies, J. V. (in preparation).
(12) Tanford, C., "Physical Chemistry of Macromolecules," J. Wiley and Sons, New York, 1961.
(13) Weber, R. E., Unpublished data, referred to in "Physical Chemistry of Macromolecules," Charles Tanford, ed., p. 516, J. Wiley and Sons, New York, 1961.

RECEIVED January 17, 1968.

33

Effect of γ-Irradiation on Aqueous Solutions of the Cyclic Dodecapeptide Polymyxin B

J. KOPOLDOVÁ

Isotope Laboratory of the Institutes for Biological Research, Czechoslovak Academy of Sciences, Prague, Czechoslovakia

As a continuation of our work on γ-irradiation of simple di- and tripeptides we have studied the radiation behavior of a more complex model—the cyclic, antibiotically active dodecapeptide polymyxin B—by irradiating its 0.5% aqueous solutions in oxygenated and oxygen-free atmospheres at doses of 1.36×10^5–131.7×10^5 rad. The radiation products were determined in the irradiated solutions and in their hydrolysates, as well as the decrease of the content and biological activity of polymyxin. Both of these amounted to 45% at a dose of 13.7×10^5 rad. It was found that the main radiation mechanisms in solutions of polymyxin correspond, in general, to those described for the radiolysis of simple peptides. The major reactions in oxygenated solutions are oxidative deamination, Garrison's cleavage of peptide bonds, and oxidative reactions in the amino acid residues. In oxygen-free media, reductive deamination and recombination reactions are the main processes.

In hitherto published work on the effect of γ-irradiation on acetylated amino acids (3) and simple di- and tripeptides (5, 9), the following main radiolysis mechanisms of these substances have been established. In oxygenated media:

(1) Oxidative deamination reactions of free $-NH_2$ groups which proceed *via* the formation of imino acids and their hydrolysis and lead to the formation of ketoacyl peptides or to the forming of the C–terminal amino acid according to the summary scheme

$$NH_2CH(R_1)CONHCH(R_2)COOH + H_2O_2 + H_2O \rightarrow NH_3 + O{=}C(R_1)CONHCH(R_2)COOH \qquad (1)$$

$$NH_2CH(R_1)CONHCH(R_2)COOH + H_2O_2 + 2H_2O \rightarrow NH_3 + CO_2 + R_1CHO + NH_2CH(R_2)COOH \qquad (2)$$

(2) Simultaneously, oxidation reactions take place on the methyl and methylene groups of the amino acid chains with the formation of the corresponding –OH, –CO, and –COOH derivatives. In peptides containing amino acids with branched chains or aromatic or heterocyclic nuclei, splitting of the carbon chain of these amino acid residues takes place.

(3) Cleavage of the peptide bond according to Garrison's reaction, which can be summarily represented by the scheme

$$RCONHCHR_2 + OH \rightarrow RCONH\dot{C}R_2 + H_2O \qquad (3)$$

$$RCONH\dot{C}R_2 + O_2 + H_2O \rightarrow RCONH_2 + RCOR + HO_2 \qquad (4)$$

In oxygen-free media these reactions are suppressed and the processes taking place in such media are:

(a) Reductive deamination of free $-NH_2$ groups leading to ammonia and the formation of acyl peptides according to the scheme

$$H + H_2NCH(R_1)CONHCH(R_2)COOH \rightarrow NH_3 + \dot{C}H(R_1)CONHCH(R_2)COOH \qquad (5)$$

$$\dot{C}H(R_1)CONHCH(R_2)COOH + NH_2CH(R_1)CONHCH(R_2)COOH \rightarrow CH_2(R_1)CONHCH(R_2)COOH + NH_2\dot{C}(R_1)CONHCH(R_2)COOH \qquad (6)$$

(b) Recombination reactions with the formation of new –C–C– bonds, which yield peptides of higher molecular weight.

(c) The cleavage of peptide bonds, which in these media takes place according to the scheme

$$H + RCONHCH(R)COOH \rightarrow RCONH_2 + CH(R)COOH \qquad (7)$$

$$\rightarrow RCO + NH_2CH(R)COOH \qquad (8)$$

The purpose of the present work was to investigate whether the mechanisms outlined above also take place when more complex peptides containing a larger number of peptide bonds are irradiated. A peptide which contains 10 to 12 amino acids and is a stable, chemically defined substance, soluble in water, appeared to be best to use for this purpose. For these reasons, the peptide antibiotic polymyxin B (sulfate) was chosen. It possesses the further advantage that in addition to chemical changes caused by radiation, it allows changes to follow in its biological activity.

Polymyxin B ($C_{56}H_{98}O_{13}N_{16}$ m.w.1202) is a cyclic peptide consisting for the major part of L-, α-, γ-, diaminobutyric acid (5 residues), aside of L-threonine (2), L-leucine (1), D-phenylalanine (1), and (+)-6-methyloctanoic acid (1). In order to be able to explain the formation of certain degradation products of this peptide it was first necessary to obtain some basic information on the radiation chemical behavior of free diaminobutyric acid whose radiolysis has not yet been described.

Experimental Procedure

0.05*M* aqueous solutions of free diaminobutyric acid (prepared by Ing. Poduška, Institute of Organic Chemistry and Biochemistry, Czechoslovak Academy of Sciences) and 0.5% aqueous solutions of polymyxin B (sulfate) (Burroughs, Wellcome and Co.) were prepared.

These solutions were in glass ampules irradiated either in oxygen-free (the ampules having been bubbled with nitrogen and sealed prior to irradiation) or in oxygenated atmospheres (in the latter case oxygen was bubbled through the ampules during irradiation).

The radiation source was a ^{60}Co device of 2.7×10^5 rad./hr. intensity. For polymyxin B solutions the doses were 1.36×10^5, 13.17×10^5, 66×10^5, and 131.7×10^5 rad. The solutions of free diaminobutyric acid were irradiated at a single dose of 131.7×10^5 rad., which was used in earlier work for irradiating free amino acids and peptides.

The decrease of the biological activity of irradiated polymyxin B solutions was determined by the diffusional microbiological method. As a test culture, we used *Bacillus subtilis* ATCC 633 and *Eschericchia coli* NCIB 8113. The experiments were quantitatively evaluated by the method of Řičicová and Podojil (*11*). The culture was cultivated according to the method of Goss and Katz (*4*).

In all the irradiated samples, free and amide-like ammonia were determined by a modification of Conway's method (*10*) and carbonyl substances were determined spectrophotometrically (*8*).

The decomposition products in irradiated solutions of polymyxin and in their hydrolysates were identified by paper electrophoresis in a pyridine-acetate buffer solution (pH 5.7, 1200 volts) and by paper chromatography using the systems butyl alcohol-acetic acid-water (4:1:5) and phenol-ethyl alcohol-water (2:1:1, in an NH_3 atmosphere). For detection, ninhydrin and 2,4-dinitrophenyl hydrazine were used.

The content of ninhydrin-positive products in hydrolysates of the irradiated samples of polymyxin was very low in comparison with the content of amino acids forming the original peptide. For their identification and quantitative determination we used quantitative paper chromatography in the modification of Heilman *et al.* (*6*). This method was also used for determining the decrease of the four basic amino acids of the peptide studied. Considering the marked grading of the radiation doses used in the present work, the attained accuracy of $\pm 5\%$ can be considered as satisfactory.

The recombination products formed in polymyxin solutions irradiated in oxygen-free atmosphere were separated from the irradiated solution on a column of Sephadex G 25 (50×1 cm.). The eluent was 0.05*M* acetic acid flowing at the rate of 6 ml./hr. Recombination products of higher molecular weight passed as the first fraction. From irradiated solutions of free diaminobutyric acid and from hydrolysates of irradiated polymyxin solutions, the recombination products were separated as the first fraction on a column of Sephadex G 10.

6-methyloctanoic acid occurring in the hydrolysates of polymyxin was qualitatively determined in the form of its methyl ester by means of gas chromatography (Argon Pye instrument, 20% Reoplex, Cellite 545, 138°C., flow rate 20 ml./min.).

Results and Discussion

Radiation Effects on Solutions of Free Diaminobutyric Acid. As has been mentioned earlier, along with the study of polymyxin solutions we have also studied radiation effects on solutions of free diaminobutyric acid, which with its five molecules is contained in the original peptide to a larger extent than any other single component. It could be expected that the establishment of the main mechanisms of radiation degradation of free diaminobutyric acid will contribute to the elucidation of polymyxin radiolysis.

It was found that the major mechanism in radiolysis of diaminobutyric acid in oxygenated solution is oxidative deamination on α- or γ-position. This is clear from a comparison of the decrease in the content of diaminobutyric acid (G/–M/2.65), with the yield of ammonia (G 2.1) and with the yields of deaminated products ($\Sigma\ G \approx 2.0$). Aside from carbonyl substances and ketoamino acids, β-alanine and aspartic acid have been found among the products of oxidative deamination. In oxygen-free atmosphere, two of the main radiation mechanisms are reductive deamination (G/–M/1.4 and G NH_3 1.2) and recombination reactions leading to products of higher molecular weight.

Radiation Effects on Solutions of Polymyxin. The decrease in the content of polymyxin and its biological activity, as well as the results of analyses for free and amide-like ammonia, total content of carbonyl substances, and the content of individual amino acids in the hydrolysates of irradiated samples are summarized in Table I.

Irradiation in an Oxygenated Solution. The lowest dose of 1.36×10^5 rad. did not produce any significant changes in the solution of polymyxin. The content of the substance and its biological activity were only slightly reduced.

On increasing the dose to 13.17×10^5 rad, both the content of polymyxin and its biological activity were reduced by about 44 to 45%. The decomposition product was a peptide-like substance with electrophoretic behavior similar to polymyxin, but it had a positive reaction to 2,4-dinitrophenylhydrazine. On hydrolyzing the irradiated solution with 4*N* HCl at 95°C., the substance was decomposed to a basic peptide, diaminobutyric acid, and to an unidentified ketoacid. Apparently, as a result of irradiation the peptide bond is attacked according to Garrison's reaction 3. From the yield of amide-like ammonia, G 1.05, it can be

Table I. Decrease in the Polymyxin B Content, Biological and Oxygen-free 0.5% Aqueous Solutions

Dose (rad)	*Medium*	*pH*	*Content of Polymyxin*	*Biological Activity*	*Free NH_3*	*Amide-like NH_3*	*Total C=O*
0		6.2	100%	100%			
1.36×10^5	O_2	+[b]	98%	97%	+	+	+
	N_2	6.1	98%	98%	+	+	+
13.17×10^5	O_2	3.7	55%	56%	0.4	1.2	2.0
	N_2	5.9	56%	55%	0.1	0.4	0.15
66.10^5	O_2	2.9	—	—	1.2	4.8	5.7
	N_2	5.4	traces	—	0.4	1.6	0.35
131.10^5	O_2	2.55	—	—	4.4	13.6	9.3
	N_2	5.1	—	—	1.2	3.6	1.25

[a] Expressed in mmol./ml. or % of original.
[b] A plus sign (+) indicates a value which was not determined.

estimated that at this dose the extent of cleavage of the peptide bond is approximately 5%.

Irradiation in oxygenated solutions also leads to oxidative deamination reactions on some of the free $-NH_2$ groups of diamino acid chains according to Reaction Scheme 1. These reactions lead to the formation of peptides which contain, in addition to diaminobutyric chains, deaminated derivatives with a carbonyl group. In a strongly oxidative medium these groups are further oxidized to $-COOH$ groups, as is witnessed by the presence of aspartic acid in the hydrolysates of these peptides. The replacement in the course of irradiation of free $-NH_2$ groups by carbonyl and carboxyl groups leads to the formation of neutral and acidic peptides, which were detected in solutions of polymyxin irradiated at doses of 66×10^5 rad. and 131×10^5 rad. The extent of cleavage of the peptide bond according to Garrison's reaction increased to 10%, and on irradiation at the highest dose it further increased to 30%. In solutions of polymyxin irradiated at these doses, small amounts of free amino acids have been found (threonine, traces of leucine and phenylalanine, and β-alanine). The presence of these amino acids can be explained by the cleavage of peptide bonds according to Reaction 2. Evidence of this can be

Activity, and Yield of Products Formed from Its Oxygenated Irradiated by the Doses 1.36 to 131.7 × 10^5 rad[a]

Decrease of Amino Acids (in hydrolyzates)				New Formed Amino Acids (in hydrolyzates)			
di-NH₂ butyric	*Thr*	*Leu*	*Phe*	*Asp*	*β-Ala*	*Gly, Se*	*butyric γ-amino*
+	+	+	+	+	+	+	+
+	+	+	+	+	+	+	+
2.3 (12%)	0.7 (8%)	0.8 (20%)	1.25 (30%)	0.3	traces	—	—
2.55 (10%)	1.25 (15%)	0.75 (18%)	1.05 (25%)	traces	—	—	0.25
6.4 (26%)	3.1 (37%)	3.1 (74%)	4.1 (98%)	1.2	0.5	traces	—
6.0 (24%)	2.7 (32%)	1.3 (32%)	3.2 (78%)	traces	—	—	0.75
10.0 (40%)	6.7 (80%)	4.15 (100%)	4.2 (100%)	2.2	0.6	0.1	—
8.5 (34%)	4.6 (55%)	2.1 (50%)	4.1 (98%)	0.1	—	—	1.5

[a] A minus sign (−) indicates zero value.

seen in the presence of β-alanine, which is probably formed by the oxidation of the amino aldehyde obtained in Reaction 2.

In addition to the above mentioned oxidative deamination reactions and Garrison's cleavage of the peptide bond, oxidation and degradation reactions also take place in the remaining amino acid chains, including the benzene nucleus of Phe, as can be inferred from the presence of dialdehydes which have been found in irradiated solutions of polymyxin. As a result of these reactions the content of individual amino acids in the hydrolysates of irradiated solutions is successively lower, the decrease being largest for Phe, Leu, and for methyloctanoic acid.

Irradiation in Oxygen-Free Solutions of Polymyxin. The smallest dose did not produce observable changes, thus the results are similar to those obtained with oxygenated solutions.

On increasing the dose, the content of polymyxin and its biological activity were reduced. On the electrophoreogram of the irradiated sample we have found, aside from the original peptide, two radiation products with markedly changed chromatographic and electrophoretic behavior. One of these products, which moves down a column of Sephadex G 25 as the first fraction, remains at the start of the electrophoreogram; apparently this is a higher molecular weight product formed by a recombination reaction. The second product is less basic than non-irradiated polymyxin.

Irradiation of polymyxin in an oxygen-free atmosphere at higher doses resulted in an almost complete loss of biological activity; the original peptide could be determined only in trace amount. Higher amounts of radiation products described in the previous section were present. In the hydrolysate of the irradiated solution, a 25 to 30% decrease was determined for all amino acids, except for phenylalanine whose decrease amounted to 78%. However, new amino acids were detected in the hydrolysates: (1) γ-aminobutyric acid and (2) α-aminobutyric acid. Both of these substances have been found in an irradiated solution of diaminobutyric acid where they represent products of reductive deamination reactions in the γ- and α-positions. The presence of γ-aminobutyric acid in the hydrolysate of irradiated polymyxin indicates that in an oxygen-free atmosphere reductive cleavage of the peptide bond apparently takes place between some of the diaminobutyric residues (*see* Reaction 7). The presence of α-aminobutyric acid indicates that reductive deamination reactions occur in irradiated solution of polymyxin, thus explaining the formation of the less basic peptides which have been detected in the irradiated samples.

Irradiation at the highest dose resulted in an increase of the recombination product which remains at the start of the paper electrophoreograms and chromatograms and gives a weak ninhydrin-positive reaction. It is strongly fluorescent in ultraviolet light. From the hydrolysate of the sample irradiated at the highest dose, we have separated on a column of Sephadex G 10 the first fractions. Their chromatographic and electrophoretic behavior (7) corresponded with that of the recombination products isolated in the same manner from an irradiated sample of free diaminobutyric acid. It can be concluded from this that the main portion of recombination products of polymyxin is formed as a result of recombination between diaminobutyric chains. However, other recombination reactions probably take place—*e.g.*, reactions between diaminobutyric, Phe, and Leu chains. This would explain the marked decrease in the content of these substances. A detailed analysis of these recombination products has not been carried out.

The results outlined enable us to conclude that when the dodecapeptide is irradiated, it is subject to the same mechanisms which have been established for irradiated solutions of simple peptides. In an oxygenated medium, radiation changes take place both in the side chains of amino acid residues and in the cyclic chain of the peptide bond.

In the first case oxidative deamination reactions occur on the free NH_2 groups of diaminobutyric residues with the formation of keto–acyl peptides. During further oxidation, these substances are changed into acid peptides by successive replacements of NH_2 groups by aldehydic and carboxylic groups. The other amino acid residues also undergo oxidation and degradation reactions, with the formation of OH derivatives, further oxidation products or splitting of the carbon chain, which is the case for Phe and Leu residues. The order of radiosensitivity of these substances is in agreement with the results given by Ambe, Kumta, and Tappel (*1*). Oxidative cleavage of –NH–CO– bonds according to Garrison's mechanism takes place simultaneously with radiation changes in chains of amino acids residues.

In an oxygen-free medium these reactions are suppressed. As with radiation changes in the peptide chain, both reductive and oxidative cleavage occur in an oxygen-free medium but to a lesser extent than in an oxygenated medium. The main reactions which occur in this medium are reductive deamination of the free $-NH_2$ groups of diaminobutyric residues and recombination reactions with the formation of higher molecular weight peptides. It cannot be excluded that recombination reactions also take place between side chains of the same polymyxin molecule, which would lead to a deformation of its original structure and thereby to a change of its behavior on Sephadex. To elucidate the course of recombination reactions would require a more detailed analysis of the recombination products. The results of this analysis could be very useful for a better understanding of radiation changes in more complex peptides or proteins.

Literature Cited

(1) Ambe, K. S., Kumta, U. S., Tappel, A. L., *Radiation Res.* **15,** 709 (1961).
(2) Conway, E. J., Berne, A., *Biochem. J.* **27,** 419 (1933).
(3) Garrison, W. M., Weeks, B. M., *Radiation Res.* **17,** 341 (1962).
(4) Goss, W. A., Katz, E., *Appl. Microbiol.* **5,** 95 (1957).
(5) Hatano, H., *J. Radiation Res. (Japan)* **1,** 38 (1960).
(6) Heilmann, J., Barrolier, J., Watzke, E., *Z. Physiol. Chem.* **309,** 219 (1957).
(7) Katrukha, G. S., Silaev, A. B., Kharzkhaeva, S. V., *Biokhimiya* **27,** 549 (1962).
(8) Lappin, G. R., Clark, L. C., *Anal. Chem.* **23,** 541 (1951).
(9) Liebster, J., Kopoldová, J., *Radiation Res.* **27,** 162 (1966).
(10) Messer, M., *Biochim. Biophys. Acta* **17,** 151 (1955).
(11) Řičicová, A., Podojil, M., *Folia Microbiologica* **10,** 299 (1965).

RECEIVED January 11, 1968.

34

Radiation Chemical Studies on Oxygen-Carrying Proteins: Hemocyanin

JACK SCHUBERT, E. R. WHITE, and L. F. BECKER, JR.

Radiation Health Division, Graduate School of Public Health, University of Pittsburgh, Pittsburgh, Pa. 15213

The oxygen-carrying capacity of the nonheme copper protein, hemocyanin, is reduced by irradiation of the oxygenated protein with gamma and x-rays with $G(-O_2) = 0.9$*–1.2. Measurements are made on hemocyanin in its own serum at relatively low doses (0–80 krads). Oxygenated hemocyanin is resistant to irradiation but loses its oxygen-carrying capacity only when deoxygenated following irradiation in the oxygenated state. Irradiation of the deoxygenated form is without effect on the oxygen-carrying capacity. The effect of irradiation on hemocyanin involves the oxidation of protein-bound copper atoms to the Cu(II) state by radiolytic hydrogen peroxide in the same manner as is produced by adding* H_2O_2 *to unirradiated hemocyanins. The effects of organic peroxides, pH, urea, catalase, and other factors on the oxygenation of hemocyanin are described.*

One of the most active areas of research in biological systems is concerned with the mechanism of activation and utilization of oxygen (*15*). Oxygen plays an important and special role with respect to radiation damage and protection in both radiobiology (*2*, *39*) and radiation chemistry (*5*, *43*). As a model radiobiological system we have chosen to investigate the effects of ionizing radiation on the oxygenation reactions of oxygen-carrying proteins under as natural conditions as possible. Since we are studying the effects of radiation on the functional behavior of proteins, we generally use relatively small total radiation doses (0–0.1 Mrad) rather than a combination of high radiation doses ($\sim$0.5–5 Mrads) and unphysiological conditions which produce gross damage, having questionable relevance to biological systems.

In this report we present further results of our investigations (*34, 37*) on the action of gamma-irradiation on the nonheme oxygen-carrying copper protein, hemocyanin. This protein serves as an especially convenient radiobiological model because its oxygenation reactions can be studied on the protein as it exists naturally in its own serum, without isolation or disruptive purification procedures. The use of a copper protein is of particular interest in view of suggestions that copper possesses some unique characteristics and roles in radiobiology (*1, 19, 35, 36*). We have already shown that the oxygen-carrying capacity of two types of hemocyanin as measured by optical absorption at 340 mμ decreases with increasing radiation dose giving initial yield values of $G(-O_2)$ of about 1.0 (*34, 37*).

Previous investigations (*4, 32, 41, 42*) on the actions of ionizing radiation on hemocyanin involved doses of 2×10^5 to 6×10^5 rads and higher. Svedberg (*41, 42*) showed that irradiation with α-particles split hemocyanin from the snail *Helix pomatia* into halves and eventually eighths. Presumably hydrogen bonds were broken by direct action of the heavy ionizing tracks. Chemical changes must have occurred because the fragments could not be reconstituted. A similar splitting takes place when hemocyanin from *Limulus polyphemus* is irradiated with x-rays (*32*). Barron (*4*) demonstrated that large doses ($4–6 \times 10^5$ rads) of x-irradiation of hemocyanin in dilute solutions caused the copper-protein bond to rupture.

Properties of Hemocyanins

The four main groups of oxygen-carrying proteins—the hemoglobins, chlorocruorins, hemerythrins, hemocyanins—possess the vital function of transport and storage of oxygen in the animal kingdom (*15, 23*). They react reversibly with molecular oxygen at relatively high partial pressures and release it to tissues where the partial pressure is low. Hemoglobins and chlorocruorins possess an iron-containing prosthetic group and a protein. The oxygen binding site resides with the iron atom centered in the porphyrin ring while the globin makes the prosthetic group soluble and its reactions with oxygen reversible. In both hemoglobin and chlorocruorin the molecular oxygen combines in a 1:1 ratio with the Fe atom.

Hemerythrin, which contains iron, and hemocyanin, which contains copper, are nonheme oxygen-carrying proteins in which the metal appears to be bound directly to the protein *via* the functional groupings of one or more amino acid residues. The metal to oxygen ratio appears to be 2:1 in both hemerythrin and hemocyanin in contrast to the 1:1 ratio found in the heme proteins (*13, 23, 26*).

The existence of other natural occurring oxygen carriers has not been proved. Presumptive evidence for an oxygen-carrying function has been ascribed to a vanadium-containing protein, hemovanadium (*16*) found in the marine organisms of the tunicate family.

Hemocyanins from varying sources contain from 0.15 to 0.26% copper, 0.8 to 1.2% sulfur, and molecular weights which vary considerably because of the aggregation of smaller units (*13, 33*). The amino acid composition of hemocyanins from ten different species have been determined (*14*). Removal of copper or oxygen does not modify the protein composition or produce any measurable change as measured by optical rotatory dispersion on the conformation of the protein structure (*7*). The state of aggregation of the subunits determines, in part, the oxygenation properties of the protein (*17, 18*). The proteins are colorless when deoxygenated and deep blue when oxygenated. The oxygenated protein is readily deoxygenated by passage of a stream of oxygen-free helium through a solution of the protein.

The protein-bound copper can be removed by dialysis against cyanide, sulfide, and other copper complexing agents. Subsequent reintroduction of the copper restores the oxygenating ability of hemocyanin. However, the resynthesis of hemocyanin from apohemocyanin can be achieved only with cuprous, not cupric salts (*6, 13*). Practically quantitative reconstitution is obtained by the use of the acetonitrile complex of copper (*21*). The apoprotein appears specific for copper since the binding of other metal ions denatures the protein (*6*).

Many investigations have been made to identify the ligands in hemocyanin responsible for the binding of copper and the oxidation state of the copper itself (*6, 9, 13, 23*). These questions have not been resolved. More recently, however, measurements of the optical rotatory dispersion (OD) and circular dichroism (CD) on hemocyanin obtained from *Octopus vulgaris* and *Loligo pealei* have produced convincing evidence, albeit circumstantial, on the binding of copper to hemocyanin (*7, 45, 46*). Van Holde (*46*) compared the CD spectra obtained for the molluscan hemocyanin with those of peptide-Cu(II) complexes. Only a histidine-containing complex showed CD spectra resembling those found for the hemocyanins. Thus, as has been inferred from other observations, the histidyl residues are at least partially responsible for the binding of copper in hemocyanins.

The investigations of Felsenfeld (*10*) on the action of hydrogen peroxide on hemocyanin has provided interesting information which, in fact, explains the radiation effects observed thus far. He found that the deoxygenated hemocyanin was much more sensitive to attack than the oxygenated hemocyanin as measured by the oxygen-carrying capacity. The peroxide appears to act by oxidizing the Cu(I) of deoxygenated hemocyanin to the Cu(II) state. The hemocyanin from the mollusk *Busycotypus canaliculatum* can be regenerated by the use of reducing agents and by the use of excess peroxide (*10*). The product of the peroxide oxidation was designated as methemocyanin in analogy to methemoglobin since in both cases specific oxidation of the metal ion occurred with a concomitant loss of physiological activity.

Hemocyanin possesses a catalase-like action (*10, 12*), albeit a weak one, in that it decomposes hydrogen peroxide into water and oxygen just as the hemeprotein catalase. The catalase-like action of hemocyanin is due to the protein-bound copper since neither copper-free hemocyanin nor free copper ions exhibit activity under equivalent conditions. Copper-amino acid complexes have been tested for catalase-like action, and it was reported that only the copper-arginine complex possesses catalase-like activity (*13*). However, we have found (*37*) as have other investigators (*29, 40*), that other amino acid complexes of copper also decompose H_2O_2.

Oxygenated hemocyanin exhibits absorption bands in the visible and ultraviolet regions at about 278, 345, and near 600 mμ. The band at 278 mμ is common to all proteins while the other two, called copper bands, disappear upon deoxygenation or removal of the copper (*13*). Neither oxygenated or deoxygenated hemocyanin give an EPR signal except when the protein is denatured at which point the copper becomes paramagnetic (*27*). However, when denatured hemocyanin is regenerated with cysteine or H_2O_2, the EPR signal disappears (*22*).

The oxidation state of the copper in hemocyanins has been the subject of much investigation and discussion (*11, 23, 24, 25, 27, 30*). Van Holde (*46*) has reviewed the evidence regarding the oxidation state of copper in copper proteins. He points out that the bond at about 340 mμ is very strong in the hemocyanins and corresponds to their ability to bind oxygen and to the presence of cupric copper. The conclusion is drawn that in oxyhemocyanin the copper is at least partially in the Cu(II) form and that the absence of an EPR signal indicates either electron pairing with the oxygen or between the cupric ions. A tentative mechanism for O_2 binding in hemocyanins is presented (*46*) in which it is assumed that in deoxyhemocyanin one coordination site on each cuprous ion is occupied by a water molecule. When these are replaced by O_2, distortion of the coordination is required because of the smaller size of O_2. Electron transfer to O_2 is facilitated by the longer bond length in the O_2^{2-} ion.

Experimental

Limulus (the horseshoe or king crab) and *Busycotypus* (*Busycon,* the channeled whelk) hemocyanin hemolymph are obtained from the

Marine Biological Laboratory, Woods Hole, Mass. The hemolymph is shipped cold in insulated containers *via* air the same day the animals are bled. The hemocyanin is "conditioned" upon arrival. This consists of removal of large clumps of clotted material with a glass rod. The solution is then filtered (Reeve Angel flutted filter paper #802). Subsequently, the sample is oxygenated by bubbling oxygen through the solution for about ten minutes at a rate of 20 ml. per minute. The oxygenated hemolymph is placed in a 350 ml. gas washing bottle with inlet and fritted disc at the bottom. The bottle is surrounded by ice, and a deoxygenation cycle is carried out by bubbling especially purified helium gas ($O_2 < 0.001\%$ by volume) at a rate of 40 ml. per minute until the solution is colorless. Two additional reoxygenation and deoxygenation cycles are carried out. After the final oxygenation the solution is filtered, a few drops of toluene added, and the solution is stored in the refrigerator at about 5°C. We do not find evidence for surface denaturation of the hemocyanins under the conditions described for the particular hemocyanin employed.

Since we are working with a biological fluid subject to deterioration, it is especially important that reliable criteria be employed to ensure that the observed responses of hemocyanin to chemical and physical stress are real and reproducible and not artefacts. The literature contains many references to the storage life of hemocyanin. Some investigators have claimed that the hemolymph can be stored for weeks or even months without deterioration as long as the material is kept cold and covered with toluene. However, the question arises as to the criteria of deterioration employed. In terms of immunological reactions (*20*), catalase activity, and total oxygen capacity, hemocyanin appears remarkably stable. We have found, however, by our criteria, that the refrigerator life of our hemocyanin is approximately twelve days. The criteria we employ is a time dependency of the oxygenated and deoxygenated optical density at 340 mμ. Some of the observations we have made regarding the usability of hemocyanin in hemolymph are:

(1) The oxygenated optical density, $(OD)_o$, for a given dilution, may be attained each day, but in a deteriorated sample, there occurs a spontaneous loss of oxygen upon standing 30–60 minutes with a concomitant drop in $(OD)_o$. Upon reoxygenation the $(OD)_o$ may rise again but only temporarily.

(2) The deoxygenated optical density, $(OD)_d$, of a deteriorated sample is higher than that of a fresh preparation and may be 25–50% higher in $(OD)_d$ than the fresh sample.

(3) The pH of fresh hemocyanin, *Busycotypus* hemocyanin in its hemolymph or serum is 8.1 ± 0.15 and that of *Limulus* is 7.6 ± 0.5. The pH undergoes small changes from day to day, but the pH change in a deteriorated sample undergoes a larger than normal drop. A normal decrease may be from 0.00 to 0.15 of a pH unit per day, but when the samples deteriorate the pH drops 0.3–0.5 of a unit.

Regulation of helium gas flow through the various solutions are satisfactorily controlled by constant differential low flow controllers manufactured by Moore Products Co., Philadelphia, Pa. By this means we are able to obtain a constant flow of gas for deoxygenation regardless of changes in downstream pressure. We employ a unit consisting of six differential flow controllers connected in parallel. Each unit can be adjusted without any effect on the others. We find that 40 ml. of helium per minute provides a satisfactory flow for rapid deoxygenation of dilute solutions of oxygenated hemocyanin. The flow rate is measured by a simple soap bubble meter.

The reoxygenation of deoxyhemocyanin by molecular oxygen is complete in a matter of seconds. However, the deoxygenation cycle in our system requires more time. With hemocyanin solutions diluted with phosphate buffer to an optical density of about 0.5, and a total volume of about 4 ml., deoxygenation is complete in about three minutes but more concentrated solutions require more time. We routinely deoxygenate for six minutes with hemocyanin solution of $(OD)_o = 0.5$ and ten minutes for solutions having an $(OD)_o = 1$. The rates of deoxygenation are little affected by the age, pH 5–9, or degree of dilution.

Dilutions are made with 0.05*M* sodium dihydrogen phosphate buffer, pH 7.00. Copper analyses are made by atomic absorption spectrophotometry; the radiation source, cobalt-60 gamma rays, delivers about 15,000 rad/min. In some cases 280 kv x-rays were used for irradiation.

Radiation doses are measured with a ferrous sulfate dosimeter based on a value of $G(Fe^{3+}) = 15.5$ (*28*). For radiation doses approaching 40,000 rads we use an oxygen-saturated ferrous sulfate solution containing 4 millimoles of iron instead of the usual 1 millimole. In this manner we can extend the useful range to at least 10^5 rads. For radiation doses below 4,000 rads we employ an optical cell with a 10 cm. path length instead of a 1 cm. path length. This permits us to obtain reliable measurements down to 400 rads total absorbed dose.

Oxygen-saturated solutions of hemocyanin are irradiated at 25°C. in 4 ml. glass vials sealed with Teflon-lined screw caps. After irradiation, oxygenated solutions are transferred to silica cell cuvettes (path length 1 cm.) capped with sleeve-type rubber stoppers with an indented area in the center so that syringe needles for passage of oxygen or oxygen-free helium can be inserted. Hemocyanin is subsequently deoxygenated by bubbling from 350 to 600 ml. of helium, at a rate of 40 ml. per minute, through the solution until complete deoxygenation occurs as measured by the deoxygenated optical density. The solution is kept in the deoxygenated state for a given time, then reoxygenated, and the oxygenated optical density is measured. Subsequent measurements are made until the $(OD)_o$ reaches a constant value. The $(OD)_o$ of hemocyanin from *Limulus* attains a constant value immediately after oxygenation. With irradiated hemocyanin from *Busycotypus*, the time required for the $(OD)_o$ to reach a stable maximum value increases with increasing radiation dose —*e.g.*, a dose of less than 8,000 rads requires less than one minute; approximately 13,000 to 20,000, one hour; 20,000 to 27,000, one to two hours; and three to four hours for doses above 34,000 rads.

After irradiation, or sometimes before, small amounts of aggregated protein may appear in suspension in the hemocyanin solutions and are removed by low speed centrifugation. The aggregated protein is colorless and probably not hemocyanin because its removal does not change the original OD's. However, their presence does raise the OD slightly ($\sim$0.05 an OD unit). If the suspended aggregates appear their effect can be compensated for in *Limulus* hemocyanin as follows: during deoxygenation the $(OD)_d$ is recorded. The sample is oxygenated and the $(OD)_o$ recorded. The oxygenated sample is centrifuged, and the $(OD)_o$ again is read. The difference in $(OD)_o$ between the centrifuged and noncentrifuged sample is subtracted from the deoxygenated sample OD to give a corrected $(OD)_d$. The same procedure is used with *Busycotypus* hemocyanin for $(OD)_o$ values, but because of rapid spontaneous reoxygenation from residual H_2O_2, a correction to the $(OD)_d$ is not feasible.

An important factor, not always appreciated in investigations of the effects of ionizing radiation on biological materials in aqueous solution, is the depletion of oxygen in the medium which occurs during irradiation. In our systems, this factor becomes important even in oxygen saturated solution above doses of 60,000 rads and at lower doses with air saturated solutions. From experience, we found that it is necessary either to bubble oxygen through the solution during irradiation or to maintain the oxygen saturated solution in a closed system during irradiation. In order to check whether our system has suffered oxygen depletion at high radiation doses, we measure the $(OD)_o$ of an irradiated oxygenated hemocyanin solution immediately after irradiation and before further oxygenation. If it decreases then we know that depletion occurred. Inasmuch as only the fully oxygenated hemocyanin is resistant to the action of the radiation produced products, it is obviously necessary that no oxygen depletion occur in the system during irradiation.

Hydrogen peroxide is formed in the irradiated oxygenated buffer solutions and the concentrations were measured iodometrically (*8*) in pH 7 phosphate buffer. Amounts of H_2O_2 formed were, in μmole/liter: 18 at 10 krad, 26 at 15 krad, 58 at 40 krads. In deoxygenated buffer no H_2O_2 was detected (< 1 μmole/liter). The results are in good agreement with other workers (*5*).

The copper in hemocyanin is directly and quantitatively involved in the oxygenation reaction. All incoming hemocyanin solutions are analyzed for copper with a Perkin-Elmer atomic absorption spectrophotometer. The analyses are carried out by diluting the stock solution with distilled water and feeding the solution to the burner.

The catalase-like properties of hemocyanin and copper-amino acid chelates have been measured manometrically using a conventional Warburg apparatus. We are now using a differential manometer technique for measuring the rates of oxygen evolution (*31*) which, for our purposes, is much superior to the conventional vertical column differential manometer, especially in sensitivity.

Results

No effect of irradiation on hemocyanin is detected as long as the hemocyanin is maintained in the oxygenated state. However, upon deoxygenation of the irradiated hemocyanin, followed by oxygenation, a decrease in oxygen-carrying capacity is observed. The amount of radiation damage—measured in terms of loss of oxygen capacity—depends on the time the irradiated hemocyanin remains in the oxygenated state (designated as oxygen reaction time, o.r.t.) before a deoxygenation and reoxygenation cycle, and in the deoxygenated state (designated as deoxygenated reaction time, d.r.t.) before reoxygenation. However, under the conditions employed, the radiation effects are independent of the o.r.t.'s for the time intervals employed. Generally, the o.r.t. was ten minutes and the d.r.t. was one hour. In the case of *Limulus* hemocyanin—*e.g.*, with an $(OD)_o$ of 0.5—the effect of irradiation on the $(OD)_o$ was identical for o.r.t.'s up to 60 minutes after the cessation of irradiation.

Samples of *Limulus* and *Busycotypus* were diluted with phosphate buffer to yield desired values of oxygenated optical density. The hemocyanin was irradiated in the oxygenated state, deoxygenated immediately after irradiation, then reoxygenated. The $(OD)_o$ decreased with increasing dose and the $G(-O_2)$ values (0.9–1.2), for both hemocyanins were about the same and independent of concentration (Figure 1).

In Figure 2 data for a one hour d.r.t. (a period beyond which no further decreases in oxygen capacity occur) show that the $(OD)_o$ drops rapidly with increasing radiation and, in fact, more than 90% of the entire oxygen capacity is lost above 35,000 rads.

Experiments with *Busycotypus* hemocyanin yielded results similar to those obtained with *Limulus* hemocyanin. However, with an $(OD)_o$ of 0.5, radiation doses above 13,000 to 16,000 rads restored the oxygen capacity, and above 70,000 rads the oxygen capacity became nearly equivalent to unirradiated hemocyanin (*37*). When the concentration of hemocyanin was increased to give an $(OD)_o$ of 0.9, the radiation dose required to produce the minimum increased to that expected—observed $= 23{,}000$ rads, calculated $= \frac{0.9}{0.5} \times 13{,}000 = 23{,}000$ rads (Figure 3).

Role of Radiolytic Hydrogen Peroxide. A series of experiments were carried out to determine the extent to which radiolytic H_2O_2 contributed to the decrease in oxygen capacity of irradiated hemocyanin. From these experiments summarized below, the conclusion is drawn that the effects of gamma irradiation of hemocyanin in solutions of hemolymph or buffer in the dose range of 0 to 60 krads are caused nearly entirely by H_2O_2. The experimental bases for this conclusion follow:

(1) The phosphate buffer was irradiated and added to unirradiated hemocyanin. The subsequent changes in oxygen-carrying capacity were identical with that observed when the hemocyanin was irradiated while in the same buffer over the entire range of radiation doses. Both *Limulus* and *Busycotypus* hemocyanin were tested. In the case of the latter, even the regeneration of oxygen-carrying capacity was reproduced (Figure 4).

(2) The presence of catalase during irradiation of hemocyanin or the addition of catalase to hemocyanin after irradiation, but before deoxygenation, eliminates the effects of irradiation on the oxygen-carrying capacity (Figure 5).

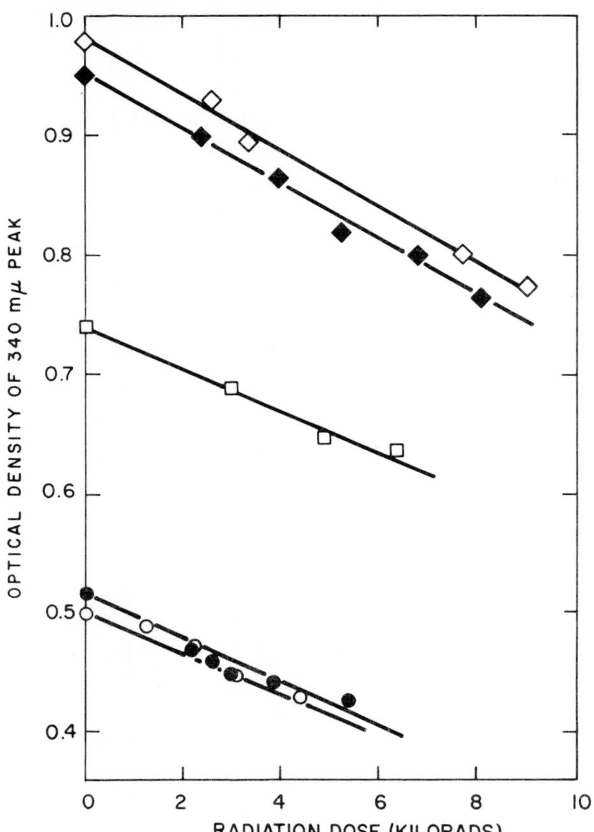

Figure 1. Effect of gamma irradiation on the oxygen-carrying capacity of different concentrations of oxygenated hemocyanins in phosphate buffer at pH 7.0. The oxygenation reaction time was 10 minutes and the deoxygenation reaction time was 30 minutes

Busycotypus
◇—[*Cu*] = *7.1* × *10*$^{-5}$M; G(*–O*$_2$) = *1.2*
□—[*Cu*] = *5.35* × *10*$^{-5}$M; G(*–O*$_2$) = *1.0*
○—[*Cu*] = *3.55* × *10*$^{-5}$M; G(*–O*$_2$) = *0.9*
Limulus
■—[*Cu*] = *7.68* × *10*$^{-5}$M; G(*–O*$_2$) = *1.1*
●—[*Cu*] = *4.04* × *10*$^{-5}$M; G(*–O*$_2$) = *0.9*

(3) The hemolymph was separated from hemocyanin by ultracentrifugation. When the protein-free hemolymph was irradiated and added to unirradiated buffered (phosphate) hemolymph, the effect was identical with that observed for the same doses of irradiation delivered to hemocyanin in hemolymph. The amount of H_2O_2 produced in hemolymph was found to be the same as that produced in pure buffer for the radiation dose range, 0–60 krads.

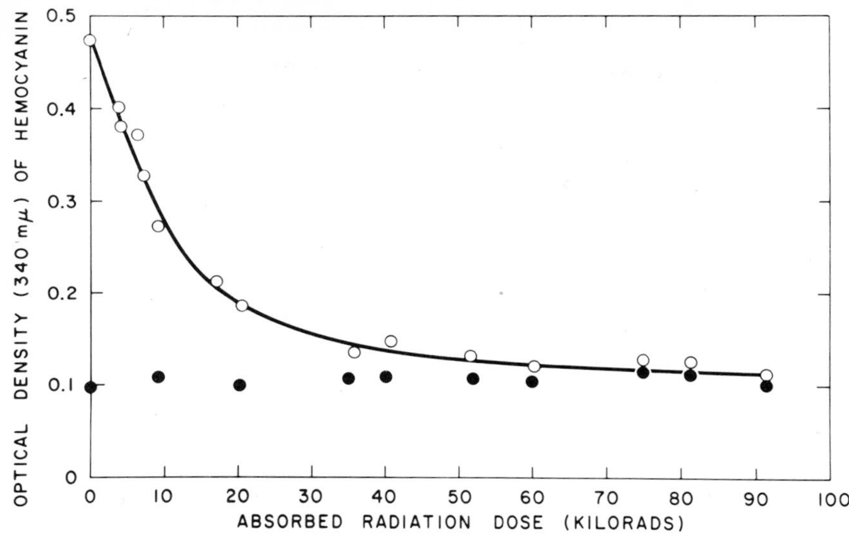

Science

Figure 2. Changes in optical densities of hemocyanin from Limulus *after irradiation at 25°C. with cobalt-60 gamma rays at a dose rate of 15 kilorads/ min. Solutions consisted of* Limulus *hemolymph diluted with 0.05*M *potassium dihydrogen phosphate buffer (pH 7.00) and saturated with oxygen. Copper concentration was 3.92 × 10^{-5}*M. *Hemocyanin was deoxygenated ten minutes after irradiation and was allowed to remain in the deoxygenated state for one hour before reoxygenation, at which time the optical densities were measured at 340 mμ. Subsequent deoxygenation provided the final deoxygenated optical densities.*

○—*oxygenated*
●—*deoxygenated*

(4) The addition of H_2O_2 to buffered solutions of hemocyanin produced effects very similar to those observed upon irradiation. These results along with those of irradiated systems, also reflect small effects caused by the catalytic decomposition of H_2O_2 by hemocyanin itself.

Effect of Organic Peroxides. The effect on the oxygen-carrying properties of *Limulus* hemocyanin by different organic peroxides was tested. The peroxides tested included: succinic acid peroxide ($(HOOC—CH_2—CH_2—CO)_2O_2$; *tert*-butyl hydroperoxide ($(CH_3)_3C—OOH$); and *tert*-butyl peroxymaleic acid ($(CH_3)_3C—OO—\overset{\overset{\displaystyle O}{\|}}{C}—CH{=}CH—COOH$). At the highest concentrations tested which included levels higher than that employed with H_2O_2, no effects on oxygen-carrying were observed. It appears that the size and shape of the hydrocarbon side chains around the peroxide oxygen are a critical factor since they determine the ability to contact protein-bound copper. These studies are continuing and are being extended to *Busycotypus* hemocyanin.

Effect of Urea, Calcium, and pH. When the concentration of chemical or radiolytic H_2O_2 exceeds that of the copper in *Busycotypus* hemocyanin, the oxygen-carrying capacity is regenerated. This is not true of *Limulus* hemocyanin, presumably caused by the relative inaccessibility of the protein-bound copper. Accordingly we attempted to "open up" the structure of *Limulus* by the use of high (6–7*M*) solutions of urea which could cause the protein structure to unfold. However, urea, under the conditions tested, had little or no effect on either the oxygen-carrying capacity or H_2O_2 regeneration of *Limulus* hemocyanin.

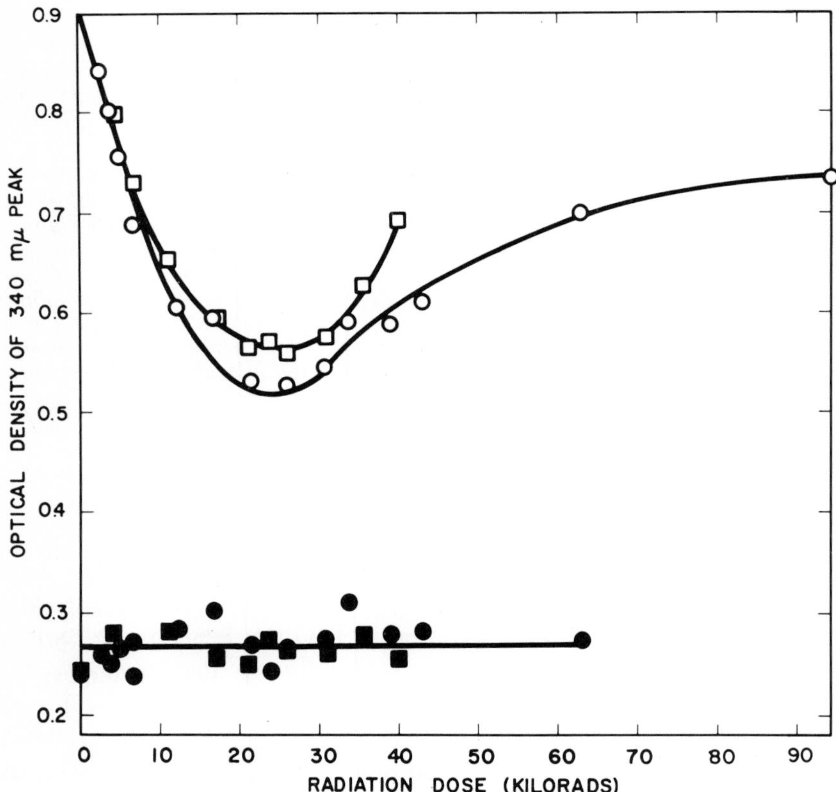

Figure 3. Effect of gamma radiation on oxygenated Busycotypus *hemocyanin in phosphate buffer, pH 7 at 25°C. Copper concentration was 7.1 ×* 10^{-5}M

○—*$(OD)_o$ at 1 hr. deoxygenated reaction time (d.r.t.)*
□—*$(OD)_o$ at 15 min. d.r.t.*
■—*$(OD)_d$ at 15 min. d.r.t.*
●—*$(OD)_d$ at 1 hr. d.r.t.*

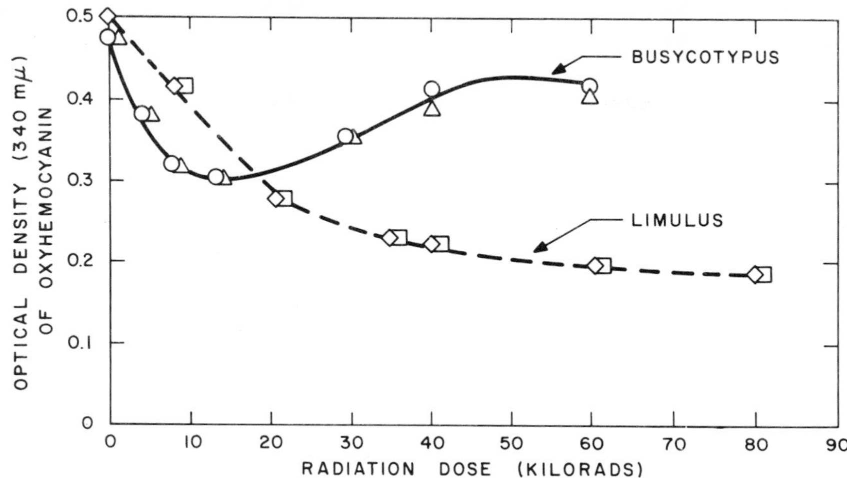

*Figure 4. Medium effects on hemocyanin. Effect of oxygenated gamma irradiated, 0.05*M*, buffer (pH 7) on unirradiated hemocyanin*

◇, ○ *Hemocyanin and buffer irradiated together*
□, △ *Irradiated buffer added to unirradiated hemocyanin*

Neither the oxygenation reactions of *Limulus* hemocyanin nor the destruction of oxygen-carrying capacity by H_2O_2 were affected by varying pH (5.5–8) and added calcium levels (0.0056–0.032*M*). Whether these particular experiments actually produced changes in the state of aggregation of the hemocyanin was not tested.

Catalytic Decomposition of H_2O_2. Hemocyanin from *Busycotypus* decomposes H_2O_2 and releases oxygen (*10*). We measured this catalytic action on samples of hemocyanin heated for 15 minutes at different temperatures and pH 7. The general effectiveness of the catalytic action was relatively unchanged up to temperatures as high as 65°C. (Figure 6). The catalytic effectiveness of *Limulus* hemocyanin is far lower than that from *Busycotypus* and was manifested only at higher concentrations and pH (Figure 6). Irradiation of hemocyanin with doses up to 100 krads did not affect the catalytic activity.

The catalase-like action of hemocyanin is probably because of copper bound to one or more amino acids in the protein. Contrary to previous claims (*12*), arginine chelates with copper are not the only catalytically active species. For example, copper chelates with histidine and histamine are also active. The rates appear to be a first power function of copper and H_2O_2. Studies now being carried out with V. S. Sharma in our laboratories indicate that the active species is the Cu(II)L form where L represents the ligand. The copper chelate forms a ternary complex with the HOO^- anion of H_2O_2 which subsequently decomposes to O_2 by free radical and molecular mechanisms. The most catalytically active ligands involve the coordination of two nitrogen atoms to copper. It is anticipated that the studies with model copper complexes may clarify the mode of attachment of copper to different hemocyanins.

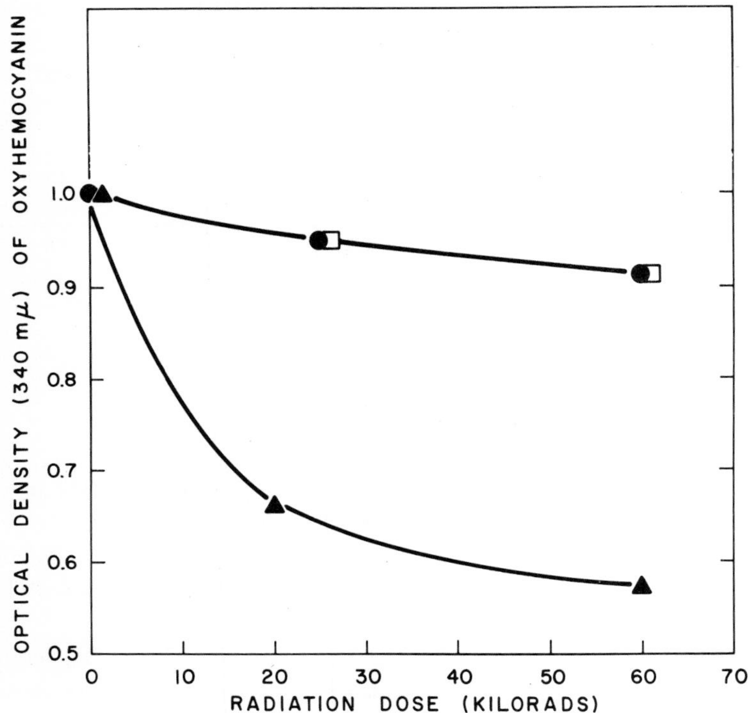

Figure 5. Effect of catalase on response of Busycotypus *hemocyanin to gamma irradiation. Catalase concentration was 20 μg/ml.*

□, ● *Catalase present during irradiation or added afterwards*
▲ *No catalase added*

Discussion

The reactivation of *Busycotypus* hemocyanin illustrates the dual nature of H_2O_2 namely, that it is also a reducing agent (*38, 44*). The radiation reactivation of *Busycotypus* hemocyanin, at the concentrations employed, is brought about by the reduction of Cu(II) to Cu(I) by H_2O_2 as occurs with H_2O_2 added to unirradiated hemocyanin (*10*).

Some of the redox reactions that may involve the protein-bound copper can be deduced (*3, 5, 44*) if we consider that we are dealing with

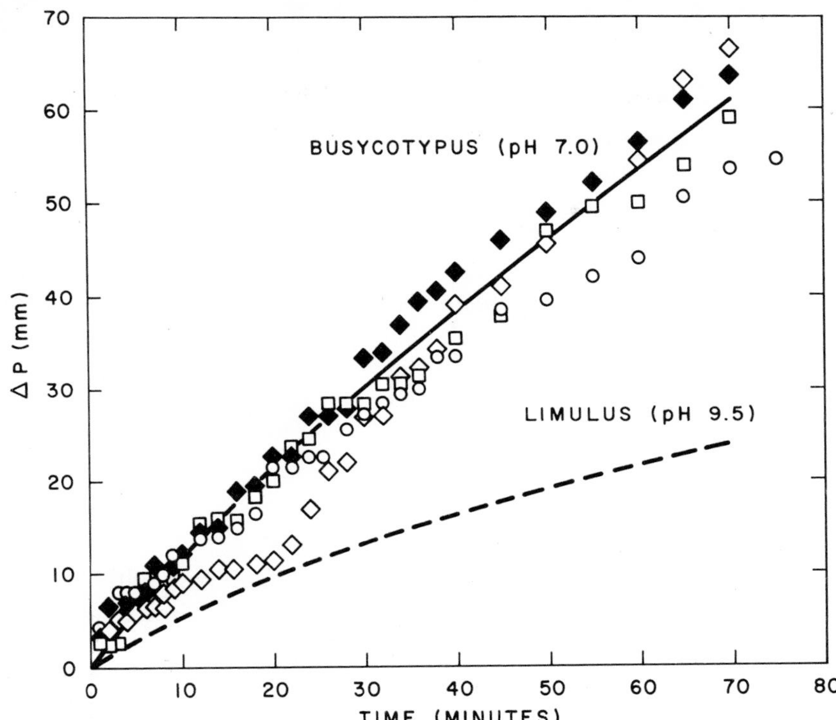

Figure 6. Liberation of oxygen from hydrogen peroxide in the presence of Busycotypus *hemocyanin at pH 7 but at different temperatures and of* Limulus *hemocyanin at 25°C. and pH 9.5. The* Busycotypus *hemocyanin solutions were heated for 15 minutes at a given temperature prior to mixing with hydrogen peroxide*

———————— Busycotypus *hemocyanin*

Warburg flask contained 14.4 μmoles H_2O_2 (0.2 ml. of 0.072M), 0.5 ml. of hemocyanin serum (7.5 × 10^{-4}M in copper) and 0.2 cc. of 0.05M pH 7 phosphate buffer. 1 mm. = 0.062 μmoles O_2: Solid line, 25°C.; ○, 35°C.; □, 45°C.; ◇, 65°C.; ◆, 65°C. and deoxygenated while heated

– – – – – – – – – Limulus *hemocyanin*

Conditions as for Busycotypus *except that the copper concentration was 2.0 × 10^{-3}M, pH 9.5, and temperature of 25°C.*

a neutral, oxygenated, aqueous medium containing organic solutes and that reduction takes place more readily in neutral than in acid media. From Reference 37 the most likely reactions in oxygenated media include: (1) Oxidation (inactivation)

$$\text{P-Cu(I)} + H_2O_2 = \text{P-Cu(II)} + OH + OH^-$$

$$\text{P-Cu(I)} + OH = \text{P-Cu(II)} + OH^-$$

(2) Reduction (reactivation)

$$P\text{-}Cu(II) + H_2O_2 = P\text{-}Cu(I) + HO_2 + H^+$$

$$P\text{-}Cu(II) + HO_2 = P\text{-}Cu(I) + O_2$$

Whether the radiation doses employed modify the hemocyanin molecule is a question which we are exploring. We have irradiated *Limulus* hemocyanin in the deoxygenated state at fairly high doses (~100,000 rads) and have found little change in the oxygenation-deoxygenation properties. We have also begun to use other techniques with which to ascertain possible effects of ionizing radiation on the hemocyanin molecule including optical rotatory dispersion and circular dichroism (*46*). For the present, it appears that the principal effect of ionizing radiation on hemocyanin is centered on the active copper sites through the promotion of the oxidation of the Cu(I) to the Cu(II) state by radiolytic hydrogen peroxide.

Acknowledgment

This investigation was supported by U. S. Public Health Service Research Grant RH 00434, National Center for Radiological Health and by AEC contract AT(30-1)-3641.

Literature Cited

(1) Anbar, M., *Nature* **200,** 376 (1963).
(2) Bacq, A. M., Alexander, P., "Fundamentals of Radiobiology," Pergamon Press, New York, 1961.
(3) Barb, W. G., Baxendale, J. H., George, P., Hargrave, K. R., *Trans. Faraday Soc.* **47,** 462, 591 (1951).
(4) Barron, E. S. G., *Ann. New York Acad. Sci.* **59,** 574 (1955).
(5) Baxendale, J. H., *Radiation Res. Suppl.* **4, 114** (1964).
(6) Bayer, E., *Liebigs Ann. Chem.* **653,** 149 (1962).
(7) Cohen, L. B., Van Holde, K. E., *Biochemistry* **3,** 1809 (1964).
(8) Egerton, A. C., Everett, A. J., Minkoff, G. J., Rudrakanchana, S., Salooja, K. C., *Anal. Chim. Acta* **10,** 422 (1954).
(9) Felsenfeld, G., *J. Cellular Comp. Physiol.* **43,** 23 (1954).
(10) Felsenfeld, G. Printz, M. P., *J. Am. Chem. Soc.* **81,** 6259 (1959).
(11) Frieden, E., Osaki, S., Kobayashi, H., *J. Gen. Physiol.* **49,** 213 (1965).
(12) Ghiretti, F., *Arch. Biochem. Biophys.* **63,** 165 (1956).
(13) Ghiretti, F., "Oxygenases," Chap. 10, O. Hayaishi, ed., Academic Press, New York, 1962.
(14) Ghiretti-Magaldi, A. Nuzzolo, Ghiretti, F., *Biochemistry* **5,** 1943 (1966).
(15) Hayaishi, O. (ed.), "Oxygenases," Academic Press, New York, 1962.
(16) Hudson, T. A. F., "Vanadium-Toxicology and Biological Significance," Elsevier Publishing Co., New York, 1964.
(17) Larimer, J. L., Riggs, A. F., *Comp. Biochem. Physiol.* **13,** 35 (1964).
(18) Johnston, W., James, T. W., and Barber, A. A., *Comp. Biochem. Physiol.* **22,** 261 (1967).
(19) Levitzki, A., Anbar, M., *J. Am. Chem. Soc.* **89,** 4185 (1967).
(20) Litt, M., Boyd, W. C., *Nature* **181,** 1075 (1958).

(21) Lontie, R. Blaton, V., Albert, M., Peeters, B., *Arch. Intern. Physiol. Biochim.* **73,** 150 (1965).
(22) Lontie, R., Witters, R., "The Biochemistry of Copper," pp. 455-462, J. Peisach, P. Aisen, W. E. Blumberg, eds., Academic Press, New York, 1966.
(23) Manwell, C., *Ann. Rev. Physiol.* **22,** 191 (1960).
(24) Mason, H. S., *Nature* **177,** 79 (1956).
(25) Mason, H. S., *Advan. Enzymol.* **19,** 79 (1957).
(26) Nagy-Keresztes, S., Klotz, I. M., *Biochemistry* **4,** 919 (1965).
(27) Nakamura, T., Mason, H. S., *Biochem. Biophys. Res. Comm.* **3,** 297 (1960).
(28) *Natl. Bur. Std. (U. S.) Handbook* **85,** 14 (1964).
(29) Nikolaev, L. A., "The Origin of Life on the Earth," pp. 263-274, F. Clark, R. L. M. Synge, eds., Pergamon Press, New York, 1959.
(30) Orgel, L. E., In *Metals and Enzyme Activity,* Symposium No. 15, Cambridge, 1958.
(31) Peterson, R. N., Freund, M., Gilmont, R., *Proc. Soc. Exp. Biol. Med.* **125,** 645 (1967).
(32) Pickels, E. G., Anderson, R. S., *J. Gen. Physiol.* **30,** 83 (1946).
(33) Redfield, A. C., "Copper Metabolism," W. D. McElroy, B. Glass, eds., The Johns Hopkins Press, Baltimore, 1950.
(34) Schubert, J., *Nature* **195,** 1096 (1962).
(35) *Ibid.,* **200,** 375 (1963).
(36) Schubert, J., "Copper and Peroxides in Radiobiology and Medicine," C. C. Thomas, Springfield, Ill., 1964.
(37) Schubert, J., White, E. R., *Science* **155,** 1000 (1967).
(38) Schumb, W. C., Satterfield, C. N., Wentworth, R. L., "Hydrogen Peroxide," p. 355, Reinhold, New York, 1955.
(39) Shchepot'yeva, E. S., Ardashnikov, S. N., Lur'ye, G. E., Rakhamanova, T. B., "Effect of Oxygen in Ionizing Radiation," State Publishing House for Medical Literature, Moscow, 1959 (Translation, U. S. At. Energy Comm., Technical Information Service, **AEC-tr-4265**).
(40) Sigel, H., Muller, V., *Helv. Chim. Acta* **49,** 671 (1966).
(41) Svedberg, T., Brohult, S., *Nature* **142,** 830 (1938).
(42) *Ibid.,* **143,** 938 (1939).
(43) Swallow, A. J., "Radiation Chemistry of Organic Compounds," Pergamon Press, New York, 1960.
(44) Uri, N., *Chem. Rev.* **50,** 375 (1952).
(45) Van Holde, K. E., Cohen, L. B., *Biochemistry* **3,** 1803 (1964).
(46) Van Holde, K. E., *Biochemistry* **6,** 93 (1967).

RECEIVED February 12, 1968.

35

Tritiated Free Radical Scavengers in the Study of the Irradiated Protein Molecule

P. RIESZ and F. H. WHITE, JR.

National Cancer Institute and National Heart Institute, National Institutes of Health, Bethesda, Md. 20014

The use of gaseous tritiated radical scavengers to determine the secondary free radical distribution in γ-irradiated lyophilized macromolecules has been explored. For proteins the similarity of the tritium distributions obtained with tritiated H_2S and HI as well as studies with $H_2{}^{35}S$, support the assumption that these distributions are an approximate measure of the secondary radical distribution. Radical distributions of several native proteins were characteristically different, those of denatured proteins approximately the same, thus demonstrating a pronounced effect of conformation. In contrast to proteins, the reaction of irradiated dry DNA with tritiated H_2S or HI gave approximately 100 times more tritium label on the DNA than expected from the initial concentration of free radicals in the DNA.

The long-lived free radicals produced by γ-radiolysis of dry proteins have been studied (*10, 20, 23*) by electron spin resonance (ESR). It was shown (*11, 22, 35*) that when proteins are irradiated at 77°K., ESR centers are formed ("primary" radicals), which on heating to room temperature are irreversibly changed to give spectra which are identical with those found after radiolysis at room temperature ("secondary" radicals). It was inferred (*23*) from the ESR spectra that on irradiation of proteins, two main types of radicals are formed at room temperature. In the one, the unpaired spin is localized at the cysteine sulfur, while in the other it is mainly associated with glycine residues.

An independent experimental method for studying the secondary free radicals located on carbon was developed recently (*30, 31, 37*). This involves exposing the γ-irradiated lyophilized proteins to tritiated radical scavengers (hydrogen sulfide or hydrogen iodide) in order to form carbon-tritium bonds in the protein. Subsequent hydrolysis, amino acid analysis, and tritium counting allow determination of the tritium distribution among the amino acids, which appears to be a measure of the secondary free radical distribution.

Experimental

Materials. Tritiated hydrogen sulfide (HST) and hydrogen iodide (TI), both with a specific activity of 224 mc/mmole and $H_2{}^{35}S$ (7.05 mc/mmole at the time of synthesis), were obtained from New England Nuclear Corp. HST and $H_2{}^{35}S$ were passed into a previously evacuated liquid nitrogen trap, and the hydrogen formed by self-radiolysis was removed before addition to protein. Iodine formed by self-radiolysis of TI was separated by two distillations from traps at dry ice temperature. For experiments with TI a silicone manometer and silicone grease were used on the vacuum line. Proteins were obtained from suppliers listed previously (*37*). All proteins were lyophilized from aqueous solutions at a starting concentration of 1 mg./ml.

Irradiation of Protein and Exposure to Tritiated Scavenger. Unless specified differently experiments were performed as follows: the lyophilized protein samples (*ca.* 20 mg.) were evacuated for 2 hours at 10^{-3} torr in a cylindrical borosilicate glass vessel (*ca.* 15 cc., 1 cm. i.d.) equipped with a breakseal sidearm. After sealing off under vacuum, the samples were irradiated at room temperature in a cobalt γ-source at a dose rate of about 8 Mrads/day, usually to about 6 Mrads. Dose rates were measured with the ferrous sulfate dosimeter in vessels identical with those used in labeling experiments. Immediately after irradiation of the protein samples, any volatile radiation products were removed, and 3.0 ml. of oxygen-free, dry HST containing 30.0 mc of tritium was added to the exposure vessel. The usual pressure was about 150 torr. After 4 hours, HST was transferred to a storage vessel. The protein was immediately dissolved in 100 ml. of water at room temperature to remove most of the exchangeable tritium and allowed to stand several hours. After lyophilization this procedure was repeated, except that the time allowed for exchange was about 17 hours. After exposure to HST, the protein contained 10–20 mc of tritium; after the exchange procedure only a few μc/mg. remained.

Acid hydrolysis of the protein was carried out with 2–8 mg. in 2 ml. of 6*N* HCl at 110°C. for 18 hours under vacuum. The hydrolysate was dried over sodium hydroxide pellets *in vacuo,* and any remaining traces of exchangeable tritium were removed by redissolving in 10 ml. H_2O and lyophilizing.

Amino Acid Analysis and Counting. An automatic amino acid analyzer (Phoenix) employing the system of Piez and Morris (*26*) was used. The eluate, before being mixed with ninhydrin, was passed through a scintillation flow counting system (*27*) (Nuclear Chicago Corp.) equipped with a digital integrator. The efficiency of the flow cells was about 2% and was determined by passing a standard sample of tritiated hydroxyproline through the analyzer and counter under the conditions of analysis.

Chromatography of Ribonuclease on IRC-50 (XE-64) Carboxylic Acid Cation Exchange Resin. This was carried out by the method of Hirs, Moore, and Stein (*15*) using a column of XE-64, 0.9 cm. in diameter and 30 cm. in length with 0.2*M* sodium phosphate (pH 6.17) as eluent. The flow rate was 5 ml. per hour.

Sephadex Chromatography. Immediately after exposure of ribonuclease to $H_2{}^{35}S$ or $H^{35}ST$, a G-25 Sephadex column (2.5 cm. diameter, 20 cm. long was used to separate protein containing ^{35}S from small ^{35}S-labeled molecules present in the mixture. 0.1*M* Acetic acid was used as eluent.

Reduction and Carboxymethylation of Proteins. Reduction of disulfide bridges with mercaptoethanol in 8*M* urea and reaction with iodoacetate to introduce the carboxymethyl (CM) group onto the protein sulfhydryl groups have been described earlier (*39*).

ESR Measurements. ESR measurements were carried out using a Varian V-4500 spectrometer with a 6-inch magnet which was regulated and scanned by "fieldial."

Treatment of Data. The distribution of tritium in various proteins is presented in terms of a normalized specific activity (NSA). Thereby, the effects of variation in specific activity and differences in molecular weights of the proteins on the specific activities of their amino acids were eliminated. NSA is defined as

$$\frac{S_i \times 100}{\Sigma S_i}$$

where S_i is the specific activity of a given amino acid in counts per μmole, and ΣS_i is the sum of specific activities of all of the amino acids of the protein under consideration.

Conditions for Determining Secondary Radical Distributions

Reactions Involved in Radical Interception. Some of the reactions which have been considered in the radical interceptor technique are shown in Reactions 1-8. Reactions 1 and 2 are schematic and do not describe the mechanism of formation of secondary free radicals in proteins by ionizing radiation. The reactions of the carbon radicals with tritiated scavengers (Reactions 3 and 3a) lead to the formation of carbon-tritium bonds.

$$\geqslant C{-}R \rightsquigarrow\, \geqslant C^{\cdot} + R^{\cdot} \qquad (1)$$

$$R + \geqslant C{-}H \rightarrow\, \geqslant C^{\cdot} + RH \qquad (2)$$

$$\geqslant C^{\cdot} + HST \rightarrow\, \geqslant C{-}T + HS^{\cdot} \quad (3) \qquad \geqslant C^{\cdot} + TI \rightarrow\, \geqslant C{-}T + I^{\cdot} \quad (3a)$$

$$2\,HS^{\cdot} \rightarrow H_2S + S \text{ or } H_2S_2 \quad (4) \qquad 2\,I^{\cdot} \rightarrow I_2 \quad (4a)$$

$$\geqslant C{-}H + HS^{\cdot} \rightarrow\, \geqslant C^{\cdot} + H_2S \quad (5) \qquad \geqslant C{-}H + I^{\cdot} \rightarrow\, \geqslant C^{\cdot} + HI \quad (5a)$$

$$\geqslant C^{\cdot} + HS^{\cdot} \rightarrow\, \geqslant C{-}SH \quad (6) \qquad \geqslant C^{\cdot} + I^{\cdot} \rightarrow\, \geqslant C{-}I \quad (6a)$$

$$>C{=}C< + HS^{\cdot} \rightarrow\, >\dot{C}{-}C(SH)< \quad (7) \qquad >C{=}C< + I^{\cdot} \rightarrow\, >\dot{C}{-}C(I)< \quad (7a)$$

$$-CH_2{-}S{-}S{-}CH_2{-} + HS^{\cdot} \rightarrow -CH_2{-}S{-}SH + {}^{\cdot}S{-}CH_2{-} \qquad (8)$$

It is important to ascertain the fate of the HS· radicals produced in the labeling reaction since some of the radical termination processes may influence the observed tritium distribution. Thus, if HS· radicals are removed by disproportionation or dimerization in the gas phase (Reaction 4) or by reaction with disulfide bridges (Reaction 8), no distortion of the tritium distribution will occur. However, Reactions 5, 6, and 7 may, under certain circumstances, lead to erroneous tritium distributions. Although the bond dissociation energy of the HS-H bond [90 kcal. (*3*)] is considerably lower than that of most C-H bonds, the possible occurrence of Reaction 5 cannot be ruled out *a priori*. If HS· radicals could abstract hydrogen from carbon (Reaction 5) to produce a new class of carbon radicals, not previously formed by γ-radiolysis, this new class would not be expected to be identical with the secondary radical distribution. Furthermore, Reaction 5 followed by 3 could lead to a chain reaction for tritium incorporation. To examine the possible contribution of Reaction 5 to HST labeling, the use of tritiated hydrogen iodide as radical interceptor was investigated (discussed later). For this reagent one can assume that Reaction 5A does not occur. This is a consequence of the low bond dissociation energy of the HI molecule [71 kcal. (*3, 36*)] and has been demonstrated by experimental work in which iodine and HI have been used as radical scavengers (*33*).

Reaction of HS· radicals, produced by Reaction 3, with the carbon radicals formed by radiolysis, may lead to distorted tritium distributions if the carbon radicals located on a particular amino acid residue react more slowly with HST than those located on other amino acid residues, but rapidly with HS· radicals.

Addition of HS· to double bonds of the aromatic amino acids (Reaction 7) will result in the formation of a new carbon radical. This unpaired spin may conceivably migrate to other amino acid residues by successive H-atom transfer reactions before the resulting radical becomes labeled by reacting with HST. Such a process could give rise to a radical chain for incorporating T into amino acid residues without labeling the aromatic amino acids. If no migration occurs before Reaction 3, a tritiated cyclohexadiene-thiol analog of the parent aromatic amino acid residue will be formed. This new tritiated compound may have a strong tendency to aromatize with loss of H_2S regenerating the original amino acid in tritiated condition. In view of these possible complications, the possible reactions of the HS· radical were explored with the help of $H_2{}^{35}S$.

In addition to the necessity for studying the radical termination reactions, there are three conditions which must be fulfilled if the tritium distribution is to correspond to the distribution of the secondary free radicals. First, the time of exposure to the tritiated radical scavenger must be sufficient to ensure that all of the free radicals on carbon react. Second, there must be no significant amount of exchange of tritium bound to carbon during removal of the exchangeable tritium bound to oxygen, nitrogen, and sulfur, or during acid hydrolysis of the protein. Third, the extent of tritium labeling induced by β-decay in presence of HST (subsequently referred to as β-labeling) must be determined in separate experiments and, unless negligible, must be subtracted from the tritium introduced into the protein as a consequence of radical formation by γ-radiolysis (γ-labeling).

ESR Studies. The reaction of free radicals with radical scavengers can be followed by observing the ESR spectrum of γ-irradiated proteins as a function of time after adding the scavenger. Previous experiments (*30, 37*) with H_2S and lyophilized ribonuclease, lysozyme, chymotrypsinogen, insulin, myoglobin, gelatin, and their reduced carboxymethylated derivatives have shown that all of the carbon radicals react with H_2S (150 torr, room temp.) in 4 hours or less. In the proteins other than myoglobin and gelatin, the decrease of the carbon radical signal is accompanied by a transient increase of the sulfur radical signal during exposure. This increase is not found when HI is used as the radical interceptor. Whatever the mechanism of this process, it does not influence our results. This follows from the similarity of the tritium distributions with HST and TI in the two cases (chymotrypsinogen and ribonuclease) where a detailed comparison has been made. Figure 1 shows the results for ribonuclease irradiated to 4.2 Mrads and exposed to HI (150 torr, room temp.). After 4 hours the carbon radical signal has disappeared, leaving only the sulfur signal. The latter is caused by sulfur radicals, formed during γ-radiolysis, which do not react with HI. The same time period has also been found ample for the complete reaction of the carbon radicals in γ-irradiated lyophilized peptides such as L-leucyl-L-leucyl-L-leucine, L-methionyl-L-methionyl-L-methionine, and poly-L-proline.

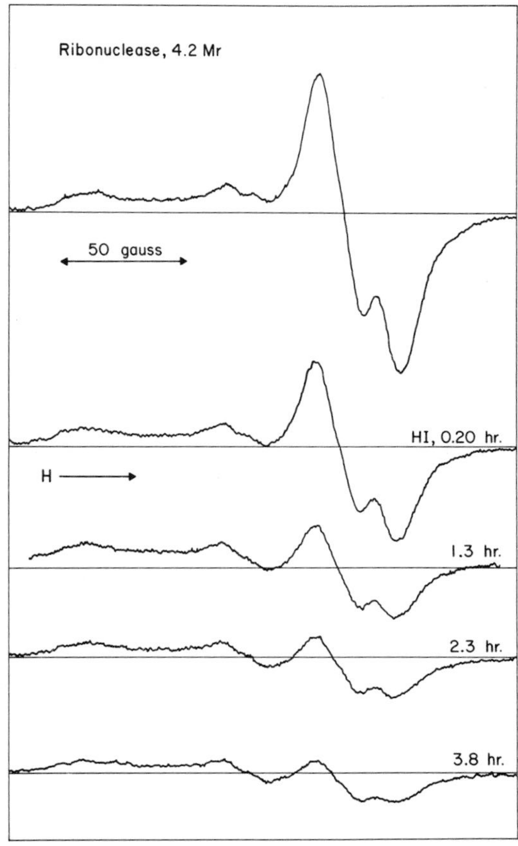

Figure 1. Reaction of free radicals on carbon in irradiated ribonuclease with hydrogen iodide, as studied by ESR. Curves represent the first derivative of the absorption curves

Removal of carbon radicals is slow when irradiated ribonuclease is treated with molecules larger than H_2S such as chloroform, isopropyl cyanide, and isoamyl mercaptan. For isoamyl mercaptan (15 torr, room temp.) less than half of the carbon radicals react in 3 hours (Figure 2). However, after 144 hours all radicals have reacted. The use of large radical scavenger molecules for studying the conformation of proteins in the dry state is discussed later.

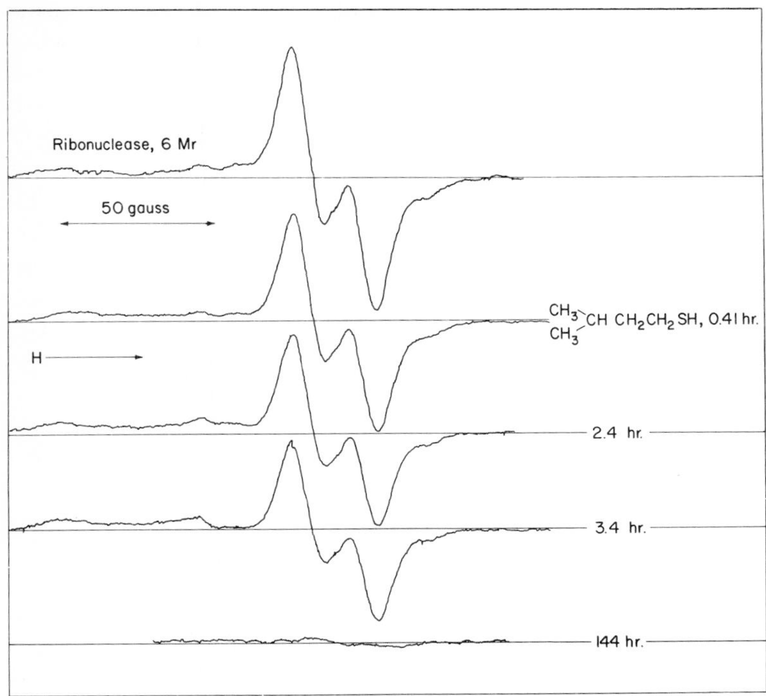

Figure 2. Reaction of free radicals on carbon in irradiated ribonuclease with isoamyl mercaptan

Exchange Studies. Previous studies (*30, 37*) of the exchange of tritium from HTO into individual amino acids and into ribonuclease under hydrolytic conditions (6*N* HCl, 110°C., 18 hours) have shown that only aspartic acid, glutamic acid, carboxymethyl cysteine, and tyrosine exchange. In the case of tyrosine this exchange takes place at positions 3 and 5 (*19*), in the other cases on the carbon atom next to the extra carboxyls (*14*). The actual positions of tritium introduced into the proteins by HST and TI labeling remain to be determined. If tritium is not introduced into the exchangeable positions, the losses during hydrolysis will not be significant for the present work. Otherwise, milder methods of complete enzymatic hydrolysis must be used.

β-Labeling. Incorporation of tritium on exposure of a nonirradiated protein to HST or TI has been termed β-labeling in contrast to γ-labeling which refers to the tritium introduced into the protein as a consequence of radical formation by γ-radiolysis. Earlier investigations (*30, 37*) showed that in the standard ($\gamma + \beta$)-labeling experiment, where the time of exposure to HST is 4 hours, β-labeling accounted for 10% or less of the total tritium incorporated for ribonuclease, chymotrypsinogen, insulin, and myoglobin and for 18% in the case of carboxymethylated reduced ribonuclease. The amount of tritium incorporated by β-labeling was approximately proportional to the time of exposure at 4 and 24 hours. When TI is used as a radical scavenger, the percentage of β-labeling is much higher (25% for ribonuclease, 45% for chymotrypsinogen) and less reproducible than with HST. Tritium distributions for β-labeling after 24 hours are shown in Figure 3 for HST (ribonuclease and lysozyme), and in Figures 4 and 5 for TI (ribonuclease and chymotrypsinogen). β-Labeling with HST produces a high specific activity in histidine, while the use of TI results in high specific activities of phenylalanine, tyrosine, and methionine for ribonuclease and of phenylalanine, tyrosine, and histidine for lysozyme.

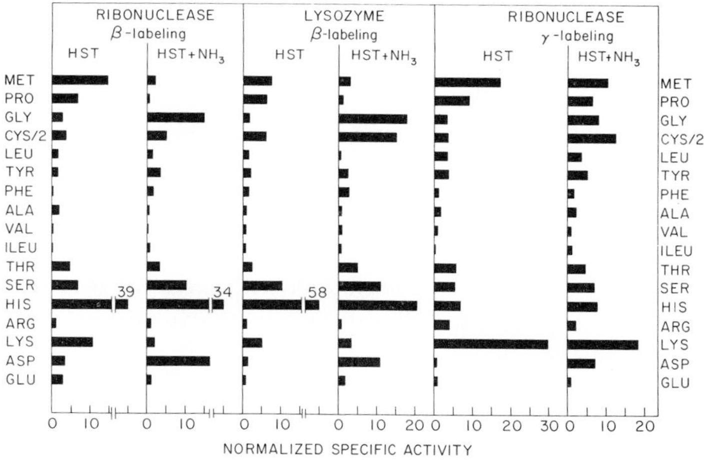

Figure 3. Effect of ammonia on tritium distributions of β-labeled ribonuclease and lysozyme and on γ-labeled ribonuclease. Bar lengths are proportional to the normalized specific activity (defined in text)

The geometrical arrangement of the exposure vessel is such that only a small fraction (< 5%) of the β-particles generated in the gas phase is absorbed by the protein. The irreversible absorption of H_2S was negligible under the conditions of our experiments; however, for HI only about two-thirds of the gas could be removed by transfer to a liquid nitrogen trap after exposure, the remainder being presumably chemically bound to basic sites in the protein. A substantial fraction (about two-thirds after 4 hours of exposure) of the total tritium initially present in the radical scavenger was transferred to the protein owing to exchange on oxygen and nitrogen. The energy released by the β-decay of this portion of the tritium is absorbed by the solid protein, leading to tritium labeling by processes analogous to those responsible for γ-labeling. Tritium may also be incorporated into the protein as a consequence of radiolysis in the gas phase. If one assumes that all of the energy available from β-decay of tritium is used for β-labeling, a minimum G value of about 6 for radical production is obtained, compared with a value of about 1 for γ-labeling. Among the highly reactive intermediates in the gas-phase radiolysis of H_2S are hydrogen atoms, sulfhydryl radicals, and H_2ST^+ ions. Hydrogen atoms formed in the gas phase are more likely to be scavenged by H_2S (*4*) than to react with the protein to produce carbon radicals. Since the ion-molecule reaction to produce H_2ST^+ ions is known to occur in the mass spectrometer (*7*), the possible role of H_2ST^+ in β-labeling was investigated. It is known (*1*) that ammonia, because of its high proton affinity, retards the ionic radiation-induced polymerization of cyclopentadiene. The possibility that ammonia reacts with neutral free radicals or hydrogen atoms can be discounted because of the high value of the H_2N-H bond dissociation energy, $D_{H_2N-H} = 106$ kcal./mole (*41*). Furthermore, H atoms do not react with ammonia in the radiolysis of liquid ammonia (*2*). In a control experiment, ribonuclease was irradiated to 5 Mrads in the presence of 3 ml. (N.T.P.) of NH_3 gas. Subsequently, 3 ml. of HST were added, and the tritium-labeling experiment was carried out in the usual manner. Figure 3 shows that ammonia affects the γ-labeled tritium distribution, although in this experiment there is no significant contribution to labeling from the gas phase. The addition of ammonia decreases the specific activities of methionine and lysine and increases those of aspartic acid and glycine. A possible explanation of the effect of ammonia on the γ-labeled tritium distribution is the formation of ammonium salts of aspartic and glutamic acids prior to radiolysis. Thus, Henriksen (*12*) has observed that the radical yield of a freeze-dried protein may vary with the pH of the solution before lyophilization. Figure 3 shows that adding ammonia to HST during β-labeling experiments with ribonuclease and lysozyme produced the same changes as in the γ-labeling experiment. We can conclude from these experiments that there is no evidence for a major contribution to labeling from H_2ST^+ ions in the gas phase. Furthermore, we can infer that if radiolysis in the gas phase is responsible for an appreciable contribution to β-labeling, the most likely intermediate would be the HS· radical. The similarity of the NH_3 effects for β- and γ-labeling also supports the assumption that a significant part of the β-labeling by HST proceeds by processes analogous to γ-labeling, whereby the carbon free radicals become labeled by abstraction of tritium from HST.

The extremely large fraction of the total tritium in phenylalanine and tyrosine for β-labeling of ribonuclease and chymotrypsinogen with TI can be understood in terms of a mechanism involving the addition of iodine atoms to aromatic rings, followed by reaction of the carbon radical with TI to give the cyclohexadiene derivative, which will tend to aromatize with loss of HI or TI to yield the tritiated parent amino acid as shown below.

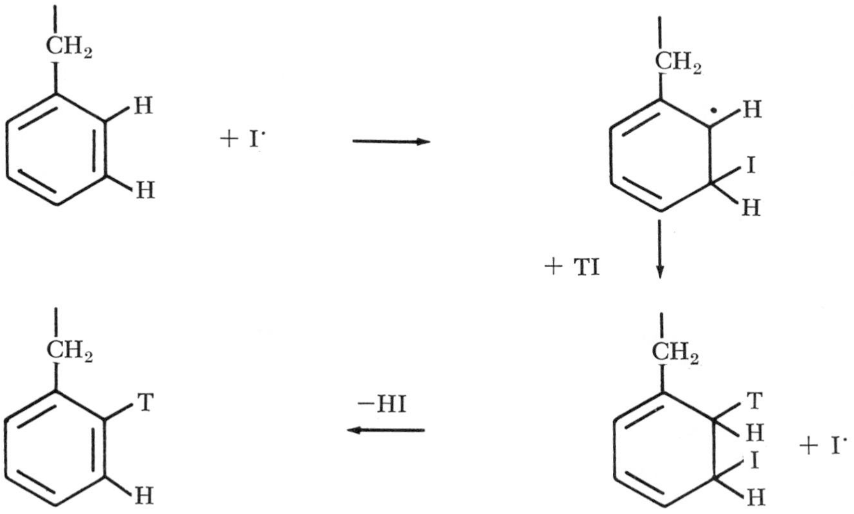

The same tritium distribution is obtained when ribonuclease is dried for a week in an evacuated drying pistol over P_2O_5 at 100°C. before β-labeling with TI. This experiment indicates that the mechanism does not involve exchange with TI dissolved in small amounts of protein-bound water.

HST and TI in γ-Labeling. In γ-labeling experiments the average specific activities (μc/mg.) for ribonuclease were 0.76 (HST), 0.23 (TI) and for chymotrypsinogen 0.76 (HST), 0.32 (TI). For β-labeling the average specific activities (4 hours) were 0.073 (HST), 0.085 (TI) and for chymotrypsinogen 0.038 (HST), 0.078 (TI). The observation that the amount of tritium incorporated is of the same order of magnitude for both interceptors is consistent with the absence of a chain reaction owing to HS· radicals. The β-labeled distributions were substracted from the observed $\gamma + \beta$ tritium distribution to obtain the corrected γ-labeled distribution. Since the total amount of β-labeling with TI was not very reproducible, the fraction of β-labeling to be subtracted was adjusted to give the observed normalized specific activity of phenylalanine or tyrosine observed with HST. The result of this subtraction is shown in Figures 4 and 5. Figure 6 shows the γ-distribution of tritium among the amino acids of ribonuclease and of chymotrypsinogen for HST and TI. There are many similarities between the tritium distributions for HST and TI. These results show that either hydrogen abstraction by HS· radicals is not a significant process in these experiments or HS· radicals abstract from the carbon-hydrogen bonds of the various amino acid residues at relative rates which accidentally parallel the secondary radical distribution produced by γ-radiolysis. The latter hypothesis appears to be less likely. The results with TI support the three major conclusions previously (*30*) obtained with HST. First, tritium is widely distributed among amino acid residues. Second, in a given protein, the specific activities vary from very high to very low. Third, the low specific activity of glycine indicates that glycine does not play a special role as a free radical site in ribonuclease and chymotrypsinogen.

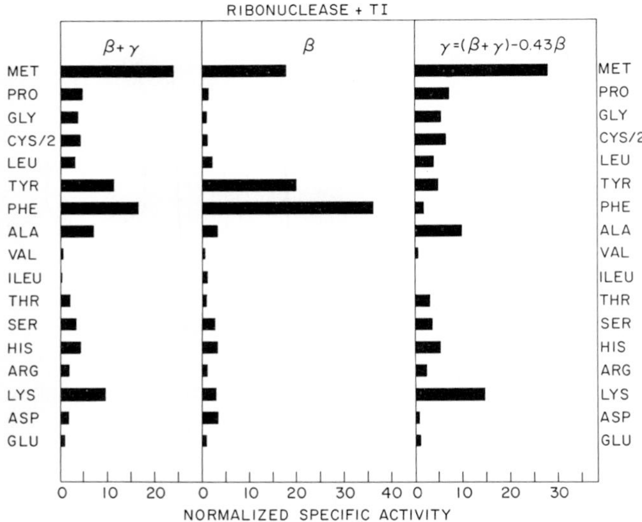

Figure 4. (γ + β)-, β-, and γ-labeled tritium distributions in ribonuclease with TI

However, the specific activities of certain amino acid residues are significantly different when the two reagents are compared. Thus, the specific activity of lysine in ribonuclease labeled with TI is lower and that of alanine is higher than for labeling with HST. It appears, therefore, that some distortion can occur when tritiated scavengers are employed. It was pointed out earlier that a possible explanation of such distortions might lie in the reactions by which the radicals produced during the labeling process are removed. These have been studied by using $H_2{}^{35}S$ as radical scavenger.

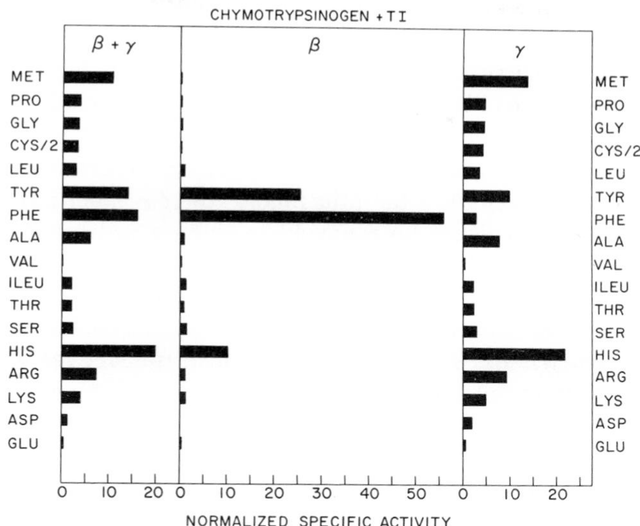

Figure 5. (γ + β)-, β-, and γ-labeled tritium distributions in chymotrypsinogen with TI

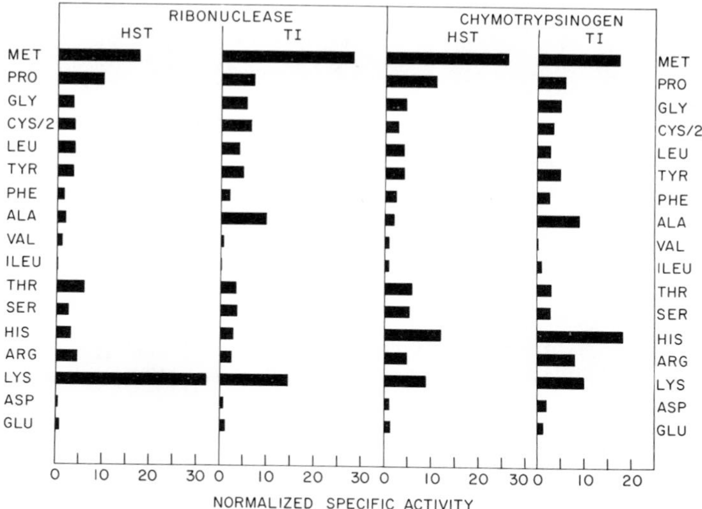

Figure 6. γ-Labeled tritium distribution of ribonuclease and chymotrypsinogen with HST and TI as radical interceptors

Experiments with $H_2{}^{35}S$ and $H^{35}ST$. Reactions 6, 7, and 8 are possible ways of removing HS· radicals produced by Reaction 3. In Reaction 6, HS· radicals react with C· radicals; Reaction 7 consists of the addition of HS· to the double bond of an aromatic amino acid residue, and in Reaction 8 the disulfide bridge is opened to give an S-SH bond and a new S· radical. All these reactions will introduce covalently bound ^{35}S into the protein molecule when $H_2{}^{35}S$ is added to the irradiated protein. However, ^{35}S introduced by Reaction 8 can be removed by treating the protein with 8*M* urea and mercaptoethanol since under these conditions the S-S bond is broken. On the other hand, the ^{35}S label introduced by Reactions 6 and 7 will not be removed by such a reduction procedure. Furthermore, the ^{35}S introduced by Reaction 7 should be associated to a large extent with tritium in the same macromolecule. Even if the carbon radicals formed by Reaction 7 were to migrate by successive hydrogen atom transfer reactions, it is unlikely that radical transfer reactions would be exclusively intermolecular.

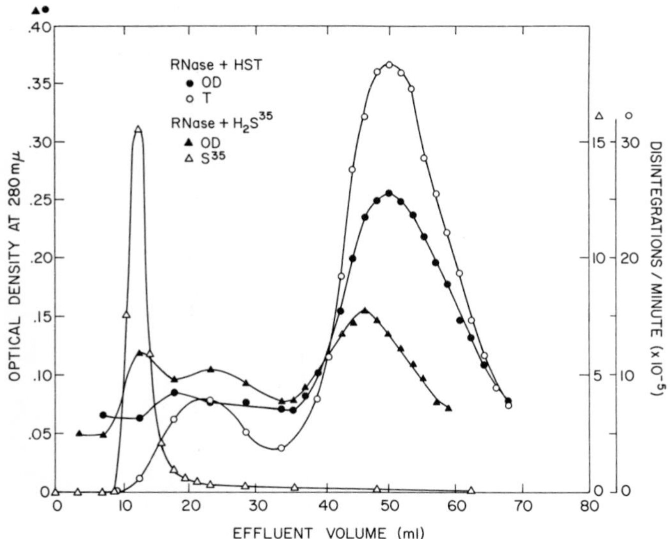

Figure 7. Chromatography of HST-labeled and $H_2{}^{35}S$-labeled ribonuclease on XE-64 carboxylic acid cation exchange resin

The results of an experiment which indicate that the irreversible addition of HS· radicals to aromatic rings is not an important process for native ribonuclease is shown in Figure 7. γ-Irradiated ribonuclease was exposed to $H_2{}^{35}S$ for 4 hours and then immediately separated from noncovalently bound ^{35}S by chromatography on Sephadex G25. After lyophilization the ribonuclease was chromatographed on an IRC 50 (XE-64) carboxylic acid cation-exchange resin column. γ-Irradiated ribonuclease exposed to HST was also chromatographed under identical conditions. A separate experiment, in which γ-irradiated ribonuclease was treated with doubly-labeled $H^{35}ST$, was performed with the same results. Figure 7 shows that the ^{35}S peak does not coincide with the T peaks, and hence T and ^{35}S are not present in the same polypeptide chain; this finding constitutes evidence against the irreversible addition of SH to aromatic rings. The double-labeling experiment proves that the noncoincidence of ^{35}S and T peaks is not the result of slightly different oxidation processes for the ^{35}SH-containing protein and the tritium-labeled protein when these are prepared in separate experiments. However, these results do not exclude the possibility that HS· radicals add to amino acid residues containing conjugated double bonds and that subsequently $H_2{}^{35}S$ is lost, and the conjugated double bond system is reformed. The analogous mechanism for TI has been described in detail earlier.

Evidence for the reaction of HS· radicals with disulfide bridges was obtained by studying the following sequence of reactions:

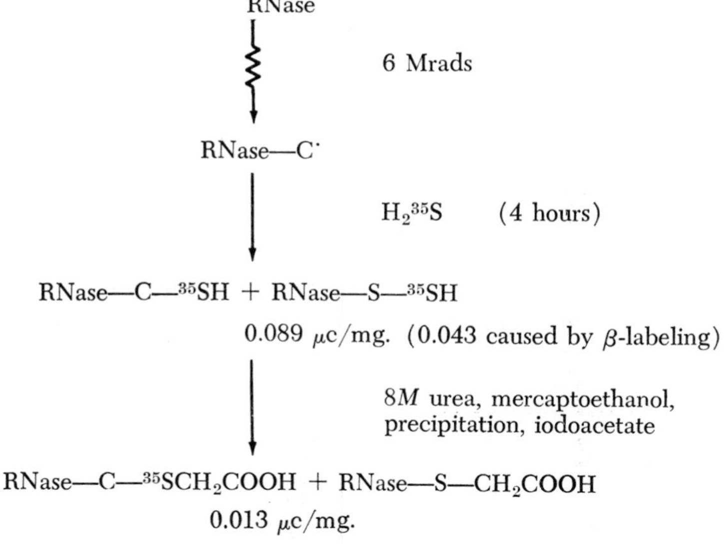

Irradiated ribonuclease is treated with $H_2{}^{35}S$ and the non-covalently bound ^{35}S is removed by Sephadex chromatography. At this stage the specific activity of the ribonuclease was 0.089 μc/mg., of which 0.043 μc/mg. was caused by β-labeling determined in a separate experiment. Reduction of this material with mercaptoethanol in 8*M* urea, precipitation, and carboxymethylation resulted in ribonuclease's having a specific activity of 0.013 μc/mg. This decrease is interpreted as resulting from the cleavage of the S-^{35}SH bond.

From the specific activities of the ^{35}S-labeled proteins and of $H_2{}^{35}S$ the number of HS· radicals which react with ribonuclease can be calculated. Table I shows that the number of SH radicals covalently bound is approximately equal to the number of carbon radicals produced by γ-radiolysis. The latter was calculated from T incorporation and from the ESR data of Hunt and Williams (*16*).

Table I. Effect of Reduction on the Specific Activity of ^{35}S-Labeled Protein [d]

	Specific Activity of RNase (μc/mg.)	*Molecules/C· or molecules/HS·*
HST	0.76	11 [a]
$H_2{}^{35}S$ [b]	0.046	12
$H_2{}^{35}S$ [c]	0.013	41

[a] Assuming no tritium isotope effect.
[b] Before reduction (corrected for β-labeling).
[c] After reduction.
[d] 1μc T = 2.07 × 10^{13} T atoms; 1μc ^{35}S = 4.00 × 10^{11} ^{35}S atoms; H_2S/HST = 129, $H_2S/H_2{}^{35}S$ = 2.02 × 10^5.

It appears that almost all of the HS· radicals formed in the labeling reaction react with the protein and do not recombine in the gas phase. In native RNase about 70% of the HS· radicals react with disulfide bridges (Reaction 8), while 30% add to carbon radicals (Reaction 6). The latter process could, under conditions previously discussed, cause a distortion of the tritium distribution. The reactions of HS· radicals in reduced proteins remain to be investigated.

Specific Activities of Proteins. The average specific activities of proteins after γ-radiolysis to a dose of about 6 Mrads (except for myoglobin which was irradiated to 23 Mrads), HST labeling and acid hydrolysis were as follows: ribonuclease, 0.76 ± 0.21; lysozyme, 0.66 ± 0.21; chymotrypsinogen, 0.76 ± 0.06; insulin, 0.18 ± 0.06; myoglobin 0.46 ± 0.23; CM reduced ribonuclease, 0.96 ± 0.38; CM reduced lysozyme, 0.98 ± 0.29; CM reduced chymotrypsinogen, 0.31 ± 0.10; CM reduced insulin, 1.80 ± 0.03; gelatin 16.4 ± 0.10 μc/mg. The very high specific activity of gelatin may indicate the existence of an unknown mechanism of tritium incorporation (perhaps related to its content of proline or hydroxyproline) and raises the possibility that the tritium distribution of this protein may not reflect its secondary free radical distribution. However, Figure 10 indicates that the tritium distribution of gelatin does not greatly differ from those of other denatured proteins.

Tritium Distribution of Native Ribonuclease. In a standard γ-labeling experiment 20 mg. of protein were irradiated at 10^{-3} torr to about 5 Mrads at room temperature and subsequently exposed to HST at a pressure of about 150 torr for 4 hours (Experiment A, Figure 8). A portion of the unfractionated protein was then hydrolyzed, after exchange, to determine the tritium distribution. The results in Figure 8 demonstrate that essentially the same tritium distribution is obtained under a variety of experimental conditions (B-F). In Experiment B, ribonuclease was irradiated at 77°K. and then allowed to warm to 298°K. before adding HST. The comparison of distributions from Experiments A and B (Figure 7) shows that the radicals formed by radiolysis at 298°K. are identical with the secondary radicals produced from the primary radicals, formed by radiolysis at 77°K. and subsequent heating to 298°K. The same conclusion was previously reached (*11, 22*) from interpretation of ESR spectra.

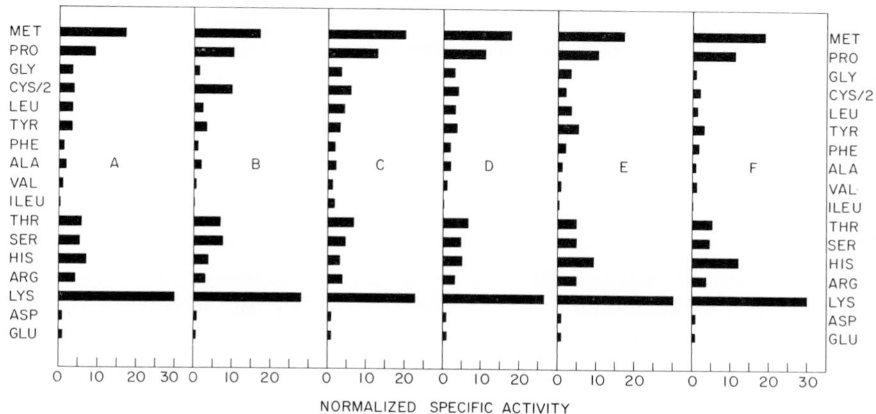

Figure 8. Effect of experimental conditions on the tritium distribution of ribonuclease

A: γ-Radiolysis (5 Mrads) at 298°K., then HST (150 torr); standard γ-labeling.
B: γ-Radiolysis at 77°K. (5 Mrads), raise temp. to 298°K., then HST.
C: γ-Radiolysis (1.5 Mrads) at 298°K. in presence of HST.
D: γ-Radiolysis at 298°K. (5 Mrads); then HST (450 torr).
E: Standard γ-labeling, then chromatography on XE-64, first peak of Figure 7.
F: Same as E, second peak of Figure 7.

In Experiment C, 4.4 mg. of ribonuclease were irradiated at room temperature in the presence of HST to a dose of 1.5 Mrads (4.5 hours). γ-Radiolysis was started immediately after HST addition. No evidence of a change in T distribution, owing to scavenging of earlier intermediates or to reactions initiated in the gas phase, was observed. The same distribution was observed earlier (*30*) for ribonuclease irradiated to 29 Mrads under standard conditions, which suggests that the distribution of radicals is independent of dose from 1.5 to 29 Mrads, even though the radical yield falls off as a function of dose (*16*) above 1 Mrad. Snipes and Horan have shown (*34*), for the case of alanine crystals, that at saturation, radical production is not zero, but radicals are being produced and destroyed at the same rate. Any detailed mechanism for the destruction of radicals needs to be consistent with the constancy of the radical distribution over a large dose range. A threefold increase in the HST pressure (Experiment D) owing to a decrease in the volume of the exposure vessel does not affect the distribution. In Experiments E and F, two fractions of ribonuclease corresponding to the two tritium peaks obtained by chromatography on XE-64 carboxylic acid cation-exchange resin (Figure 7) were studied separately; each had approximately the same distribution as unfractionated ribonuclease.

Tritiated Products Other than Normal Amino Acids. Analyses of all proteins investigated revealed radioactive components which were not detectable by color reaction with ninhydrin. In experiments with HST these components contained 10% or less of the total tritium incorporated into each protein, except for myoglobin and carboxymethylated reduced chymotrypsinogen (17 and 19%, respectively). Such components may arise by reaction of HST with free radicals resulting from the cleavage of bonds other than C-H bonds. Recently Haskill and Hunt (*9*) have concluded that main chain scission is an important process in the γ-radiolysis of dry ribonuclease contrary to the results of Ray and Hutchinson (*29*). However, the present experiments do not necessarily have any bearing on the question of whether or not main chain breaks occur during the formation of primary radicals, since it is possible that such primary radicals may abstract hydrogen from C-H bonds to give the secondary radical population which is tritium labeled in the present experiments.

Tritium Distributions

Normalized Specific Activities Among Native Proteins. Figure 9 shows a comparison of tritium distributions for native proteins irradiated to about 6 Mrads (except for myoglobin which was irradiated to 23 Mrads). Each bar represents the average normalized specific activity of five separate labeling experiments for ribonuclease and of two for each of the other proteins. The tritium distributions have many similarities. The activities of proline and methionine are generally high. Lysine and histidine are heavily labeled in most proteins, while threonine and serine exhibit less activity. Many other residues—*e.g.*, alanine, valine, isoleucine, leucine, phenylalanine, and glycine, have much lower activities.

Each protein has, within this general pattern, its own characteristic radical distribution. In ribonuclease, lysine exhibits a much higher activity than do the remaining amino acids. Lysine and methionine are the most heavily labeled residues in lysozyme. In myoglobin, histidine has the highest activity. Methionine is the most heavily labeled amino acid in chymotrypsinogen, as is proline in insulin. Despite the similarities, therefore, each native protein exhibits a characteristic tritium distribution.

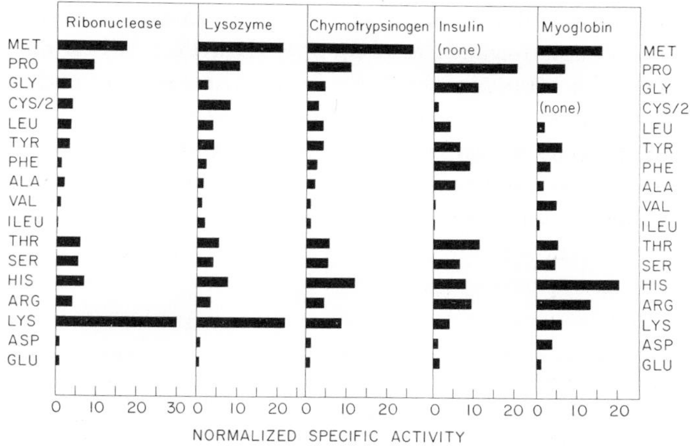

Figure 9. Comparison of tritium distributions in native proteins

There does not appear to be any special significance to glycine as a free radical site, contrary to conclusions drawn from ESR studies (*23*) since the specific activities of glycine are low for all proteins studied. However, the percentage of the total T on glycine increases with increasing glycine content. Thus, for ribonuclease, lysozyme, chymotrypsinogen, insulin, and gelatin, for which the percentages of glycine residues are 2.5, 9.6, 9.6, 8.3, and 35, respectively, the corresponding percentages of the total tritium on glycine are 1.5, 5.8, 10.7, 14.3, and 35, respectively. Thus, in proteins of high glycine content, such as collagen, gelatin, or silk, glycine radicals would be expected to contribute considerably to the ESR spectra. This is in agreement with the results of Gordy and Shields (*8*), who interpreted the ESR spectrum of irradiated oriented silk in terms of the glycine radical.

The method of labeling secondary free radicals by exposure to tritiated hydrogen sulfide cannot give any information about the presence of radicals on sulfur since hydrogen attached to sulfur exchanges rapidly with water when the protein is dissolved. When proteins containing cystine are irradiated at 295°K., an appreciable percentage of the unpaired spins resides on sulfur. Although the exact percentage depends on the detailed experimental conditions (*e.g.*, dose rate and time of storage after radiolysis) the following results (*13*) are typical: ribonuclease, insulin and lysozyme, irradiated at a dose of 0.15–0.45 Mrads at 295°K., contained 70, 60, and 40% of sulfur radicals, respectively, shortly after irradiation.

Strong evidence has been presented (*10, 13, 18*) that the sulfur pattern in the ESR spectra of irradiated proteins is caused by the —CH_2—S· radicals formed from cystine. However, when ribonuclease is irradiated to 34 Mrads in the absence of air and subsequently dissolved in water, definitive chemical experiments (*28*) show no appreciable breaking of disulfide bridges. Possibly these apparently conflicting results might be reconciled by supposing that broken disulfide bridges (one per molecule) may rejoin in aqueous solution.

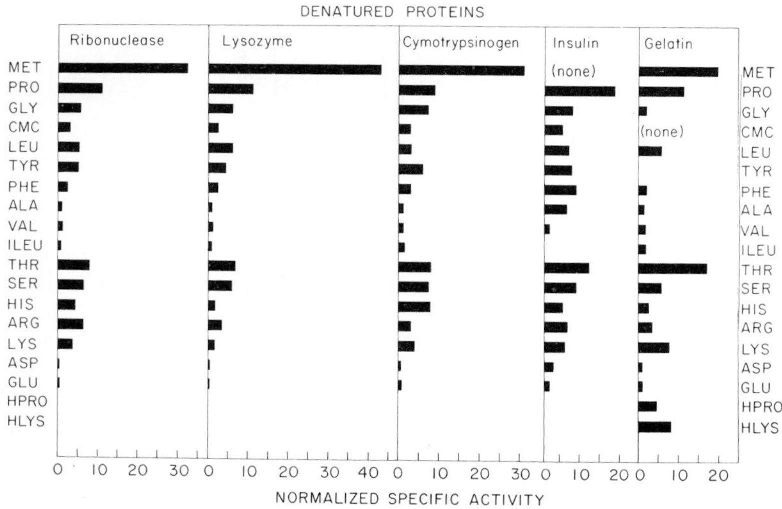

Figure 10. Comparison of tritium distributions in denatured proteins

Denatured Proteins. Gelatin as well as carboxymethylated reduced proteins is included in this group. It can be seen from Figure 10 and shown by analysis of the product-moment correlation coefficients (*32*) that the tritium distributions of the CM-reduced proteins are more similar

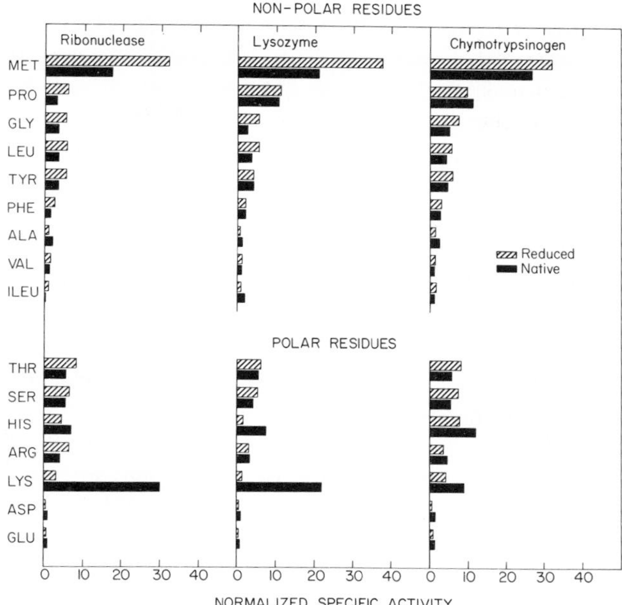

Figure 11. Effect of loss of secondary and tertiary structure on the normalized specific activities of nonpolar and polar amino acid residues

than those of the native proteins (Figure 9). The marked differences for the native proteins, therefore, appear to be caused by their secondary and tertiary structures. The similarity of the tritium distributions for the more nearly random polypeptide chains implies that the probability of forming a secondary radical on a given residue of a long polypeptide chain is independent of primary sequence and of chain length. The results of Figure 11 show that when the random polypeptide chain is folded to a biologically active conformation, the probability of secondary radical formation on nonpolar residues decreases, while that for the polar residues lysine, histidine, aspartic and glutamic acid generally increases. X-ray diffraction studies (*14, 20, 21*) have shown that nonpolar amino acids are chiefly contained in the interior of the protein molecule, with the exception of glycine and alanine which often appear on the surface. Assuming that this generalization applies to the lyophilized as well as to the crystalline state, the lower specific activities of the nonpolar residues in the native protein suggest a smaller probability for free radicals to accumulate on a given residue if this residue is located in the interior of the native protein.

Individual Residues of Lysozyme. The importance of conformation as an influence on the secondary radical distribution is demonstrated by the recent work of White (*40*) on the tritium distribution among the individual residues of lysozyme. Tritiated lysozyme prepared by the standard procedure was reduced, carboxymethylated, and digested with chymotrypsin. The digest was subjected to ion-exchange chromatography and electrophoresis to separate the peptides, which were then analyzed to determine the specific activities of 78 of the 129 residues in the protein chain. The tritium was widely distributed along the polypeptide chain with only 12 residues containing less tritium than could be detected by the flow-counting system. Different amino acid residues of the same amino acid were found to have markedly different specific activities depending on their location within the protein molecule. Thus, the relative specific activities (RSA) of lysine, one of the two most heavily labeled amino acids in lysozyme, are 1.78, 0.19, 0.79, 1.28, and 0.69 for positions 1, 13, 96 plus 97, and 116, respectively. (RSA is the ratio of the specific activity of a given residue to the average specific activity for all residues of the same kind within the protein). Most of the residues of RSA > 1.5 were found in several small clusters when the tritium distribution was related to the three-dimensional structure of crystalline lysozyme (*25*). These clusters consist of four groups:

(1) Residues 16, 18, 19, 21, 23, 29, 31, and 32, which are close to 105, 110, 113, and 115.

(2) Residues 50, 54, and 57, associated with 83, 84, and 88.

(3) At the amino end of the chain 1 and 6.

(4) At the carboxyl end 118, 119, and 121.

Although the reasons underlying this spatial relationship are not known, its existence is additional evidence for conformation as a significant factor in determining the free radical distribution.

Other Applications of Tritiated Radical Scavengers

Conformational Studies in the Lyophilized State. It is difficult to obtain evidence regarding the conformation of proteins in the lyophilized state. Studies (*5*) of amorphous ribonuclease-S suspended in 90% saturated ammonium sulfate solutions suggest that it may be enzymatically active and therefore possess native conformation, although it is difficult to exclude completely the possibility that the observed activity may be caused by crystalline regions formed on the surface of the lyophilized material. Radical scavengers might be used to distinguish between the surface and interior in lyophilized proteins in the following manner. The irradiated lyophilized enzyme is first treated with an unlabeled radical scavenger whose molecules are so bulky that they cannot react with radicals on the interior residues and will donate H atoms only to surface residues. Subsequently, this radical scavenger is removed, and HST is added to label the interior residues with tritium. Figure 2 shows that isoamyl mercaptan reacts much more slowly with the carbon radicals of ribonuclease than H_2S. However, it does not fulfill the requirements for the ideal bulky interceptor (stated above) since after 144 hours all of the carbon radicals have reacted. It is not known whether the rate-controlling step is diffusion into the interior of the protein molecule or diffusion into the interior of the particles of the lyophilized solid. The results of an experiment in which irradiated ribonuclease is exposed first to unlabeled isoamyl mercaptan at 15 torr for 3 hours and then to HST for 4 hours are shown in Figure 12. The most striking difference from the tritium distribution of the standard labeling experiment is the decrease in the specific activity of lysine. The percentage of the total tritium in nonpolar residues increases from 25 to 39, that of the polar residues decreases from 75 to 61. If it is assumed that the radical distribution in molecules on the surface and in the interior of the solid particles is the same, then these results indicate that most of the lysines are surface residues in the lyophilized state.

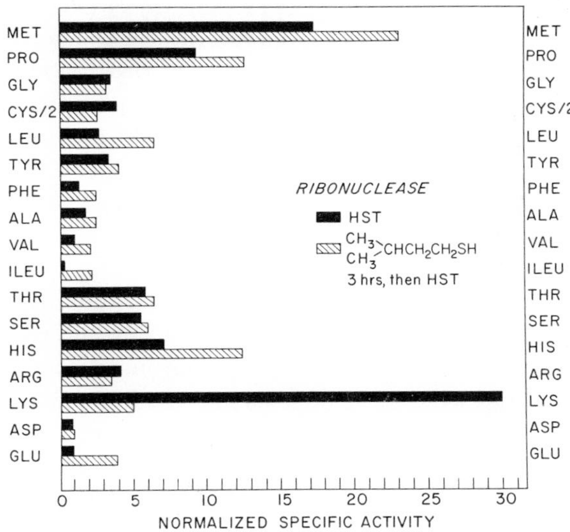

Figure 12. Effect of pretreatment of γ-irradiated ribonuclease with isoamyl mercaptan (3 hours) followed by HST exposure

Conformation of Proteins in Aqueous Solution. Determination of the macromolecular conformation of a globular protein in solution is in principle a difficult problem, likely to occupy protein chemists for many years to come. Introduction of a new experimental technique into this field would be desirable. Radiolysis of deaerated aqueous protein solutions leads to the formation of carbon radicals on the protein. In the presence of a reactive T-donor it may be possible, at suitable concentration ratios and dose rates, to favor the reaction of the protein radicals to abstract tritium from the T-donor and suppress the reaction with other radicals in the system. Moreover, if the T-donor is of sufficient size, only the surface protein radicals will be labeled. Since tritium donors of high specific activity must be used, it is preferable to choose T-donors which are not in isotopic equilibrium with water but have weak C-T bonds. Saunders *et al.* (*32*) have reported that the use of tritiated chloroform leads to the introduction of μc/mg. amounts of tritium into chymotrypsinogen. Subsequently, similar results were observed in our laboratory with tritiated isopropyl cyanide and chloroform in aqueous lysozyme solutions. However, when samples of tritiated chymotrypsinogen and lysozyme were subjected to acid hydrolysis, amino acid analysis, and counting, most of the tritium eluted shortly after the void volume of buffer had passed through the ion-exchange column, and only a negligible portion of tritium was associated with the normal amino acids. Further studies involving the same general approach are in progress.

Experiments with Dry Deoxyribonucleic Acid. Ormerod and Riesz (*21*) have attempted to determine the radical distribution in irradiated dry deoxyribonucleic acid (DNA) from salmon sperm using either tritiated H_2S or hydrogen iodide. Approximately 100 times more tritium is introduced into DNA than expected from the initial concentration of free radicals on DNA. Furthermore, these reactions do not selectively label the DNA at the sites of the stable free radicals, in contrast to results previously obtained with proteins. The results can be understood in terms of a mechanism in which HS· and I· radicals, produced in the labeling step, add to the double bonds of the purine and pyrimidine rings, thus giving rise to a chain reaction for tritium incorporation. A possible explanation for the occurrence of a chain reaction with DNA, but not with proteins, is that the geometrical arrangement of the bases in DNA may permit the SH radical, formed in the labeling reaction, to be in a favorable location for addition to a neighboring base. The number of double bonds per unit molecular weight is also larger for DNA by a factor of about 5.

Labeling of Biological Macromolecules. Chromatography of tritiated ribonuclease (Figure 7) has shown that 85% of the radioactivity elutes with the native peak during ion exchange chromatography. A similar result has been found for tritiated lysozyme. Repeated crystallization (*6*) of tritiated lysozyme at pH 9.6 lowers the specific activity. However, the activity remained nearly constant with the fourth and fifth crystallizations, finally approximating the value of 0.77 μc/mg., which had been obtained for the hydrolysate of tritiated lysozyme after two lyophilizations. The value so obtained indicated the radioactivity arising from tritium on carbon after the complete removal of exchangeable tritium. These results indicate that this method may find wider use for labeling biological macromolecules (*38*).

Acknowledgment

We thank Hideo Kon for valuable discussions and for ESR measurements.

Literature Cited

(1) Busler, W. R., Martin, D. H., Williams, Ff., *Discussions Faraday Soc.* **36,** 102 (1963).
(2) Cleaver, D., Collinson, E., Dainton, F. S., *Trans. Faraday Soc.* **56,** 1640 (1960).
(3) Cottrell, T. L., "The Strengths of Chemical Bonds," 2nd Ed., Butterworth Scientific Publications, London, 1958.
(4) Darwent, De B., Roberts, R., *Proc. Roy. Soc. (London)* **A216,** 344 (1953).
(5) Doscher, M. S., Richards, F. M., *J. Biol. Chem.* **238,** 2399 (1963).
(6) Fevold, H. L., Alderton, G., "Biochemical Preparations," pp. 67-71, Wiley, New York, 1949.
(7) Field, F. H., Lampe, F. W., *J. Am. Chem. Soc.* **80,** 5583 (1958).
(8) Gordy, W., Shields, H., *Proc. Natl. Acad. Sci., U. S.* **46,** 1124 (1960).
(9) Haskill, J. S., Hunt, J. W., *Radiation Res.* **32,** 827 (1967).
(10) Henriksen, T., "Electron Spin Resonance and the Effects of Radiation on Biological Systems," p. 81, National Academy of Sciences, Washington, D. C., 1966.
(11) Henriksen, T., Sanner, T., Pihl, A., *Radiation Res.* **18,** 147 (1963).
(12) Henriksen, T., *Acta Chem. Scand.* **20,** 2898 (1966).
(13) Henriksen, T., "Electron Spin Resonance Studies on the Formation and Properties of Free Radicals in Irradiated Sulfur-Containing Substances," University Press, Oslo, 1963.
(14) Hill, J., Leach, S. J., *Biochem.* **3,** 1814 (1964).
(15) Hirs, C. H. W., Stein, W. H., Moore, S., *J. Biol. Chem.* **200,** 493 (1953).
(16) Hunt, J. W., Williams, J. F., *Radiation Res.* **23,** 26 (1964).
(17) Kendrew, J. C., *Science* **139,** 1259 (1963).
(18) Kurita, Y., Gordy, W., *J. Chem. Phys.* **34,** 282 (1961).
(19) Martin, R. B., Morlino, V. J., *Science* **150,** 493 (1965).
(20) Ormerod, M. G., Singh, B. B., *Biochim. Biophys. Acta* **109,** 204 (1965).
(21) Ormerod, M. G., Riesz, P., *Biochim. Biophys. Acta* **149,** 451 (1967).
(22) Patten, F., Gordy, W., *Proc. Natl. Acad. Sci., U. S.* **46,** 1137 (1961).
(23) Patten, R. A., Gordy, W., *Radiation Res.* **22,** 29 (1964).
(24) Perutz, M. F., *Science* **140,** 863 (1963).
(25) Phillips, D. C., *Sci. Am.* **215** (5), 78 (1966).
(26) Piez, K. A., Morris, L., *Anal. Biochem.* **1,** 187 (1960).
(27) Piez, K. A., *Anal. Biochem.* **4,** 459 (1962).
(28) Ray, D. K., Hutchinson, F., *Biochim. Biophys. Acta* **147,** 347 (1967).
(29) *Ibid.,* p. 357.
(30) Riesz, P., White, F. H., Jr., Kon, H., *J. Am. Chem. Soc.* **88,** 872 (1966).
(31) Riesz, P., White, F. H., Jr., *Nature* **216,** 1208 (1967).

(32) Saunders, M., Jung, H. A., Hamilton, W. L., *J. Am. Chem. Soc.* **89**, 472 (1967).
(33) Schuler, R. H., Fessenden, R. W., "Radiation Research," p. 99, North-Holland, Amsterdam, 1967.
(34) Snipes, W., Horan, K. P., *Radiation Res.* **30**, 307 (1967).
(35) Stratton, K., Koehler, A. M., *Abs. Radiation Res.* **22**, 240 (1964).
(36) Tedder, J. M., *Quart. Rev.* **14**, 336 (1960).
(37) White, F. H., Jr., Riesz, P., Kon, H., *Radiation Res.* **32**, 744 (1967).
(38) White, F. H., Jr., Riesz, P., *Biochem. Biophys. Res. Comm.* **30**, 303 (1968).
(39) White, F. H., Jr., *J. Biol. Chem.* **236**, 1353 (1961).
(40) White, F. H., Jr. (in preparation).
(41) Williams, J., *J. Am. Chem. Soc.* **84**, 2895 (1962).

RECEIVED December 14, 1967.

Dosimetry

36

The Optical Approximation, Primary Radiation Chemical Yields, and Structure of the Track of an Ionizing Particle

IVAN SANTAR and JAROSLAV BEDNÁŘ

The Nuclear Research Institute, Czechoslovak Academy of Sciences, Řež, Czechoslovakia

A survey is given of the theory of the physical stage of radiolysis. Using the optical approximation to cross sections for the interaction between fast electrons and molecules, expressions have been derived for the yield g° *of primary optical activations, and for the total absorbed energy* Q_{tot}*. It is shown that the total yield* g *of primary activations is conveniently discussed as a sum* $g^{\circ} + g^{s}$*, where the first term includes the action of fast electrons, while* g^{s} *describes the action of slow electrons (kinetic energy less than about 100 e.v.) on molecules of the medium. This approach is compared with Platzman's considerations on primary yields and the differences are pointed out. Finally, theoretical results of the present approach are applied to the analysis of the initial structure of the track of a fast electron, consisting of spurs, blobs, and short tracks.*

There is no doubt that of all phenomena connected with the interaction of high-energy radiation with matter, the radiation-chemical response of matter is the most complicated one. Between the primary acts by which the radiative energy is transferred to the medium and the resulting chemical changes there lies a complicated interplay of subsequent physicochemical and chemical processes. However, the whole present experience of radiation chemistry, brought together in the ubiquitous term "radiation-chemical yield," suggests a proportionality between the measured effects and the amount of initially absorbed energy of radiation. This fact should stimulate the efforts towards the theoretical description of radiolytic processes.

The absorption of energy of radiation passing through a medium can be theoretically investigated at three levels of increasing complexity:

(1) Quite pragmatically as a process occurring continuously in the whole irradiated volume. Consequently, we characterize this process by a single quantity called the dose, which gives the amount of energy absorbed in a volume or mass unit. This was the pragmatic basis for the introduction of the empirical notion of the "100 e.v.-yield."

(2) As a process occurring continuously along the paths of individual ionizing particles. Then the decisive quantity appears to be the LET giving the mean energy loss of the particle per unit path-length.

(3) As an ensemble of individual elementary acts of energy transfer, as it corresponds to the physical reality of this phenomenon.

Except for the work of Platzman (*5, 12, 13*) and Magee (*6, 7*), the theoretical considerations in radiation chemistry have been limited to the first two items only. Recently, the most general procedure (item 3) has been applied to both the theory of primary radiation chemical yield (*1, 14, 16, 17, 19*) and to the theory of initial structure of the track of an ionizing particle (*10, 19*). The purpose of this paper is to compare these two aspects of absorption of ionizing radiation.

Primary Radiation Chemical Yield

The most characteristic type of primary activations are the electronic transitions of molecules which are much faster than other response of the irradiated medium. This enables one to consider separately the physical stage of radiolysis, at the end of which a certain ensemble of excited and ionized molecules is formed in the medium. Each of the activated molecules possesses a particular amount of energy available for subsequent processes. The initial distribution and yields of individual primary activations are dealt with by the theory of primary radiation chemical yield (PRCY). We have studied the application of this theory to the radiolysis of gases in detail during the last years (*16, 17, 18, 19, 20*). Thus, in the formal expression—*see* (*5*), for the yield $G(\mathrm{X}) = \Sigma_n g_n \phi_n(\mathrm{X})$ of a particular (final or intermediary) product X, we are primarily interested in the primary g_n-values for the individual types of primary activations. The probabilities $\phi_n(\mathrm{X})$ of the formation of product X because of primary activation of nth type implicitly involve the complex sequence of all possible consecutive and/or competitive reaction ways and remain much more obscure at the present.

The physical stage of a β- or γ-radiolysis of a sufficiently diluted medium is described in this theory (*see* Table I) as the interaction of the degradation spectrum of electrons with the ensemble of isolated molecules of the gas. The probabilities of individual inelastic collisions are characterized by their cross sections and the solution of the problem is, in principle, statistical. In the general method developed by Fano and Platzman [*see* Refs. *1, 12, 14, 17, 18*], the yield of a particular primary product is given simply by the corresponding cross section averaged over the actual degradation spectrum calculated for a single primary electron of a given energy. As the result of this treatment we obtain the average distribution of absolute numbers of primary activations brought about by absorption of a given amount of energy. The individual elementary acts are regarded as fully independent and uncorrelated in space and time. The macroscopic homogeneity of the statistics used entirely corresponds to the natural situation in gases: Indeed, the activated molecules are formed there in independent and isolated primary acts and react in later stages of radiolysis according to the laws of homogeneous kinetics of gases.

We shall summarize briefly the underlying conceptions and assumptions of the theory of PRCY and present some recent results of its application.

In the radiolysis by β- or γ-radiation with maximum energy of about 1 Mev. the most typical process (*see* Table II) is the electronic transitions of valence electrons of molecules. Other processes like direct vibrational excitations of the ground state or electron capture by molecules are characteristic only for the subexcitation electrons with kinetic energy below the threshold E_0 of electronic excitations. By the interactions of subexcitation electrons a fraction of about 10 to 15% of the total absorbed energy is dissipated. This fraction may partially be utilized for chemical changes; however, the corresponding yield should always be considered separately since the mechanisms are much more intricate here and depend strongly on the nature of the medium.

Fast electrons with kinetic energy $T \gtrsim 100$ e.v. excite and ionize molecules predominantly in optical collisions inducing the same type of transitions of valence electrons as does the absorption of photons. This abundant type of primary activations shows, therefore, a very close connection with the optical spectra of molecules. Thus, foundations are laid for the use of the so-called optical approximation in radiation chemistry, as suggested by Platzman (*13*). More explicitly, the theory of cross sections for optical collisions leads in first approximation to the following formula for the yield of a particular electronic transition n:

$$g_n = \text{const} \times f_n/E_n \tag{1}$$

Here E_n is the energy of the transition and f_n is the corresponding optical oscillator strength, characterizing the relative contribution of that transition to the optical spectrum of the molecule.

In addition, sufficiently energetic electrons induce, in a small yield, the optical transitions of inner electrons [g_K being (*1, 11*) of the order of

Table I. Structure of

Theory	diluted PRCY
Primary activation	isolated
Development of the activation	isolated
System	ionizing particle + molecule
Statistics	homogeneous (degradation spectrum + ensemble of isolated molecules)
Space and time element	—
The theory	
–operates in stage	physical (P)
–extensible to stages	physicochemical (PC) chemical (C)

0.01 for the *K*-electrons of the elements from the second period]. Characteristic result of these transitions is the Auger effect. Its importance as a specific minor effect in radiation chemistry stems from the deep destruction of the molecule into small fragments (*11*).

Finally, fast electrons also undergo infrequent hard collisions with molecules, in which the latter are ionized and secondary electrons with appreciable kinetic energy of the order of hundreds of e.v. are ejected (δ-electrons). These collisions thus contribute (*6, 17*) by a small amount $g^* \sim 0.1$ to the yield of ionizations. A distinct specific role of them is apparent only in radiolysis of condensed media, where they constitute a pronounced structural track effect and may contribute to certain minor processes (*see* below).

No corresponding detailed theory of the action of slow electrons exists. Their fraction in the degradation spectrum is nevertheless so substantial that their contribution to the radiolysis must be considered as very important. The reason is that they are formed abundantly as secondary electrons from optical ionizations and contribute considerably

Radiation-Chemical Theories

M E D I U M

dense		
Magee	*Fano*·	*not existing yet*
isolated	non-isolated	non-isolated
non-isolated		non-isolated
track of ionizing particle in isolated molecules	ionizing particle + matrix of molecules	track of ionizing particle in matrix of molecules
in track (individual particle + ensemble of isolated molecules)	homogeneous (degradation spectrum + plasma of molecular electrons)	in track (degradation spectrum + plasma of molecular electrons + ensemble of interacting molecules)
+	+	+
P	P	P
PC, C		(PC, C) ?

FUTURE PROGRESS

to the excitations and ionizations of valence electrons, the latter usually being precursors of a major part of the chemical changes observed.

The general method for the calculation of yields is inapplicable to slow electrons, therefore will be replaced by an approach combining the convenient use of the optical approximation for fast electrons with the possibility of avoiding any need for detailed knowledge of the distribution and the interactions of slow electrons. In view of the fact that the small yields of hard collisions and inner-shell ionizations represent at most a few per cent of the total ionization, and that, moreover, the δ- and Auger electrons produced are fast and lose most of their energy again in optical collisions, secondary electrons from optical ionizations caused by fast electrons may be said to practically predominate in the slow region of the degradation spectrum. The essential point of the theory of PRCY is (*17, 18*) therefore a corresponding subdivision of the degradation spectrum into the fast and slow regions whose contributions to the total yield g of primary activations are considered separately (*see* Figure 1):

$$g = g^{o} + g^{s} \tag{2}$$

Table II. Survey of Types

D E G R A D A T I O N

Process	*FAST ELECTRONS $T > 100$ e.v.*		
	Optical excitations of		Hard collisions
	valence electrons (100 e.v. $> E > E_0$)	inner electrons ($E \sim I_K$)	($E > 100$ e.v.)
g	$g^\circ \sim 4$–5	$g_K \sim 0.01$–0.02	$g^* \sim 0.1$–0.2
% Q_{tot}	50–60%	0.1–0.2%	1–2%

The optical yield g° caused by the fast electrons can be expressed explicitly using the optical approximation. In the differential form concerning the energy transferred between E and $E + dE$ we then obtain (*16, 17, 18, 19*):

$$g^\circ(E)dE = \frac{100}{Z^\circ_{\mathrm{eff}}} \frac{1}{E} \frac{df}{dE} dE. \tag{3}$$

Z°_{eff} is the effective number of valence electrons in the molecule, df/dE is the differential form of the oscillator strength f_n from Equation 1.

Essentially all slow electrons originate in ionizing optical collisions and their kinetic energy, though dissipated in a number of subsequent interactions, is thus integrally included in the energies E of these collisions. This is the reason why the total absorbed energy may be approximated by the energy transferred in optical collisions of fast electrons. From the optical approximation (Equation 3), it may then be shown (*17*) that the total absorbed energy Q_{tot} is

$$Q_{tot} \doteq \mathrm{const} \times Z^\circ_{\mathrm{eff}}, \tag{4}$$

from where the importance of valence electrons in the partition of energy

of Primary Activations

S P E C T R U M

SLOW ELECTRONS 100 *e.v.* $> T > E_o$		*SUBEXCITATION ELECTRONS* $T < E_o$
Excitations optically		Other processes
allowed	forbidden	(vibrational excitations, electron capture, . . .)
$g^s \sim 3\text{–}4$	important perhaps for low-lying lowest triplets	g^{se} varying between 0 and g_{ion}
25–35%	small fraction?	10–15%

in mixtures can clearly be seen. It further follows for the distribution of absorbed energy among the various optical collisions that

$$\frac{1}{Q_{tot}} \frac{dQ_{tot}}{dE} = \frac{1}{Z^{\circ}_{eff}} \frac{df}{dE}. \tag{5}$$

The optical spectrum df/dE, and the derived excitation (*14*) spectrum $(1/E)(df/dE)$ are thus seen to be the most important characteristics of a molecule even from the point of view of its radiolytic properties. By integrating the differential yields given by Equation 3 over relevant parts of molecular spectra we can, of course, obtain the partial yields for particular types of transitions—*e.g.*, the yields of all excitations, ionizations, etc., as well as the total yield of all primary optical transitions:

$$g^{\circ} = \frac{100M^2}{RZ^{\circ}_{eff}}, \text{ where } M^2 = \int_{\text{spectrum}} \frac{R}{E} \frac{df}{dE} dE. \tag{6}$$

Analogous general procedure for the remaining part g^s (caused by collisions of slow electrons) of the total yield g is not available at present. We must therefore content ourselves with a rather crude estimation of g^s from an energy balance using appropriate average values of energies of secondary excitations and ionizations by slow electrons together with an estimate of shape of the energy spectrum of these electrons.

Results of our calculations (*20*) for several molecules are shown in Table III. For calculations of optical yields, data on optical spectra of molecules can be used, above all. Besides that, the total optical yield g°, which is an integral over the entire spectrum, is connected with a number of optical properties of molecules. Thus, for example, an approximative formula, derived by us (*20*), can be used for its estimation:

$$g^\circ \approx 5.4 \sqrt{\frac{P_E}{Z^\circ_{\text{eff}}}} \tag{7}$$

This formula connects the total optical yield with the molar polarization P_E (in cc.) of the molecule.

Table III. Survey of Calculated Yields for Certain Molecules

Molecule	CH_4	H_2O	NH_3	$(CH_2)_n$	O_2	*Ne*	*He*	H_2
g	6.9-6.4	7.6-5.5	10.0-7.4	~8	9.2-6.5	~3.7	~3.4	~6.2
g^o	4.8	3.7	4.5	4.7	2.8	1.7	2.8	5.8
g^s	2.1-1.6	3.9-1.8	5.5-2.9	3.3	6.4-3.7	2.0	0.6	0.4
g_{exc}	3.3-2.8	4.3-2.2	6.2-3.6	3.5	6.0-3.3	1.0	1.0	3.4
$g^o{}_{exc}$	1.7	1.0	1.2	0.7	0.4	0.2	1.0	3.1_5
$g^s{}_{exc}$	1.6-1.1	3.3-1.2	5.0-2.4	2.8	5.6-2.9	0.8	0.1	0.2_5
g_{ion}	3.6	3.3	3.8	4.5	3.2	2.7	2.4	2.8
$g^o{}_{ion}$	3.1	2.7	3.3	4.0	2.4	1.5	1.8	2.6_5
$g^s{}_{ion}$	0.5	0.6	0.5	0.5	0.8	1.2	0.6	0.1_5
γ	0.9-0.8	1.3-0.7	1.6-1.2	0.8	1.8-1.0	0.4	0.4	1.2
γ^o	0.52	0.39	0.35	0.2	0.18	0.11	0.53	1.19
γ^s	3.3-2.0	4.8-1.7	10.6-5.3	5.6	6.5-3.4	0.7	0.2	2.0

The yield $g^\circ{}_{\text{ion}}$ can be determined from the spectra of photoionization or from measurements of molecular ionization cross sections for fast electrons. For a number of compounds the data on W, the mean energy expenditure per ion pair, are further available. They are related to the total yield of ionization by a simple formula

$$g_{\text{ion}} = 100/W. \tag{8}$$

The main uncertainty in the values of g in Table III is introduced by the less accurate estimation of $g^s{}_{\text{exc}}$ from the energy balance.

The main conclusion which can be drawn from Table III is that both the optical and the total yields, as well as the ratios $\gamma = g_{\text{exc}}/g_{\text{ion}}$ of excitations to ionizations, are markedly influenced by the molecular nature of the medium (*20*). Characteristic values vary from 3 to 6 for g°, from 6 up to 10 for g, from 0.2 to 0.6 for γ°, and from 0.5 possibly up to 1.5 for γ. The optical yield g° is determined essentially by the overall shape of the optical spectrum of a molecule, whereas the yield g^s and consequently also the total primary yield g are presumably more strongly dependent on the individual molecular nature and on details of the low-energetic part of the optical spectrum. The differences found between γ° and γ illustrate the necessary caution which should be taken when applying the optical approximation to predict observable overall effects in radiolysis.

One important point remains to be resolved, however. Platzman has recently (*14*) summarized his efforts for introducing the optical approximation into the theory of radiation chemistry and suggested a formula for the overall yield g_{OA} of primary activations:

$$g_{OA}(E)dE = \frac{100}{W} \frac{(R/E)(df/dE)}{M_{ion}^2} dE. \tag{9}$$

This formula combines optical data such as df/dE and M^2_{ion}, which is an integral over all ionized states analogous to M^2 in Equation 6, with empirical radiation-chemical data on W. Equation 9 is essentially of the form $g = \text{const} \times g^\circ$ and thus represents an alternative to, and should be compared with our view, $g = g^\circ + g^s$. It does, in fact, extend the optical approximation expressed by Equation 1 to the totality of primary activations in the physical stage and yields, in particular, the approximative conclusion $\gamma = \gamma^\circ$.

Without going into details to be discussed elsewhere (*20*), we may point out the main difference between the two approaches as follows: While our approach tends to emphasize the contribution g^s of slow secondary electrons to the primary yields, Platzman's treatment puts generally more emphasis on the internal energy of the ionized species than we do. Consequently, his absolute values of primary yields are, in general, lower than ours, and a significant part of the observed decomposition is implicitly expected to occur in subsequent physicochemical and chemical stages of radiolysis. In contrast, our approach explains most of the observed decomposition by the primary processes of the physical stage.

Any decisive conclusions about the problem in the future will necessarily devolve upon a detailed knowledge of energy distribution of ionization processes and secondary electrons, and possibly also upon a better understanding of the physicochemical and chemical processes of radiolysis.

Initial Structure of the Track of an Ionizing Particle

In condensed media the elementary acts acquire much more complicated character (*see* Table I) since the concept of collision of an electron with an isolated molecule loses its meaning. The ionizing particles interact in a dense medium more or less with the electromagnetic field of a plasma of molecular electrons not necessarily belonging to a single molecule. Consequently, the resulting activation may be delocalized at the very beginning. Fano's theory (*2, 3, 4*) of electromagnetic interactions in dense media suggests that the optical spectrum can be appreciably modified in comparison with that of an isolated molecule. Our knowledge of the spectral properties of condensed matter is very poor at present, but estimations of Platzman (*14*) indicate that the picture developed for the gaseous phase may serve as a first approximation even for the condensed phase. In view of the possible delocalization of the primary activations the space element already enters the considerations on the primary act. On the macroscopic scale, however, the picture remains analogous to the dilute gas so that for the description of the energetic distribution of primary activations the homogeneous statistic picture could again be used.

However, the density of the medium affects the course of radiolysis in another well-known, and very important way. Long-living reactive intermediates such as free atoms and radicals remain localized for an appreciable period of time in the close neighborhood of the parent activations because of their limited mobility in condensed phase. Hitherto neglected space and time correlations between the individual elementary acts thus begin to influence considerably the subsequent processes. This fact has to be taken into account in the theory of primary processes.

At usual intensities of irradiation, the tracks of individual primary electrons are well isolated. On the other hand, the average distance between subsequent collisions along the track of a particular electron is much reduced in the condensed medium. This enhances the probability of mutual interaction of the intermediates within the track. This fact has led to the idea of an isolated track of an ionizing particle as a web along which the physicochemical and chemical events develop in space and time.

The usual extrapolation of experimental knowledge back along the time sequence of radiolytic processes has provided us with the picture of a radical track which is formed at the beginning of the chemical stage. While the further development of this track by diffusion and chemical reactions had been successfully treated in great detail by the theory of diffusion kinetics, the initial structure of the track was pictured only by very crude and approximate models. The reason for this was the principal incapability of the chemical experience to yield, by back extrapolation, physical information.

The original idea (*15*) was that of a string of isolated centers (spurs) along the track, in each of which an energy of the order of tens of e.v. had been deposited in the primary act. However, the physical nature of spur formation remained rather unidentified and unexplained in detail (*6*). On the other hand, it is seen from the foregoing that the track formation involves a number of both qualitatively and quantitatively different processes which tend to complicate the initial structure of the track.

Quite recently Magee and his co-workers (*7, 9, 10*) endeavoring to stimulate further development of the theory of track took up a more detailed analysis of these primary processes of track formation (*see* Table IV). Depending on the energy loss E of the primary particle Mozumder and Magee (*9*) divided the collisional processes along the track into the following groups: 1. spurs, 2. blobs, 3. short tracks, and 4. branch tracks.

The by far most frequent *spurs* corresponding to low energy losses below 100 e.v. can be identified with the optical collision of fast electrons (*see* Table IV). It is important here that the secondary electron from an optical ionization is so slow that it loses its energy very near to the point of the primary collision. Because of this, all secondary excitations and ionizations induced by this electron occur within the same single spur. The action of slow electrons is thus completely included in the spurs, and only fast electrons are considered as ionizing particles forming the characteristic entities in the track. This situation is exactly analogous to the splitting of the degradation spectrum into slow and fast electrons in the theory of PRCY: Total yield of spurs is equal to the yield g° of optical collisions.

In the case of dilute gases there was no need for any further subdivision of fast electrons since the mean free path of all of them was always so large that all primary activations were well separated. On the other hand, in condensed media the free path of electrons having an energy close to the lower limit of the fast region is reduced to the extent that the spurs formed by them tend to overlap from the very beginning. Secondary electrons with energies of 100 to 500 e.v. form pear-like *blobs* with a high local concentration of overlapping spurs. Still faster δ-electrons with T between 500 and 5000 e.v. form cylindrical *short tracks* with high LET, in which the extent of the overlap of spurs is still appreciable. Only the electrons of energies higher than 5000 e.v. are actually considered as producing the branch tracks composed of isolated spurs, blobs,

Table IV. Survey

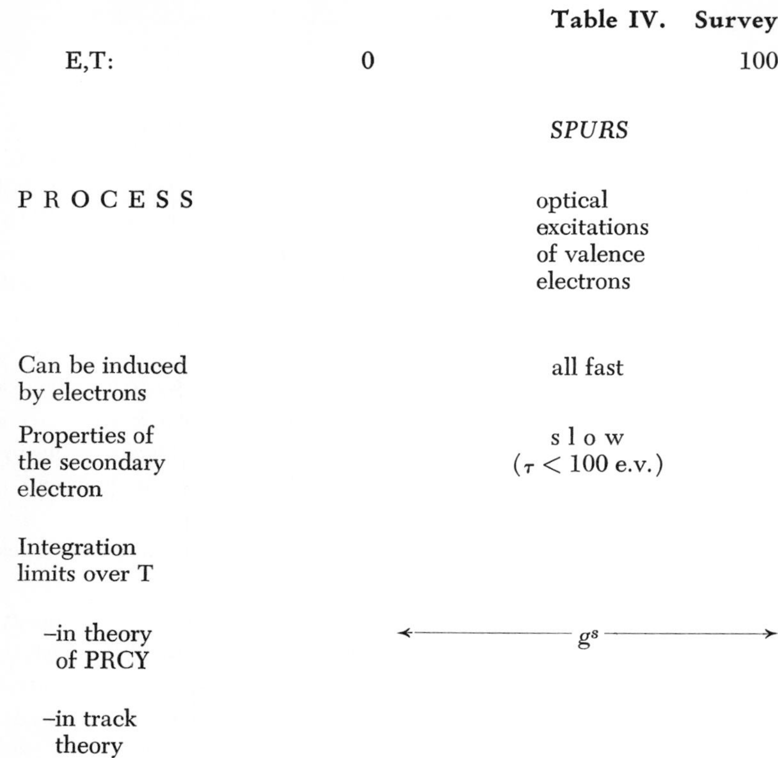

E,T:	0		100
		SPURS	
PROCESS		optical excitations of valence electrons	
Can be induced by electrons		all fast	
Properties of the secondary electron		slow ($\tau < 100$ e.v.)	
Integration limits over T			
–in theory of PRCY	←	g^s	→
–in track theory			

etc. The total yield of all blobs, short tracks, and branch tracks corresponds, of course, to the small yields g^* of δ-electrons from hard collisions and g_K of Auger electrons from the inner-shell ionizations.

Magee does not regard the branch tracks as particular entities but he develops them in the same way as the track of the primary fast electron. To compare his results with the theory of PRCY it is, however, necessary (*20*) to develop even the blobs and the short tracks into their constituting spurs. For the corresponding partition of the total yield of spurs we then obtain

$$g^\circ = g(\text{spur}) + g(\text{spur})_{\text{bl}} + g(\text{spur})_{\text{st}}. \qquad (10)$$

The results of Magee's calculations (*7, 10*) of track structure represent either the term $g(\text{spur})$ for isolated spurs only or the sum $g(\text{spur}) + g(\text{spur})_{\text{st}}$ if the short tracks had further been developed into spurs. Simply, it matters where the limit of energy is put above which the electron is still ascribed the ability to generate isolated activations. In the language of degradation spectrum this statement is equivalent to the shifting of the borderline between fast and slow electrons, the latter as if dissipating their energy "at the spot"—*i.e.*, within a single entity. Thus,

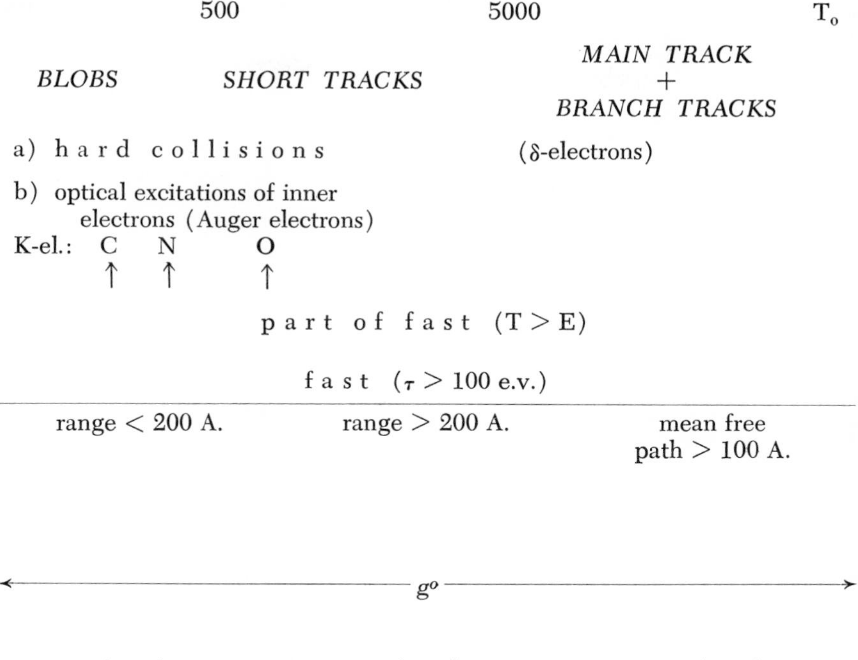

again, we meet the necessity of a resolution into parts of the degradation spectrum, and of separate evaluation of contributions of these parts to the total yield.

An approximate solution of this problem (*11*) is given in Figure 1, where the relative contributions of electrons of different energies to the total yield g are shown. The part of the curve for g° is based on theoretical calculations of the degradation spectrum (8), the contribution g^s is extrapolated schematically. From this Figure we get as a rough first approximation the ratios 65:22:13 for the percentage of the terms on the right-hand side of Equation 10.

Since the optical approximation is valid for all fast electrons, and since the latter are all able to induce the entire spectrum of optical transitions, the energy distribution of spurs is the same for isolated spurs and for the spurs in blobs or short tracks. The average energy per spur is thus equal in all entities and the partition of energy between spurs, blobs, and short tracks is approximately given by the above ratios, too. This is one of the reasons why the yield g^s caused by slow electrons is uniformly added to the whole area of the yield g° of spurs in Figure 1.

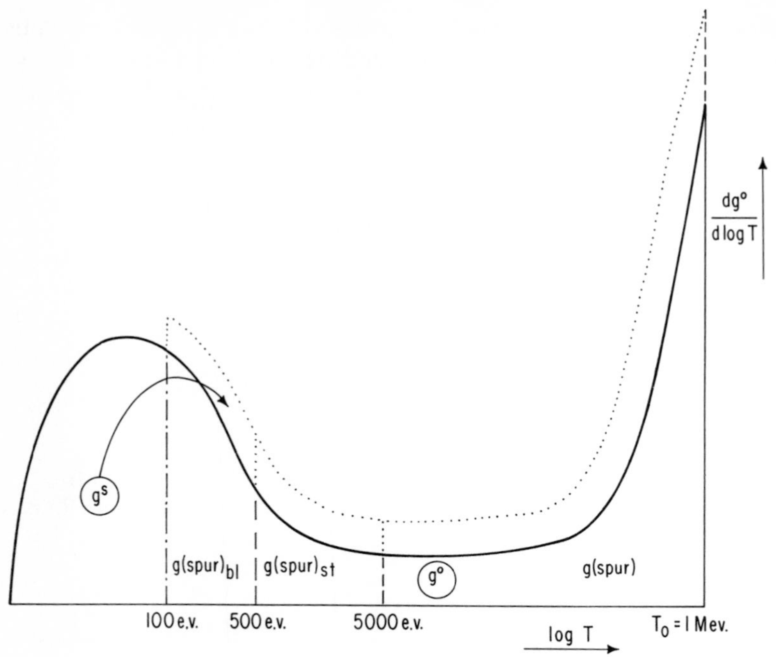

Figure 1. Subdivision of the degradation spectrum and contributions of its various regions to the total yield of primary activations

Our conclusions are corroborated by an analysis of Magee's results. His approach (*10*) is to simulate the track by a Monte Carlo method. The computer generates pairs of random numbers with which the free paths of the electrons before particular collisions, and the energy losses in these collisions, are univocally associated on the basis of a particular form of the cross sections.

The result of this algorithm is the distribution of numbers and energies of isolated spurs, blobs, and short tracks formed during the complete absorption of a primary 1 Mev. electron. It can be seen from Figure 2 that the histograms (*10*) for water agree in shape very well with the spectrum of oscillator strength and with the derived excitation spectrum $(1/E)(df/dE)$, which Magee used. This is in full agreement with our conception of the optical approximation (*see* Equations 3 and 5). On the other hand, the absolute values are different since Magee used a substantially different optical spectrum for water than we previously did (*16*).

We made a number of calculations (*20*) of the track structure by our method, which has been briefly mentioned above. Table V again shows a pronounced effect of the chemical nature of molecules on the fundamental radiation-chemical properties. While the yields of blobs and short tracks remain roughly unchanged, the yields of spurs vary within a factor of two. This may be important indeed in considerations of track effects in different liquids.

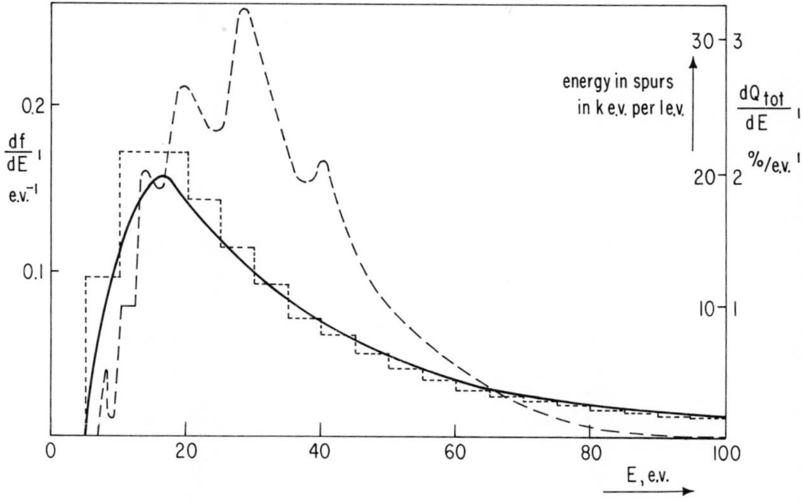

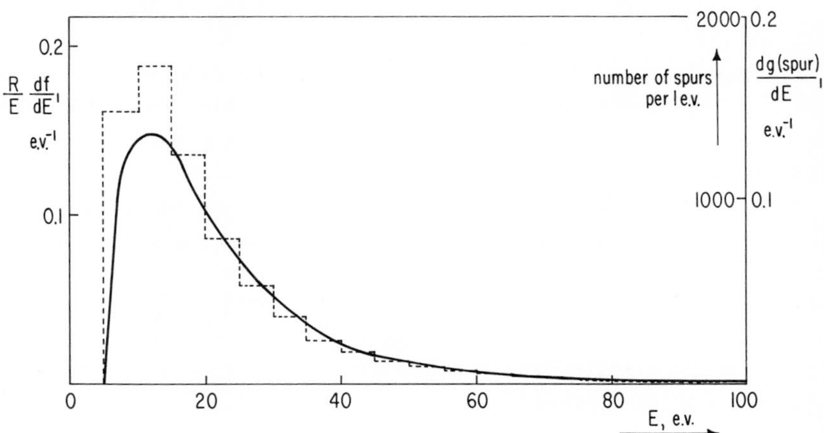

Figure 2. Comparison between the optical spectra used and the spur-distribution histograms obtained for a 1 Mev. primary electron absorbed in water (—— spectra df/dE, (R/E)(df/dE) used by Magee (10), *- - - - - resulting histograms of number and energy distribution of spurs, by Monte Carlo method, - - - spectrum df/dE for an isolated water molecule* (16)

Table V. Effect of Chemical Composition of the Medium on the Track Structure

	g^o	$g(spur)_{bl}$	$g(spur)_{st}$	$g(spur)$	$g(blob)$	$g(s.t.)$
H_2	5.8	1.5	0.8	3.5	~0.1	~0.01
CH_4	4.8	1.2	0.7	2.9		
H_2O	3.7	1.0	0.5	2.2		
O_2	2.8	0.7	0.4	1.7		

In conclusion, it may be said that, at present, theory appears to be able to provide a useful *a priori* information on primary radiolytic processes and yields.

Literature Cited

(1) Durup, J., Platzman, R. L., *Discussions Faraday Soc.* **31,** 156 (1961).
(2) Fano, U., *Phys. Rev.* **103,** 1202 (1956).
(3) *Ibid.,* **118,** 451 (1960).
(4) Fano, U., *Ann. Rev. Nucl. Science* **13,** 1 (1963).
(5) Hart, E. J., Platzman, R. L., "Mechanisms in Radiobiology," Vol. I, p. 93, A. Forssberg, M. Errera, eds., Academic Press, New York, 1961.
(6) Magee, J. L., *Ann. Rev. Phys. Chem.* **12,** 389 (1961).
(7) Magee, J. L., Funabashi, K., Mozumder, A., *Proc. 6th Japan Conf. Radioisotopes, Tokyo,* p. 755, 1965.
(8) McGinnies, R. T., *U. S. Natl. Bur. Stds. Circ.* **No. 597** (1959).
(9) Mozumder, A., Magee, J. L., *Radiation Res.* **28,** 203 (1966).
(10) Mozumder, A., Magee, J. L., *J. Chem. Phys.* **45,** 3332 (1966).
(11) Ore, A., "Radiation Research," p. 54, G. Silini, ed., Proc. Intern. Congr. of Radiation Res., 3rd, North-Holland Publ. Co., Amsterdam, 1967.
(12) Platzman, R. L., *Intern. J. Appl. Radiation Isotopes* **10,** 116 (1961).
(13) Platzman, R. L., *The Vortex* **23,** 372 (1962).
(14) Platzman, R. L., "Radiation Research," p. 20, G. Silini, ed., Proc. Intern. Congr. Radiation Research, 3rd, North-Holland Publ. Co., Amsterdam, 1967.
(15) Samuel, A. H., Magee, J. L., *J. Chem. Phys.* **21,** 1080 (1953).
(16) Santar, I., Bednář, J., *Coll. Czech. Chem. Commun.* **32,** 953 (1967).
(17) *Ibid.,* **33,** 1 (1968).
(18) Santar, I., Bednář, J., "The Chemistry of Excitation and Ionization," p. 217, G. R. A. Johnson, G. Scholes, eds., Taylor & Francis, London, 1967.
(19) Santar, I., "To the Theory of Primary Radiation—Chemical Yield" (in Czech), Dissertation, The Nuclear Research Institute, Czechoslovak Academy of Sciences, Rež (1967).
(20) Santar, I., Bednář, J. (to be published).

RECEIVED January 2, 1968.

37

The Dosimetry of Very High Intensity Pulsed Electron Sources Used for Radiation Chemistry: II. Dosimetry for Gaseous Samples

C. WILLIS, O. A. MILLER, A. E. ROTHWELL, and A. W. BOYD

Research Chemistry Branch, Chalk River Nuclear Laboratories, Atomic Energy of Canada Ltd., Chalk River, Ontario, Canada

Adiabatic calorimetry has been used to measure the mean dose in a cell used for the irradiation of gaseous samples with very high intensity electron pulses at a dose rate of about 10^{27} e.v./gram sec. The calorimeter was a thin aluminum disc, and the temperature rise caused by the pulse was measured by an attached thermocouple. By using discs of different thicknesses and extrapolating to zero thickness, the dose in an infinitely thin absorber was obtained. This was corrected for the difference in electron stopping power between aluminum and the gases. Using this dose, the nitrogen yield from nitrous oxide was found to be $G(N_2) = 12.4 \pm 0.2$. *The temperature of the nitrous oxide was initially 25°C. but increased to* $\sim$*50°C. on irradiation. The hydrogen yield from ethylene was found to be pressure dependent. At one atm.,* $G(H_2) = 1.9$ *and decreases to 1.0 at 10 atm.*

The observation by optical spectroscopy of transient species formed in short bursts of radiation requires a reasonable number of these transients to be formed. For the pulse radiolysis of liquids the dose per pulse required is 1–10 Krad. delivered in about 0.1 μsec. At a pressure of a few atmospheres, however, the stopping power of gases per unit volume is small and to produce a reasonable number of transient species, a much higher dose per pulse is required.

Recently several types of machines capable of producing intense electron pulses have become available. These are being used for pulse studies and dose rate studies in the radiation chemistry of gases. The machines are typically capacitor-discharge circuits using the field emission effect to obtain a high current of electrons from fine tungsten needles in a vacuum tube.

The measurement of the radiation energy absorbed in a sample, a necessity for accurate radiation chemistry studies, cannot be done by conventional methods at these very high intensities.

Ion chambers, the common standard for dosimetry of gases at lower intensities, cannot be used. A 1 Mrad pulse in air produces about 2×10^6 esu. per cc. in 100 nsec., which is orders of magnitude higher than can be used in ion chambers (*5*).

The extrapolation of any chemical dosimeter calibrated at much lower dose rates cannot be used directly because the relative concentration of radicals produced with such pulses is so high that radical-radical reactions may predominate so that the yields of products may be different.

Adiabatic calorimetry is the obvious absolute method for use at these dose rates and in a previous paper (*16*) we reported on its use for dosimetry of liquid samples. It is the object of the present paper to report upon its use for gas phase dosimetry.

With liquids it was not possible to stop the total beam in the sample, and therefore the stopping thickness of the calorimeter was matched to the sample. This was necessary as the electrons in a pulse are not monoenergetic. Also, by using thin liquid samples so that the depth of the cell is small compared with the divergence of the beam it was possible to match the geometry of the calorimeter and the sample fairly well. Such a procedure is not possible for gases. A fairly large volume ($\sim$ 50 ml.) of gas must be irradiated to give a measurable yield of products; hence, considerable differences in geometry exist between the calorimeter and sample. The matching of stopping thicknesses is also not possible. For the cell used in our experiments, ethylene at one atm. pressure corresponds to an aluminum calorimeter 0.0013 cm. thick. Such a calorimeter would not have sufficient structural strength.

We have measured the dose in calorimeters of various thicknesses and extrapolated to zero thickness. The calorimeters were used in various positions within the cell to obtain an average dose over the cell volume.

In attempts to find a suitable chemical dosimeter, both the nitrogen yield from the irradiation of nitrous oxide (*7, 8*) and the hydrogen yield from the irradiation of ethylene (*3, 12*) have been used to measure the doses absorbed in gases. We have irradiated both of these gases and, using the dose from the calorimetry, we have measured the yields at very high dose rates.

Apparatus

Pulsed Electron Accelerator. The very high intensity pulsed electron accelerator used was a 705 Febetron (Field Emission Corporation, McMinnville, Oregon, U.S.A.). This is nominally a 2 Mev. accelerator. Its mode of operation has been described previously (*16*).

The current-time profile and the energy spectrum of the pulse are shown in Figures 1a and 1b. This current-time profile was obtained

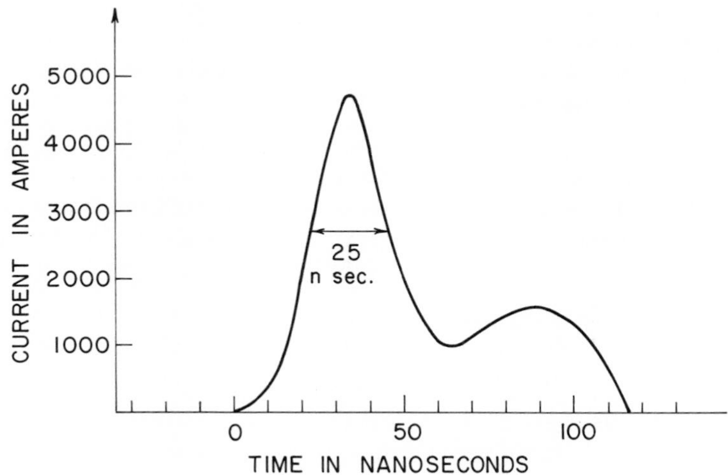

Figure 1a. Current waveform of electron pulse

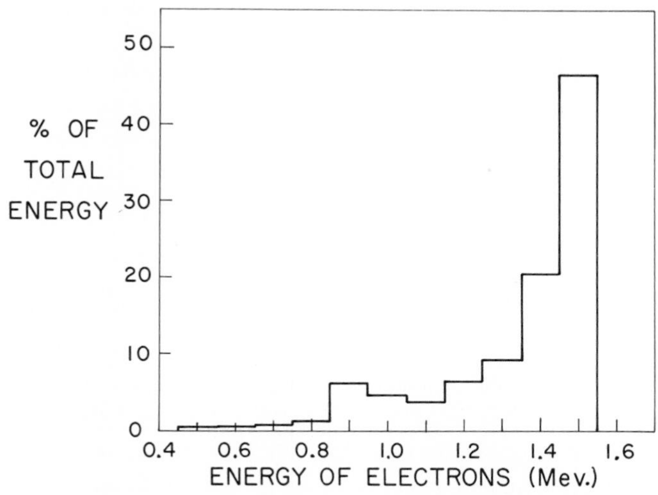

Figure 1b. Energy spectrum of electron pulse after passing through 0.005 inch stainless steel window

from a Faraday cup placed directly over the electron window of the Febetron. The energy spectrum shown was obtained by correcting the initial energies of the electrons for absorption by the stainless steel window of the irradiation cell. The initial energy spectrum was determined both from measurement of the voltage and current waveforms and the range of the electrons in aluminum by the Field Emission Corporation.

The electron beam has a diameter of between 3 and 4 cm. at the window and is diverging. In any hundred consecutive pulses, for a given tube, there is a reproducibility of ±3% (standard deviation) of the dose per pulse, but over several hundred pulses there appears to be a gradual increase in dose per pulse.

Irradiation Cells and Calorimeters. The cell used for gas phase irradiations with the Febetron was made of stainless steel. The gas volume was a cylinder 4.0 cm. in diameter and 3.0 cm. deep behind a 0.0127 cm. stainless steel electron window. The electron window was welded around the edge of the cell. Welded to the rear of the cell was a small filling tube with a stainless steel Hoke vacuum valve. The whole assembly could be pumped and baked. Gases were frozen into the filling tube volume with liquid nitrogen and allowed to expand into the cell on warming.

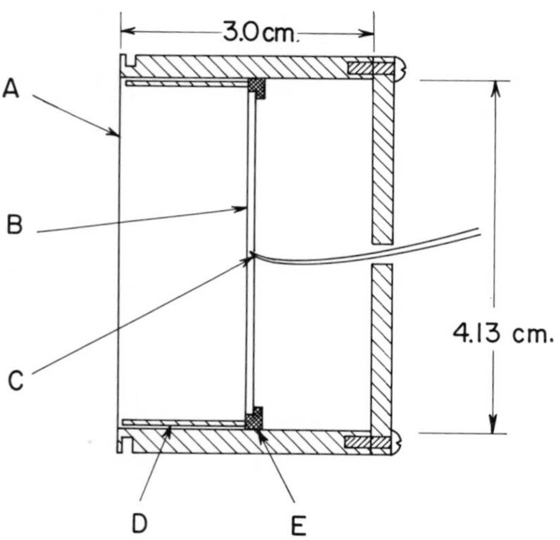

Figure 2. Irradiation cell used for calorimetry

(A) 0.0127 cm. thick stainless steel electron window, (B) calorimeter, (C) thermocouple, (D) stainless steel spacer ring, and (E) nylon calorimeter mounting ring

The cell used for calorimetric measurements shown in Figure 2 was essentially identical to that used for the gas irradiations. The front stainless steel window was welded to the cell body and the back plate was removable. The cell internal diameter was 4.13 cm. so as to allow 4.0 cm.

diameter calorimeters to be used with a 0.065 cm. gap for a nylon calorimeter mount that also acted as thermal insulation. The calorimeters fitted snugly into the mount and were secured by a small amount of Glyptal cement at various points around the circumference. The calorimeters were made of super-pure aluminum and had thicknesses of 0.0203, 0.0280, 0.076, and 0.127 cm.

The assembly fitted tightly into the cell and was pushed against a stainless steel spacer (0.04 cm. thick) that defined the position of the calorimeter relative to the front window. Spacers of lengths 0.2, 1.0, 1.5, 2.0, and 2.7 cm. were used. A 0.1 cm. hole was drilled through each calorimeter at about half radius to allow air interchange between the rear and front of the cell. This was found to be necessary as the thermal expansion because of the heating by the electron pulse of the air trapped in the front section was sufficient, in some cases, to displace the calorimeter assembly.

The thermocouples were made from copper and constantan wire 0.0127 cm. in diameter. The junction was soldered with silver and the thermocouple was either peened into or spot welded to the calorimeter roughly at its center. The leads of the thermocouple were led out through a small hole in the end plate of the cell. Identical temperature rises were obtained with and without an ice-bath cold-junction and in general the wires were joined directly to the recorder inputs.

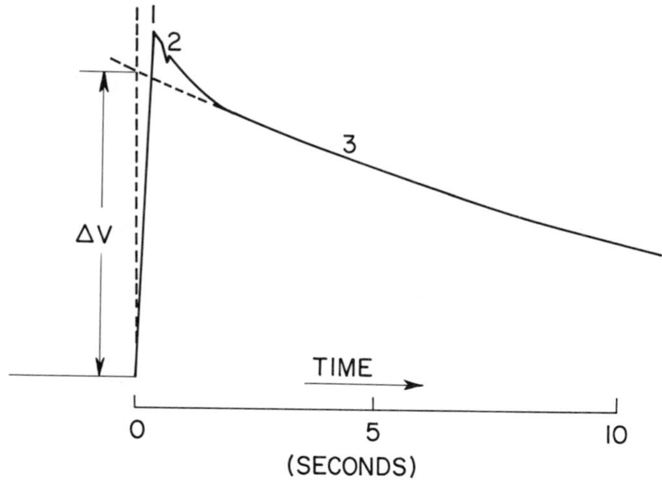

Figure 3. Typical trace of thermocouple for aluminum calorimeter

A sensitive Moseley strip-chart recorder was used to measure the voltage output of the thermocouple. This recorder has a full scale response time of 0.5 sec. A typical trace is shown in Figure 3. Peak 1 is the instantaneous temperature registered by the thermocouple. This is not the equilibrium temperature of the calorimeter. The thermocouple materials have specific heats lower than aluminum and also, since the beam intensity is not uniform across its diameter, the center of the calorimeter is initially hotter than the circumference. Peak 2 is induced by the switching off the Febetron focussing magnetic field ~ 1 sec. after the pulse. Curve 3 is the normal cooling curve of the calorimeter assembly. The induced voltage ΔV extrapolated to time zero using part 3 of the cooling curve corresponds to the irradiation dose absorbed by the calorimeter. That this is an accurate measure of the average dose over the area of the calorimeter has been shown (*16*) by agreement between calorimeters of different materials. After corrections for electron stopping power and backscatter the doses from aluminum graphite and nickel calorimeters agreed within 2%. Since these elements have considerably different thermal conductivities and specific heats it is unlikely that the heat losses from the calorimeter were significant during the time required to reach thermal equilibrium within the calorimeter.

Gases. Medical-grade nitrous oxide (Liquid Air Company Ltd.) and research-grade ethylene (Phillips) were used directly from the bottle after several freeze-pump-thaw cycles to remove any non-condensible impurities. The irradiation products were measured by freezing out with a liquid nitrogen cold trap and pumping the non-condensible gases into

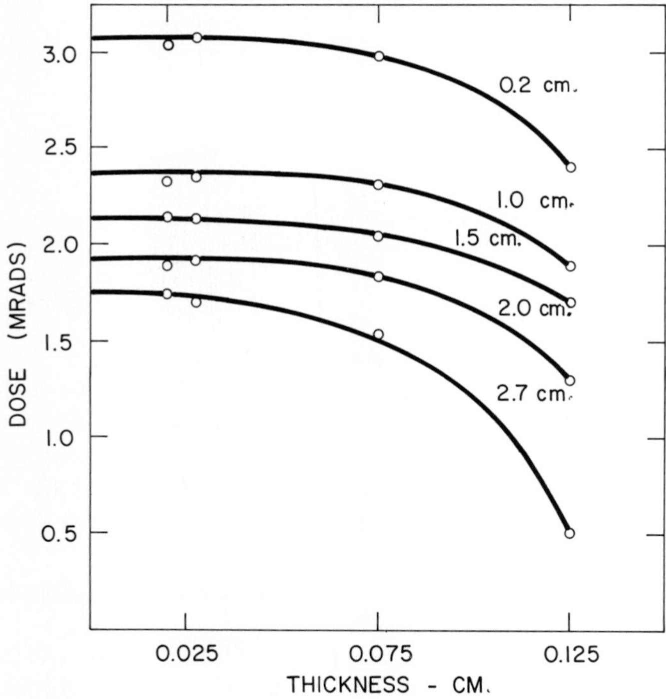

Figure 4. Doses measured in aluminum calorimeters of different thicknesses at various distances from front window of cell

a standard volume. With ethylene a supplementary solid nitrogen trap was used. The measured volume of gas was analyzed by mass spectrometry.

Irradiations were carried out at 24 ± 1°C.

The gas cell used for the ethylene irradiations was baked at 550°C. in air after each irradiation to remove the polymer formed.

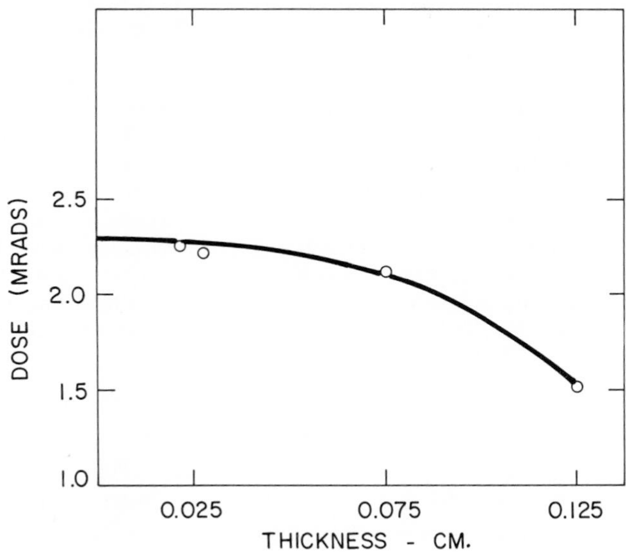

Figure 5. Mean dose for gas cell as a function of calorimeter thickness

Results

Calorimetry. The doses absorbed in the calorimeters in different positions within the cell are shown in Figure 4. Each point is the mean of five pulses. Oswald *et al.* (*11*) using higher energy electron pulses found an increase of ~ 30% in dose with aluminum calorimeters between a thickness of 0.013 cm. and 0.125 cm. The difference between their results and ours may be because of the higher energy of the electrons they used.

For each calorimeter thickness a mean dose for the cell volume can be determined. This mean dose equals $\int \frac{(\text{Dose})\,dl}{l}$, where l is the depth of the cell and the (Dose) is that measured at different depths. A plot of the mean dose for the different thicknesses of aluminum is shown in Figure 5. The doses are applicable to the various gases after correction

Table I. Relative Stopping

	Electron Fraction *f*.	Stopping Power per Electron Relative to Air, S.	S. × *f*. Relative to Aluminum
Aluminum	0.4815	0.927[a]	1.000
Gas			
Nitrous Oxide	0.5000	1.000[b]	1.120
Ethylene	0.5714	1.052[b]	1.347
Ammonia	0.5882	1.053[b]	1.388
Water	0.556	1.033[b]	1.286
Carbon Monoxide	0.5000	1.005[b]	1.126
Cyclohexane	0.5714	1.052[b]	1.347

[a] From Ref. 2.
[b] These are calculated assuming mixture law using the values from Ref. 2 and Ref. 4, S for C = 1.011, H = 1.30, O = 1.00, N = 1.00.
[c] Calculated from the measured dose in aluminum.

for the electron stopping parameters. Table I gives the various stopping parameters for sime simple gases. These apply only for transmitted electrons. However, using the data of Seliger (*13*) and Agu *et al.* (*1*), it can be shown that for a pulse with a spectrum as shown in Figure 1 over 99% of the electrons are transmitted through 0.01 cm. of aluminum. The backscatter from targets in this range of thickness ($\sim$30 mg./cm.^{2}) is negligible. Charbonnier (*6*) has derived that the energy backscatter from a thick aluminum target is only $\sim$ 3% from Spencer's calculations (*14*), and Yaffe and Justus (*17*) have shown that it falls off to zero below 200 mg./cm.^{2}.

Nitrous Oxide Irradiations. The measured yields of nitrogen and oxygen from one pulse irradiations ($\sim$ 1.6 $\times$ 10^{20} e.v./gram) of nitrous oxide are given in Table II.

The nitrogen yield $G(N_2)$ = 12.4 $\pm$ 0.2 is independent of pressure over the range studied. This value should be compared with Johnson's value of $G(N_2)$ = 12.4 $\pm$ 0.4 for ^{60}Co γ-radiation (*7*) and to Jones' and Sworski's value of $G(N_2)$ = 10.0 $\pm$ 0.2 for 1 Mev. electron irradiations (*8*). Both these values are for conventional dose rates of 10^{16}–10^{19} e.v./gram sec. Agreement with these values is quite good and the nitrogen yield from nitrous oxide seems to be constant up to a dose rate of 10^{27} e.v./gram sec.

Under the adiabatic conditions of our irradiations a 2.6*M* rad pulse raises the temperature of nitrous oxide by 28°C. At this temperature (52°C.), using data given by Jones and Sworski (*8*), $G(N_2)$ = 11.5 $\pm$

Powers for Electrons

Doses in Gas Cell (Mrads)[c]	*Stopping Thickness per atm. 3.0 cm. Cell (mg./cm.*^{2}*)*	*Equivalent Thickness of Aluminum per atm. (cm.)*
2.30		
2.58	5.4	0.0020
3.10	3.5	0.0013
3.19	2.2	0.0008
2.96	2.3	0.0008
2.59	3.5	0.0013
3.10	10.5	0.0039

0.3. This gives better agreement with our value but it is not certain that the effective temperature is as high as 52°C.

The major products formed in the irradiation of nitrous oxide are nitrogen, oxygen, and nitric oxide (*8*). However, if a liquid nitrogen cold trap is used in the analysis the nitric oxide and oxygen react to form nitrogen dioxide which condenses. Only the nitrogen yield and part of the oxygen yield are measured. Any small changes in the nitric oxide and oxygen yields lead to relatively large changes in the observed oxygen yields. Thus, although the oxygen yields shown in Table II appear to show a pressure dependence this may not be significant. The yield of oxygen at 10^{18}–10^{19} e.v./gram sec. at a pressure of 400 torr and a dose of 10^{20} e.v./gram is 2.0 at 24°C.

Table II. Yields from Nitrous Oxide Irradiations

Pressure	$G(N_2)$[a]	$G(O_2)$[a]
0.5 atm.	12.8	2.70
1.0 atm.	12.5	2.42
1.0 atm.	12.4	2.27
2.5 atm.	12.2	1.52
5.0 atm.	12.3	1.58
Mean	12.4 ± 0.2	

[a] These are calculated using the dose given in Table I.

Ethylene Irradiations. The hydrogen yields from single pulse irradiations of ethylene are given in Table III. The hydrogen yields vary with pressure from $G(H_2) = 1.9$ at 1 atm. to $G(H_2) = 1.0$ at 10 atm. At conventional dose rates $G(H_2) = 1.2 \pm 0.1$ from 0.2 to 15 atm. (*12, 15*). The pressure dependence must, therefore, be because of dose rate dependent processes.

The methane yields are much higher than at lower dose rates (*10*) and show a pressure dependence similar to that shown by the hydrogen yields. At 2 atm. pressure, $G(CH_4) \sim 0.5$ and decreases to $G(CH_4) \sim 0.25$ at 10 atm.

Both the high methane yield and the pressure dependence of the yields present an interesting facet to the radiation chemistry of ethylene, but without a much more complete product analysis no conclusions can be drawn. This is not within the scope of the present paper.

Table III. Hydrogen Yields from Ethylene Irradiations

Pressure	$G(H_2)$[a]
0.5 atm.	1.90
1.0 atm.	1.81
1.0 atm.	1.80
2.5 atm.	1.72
5.0 atm.	1.48
8.0 atm.	1.25
10.0 atm.	1.04

[a] These are calculated using the dose given in Table I.

Discussion

The use of calorimetry as a standard for radiation dosimetry is well established (*9*) and we have previously demonstrated that adiabatic calorimetry in stainless steel cells can be used for very high intensity electron pulses (*16*). The electron stopping parameters given in Table I are from experimental papers but agree within 1% with those calculated by Meisels (*10*) from Bethe's equations and any errors introduced by these must be insignificant. Calorimetry then, can be considered to be an acceptable standard for gas phase dosimetry of intense electron pulses.

Calorimetry can be used for routine monitoring of these electron pulses for liquid irradiations. However, even for the simple cells described in this paper, it requires too many pulses and is too time consuming to be used routinely for gases. In the larger more complex cells used for pulse radiolysis studies, calorimetry is impractical. Thus, a chemical gaseous dosimeter is required.

Of the two gaseous systems studied, nitrous oxide and ethylene, nitrous oxide best meets this requirement.

The *G* value for nitrogen from nitrous oxide is large and consequently the volume of product gas is easy to measure. This minimizes the errors of measurement. The temperature dependence shown by the nitrogen yield does leave some uncertainty in the $G(N_2)$ value for different dose rates as the temperature rise per pulse will be different. This can be resolved by measuring the nitrogen yield at lower doses where the temperature rise will be less. Such a study is being carried out but requires very careful calorimetric measurements.

Ethylene does not appear to be a good choice for a dosimeter at very high dose rates. Although the hydrogen yield is independent of temperature and pressure (*12, 15*) at normal dose rates, this does not appear to be the case for the present study. The small hydrogen yield and the inherent difficulties of ethylene irradiations do not encourage a more careful study at the present time.

Literature Cited

(1) Agu, B. N. C., Burdett, T. A., Matsukawa, E., *Proc. Phys. Soc.* **72**, 727 (1959).
(2) Attix, F. H., DeLaVergne, L., Ritz, V. H., *J. Res. Natl. Bur. Std.* **60**, 235 (1958).
(3) Back, R. A., Woodward, T. W., McLaughlan, K. A., *Can. J. Chem.* **40**, 1380 (1962).
(4) Baily, N. A., Brown, G. C., *Radiation Res.* **11**, 745 (1959).
(5) Boag, J. W., "Radiation Dosimetry," Vol. II, p. 2, F. H. Attix, Roesch, eds., Academic Press, N. Y., 1966.
(6) Charbonnier, F. M. (private communication).
(7) Johnson, G. R. A., *J. Inorg. Nucl. Chem.* **24**, 461 (1962).
(8) Jones, F. T., Sworski, T. J., *J. Phys. Chem.* **70**, 1546 (1966).
(9) Laughlin, J. S., Genna, S., "Radiation Dosimetry," Vol. II, p. 389, F. H. Attix, Roesch, eds., Academic Press, N. Y. 1966.
(10) Meisels, G. G., *J. Chem. Phys.* **41**, 51 (1964).
(11) Oswald, R. B., Jr., Eisen, H. A., Conrad, E. E., *IEEE Trans. on Nucl. Sci.* **NS-13**, 229 (1966).
(12) Sauer, M. C., Dorfman, L. M., *J. Phys. Chem.* **66**, 322 (1962).
(13) Seliger, H. H., *Phys. Rev.* **100**, 1029 (1955).
(14) Spencer, L. V., *Natl. Bur. Std. (U. S.) Monograph* **1** (1959).
(15) Srinivasan, S., Smith, W. E., *Intern. J. Radiation Isotopes* **17**, 643 (1966).
(16) Willis, C., Miller, O. A., Rothwell, A. E., Boyd, A. W., *Radiation Res.* (in press).
(17) Yaffe, L., Justus, K. M., *J. Chem. Soc. (London)* **S341** (1949).

RECEIVED January 2, 1968.

38

A Significant Correction Factor in Gamma Ray Dosimetry

ARI BRNJOLFSSON

U. S. Army Natick Laboratories, Natick, Mass. 01760

*Softening of the gamma rays as they penetrate light materials may cause very large differences in the radiation doses absorbed in the samples and in the dosimeters. This is illustrated in the present paper by calculating the dose in 14 dosimeters and several other materials placed at distances of 0, 1, 2, and 4 relaxation lengths from a point isotropic ^{60}Co source embedded in a large water container. These calculations show for instance, that the doses in water, Lucite, Fricke dosimeter, lithium fluoride, poly(vinyl chloride) and 0.4*M *ceric sulfate solution at zero distance from the source are in the ratios: 100: 96: 100: 83: 92: 99; at a distance corresponding to $\mu_t \cdot r = 1$ the dose ratios are 100: 95: 100: 85: 124: 169; and at a distance corresponding to $\mu_t \cdot r = 4$ the similar ratios are: 100: 93: 101: 87: 162: 251.*

Absorbed dose in a sample irradiated by gamma rays is usually determined by measuring the absorbed dose in a dosimeter; for instance, a Fricke dosimeter placed in the position of the sample. This absorbed dose in the dosimeter is, however, generally different from that in the sample. To arrive at the absorbed dose in the sample, corrections must be made for the difference. These corrections are partly caused by gamma electron non-equilibrium at the boundary, transfer of energy of excited states across the boundary, and partly caused by differences in mass energy transfer coefficients which are functions of the atomic number and the gamma ray energy. The corrections caused by boundaries will not be considered in this paper, but only the corrections caused by mass energy transfer coefficients.

In radiation dosimetry the energy absorbed per ml. of sample is usually the quantity of interest. To arrive at the energy absorbed per ml.

of the sample, the dose D_d in the dosimeter—*i.e.*, the Fricke dosimeter, is first multiplied by the ratio $\frac{\rho_s}{\rho_d}$, *i.e.*, the ratio of density ρ_s of the sample solution to the density ρ_d of the dosimeter solution. Secondly, the dose D_d is multiplied by the ratio $\frac{\mu_s}{\rho_s} \cdot \frac{\rho_d}{\mu_d}$, *i.e.*, the ratio of the mass energy transfer coefficients. These two corrections factors are usually applied.

The third correction factor, which is the ratio of the adsorbed dose buildup factors in the sample and the dosimeter, is usually ignored, but is shown in this paper to be very important. The absorbed dose buildup factor is defined in this paper analogous to the dose buildup factor, a notation used when the unit roentgen was still the unit of radiation dose. This paper shows the magnitude of this third correction factor, which is caused by differences in gamma-ray attenuation coefficients and softening of the gamma-ray spectrum. As an illustrative example, the dose in different dosimeters is calculated as a function of the distance from a point isotropic cobalt-60 source in water.

Calculations of Absorbed Dose

The gamma-ray energy in rads per second absorbed in an infinitesimal volume dx·dy·dz at the point P(x, y, z) is given by

$$d = 1.60209 \cdot 10^{-8} \int_0^{E_{max}} E \cdot \frac{d\phi(E)}{dE} \cdot \frac{\mu_k(E)}{\rho} \cdot dE \qquad (1)$$

$$= 1.60209 \cdot 10^{-8} \int_0^{E_{max}} \frac{dI(E)}{dE} \cdot \frac{\mu_k(E)}{\rho} \cdot dE$$

where

d = dose rate in rads/sec. = 100 erg/gram sec.

E = photon energy in Mev.

$\phi(E)$ = photon flux density = the total number of photons of energy less than E which enter a sphere of cross-sectional area 1 cm.^{2} per sec. at the considered point P. $\phi(E)$ is in units of cm.$^{-2}$ sec.$^{-1}$ (total number of photons per cm.^{2} per sec.).

$\frac{d\phi(E)}{dE}$ = photon flux density spectrum = number of photons in the energy interval E to $E + dE$ which enter a sphere of cross-sectional area 1 cm.^{2} per sec. at the considered point P.

$\frac{d\phi(E)}{dE}$ is in units of Mev.$^{-1}$ cm.$^{-2}$ sec.$^{-1}$ (number of photons per Mev. per cm.^{2} per sec.).

$\frac{\mu_k(E)}{\rho}$ = mass energy transfer coefficient in cm.^{2}/gram of the dosimeter at P for photons in the energy interval E to E + dE. ρ is the density in gram/cc.

$I(E)$ = the energy flux density or intensity—*i.e.*, the total energy of all the photons with energy less than E that cross a sphere of cross-sectional area of 1 cm.^{2} per sec. at the point P. $I(E)$ is in units of Mev. · cm.$^{-2}$ · sec.$^{-1}$ (energy in Mev. per cm.^{2} per sec.).

$\frac{dI(E)}{dE}$ = the energy flux density spectrum or intensity spectrum—*i.e.*, total energy of the photons in the energy interval E to $E + dE$ that cross a sphere of cross-sectional area of 1 cm.^{2} per sec. at the considered point P · $\frac{dI(E)}{dE} = \frac{d\phi}{dE} \cdot E$ is in units of cm.$^{-2}$ sec.$^{-1}$ (energy in Mev. per Mev. per cm.$^{-2}$ per sec.).

The Absorption Coefficient. In Equation 1 the mass energy transfer coefficient $\frac{\mu_k}{\rho}$ should be used and not the mass energy absorption coefficient $\frac{\mu_e}{\rho}$ given by

$$\frac{\mu_e}{\rho} = \frac{\tau}{\rho} + \frac{\sigma_a}{\rho} + \frac{\kappa}{\rho} \qquad (2)$$

where

$\frac{\tau}{\rho}$ = photoelectric mass attenuation coefficient in cm.^{2}/gram.

$\frac{\sigma_a}{\rho}$ = $\frac{\sigma_t}{\rho} \cdot \frac{E_e}{h\nu}$ the absorption component of the total Compton cross section in cm.^{2}/gram, E_e is the average energy given to the electrons in the Compton process with total cross section $\frac{\sigma_t}{\rho}$ in cm.$^{-2}$/gram for incoming photons of energy $h\nu$.

$\frac{\kappa}{\rho}$ = the cross section for the pair production in cm.^{2}/gram.

The mass energy transfer coefficient is similarly given by

$$\frac{\mu_k}{\rho} = \frac{\tau_a}{\rho} + \frac{\sigma_a}{\rho} + \frac{\kappa_a}{\rho} \qquad (3)$$

where

$$\frac{\tau_a}{\rho} = \frac{\tau}{\rho}\left(1 - \frac{\delta}{h\nu}\right) \qquad (4)$$

$$\frac{\kappa_a}{\rho} = \frac{\kappa}{\rho}\left(1 - \frac{2mc^2}{h\nu}\right) \qquad (5)$$

where

δ = average energy emitted as fluorescent radiation per photon absorbed in the photoelectric process.

$\frac{2mc^2}{h\nu}$ = is the correction for escaping radiation from the annihilation of the positron.

δ is mainly determined by the fluorescence yield ω_K in the *K*-shell. ω_K is, according to Hagedoorn and Wapstra (*4*) given by

$$\frac{\omega_K}{1-\omega_K} = (-6.4 \cdot 10^{-2} + 3.4 \cdot 10^{-2} \cdot Z - 1.03 \cdot 10^{-6} Z^3)^4; \qquad (6)$$

where

Z = atomic number

$\omega_K = \frac{\text{number } K\text{-shell vacancies}}{\text{number } K\text{-shell x-rays}}$

ω_K as a function of the atomic number (Z) is shown in Table I.

Table I. Fluorescent Yield

Atomic Number 2	Element	*Fluorescent Yield* $\omega_K \cdot 100 = \frac{K_x \cdot 100}{K_x + K_{Au}}$ *in %*	*Electron Binding Energy in Kev.* *K-Shell*	*L-Shell*	*Absorptions Coefficient in cm.²/gram in Water at the Gamma Energy*
8	O	0.18	.532		33,000
10	Ne	0.57	.867	.019	7,200
14	Si	2.7	1.839	.118	800
16	S	4.9	2.472	.193	320
20	Ca	12	4.038	.400	72
26	Fe	29	7.112	.842	13.5
29	Cu	39	8.972	1.100	6.8
30	Zn	43	9.659	1.196	5.4
40	Zr	70	17.998	2.532	0.76
50	Sn	83	29.200	4.465	0.157
56	Ba	88	37.441	5.987	0.075
58	Ce	89	40.444	6.549	0.062
60	Nd	90	43.568	7.126	0.053

In light elements δ is always small, because most of the energy is taken up by the Auger electrons and $\frac{\tau_a}{\rho}$ can then be replaced by $\frac{\tau}{\rho}$. As the atomic number increases, the fluorescent radiation increases. A portion of the fluorescent radiation, especially from the *L*-shell or the higher shells, is often absorbed within the dosimeter; for instance, the 1,000 e.v. x-rays from the *L*-shell in copper penetrate only $2 \cdot 10^{-4}$ cm. of water.

Therefore, in these calculations we have neglected this fluorescent radiation and used $\frac{\mu_e}{\rho}$ instead of $\frac{\mu_a}{\rho}$ in Equation 3. This approximation is adequate for samples and dosimeters containing atomic number $Z < 30$. But for samples containing high atomic number—*e.g.*, ceric sulfate solutions—this approximation in the calculations leads to an absorbed dose which is slightly too high. In case of ^{60}Co radiation, the pair production is negligible in light elements, while in cerium, the heaviest considered here, it is 0.8%.

The values of the absorption coefficients used in this report are those reported by Storm *et al.* (*10*).

Energy Flux Density Spectrum. $\frac{dI(E)}{dE}$ has been calculated for a point isotropic ^{60}Co source embedded in a large water container by Goldstein and Wilkins (*3*). (The nomenclature in this paper is that recommended by the International Commission on Radiological Units and Measurements (*6*), which differs from that used by Goldstein and Wilkins who used I for the same quantity as $\frac{dI}{dE}$ in this paper.) Corresponding energy buildup factors in water were measured by G. R. White (*12*), Van Dilla and Hine (*2*), Bibergal *et al.* (*1*), and by Sehested *et al.* (*8*). These experimental buildup factors were found to agree with the theoretically calculated ones within experimental and calculated accuracy of 10%. Weiss and Bernstein (*11*) studied the energy spectrum below 150 Kev. and found agreement with Spencer's and Fano's calculated values (*9*), whose calculations were the basis for the report by Goldstein and Wilkins (*3*). All this indicates that the intensity spectrum $\frac{dI(E)}{dE}$ reported by Goldstein and Wilkins for a point isotropic ^{60}Co source in water is fairly correct and it will, therefore, be used in Equation 1. The spectra are shown in Figure 1.

Calculation of Equation 1. Goldstein and Wilkins list only a few points on the spectral curves. We have graphically interpolated these points so that small intervals could be used in the numerical integration of Equation 1. Further, an extrapolation of the spectral values beyond the lowest value reported by Goldstein and Wilkins was done by assuming that at the low energies the spectral distribution is similar to that for a primary photon energy of 1 Mev.

Equation 1 was integrated numerically, because neither $\frac{dI}{dE}$ nor $\frac{\mu_k}{\rho}$ can be expressed accurately with simple functions. The widths of the energy intervals used in the integration were 0.01 Mev. from 0.025 Mev. to 0.175 Mev.; 0.0125 Mev. for photons of 0.1750 Mev. to 0.1875 Mev.; 0.025 Mev. for photons of 0.1875 Mev. to 1.2125 Mev.; and 0.0375 Mev.

for photons of 1.2125 Mev. to 1.2500 Mev. For the primary photons from ^{60}Co 1.17 Mev. and 1.33 Mev., an average energy of 1.25 Mev. was used.

Goldstein and Wilkins (*3*) do not list the photon intensity spectrum $\frac{dI}{dE}$ directly but the value of

$$4\pi r^2 \cdot \frac{dI_s(E)}{dE} \cdot \exp(\mu_t \cdot r)$$

where

$\mu_t = 0.0632$ cm.$^{-1}$ is the total absorption coefficient in water at the primary photon energy E_o

We have, therefore, first calculated the value

$$d \cdot 4\pi r^2 \cdot \exp(\mu_t \cdot r) = 1.602 \cdot 10^{-8} \cdot 3.7 \cdot 10^{10} C \cdot$$

$$4\pi r^2 \cdot \exp(\mu_t \cdot r) \cdot \left[\frac{2.5 \exp(-\mu_t \cdot r) \cdot \mu_k(E_o)}{4\pi r^2 \cdot \rho} + \right. \tag{7}$$

$$\left. \int_0^{E_o} \frac{dI_s}{dE} \cdot \frac{\mu_k}{\rho} \cdot dE \right]$$

The first term in the bracket is the contribution from the primary gamma rays (1.17 and 1.33 Mev.) at the point *P*, *r* cm. from the point source and the last term is the contribution from the scattered gamma rays at the point *P*. *d* is the dose rate in rads per sec.; *r* is the distance in water from the point isotropic ^{60}Co source of *C* curies; $\mu_t = 0.0632$ cm.$^{-1}$ is the total linear absorption coefficient in water for 1.25 Mev. photons; $\frac{dI_s}{dE}$ is the scattered gamma ray intensity spectrum; and $\frac{\mu_k(E)}{\rho}$ is the energy transfer coefficient in the dosimeter. It is assumed that the dosimeter is small enough not to change the energy intensity spectrum in the water at the point *P*, and that it is large enough to make the effect of gamma electron nonequilibrium negligible.

Definition of Absorbed Dose Buildup Factor. In the analysis of the dose variation, the concept of dose buildup factor is useful. The usual definition of dose buildup factor (*3, 5, 7*) limits its use to dose in an air dosimeter. The present definition of absorbed dose measured in rads, by which dose in any material or in any dosimeter is defined (*6*) makes the previous definition of dose buildup factor too restrictive. We will, therefore, replace the dose buildup factor by defining the absorbed dose buildup factor $B(r)$ for a given dosimeter in a given medium as the ratio of the actual absorbed dose in the dosimeter to the absorbed dose that would be measured in the dosimeter if there was no scattered radiation. The value of Equation 7 was, therefore, divided by the absorbed dose rate from the unscattered photons, the first term on the right side in Equation 7. This quotient value we call $B(r)$, *i.e.*,

$$B(r) = \frac{\frac{\mu_{k(E_0)}}{\rho} \cdot I_o + \int_o^{E_o} \exp(\mu_t \cdot r) \cdot 4\pi r^2 \frac{dI_s}{dE} \frac{\mu_k(E)}{\rho} \cdot dE}{\frac{\mu_{k(E_0)}}{\rho} \cdot I_o} \quad (8)$$

where I_o = 2.5 Mev. per one disintegration of ^{60}Co.

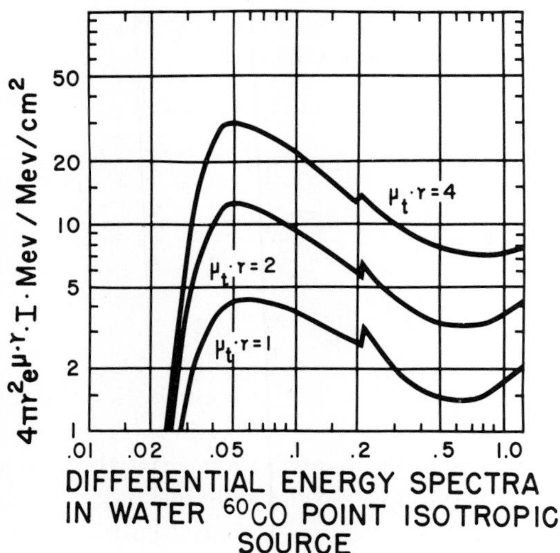

Figure 1. Energy spectra $\frac{dI}{dE}$ *in water at a distance* r *corresponding to* $\mu_t \cdot r = 1$; $\mu_t \cdot r = 2$; *and* $\mu_t \cdot r = 4$ *from a point isotropic* ^{60}*Co source. The ordinate shows and* $4\pi r^2 \exp(\mu_t \cdot r) \cdot \frac{dI}{dE}$; *the abscissa the photon energy in Mev.*

The absorbed dose buildup factor $B(r)$ in Equation 8 is the ratio of the actual dose in the dosimeter at a point P, r cm. from a point isotropic ^{60}Co source imbedded in large water container, to the dose that would be measured at the same point if there were no scattered radiation. In this equation I_o is the energy emitted by the source; I_s is the scattered radiation flux at P; μ_t is the total absorption coefficient of water (0.0632 cm.$^{-1}$); and $\frac{\mu_k}{\rho}$ is the energy transfer coefficient in cm.^{2}/gram in the dosimeter.

The integral in Equation 8 was calculated for ten elements common in applied dosimeters. These ten elements were H, C, O, Al, Si, S, Cl, Fe,

Cu, and Ce. The corresponding buildup factors calculated according to Equation 8 are listed in Table II.

Table II. Dose Buildup Factors in Elements at Different Distances in Water from a Point Isotropic ^{60}Co

Element	*Buildup Factors at $\mu_t \cdot r =$* 1	2	4	*Element*	*Buildup Factors at $\mu_t \cdot r =$* 1	2	4
*H 1	1.958	3.101	5.618	K 19	3.94	8.8	19.1
He 2	1.96	3.10	5.62	Ca 20	4.31	9.9	21.5
Li 3	1.96	3.11	5.64	Sc 21	4.71	11.2	24.4
Be 4	1.97	3.13	5.68	Ti 22	5.19	12.5	27.5
B 5	1.98	3.16	5.74	V 23	5.75	14.0	31.0
*C 6	1.995	3.201	5.850	Cr 24	6.17	15.6	34.7
N 7	2.02	3.27	6.01	Mn 25	7.00	17.3	39.0
*O 8	2.051	3.363	6.228	*Fe 26	7.66	19.24	43.29
F 9	2.10	3.50	6.59	Co 27	8.2	21.2	48.0
Ne 10	2.17	3.69	7.20	Ni 28	9.0	23.2	52.8
Na 11	2.25	3.92	7.62	*Cu 29	9.86	25.43	57.7
Mg 12	2.36	4.25	8.32	Zn 30	10.8	28	64
*Al 13	2.494	4.627	9.179	Br 35	16	43	97
*Si 14	2.665	5.115	10.32	Zr 40	23	62	138
P 15	2.86	5.65	11.50	Rh 45	31	85	190
*S 16	3.106	6.367	13.24	Sn 50	40	112	252
*Cl 17	3.38	7.14	15.04	I 53	45	130	295
A 18	3.61	7.90	17.00	*Ce 58	38.5	103.6	241.1

Interpolation of the Values of *B*. The energy absorption coefficient can be approximated by:

$$\frac{\mu_e}{\rho} = \frac{a(E) \cdot Z}{A} + \frac{b(E) \cdot f(Z)}{A} \quad (9)$$

where

Z = atomic number

A = atomic weight

$\frac{a(E) \cdot Z}{A}$ = Compton absorption

$a(E)$ = a function of the photon energy E, but independent of Z and A.

$b(E) \cdot f(Z)$ = photoelectric absorption

$b(E)$ = a function of the photon energy E but independent of Z and A.

$f(Z)$ = a function of the atomic number but independent of E

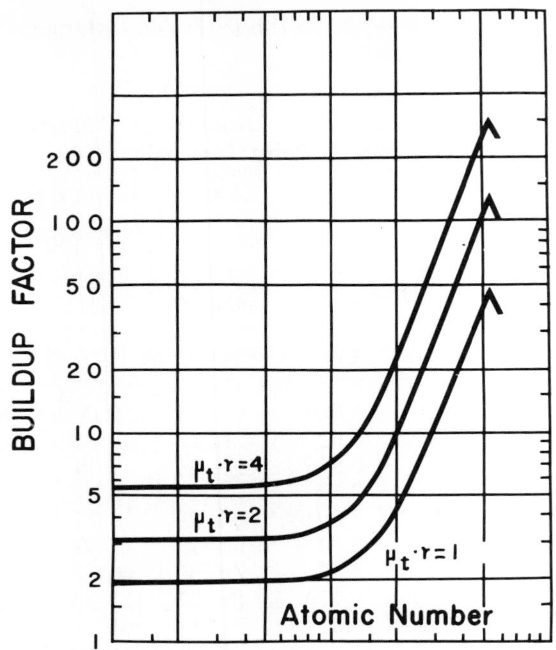

Figure 2. Absorbed dose buildup factors at distances r in water corresponding to $\mu_t \cdot r = 1$; $\mu_t \cdot r = 2$; and, $\mu_t \cdot r = 4$ from a point isotropic ^{60}Co source as a function of the atomic number Z

Table III. Dose Buildup Factors in Compounds at Different

Chemical Compound	*Molecule Weight*	$\frac{\mu_k}{\rho} \cdot 100$ *in cm.²/gram at 1.25 Mev.*
H_2O	18.015	2.975
LiF	25.937	2.471
$(CH_2)n$	14.027	3.042
Lucite $C_5H_8O_2$	101.017	2.852
Polyvinyl Chloride $(H_3C_2Cl)_n$	62.499	2.738
SiO_2	60.084	2.67
NaCl	58.453	2.563
H_2SO_4	98.076	2.706
$FeSO_4$	151.907	2.599
$CuSO_4$	159.600	2.587
$Ce(SO_4)_2$	332.240	2.630
SO_4^{2-}	96.06	2.6514
Bone (Z eff. = 13.8)		

The integral in Equation 1 can then for each distance r be written as:

$$d = a_1 \cdot \frac{Z}{A} + b_1 \cdot \frac{f(Z)}{A}; \qquad (10)$$

where a_1 and b_1 are functions of the distance r from the source but independent of Z.

The buildup factor in Equation 8 can then be expressed as:

$$B(r) = 1 + a_2 + b_2 \cdot f(Z) \cdot Z^{-1} \qquad (11)$$

insofar as the photoelectric absorption and the pair production can be neglected at 1.25 Mev. photon energy. a_2 and b_2 are functions of r, but independent of Z. The variation of f (Z) was determined from the photoelectric absorption at $E = 0.045$ Mev. The values so determined were used to calculate the values of a_2 and b_2 for each distance that gave close fit to the more exactly calculated values for the ten elements mentioned above. Equation 11 was then used to interpolate B-values for other atomic numbers. The values so found, together with the more exactly calculated values, are reported in Table II, and Figure 2.

The Buildup Factor of a Chemical Compound or Mixture. The absorbed dose buildup factor $B(r)$ of a compound consisting of the elements X_1, X_2, X_3, . . . with the buildup factors B_1, B_2, B_3, . . . and mass energy transfer coefficients $\frac{\mu_1}{\rho_1}, \frac{\mu_2}{\rho_2}, \frac{\mu_3}{\rho_3}$, —at 1.25 Mev. photon energy, and

Distances in Water from a Point Isotropic ^{60}Co Source

Buildup Factor at $\mu_t \cdot r = 0$	*Buildup Factor at* $\mu_t \cdot r = 1$	*Buildup Factor at* $\mu_t \cdot r = 2$	*Buildup Factor at* $\mu_t \cdot r = 4$
1.000	2.033	3.311	6.106
1.000	2.072	3.435	6.415
1.000	1.986	3.176	5.792
1.000	2.006	3.234	5.928
1.000	2.738	5.288	10.722
1.000	2.338	4.182	8.141
1.000	2.944	5.928	12.146
1.000	2.385	4.315	8.450
1.000	4.261	9.622	20.357
1.000	5.246	12.402	27.324
1.000	17.414	45.572	105.134
1.000	2.405	4.928	11.946
	2.65	5.1	10.

Table IV. Buildup Factors in Dosimeters at Different

Chemical Mixtures and Solutions	*Weight Percent*	*Density*
Air Dry		
N_2	75.56	0.00129
O_2	23.15	
Ar	1.29	
Sulfuric Acid		
0.4*M* H_2SO_4	3.832	1.0239
H_2O	96.168	
Sulfuric Acid		
0.005*M* H_2SO_4	0.049	1.00025
H_2O	99.951	
Fricke Dosimeter		
0.001*M* $FeSO_4$	0.015	1.0240
0.400*M* H_2SO_4	99.985	
H_2O		
Fricke Dosimeter		
0.001*M* $FeSO_4$	0.0152	1.0240
0.001*M* NaCl	0.0023	
0.400*M* H_2SO_4	99.9825	
H_2O		
Ferrous Cupric Dosimeter		
0.001*M* $FeSO_4$	0.015	1.002
0.010*M* $CuSO_4$	0.159	
0.005*M* H_2SO_4	99.826	
H_2O		
Ferrous Cupric Dosimeter		
0.006*M* $FeSO_4$	0.091	1.011
0.060*M* $CuSO_4$	0.950	
0.005*M* H_2SO_4	98.959	
H_2O		
Ceric Dosimeter		
0.01*M* $Ce(SO_4)_2$	0.323	1.0279
0.40*M* H_2SO_4	99.677	
H_2O		
Ceric Dosimeter		
0.10*M* $Ce(SO_4)_2$	3.12	1.066
0.40*M* H_2SO_4	96.88	
H_2O		
Ceric Dosimeter		
0.40*M* $Ce(SO_4)_2$	10.53	1.262
0.40*M* H_2SO_4	89.47	
H_2O		

Distances in Water from a Point Isotropic ^{60}Co Source

$\frac{\mu_k}{\rho} \cdot 100$ in cm./gram at 1.25 Mev.	Buildup Factor at $\mu_t \cdot r = 1$	Buildup Factor at $\mu_t \cdot r = 2$	Buildup Factor at $\mu_t \cdot r = 3$
2.669	2.046	3.355	6.210
2.965	2.045	3.346	6.188
2.975	2.033	3.311	6.107
2.965	2.046	3.347	6.190
2.956	2.046	3.347	6.191
2.974	2.038	3.325	6.138
2.971	2.061	3.391	6.294
2.964	2.089	3.468	6.472
2.955	2.474	4.518	8.934
2.930	3.498	7.338	15.54

with the weight fractions A_1, A_2, A_3, —can be calculated according to

$$B(r) = \frac{B_1(r) \cdot \frac{\mu_1}{\rho_1} \cdot A_1 + B_2 \cdot \frac{\mu_2}{\rho_2} \cdot A_2 + \ldots\ldots + \ldots}{\frac{\mu_1}{\rho_1} \cdot A_1 + \frac{\mu_2}{\rho_2} \cdot A_2 + \ldots\ldots} \qquad (12)$$

In the present case, the average energy of 1.25 Mev. can be used. Several such values calculated using Equation 12 are shown in Tables III and IV and in Figures 3 and 4.

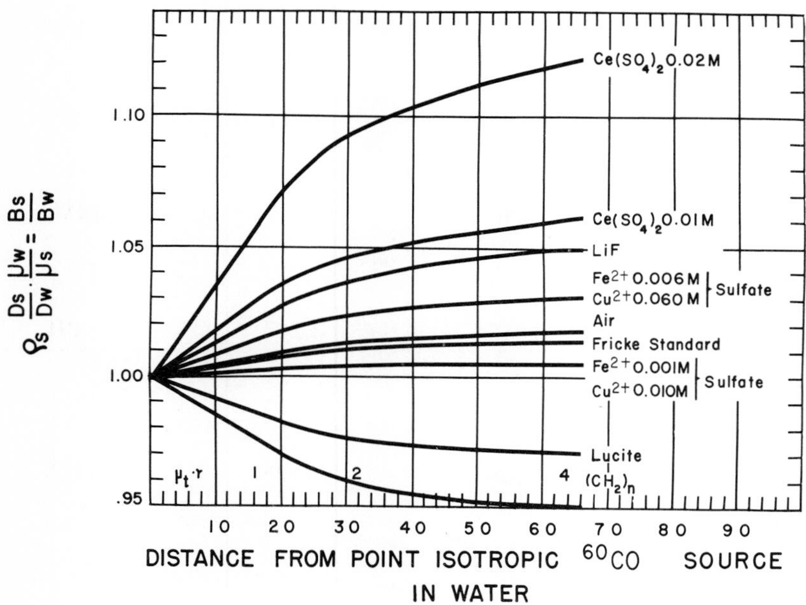

Figure 3. Absorbed dose buildup factors in different dosimeters relative to that of water as a function of the distance r *in cm. from a point isotropic* ^{60}*Co source embedded in a large water container*

Dose as a Function of the Distance from the ^{60}Co Sources. From Equations 7 and 8 we derive Equation 13 for the dose d in a dosimeter with an absorbed dose buildup factor B, r cm. from a point isotropic ^{60}Co source in water.

$$d = \frac{\mu_k}{\rho} \cdot B \cdot 1482 \cdot C \cdot \frac{e^{-\mu_t r}}{4\pi r^2} \text{ rads/sec.} \qquad (13)$$

$\frac{\mu_k}{\rho}$, and B depend on the dosimeter, while the source strength C in curies ^{60}Co, the total absorptions coefficient $\mu_t = 0.0632$ cm.^{2}/gram in water, and the distance r in cm. from the source are independent of it.

$\frac{\mu_k}{\rho}$, the energy transfer coefficient in cm.²/gram at the primary photon energy is almost equal to $\frac{\mu_e}{\rho}$, the energy absorption coefficient; B is found in Tables II, III, and IV.

It is illustrative to consider the ratio of the dose $d_s(r)$ in a dosimeter with an energy transfer coefficient $\frac{\mu_{ks}}{\rho_s}$ to the dose $d_w(r)$ in water with energy transfer coefficient $\frac{\mu_{kw}}{\rho_w}$ at the distance r cm. from the source. According to Equation 13 this ratio is given by:

$$\frac{d_s}{d_w} = \frac{\mu_{ks}/\rho_s}{\mu_{kw}/\rho_w} \cdot \frac{B_s(r)}{B_w(r)} = \frac{\mu_{ks}}{\mu_{kw}} \cdot \frac{\rho_w}{\rho_s} \cdot \frac{B_s}{B_w} \tag{14}$$

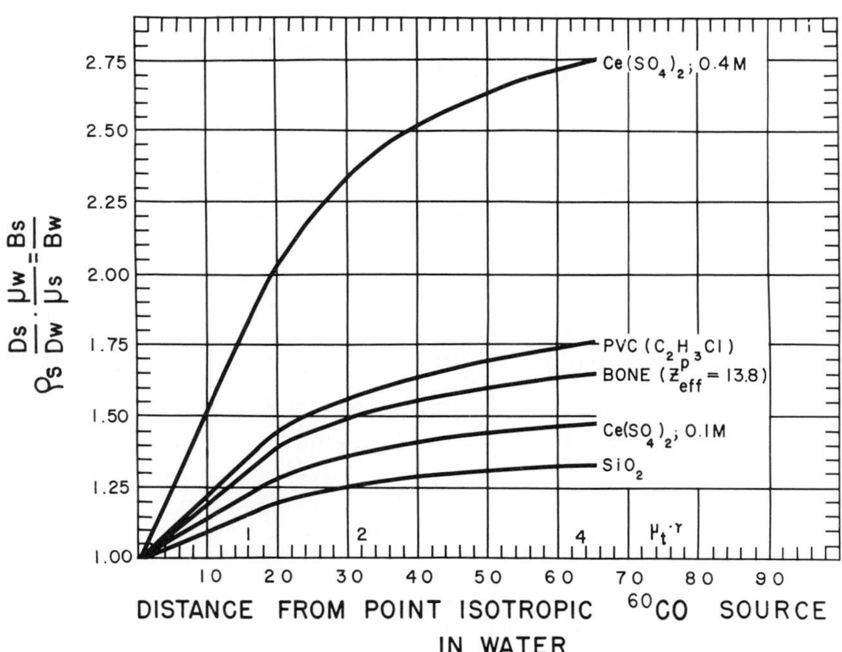

Figure 4. Absorbed dose buildup factors in different dosimeters relative to that of water as a function of the distance r *in cm. from a point isotropic* ^{60}*Co source embedded in a large water container*

The values of the energy transfer coefficients at E_0 can be found in the Tables by Storm *et al.* (*10*), while the ratio $\frac{B_s}{B_w}$ is shown for several dosimeters in columns 3, 4, and 5 of Table V, and the corresponding

Table V. The Absorbed Dose Buildup Factors and the Dose in Function of the Distance *r* in Water

Name	Formula		$\frac{B_s}{B_w}$ *the buildup factors* B_s *relative to the buildup factor* B_w *of water at*		
			$\mu_t \cdot r = 1$	$\mu_t \cdot r = 2$	$\mu_t \cdot r = 4$
Hydrocarbon	$(CH_2)_n$		0.977	0.959	0.949
Lucite	C_5H_8O		0.987	0.977	0.971
Draganić Dosimeter	0.1*M*	$(COOH)_2$	1.000	1.000	1.000
Water	H_2O		1.000	1.000	1.000
Ferrous Sulfate Cupric Sulfate Sulfuric Acid	0.001*M* 0.010*M* 0.005*M*	$FeSO_4$ $CuSO_4$ H_2SO_4	1.002	1.004	1.005
Fricke Dosimeter	0.001*M* 0.4*M*	$FeSO_4$ H_2SO_4	1.006	1.011	1.014
Air	75.56% 23.15% 1.29%	N_2 O_2 Ar	1.006	1.013	1.017
Ferrous Sulfate Cupric Sulfate Sulfuric Acid	0.006*M* 0.060*M* 0.005*M*	$FeSO_4$ $CuSO_4$ H_2SO_4	1.014	1.024	1.031
Lithium Fluoride	LiF		1.019	1.037	1.051
Ceric Sulfate	0.01*M* 0.4*M*	$Ce(SO_4)_2$ H_2SO_4	1.028	1.047	1.060
Quartz	SiO_2		1.150	1.263	1.333
Ceric Sulfate	0.10*M* 0.4*M*	$Ce(SO_4)_2$ H_2SO_4	1.217	1.365	1.463
Poly(vinyl chloride)	H_3C_2Cl		1.347	1.597	1.756
Ceric Sulfate	0.4*M* 0.4*M*	$Ce(SO_4)_2$ H_2SO_4	1.720	2.216	2.545

ratio $\frac{d_s}{d_w}$ in columns 6, 7, 8, and 9 of the same table. For other materials it may be derived by using Table II, Equation 12, and Equation 14.

Significance in Practical Problems. Close to the source, the Compton scattering of the primary gamma rays is the main process. In cobalt, for instance, the total Compton cross section is 0.054 cm.²/gram; and the photoelectric cross section is 0.00028 cm.²/gram at 1.25 Mev. This

Dosimeters Relative to the Corresponding Values in Water as a from an Isotropic ^{60}Co Point Source

$\frac{d_w}{d_s}$; the dose d_s relative to the dose d_w of water at			
$\mu_t \cdot r = 0$	$\mu_t \cdot r = 1$	$\mu_t \cdot r = 2$	$\mu_t \cdot r = 4$
1.023	0.999	0.981	0.971
0.959	0.946	0.937	0.931
0.999	0.999	0.999	0.999
1.000	1.000	1.000	1.000
1.000	1.002	1.004	1.005
0.997	1.002	1.008	1.011
0.897	0.902	0.909	0.912
0.999	1.013	1.023	1.030
0.831	0.847	0.862	0.873
0.996	1.024	1.043	1.056
0.897	1.032	1.133	1.196
0.993	1.208	1.355	1.453
0.920	1.239	1.469	1.616
0.985	1.694	2.183	2.507

means that the gamma ray spectrum close to the source is fairly independent of the material immediately surrounding the source. For example, the spectrum of the gamma rays after penetrating 1 cm. of cobalt with density ρ_{Co} is the same, or very similar, to the spectrum of the gamma rays after penetrating $\frac{18}{10} \cdot \frac{27}{59} \cdot \rho_{Co} = 7.4$ cm. of water except for the very lowest end of the spectrum. If this gamma ray spectrum then penetrates a few cm. of water, the low energy portion of the gamma ray spectrum would be fairly well re-established. In many experiments the scattering of the gamma rays in the source, source encapsulation, surrounding ^{60}Co slugs, and in the sample and sample containment is of this magnitude. The effect discussed in the present paper is therefore of great significance in many experiments.

Let us assume that we want to measure the *G*-value, number of molecular changes per 100 e.v., of $Ce^{4+} \rightarrow Ce^{3+}$ in a ceric-sulfate solution as a function of the concentration. We measure the dose in a Fricke dosimeter vial or ferrous-cupric dosimeter vial at the same place as the vial containing the ceric solution, and then, as is usual, we correct for the difference in the energy transfer coefficient at 1.25 Mev. and for the difference in density of the solutions. However, as shown in Equation 14 and in Table V and Figures 3 and 4, these corrections are entirely inadequate because of the large difference in buildup factors. For 0.4*M* ceric sulfate solution, the correction caused by the buildup factor is 72% at $\mu_t \cdot r = 1$; 122% at $\mu_t \cdot r = 2$; and 155% at $\mu_t \cdot r = 4$.

If the dose is corrected for the difference in energy transfer coefficient at 1.25 Mev. and for the differences in density of the solutions but not for the differences in buildup factors; the *G*-value, even if actually constant, would behave as if it increased with concentration. This may partly explain the great increase in the *G*-values with concentration of ceric sulfate observed in the past by some authors. For poly(vinyl chloride) the buildup factors differ also greatly from those of water as is seen in Table III. This difference in buildup factors may explain some of the difficulties encountered in its use in gamma-ray facilities.

Acknowledgment

Parts of this work were initiated in 1964 and 1965 while still employed at the Danish Atomic Energy Commission Research Establishment at Risö, Denmark, where the computer calculations of Equations 7 and 8 were carried out.

Literature Cited

(1) Bibergal, A. V., Leschensky, N. I., Margulis, V. Y., Drucker, V. G., *IAEA Conf. Proc., Warsaw,* pp. 163-177, IAEV, Vienna (Sept. 1959).
(2) van Dilla, M. A., Hine, G. J., *Nucleonics* **10,** No. 7, 54 (1952).
(3) Goldstein, H., Wilkins, J. E., *U. S. At. Energy Rept.* **NYO-3075,** 149 (1954).
(4) Hagedoora, H. L., Wapstra, A. H., *Nucl. Phys.* **15,** 146 (1960).
(5) Hine, G. J., Brownell, G. L., eds., "Radiation Dosimetry," p. 774, Academic Press, New York, 1956.
(6) International Commission on Radiological Units and Measurements (ICRU), Report 10b, 1962, *Natl. Bur. Stds. (U. S.) Handbook* **85,** 102 (1964).

(7) Moteff, J., Miscellaneous Data for Shielding Calculations, (Aircraft Nuclear Propulsion Department, Atomic Products Division, General Electric) APEX 176 (Dec. 1954).
(8) Sehested, K., Brynjolfsson, A., Holm, N. W., *Danish At. Energy Comm., Risö Rept.* **62** (1963).
(9) Spencer, L. V., Fano, U., *J. Res. Natl. Bur. Stds.* **46,** No. 6, 446 (1951).
(10) Storm, E., Gilbert, E., Israel, H., *Los Alamos Scientific Lab. Rept.* **LA-2237** (1958).
(11) Weiss, M. M., Bernstein, W., *Phys. Rev.* **92,** No. 5, 1264 (1953).
(12) White, G. R., *Phys. Rev.* **80,** 154 (1950).

RECEIVED March 21, 1968.

39

The Oxalic Acid Dosimeter Procedure

NIELS W. HOLM and K. SEHESTED

The Danish Atomic Energy Commission, Research Establishment Risö, Roskilde, Denmark

A review is given on the experiences with the oxalic acid dosimeter. The system was first suggested by Draganić, who has carried out extensive investigations on the dosimetric properties. Further experiments have been carried out at various laboratories—e.g., *in the United States, Japan, and Denmark. Although the system suffers from some systematic weaknesses, it can be applied successfully, when properly calibrated under the conditions where it is to be used. The present report describes its application for ^{60}Co and high dose-rate electron dosimetry.*

The oxalic-acid dosimeter has a history comparable to that of the ceric-sulfate dosimeter. Much work has been carried out, promising results have been obtained, and an abundance of publications have appeared; but only few people really use these systems. Still both the ceric-sulfate dosimeter and the oxalic-acid dosimeter may be applied successfully, once they are "debugged" by the people who are to use them in the daily routine. Both systems deserve much attention as they are among the few promising candidates of aqueous chemical dosimeters for use in the megarad range.

The oxalic-acid dosimeter has some substantial advantages over the ceric-sulfate dosimeter, which made us investigate it more closely: (1) it is quite insensitive to impurities, (2) it has very good energy-absorption characteristics, and (3) the system is very stable to normal storage before and after irradiation. The system also has some drawbacks: (1) the decomposition of oxalic-acid does not proceed linearly with the absorbed dose, and (2) the chemical yield is not fully independent of the radiation conditions. Other difficulties have been reported and have hampered the practical use.

This paper identifies some of these difficulties and suggests practical solutions. On basis of newer evidence, it is believed by the authors that the system is very well suited for dosimetry in—*e.g.*, radiation sterilization of food and medical products.

Historical Background

The system was first described in 1955 (*3*) by Draganić, who pointed out the advantages listed above. In later publications (*4, 6, 7, 11*), detailed procedures were reported for ^{60}Co as well as for reactor use.

The routine procedure was based on the following:

(1) The oxalic acid decomposes when subjected to radiation, and the absorbed dose is determined from the decrease in oxalic-acid concentration upon irradiation.

(2) The oxalic-acid concentration measurements are performed by (a) $KMnO_4$ titration (*3*), (b) cupribenzidine spectrophotometry (*11*), or (c) NaOH titration (*19*).

(3) The chemical change is not a linear function of the dose. As an approximation it was suggested to use $G = 4.9$ up to 30% decomposition, and from then on calculate the dose from an expression of the form

$$\log D = a \log C + b,$$

where D is the absorbed dose in e.v./gram, C the number of molecules decomposed per gram, and a and b constants depending on the oxalic-acid concentration before and after irradiation.

On this basis the system was used successfully at the laboratories at Risö and Vinca (Boris Kidrich Institute of Nuclear Sciences, Belgrade, Yugoslavia). While the $KMnO_4$-titration method was discarded as less accurate, the cupribenzidine method was developed further (*11*) and proven to be satisfactory for routine use. The NaOH titration was considered a good alternative method. The G-value for less than 30% decomposition was re-determined at Vinca (*20*) by calorimetry, and an independent G-value determination was carried out elsewhere (*15*). Concurrent investigations for pulsed electron beams took place at Risö (*9*).

During these years, the system gained interest in the United States (*6*) as a prospective substitute for the ceric-sulfate dosimeter in food-irradiation dosimetry. An ASTM (American Society for Testing & Materials) subcommittee dealing with dosimetry problems worked out tentative recommended procedures, and circulated them for testing in a number of laboratories. The suggestions for the analytical procedure included both spectrophotometry and NaOH-titration.

First ASTM Round Robin Test

Two members of the ASTM-committee have published the results of their investigations. Glass (*13*) found that the spectrophotometric procedure yielded results 7–16% lower than those obtained by the Fricke dosimeter. In the titration procedure, the results were 2–6% lower. These measurements comprised 100 m*M*, 300 m*M*, and 750 m*M* oxalic-acid solutions.

Connally and Gevantmann (*2*) used the spectrophotometric method and found, within ±5–10%, agreement with values extrapolated from measurements with the Fricke dosimeter.

Harmer (*14*) and Weiss (*22*) had indications of instability to ultraviolet light of the diluted complex solution for the spectrophotometric measurement.

Cheek and Linnenbom (*1*) found for the spectrophotometric method standard deviations of the order of ±10% based on a *G*-value of 4.9. For the NaOH-titration method they emphasized the importance of effective removal of CO_2 from the irradiated solution. As an alternative to heating they proposed to remove the CO_2 by purging the solution with a stream of H_2O-saturated, CO_2-free air. By titration they found the *G*-value to be 4.4 for a 75 m*M* oxalic-acid solution.

Fenger (*12*) used the dosimeter for gamma-flux measurements in the thermal column of the DR 2 reactor and calibrated the system in the Risö Co-60 facility. He found for a 50 m*M* oxalic-acid solution a *G*-value of 4.6 ± 0.3.

The earlier experiences of this laboratory were good in so far as the accuracy obtained with the system was in accordance with what had been stated by Draganić (better than 10%). The difficulty in obtaining good results as reported above, however, made us re-examine the procedure. (This work was started by one of the authors (N. W. H.) during a one-year stay as visiting scientist at the Radiation Sources Branch of the U.S. Army Natick Laboratories, Natick, Mass., United States.)

Re-examination of Procedure

The information accumulated by the first ASTM round robin test indicated two kinds of difficulties:

(1) The scattering of results in individual tests at any particular laboratory indicated that the analytical procedure was either too complicated for routine use, or inaccurate owing to systematic errors—*e.g.*, instability to ultraviolet light of the cupribenzidine complex solution.

(2) Application of $G = 4.9$ for 0–30% decomposition and of the log-log equation did not fit the true decomposition curve adequately.

Analytical Procedures. The demands on the chemical analysis are very strict as the absorbed dose is determined as a difference between two concentrations. Three analytical methods have been suggested for use in oxalic-acid dosimetry:

(1) TITRATION WITH $KMnO_4$ (*4, 6*). This method is not very specific as hydrogen peroxide and organic by-products formed by the radiolysis are titrated together with the oxalic acid. Good reproducibility is dependent upon a subjective kind of routine on the part of the operator, and the method is therefore not considered suitable as a standard dosimetry procedure.

(2) SPECTROPHOTOMETRY OF THE CUPRIBENZIDINE COMPLEX OF OXALIC ACID (*4, 5, 6*). Z. Draganić and I. Draganić (*10, 11*) have developed a method for spectrophotometric determination of oxalic acid by means of a reagent made up of an aqueous solution of cupric acetate, benzidinedihydrochloride, and acetic acid. The oxalic-acid solution is diluted and mixed with the complexing reagent, and the optical density is read at 246 mμ. The molar extinction coefficient of the complex is reported to be 2490, and it is stated that it may vary within 10% from batch to batch according to reagent purity (*6*). A negative temperature coefficient of 0.7%/°C. is reported for the complex and the cell compartment should therefore be temperature controlled.

(3) TITRATION WITH NaOH. This method was suggested by Matsui (*19*), who removed the carbon dioxide from the irradiated solution by heating the sample in a water bath for 30 minutes. Other experimenters (*6, 13, 17*) have checked this method, but the agreement obtained was not quite satisfactory. The reason seems to be inadequate removal of carbon dioxide.

The experiments at Natick and at Risö regarding the analytical procedures gave the following results (*9*):

(1) SPECTROPHOTOMETRY. The analytical reagents were prepared as described by Draganić *et al.* (*5*) and the analytical procedure was checked by preparing a set of 0.1, 0.2, and 0.3 m*M* oxalic-acid complex solutions. The measurements were carried out on a Cary model 15, dual-beam spectrophotometer (Natick) and on a Zeiss PMQII single-beam spectrophotometer (Risö), both with temperature-controlled cell compartments.

A calibration curve obtained with the standard Draganić (*5*) reagent is shown in Figure 1. The O.D. of a 0.1 m*M* oxalic-acid complex solution was determined to be 0.250 (corresponding to a molar extinction coefficient of 2500). Assuming Lambert-Beer's law to be valid it was then expected that the O.D. of a 0.2 m*M* and 0.3 m*M* would be 0.500 and 0.750 respectively. The readings, however, were persistently higher, namely 0.530 and 0.815. This was observed at both laboratories and checked in several determinations. (In accelerator-irradiated solutions we found that some of the reaction products from the radiolysis had an absorption of their own, which interfered (up to 5–10%) with the oxalic-acid determination.) A systematic investigation was undertaken to clarify whether other stoichiometric compositions might lead to a better straight-line relationship. It was found that the following concentrations gave a better approximation to a straight line: (1) *Solution A:* Dissolve 51.4 mg. benzidinehydrochloride in 10 ml. 30% vol. acetic acid and dilute with distilled water to 250 ml. (0.8 m*M*); and (2) *Solution B:* Dissolve 159.7 mg. cupric acetate in 250 ml. distilled water (3.2 m*M*).

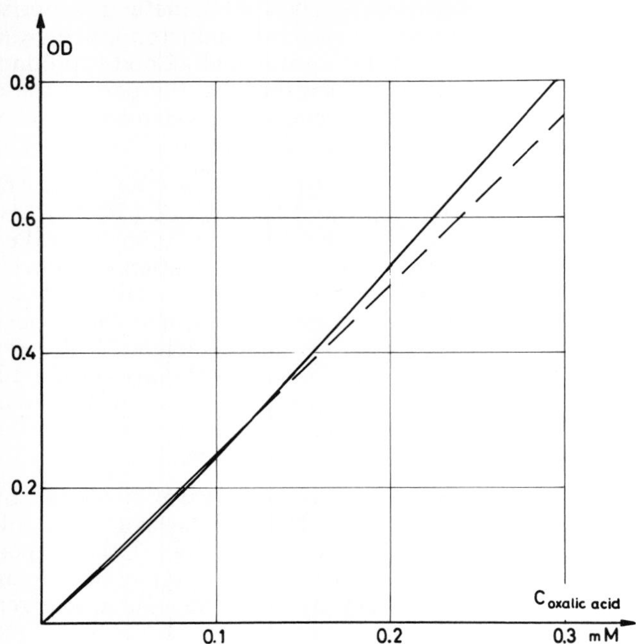

Figure 1. "Lambert-Beer" curve; O.D. as a function of oxalic-acid concentration for Draganić's complexing reagent

The molar extinction coefficient of the complex was 2100. The reagent was used in a 1:4 ratio as earlier.

The stability of the reagent has been questioned by some users, and a test was made to examine this problem. A set of solutions A and B was stored for one month. Another set of solutions was mixed to (A + B) and similarly stored. After the storage period a fresh set of reagents was prepared, and all three sets of reagents were tested. They gave identical readings, but the premixed and stored reagent was unstable in the spectrophotometer.

Another kind of instability was observed in the work with the Cary spectrophotometer at Natick. The O.D. readings decreased as if a decomposition of the complex was taking place. This phenomenon was not observed with the single-beam spectrophotometer at Risö. A simple test in which a complex solution was exposed to intense ultraviolet light showed that a few minutes' exposure decreased the optical density some 50%. A procedure, which takes care of this problem is described in Ref. *15*.

NaOH Titration. The only problem with this method is the quantitative removal of CO_2, produced by the decomposition of oxalic acid. Purging of the solution with water-saturated air works well. An easier method is to take an aliquot from the irradiated sample, weigh it, dilute with distilled water, and heat the solution for 30 minutes before titration.

CONCLUSION. The experiments showed that the spectrophotometric method as well as the titrimetric method could render reproducible results (within ±2–3%). The titrimetric method may be preferred as being more reliable and simple in routine use.

Decomposition Curve. The refinements in the analytical procedure permitted a more accurate determination of the oxalic-acid decomposition curve. The experimental data demonstrated that the yield decreases continuously with increasing dose throughout the decomposition range. A decomposition curve for a 100 m*M* oxalic-acid solution obtained at Risö is shown in Figure 2.

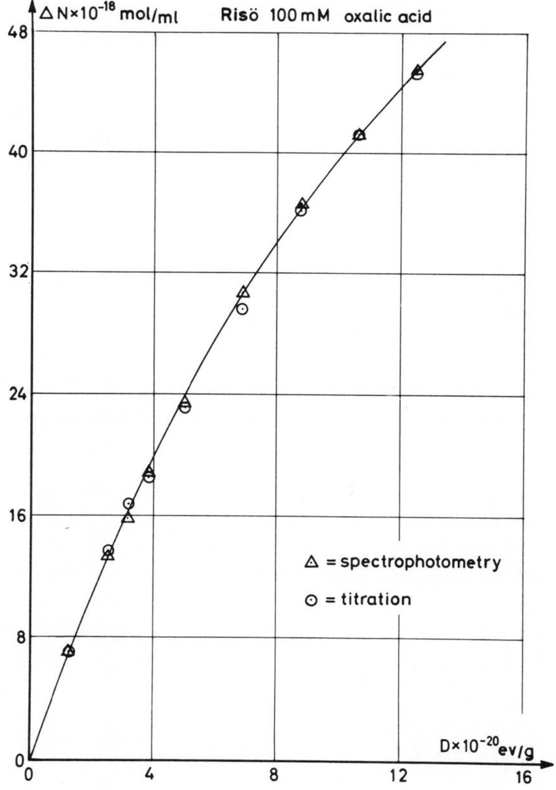

*Figure 2. Calibration curve for oxalic-acid decomposition vs. absorbed dose as determined by titration and by spectrophotometry for 100 m*M *oxalic acid*

Draganić suggested (*8*) that first order reaction kinetics would apply for the radiolytic decomposition.

Such a relation corresponds very well with the experimental results obtained at Risö and at Vinca as seen in Figures 3a, 3b, and 3c. The data from the titration analysis are used as they are considered to be more accurate. Recent data obtained at Vinca (*18*) by spectrophotometry are plotted for comparison.

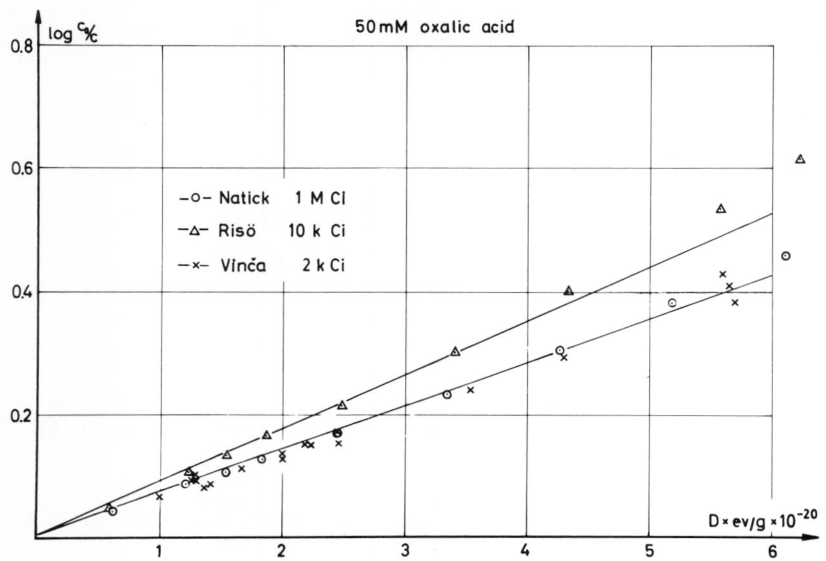

Figure 3a. Calibration curves for oxalic-acid decomposition (log c_0/c *vs. absorbed dose) obtained at Natick, Risö and Vinca (Ref.* 18*)*

CONCLUSION. From Figures 3a, 3b and 3c, it may be seen that:

(1) The validity of a logarithmic equation is supported by all the experimental data.

(2) A systematic bend-off of data from the straight line can be seen at higher decomposition values, owing to the build-up of radiolytic by-products which take part in the process. This sets an upper limit of approx. 60% decomposition to the range of useful application of the dosimeter at a particular initial concentration.

(3) Results obtained at the different installations show different yields—*i.e.*, different proportionality factors in a logarithmic equation. It is believed that the differences in yield between the different installations may be caused by a "length of irradiation" effect. Among the first products formed are glyoxal and glyoxylic acid (*21*), which react further in slow condensation reactions. When the irradiation time is of the same order of magnitude—or less—than the "lifetime" of glyoxal and glyoxylic acid in the solution, these products will react to a greater extent with the primary radicals thus decreasing the yield. For the conditions examined here the difference in yield can be more than 10%.

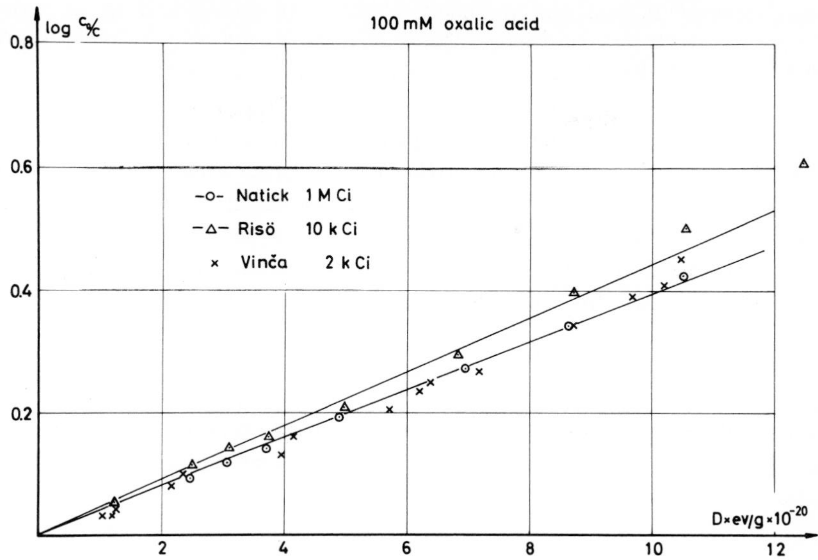

Figure 3b. *Calibration curves for oxalic-acid decomposition (log* c_0/c *vs. absorbed dose) obtained at Natick, Risö and Vinca (Ref.* 18)

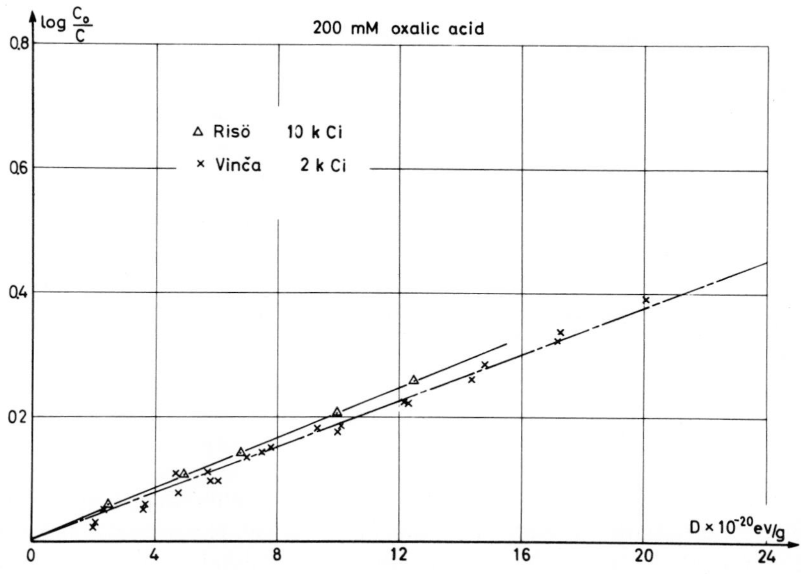

Figure 3c. *Calibration curves for oxalic-acid decomposition (log* c_0/c *vs. absorbed dose) obtained at Natick, Risö and Vinca (Ref.* 18)

Second ASTM Round Robin Test

The second round robin test which took place in 1966 was based on a proposed procedure worked out by Holm (*15*). Five laboratories in the United States took part in testing the procedure, which was based on NaOH-titration. It showed that laboratories accustomed to working on analytical-chemical problems got fairly consistent and reproducible results. When the results were recalculated so as to express a values, these values ran from 37 to 49 (*16*). At Vinca where these data were compiled for comparison, the dose relation is used in the following form:

$$D = a \cdot c_0 \log \frac{c_o}{c}.$$

D is the absorbed dose in e.v./grams, a a proportionality factor and c_o and c the concentrations in molecules per ml. before and after irradiation.

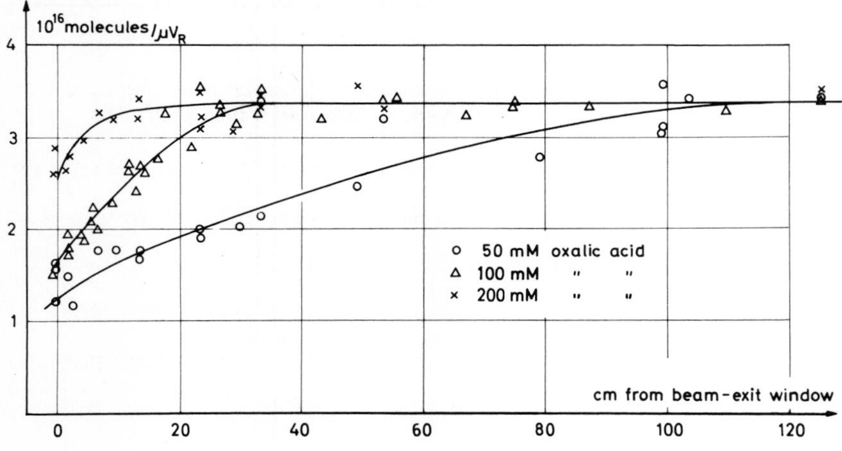

Figure 4. Dose-rate dependence of 50 mM, 100 mM and 200 mM oxalic-acid solutions, plotted as the number of molecules decomposed per unit energy input vs. *the distance in centimeters from the beam exit window*

Conclusions for Co^{60} *Dosimetry*

Experience has shown that the oxalic-acid dosimeter is not as simple in use as originally anticipated. The more recent experiments have led to refinements in the analytical procedures and added to the understanding of the decomposition process. It is necessary though to calibrate the system under the conditions where it is to be used. When that is done, the system can be expected to render precise, reliable and simple service.

Application of the Oxalic-Acid Dosimeter for High Dose-Rate Work

A number of experiments have been carried out at Risö (*8, 9*) on the behavior of the oxalic-acid system at extreme high dose rates.

The results of those experiments are summarized in Figure 4, which shows the number of molecules decomposed per unit energy input *vs.* the distance in cm. from the beam exit window. Based on a dose calibration, these figures could be recalculated so as to express the yield as a function of dose rate in the pulse at a total decomposition of 25%. It was found that the decomposition for a given dose is independent of dose rate up to:

2×10^8 rads/sec. for 50 m*M* oxalic acid

2×10^9 rads/sec. for 100 m*M* oxalic acid

2×10^{10} rads/sec. for 200 m*M* oxalic acid

It is important to note that the system is only safe in a reasonably homogeneous field. In a very inhomogeneous field a large spectrum of total absorbed doses is found in the sample and therefore also large differences in chemical yields.

Literature Cited

(1) Cheek, Linnenbom, Naval Research Laboratory, Washington, D. C., private communication (1964).
(2) Connally, E. F., Gevantmann, L. H., *U. S. Naval Radiol. Defense Lab.* **USNRDL-ER-14** (1963).
(3) Draganic, I. G., *J. Chim. Phys.* **52,** 595 (1955).
(4) *Ibid., J. Chim. Phys.* **56,** 9 (1959).
(5) Draganić, I. G., Holm, N. W., Maul, J. E., *Risö Report* **No. 22** (1961).
(6) Draganić, I. G., *Nucleonics 21* **No. 2,** 33-35 (1963).
(7) Draganić, I. G., Radak, B. B., Marković, V. M., *Intern. J. Appl. Radiation Isotopes* **16,** 145-152 (1965).
(8) Draganić, I. G., *Proc. Symp. Radiation Chem. 2nd,* Budapest, Hungary, 1967.
(9) Draganić, I. G., Sehested, K., Holm, N. W., *Risö Report* **No. 112** (1967).
(10) Draganić, Z. D., Draganić, I. G., *Bull. Inst. Nucl. Sci. "Boris Kidrich" (Belgrade)* **7,** No. 126 (1957).
(11) Draganić, Z. D., *Anal. Chim. Acta* **28,** 394 (1963).
(12) Fenger, J., *Risö Report* **No. 67** (1963).
(13) Glass, A. L., *AML Report* **No. NAEC-AML-1854** (1964).
(14) Harmer, D., Dow Chemical Company, private communication (1964).
(15) Holm, N. W., Bjergbakke, E., Sehested, K., Draganić, I. G., *Risö Report* **No. 111** (1967).
(16) Holm, N. W., Draganić, I. G. (in press).
(17) Josimović, Lj., Draganić, I., *Sci. Paper I.P.C.R. Japan,* **57, No. 1,** 29-30 (1963).
(18) Marković, V., Draganić, I. G., *IBK Report* (to be published)–and unpublished results.
(19) Matsui, M., *Sci. Paper I.P.C.R. Japan* **53, No. 1528** (1954).
(20) Radak, B. B., Karapandzić, M., Gal, O., *Nucleonics* **22, No. 11,** 52-54 (1964).

(21) Sehested, K., Bjergbakke, E., Holm, N. W., *Proc. Symp. Radiation Chem. 2nd,* Budapest, Hungary, pp. 149-160, 1967.
(22) Weiss, J., HIRDL, Brookhaven National Laboratory, private communication (1964).

RECEIVED January 16, 1968.

The Ferrous-Cupric Dosimeter

E. BJERGBAKKE and K. SEHESTED

Danish Atomic Energy Commission, Research Establishment Risö, Roskilde, Denmark

Air-free, air-saturated, and oxygenated solutions of the Fe^{2+}-Cu^{2+} dosimeter have been investigated for ^{60}Co and high dose-rate electron dosimetry. It has been shown that the dosage curves are not completely linear, but that an oxygenated or deaerated system may be used in the range 50 to 800 krad with an accuracy of 1%. The oxygenated system is for a 1.1 μsec. pulse independent of dose-rate up to 100 rads/pulse, and the deaerated solution up to 500 rads/pulse.

The Fe^{2+}–Cu^{2+} dosimeter was suggested in 1954 by Hart and Walsh (*5*), and the reaction mechanism has been described by Hart (*4*). The range of the system (50–900 krad) makes it a useful prospective dosimeter—*e.g.*, food-pasteurization processing—therefore, the system is of interest to many people. A suggested ASTM procedure for testing at a number of laboratories last year, and the present results have been accumulated for the purpose of evaluating this procedure.

Experimental

Irradiations were carried out at the ^{60}Co-gamma facility at Risö (*2*) and at the 10 Mev. linear electron accelerator at Risö (*1*). All solutions were irradiated in 5 cc. borosilicate glass cells, fitted with 5/20 standard taper joints. The method of evacuation, saturation, and filling is being described elsewhere by Sehested *et al.* (*7*).

At all gamma irradiations, doses were determined with the Fricke-dosimeter using $G_{Fe^{3+}} = 15.6$. At the electron irradiations, 10 m*M* $FeSO_4$, O_2-saturated, 0.4*M* H_2SO_4 ($G_{Fe^{3+}} = 16.1$), which is proven to be dose-rate independent over the dose-rate range studied (*7*), were used for dose calibration. Methods and equipment for dose calibration at the electron irradiations are discussed in detail elsewhere (*7*). The dose homogeneity in the irradiation cell is estimated to be better than 25%. The temperature range during irradiations was 20° to 25°C.

The water was purified by conventional three-stage distillation (3). All glassware was cleaned by conventional means and heated to 550°C. for 10 hours. The following reagents were used without further purification:

H_2SO_4	(AnalaR)
$CuSO_4,5H_2O$	(Merck, Analytical)
$FeSO_4(NH_4)_2SO_4,6H_2O$	(Merck, Analytical)
30% aqueous H_2O_2	(Merck, Analytical)

Ferric-ion concentrations were determined by measuring optical density at 3020 A. with a Cary 15 dual-beam spectrophotometer at 25°C.

Experimental Results

The effect of sulfuric acid concentration on the extinction of ferrous-ferric sulfate solutions with and without 10 m*M* $CuSO_4$ is shown in Figure 1a. The results for ferric sulfate without $CuSO_4$ is in agreement with results reported by Haybittle *et al.* (6).

When the optical density is plotted against the sulfate concentration instead of sulfuric acid concentration, the curves for 1 m*M* $CuSO_4$, 1 m*M* ferric-ferrous sulfate, and 1 m*M* ferric-ferrous sulfate become parallel (Figure 1b).

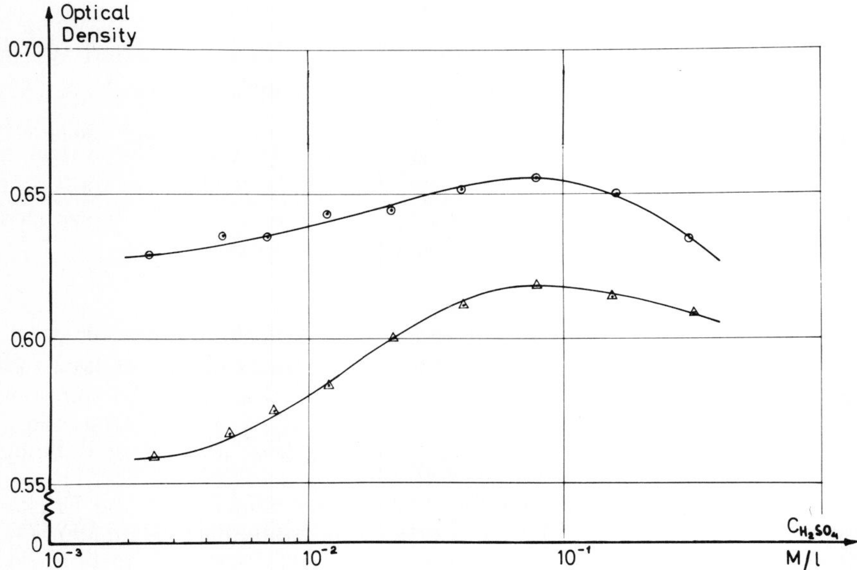

Figure 1a. Optical density as function of sulfuric-acid concentration in Fe^{2+}/Fe^{3+} and Fe^{2+}/Fe^{3+}-Cu^{2+}-solutions

⊙ *H_2SO_4 + 10mM $CuSO_4$ + 1mM Fe^{2+}/Fe^{3+}*
▲ *H_2SO_4 + 1mM Fe^{2+}/Fe^{3+}*

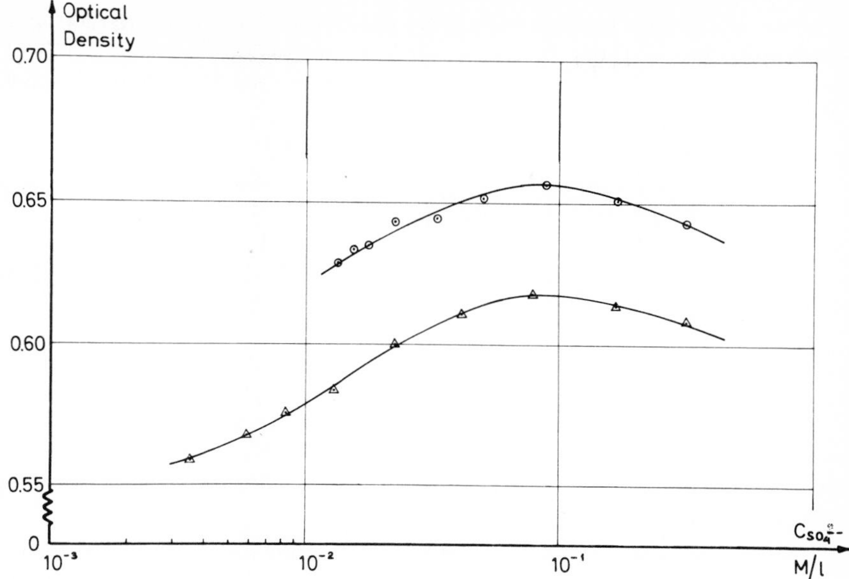

Figure 1b. Optical density as function of sulfate-ion concentration in Fe^{2+}/Fe^{3+} and Fe^{2+}/Fe^{3+}-Cu^{2+}-solutions

⊙ *H_2SO_4 + 10mM $CuSO_4$ + 1mM Fe^{2+}/Fe^{3+}*
△ *H_2SO_4 + 1mM Fe^{2+}/Fe^{3+}*

The recommended extinction coefficient for Fe^{3+} in 0.4*M* H_2SO_4 was $\epsilon_{Fe^{3+}} = 2197M^{-1}$ cm.$^{-1}$ (*6*). Using this value as a reference, $\epsilon_{Fe^{3+}}$ measured in 10m*M* $CuSO_4$, 0.005*M* H_2SO_4 is $2167M^{-1}$ cm.$^{-1}$.

The Fe^{3+} yield was determined as a function of gamma dose for 1 m*M* $FeSO_4$, 10 m*M* $CuSO_4$, 0.005*M* H_2SO_4 in

(1) air-free (argon saturated) solution
(2) oxygen-saturated solution
(3) solutions containing different amounts of atmospheric air.

Figure 2 shows the dosage curves for air-free and oxygen-saturated solutions.

The curves are not fully linear as seen from the figure. Initial *G*-values

G(Fe^{3+}), O_2 saturated solution = 0.76 (dotted lines)
G(Fe^{3+}), air-free solution = 0.63 (dotted lines)

Solutions containing different amounts of air gave initial *G*-values from 0.65 to 0.70.

The dose-rate dependence of O_2-saturated an air-free solutions (1 m*M* $FeSO_4$, 10 m*M* $CuSO_4$, 0.005*M* H_2SO_4) was determined in the dose-rate region 50-18,000 rad per pulse. The pulse length was 1.1 μsec. with approx. 0.2 μsec. rise- and fall time. The *G*-values were calculated at each dose-rate from a dosage curve of four doses up to 200 krad absorbed dose.

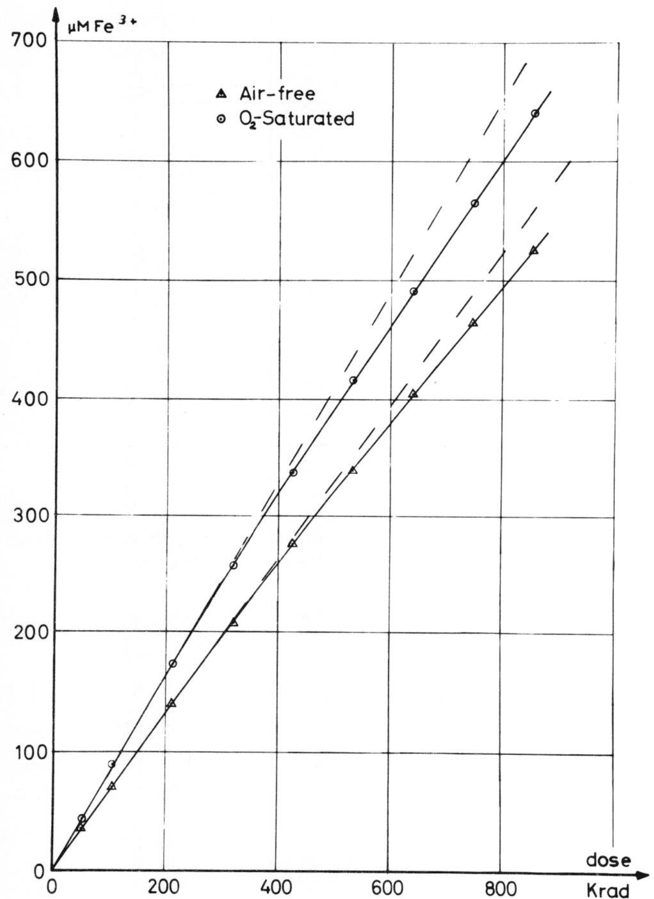

Figure 2. Dosage curves for air-free and oxygen-saturated Fe^{2+}-Cu^{2+}-solutions

Figure 3 shows $G(Fe^{3+})$ as a function of dose-rate for electron pulse lengths of 1.1 μsec. For O_2-saturated solutions there is no dose-rate dependence up to 100 rad/pulse. For air-free solution there is no dose-rate dependence up to 500 rad/pulse.

Discussion

Hart (*4*) claimed that the dose curve is linear in the range 0 to 650 krad. The present work shows that the *G*-value decreases with increasing dose, although the best straight line will only give standard deviations of the order of 2% up to 650 krad. Furthermore, the present work shows that the initial G-value is increasing with increasing O_2-concentration.

The dose-rate dependence in the air-free solution is probably mostly caused by $H + H \rightarrow H_2$, and in the O_2-saturated solution to $HO_2 + OH \rightarrow H_2O_3$, which transfers a reducing specie into an oxygenating specie.

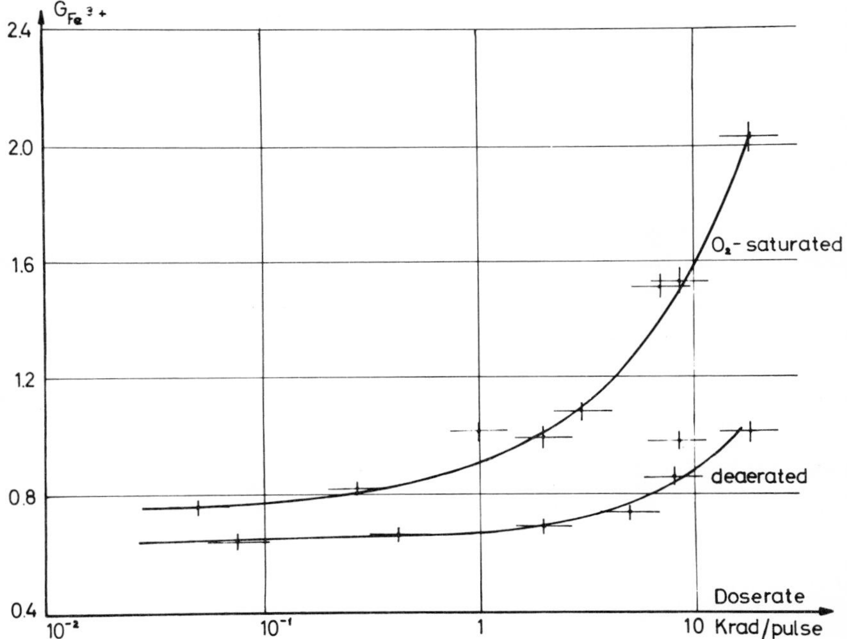

Figure 3. $G_{Fe^{3+}}$ *as function of dose-rate from a linear electron accelerator*

The reliability of the conventional system 10 mM $CuSO_4$, 1 mM $FeSO_4$, 10 mN H_2SO_4 as a dosimeter depends on the concentration of gases in the solution. We believe that it is easier to prepare an adequate oxygenated solution than a completely deaerated solution. We therefore recommend using the oxygenated system and including the following steps in the procedure:

(1) The oxygen concentration should be defined and reproducible —*e.g.*, oxygen bubbling for 30 minutes.

(2) The system should be checked against the Fricke-dosimeter to prove the adequacy of the oxygenation.

(3) New solution should be made every day (simply by adding $CuSO_4$ to a stock solution of 1 mM $FeCO_4$ in 10 mN H_2SO_4).

The advantages and applicability of the Fe^{2+}–Cu^{2+} system may be summarized as follows:

(1) The dosimeter can be used with an accuracy of 1% in the region 50–800 krad.

(2) The measurements involved are rapid, simple, and accurate.

(3) The dosimeter is rather insensitive to impurities and standard sealed glass-ampules can be used as irradiation cells.

(4) The air-free Fe^{2+}–Cu^{2+} system is dose-rate independent up to 500 rad/μsec. The O_2-saturated Fe^{2+}–Cu^{2+} system is dose-rate independent up to 100 rad/μsec.

Literature Cited

(1) Brynjolfsson, A., Holm, N. W., Sehested, K., Thaarup, G., Proc., Ind. Uses of Large Radiation Sources, Vol. II, IAEA (1963), pp. 281-295.
(2) Brynjolfsson, A., Holm, N. W., Proc., Large Radiation Sources in Ind., IAEA (1960), pp. 115-120.
(3) Fricke, H., Hart, E. J., "Radiation Dosimetry II," p. 167, Academic Press, N. Y., 1966.
(4) Hart, E. J., *Radiation Res.* **2**, 33 (1955).
(5) Hart, E. J., Walsh, P. D., *Radiation Res.* **1**, 342 (1954).
(6) Haybittle, J. L., Saunders, R. D., Swallow, A. J., *J. Chem. Phys.* **25**, 1213 (1956).
(7) Sehested, K., Lang-Rasmussen, O., Fricke, H., *J. Phys. Chem.* **72**, 626 (1968).

RECEIVED January 23, 1968.

41

Hydrated Electron and Thermoluminescent Dosimetry of Pulsed X-ray Beams

E. M. FIELDEN[1] and EDWIN J. HART

Argonne National Laboratory, 9700 South Cass Avenue, Argonne, Ill. 60439

Two dosimeters suitable for monitoring single pulses of x-rays with doses in the range 1 to 100 rads at dose rates greater than 10^3 rads/sec. are described. Both systems were independently referred to Fricke dosimetry as the absolute standard and cross checked under pulse conditions. In one system the transient hydrated electron absorption produced by the pulse is measured by kinetic spectrophotometry as an indication of the dose. In the other, doped LiF crystals of about 50 mg. are irradiated in sealed polyethylene bags under conditions of electronic equilibrium. Readout of the irradiated crystals was done on a standard commercial machine. Both methods were readily capable of 5% precision and with a little care better than 3% is obtainable.

Dosimetry of linear accelerator radiation presents special problems and in particular the dosimetry of a single pulse can be difficult. Dose rates used in pulse radiolysis are as high as 10^{11} rads/sec. but the largest dose per pulse used is typically of the order of 2×10^4 rads. Although such a pulse is detectable by the majority of dosimeters, its high dose rate takes it out of the linear range of many of them. With pulses 1/100th as great but of similar duration, dose rate ceases to be a problem but then the amount of change produced by a single pulse is too small for accurate determination by most dosimeters. Doses in the range 1 to 100 rads are being increasingly used in pulse radiolysis studies and the need for an accurate single pulse dosimeter in this range prompted the work described here.

[1] Present address: Physics Department, Institute of Cancer Research, Belmont, Sutton, Surrey, England.

Radiation-induced thermoluminescence has been developed as a general system of dosimetry and in particular has been applied to personnel and therapy dosimetry. The technique has been reviewed (*3, 13, 15, 16*). The published data indicate that lithium fluoride should be an excellent material for single pulse dosimetry as it is dose rate independent up to 10^8 rads/sec. (*10*) and is practically linear up to total doses of 10^5 rads (*12, 14*). Since this work was performed, dose rate independence up to 2×10^{11} rads/sec. has been reported (*5*) making this method of dosimetry applicable over the full range of pulsed radiation dose. Powdered LiF is normally used but a spurious background signal from the powder becomes increasingly important at doses below 10 rads (*10*). Single crystals of LiF were used in this work and it was found that their much greater freedom from spurious signals allowed their use down to 1 rad without any special precautions.

The reported irradiation energy independence of the LiF dosimeter (*1*) permits its use as a secondary standard when calibrated against ^{60}Co γ-rays in measuring the parameters required for a hydrated electron dosimeter.

The majority of laboratories using the pulse radiolysis technique use the method of kinetic spectrophotometry to detect and measure radiation-induced changes. With such apparatus it is thus possible to use transient as well as permanent optical changes as a measure of the effects of a radiation pulse. A convenient transient absorption is the hydrated electron (*6, 11*) which has the very high extinction coefficient of 1.85×10^4 cm.$^{-1}$ at 7000 A. Use of the hydrated electron as a dosimeter has already been discussed (*4, 9*), and it has found widespread use among workers in pulse radiolysis as an approximate dosimeter. This work set out to measure the parameters under which the hydrated electron could be used as an accurate dosimeter for low dose pulses. As the amount of hydrated electron present at the end of the irradiation pulse is used as a measure of dose, it is important that the lifetime of the e^-_{aq} is long compared with the pulse length.

The reaction of e^-_{aq} with H^+ can be suppressed by using an alkaline solution and then the limiting decay process is:

$$e^-_{aq} + e^-_{aq} \xrightarrow{2H_2O} H_2 + 2OH \qquad (1)$$

Saturating the solution with hydrogen converts the OH radicals into H atoms:

$$OH + H_2 \rightarrow H + H_2O \qquad (2)$$

and in alkaline solution the H atoms are converted into e^-_{aq}:

$$H + OH^- \rightarrow e^-_{aq} + H_2O \qquad (3)$$

The addition of H_2 to an alkaline solution thus doubles the yield of e^-_{aq} which is observed. However, the half-life of Reaction 2 with H_2 dissolved at 1 atm. is some 25 μsec. and if the loss of OH radicals by the competing reaction,

$$OH + OH \rightarrow H_2O_2 \qquad (4)$$

with $2k_4 = 9 \times 10^9$ M^{-1} sec.$^{-1}$, is to be kept small, then the dose per pulse must not exceed about 100 rads. Thus, when the doubled yield provided by Reactions 2 and 3 is desired, only small doses can be measured. At pH 12, Reaction 3 is rapid and it has been shown (*2*) that at this pH all H and OH radicals are converted into e^-_{aq} in a hydrogen saturated solution. Such a solution also reaches a reproducible e^-_{aq} decay when irradiated (*2, 7*) by continuous or repetitive pulse irradiation and hydrogen peroxide is not built up beyond a very low concentration (*8*). Similarly, initial traces of oxygen and hydrogen peroxide are reduced by pre-irradiation to their very low equilibrium concentrations. As there is no net chemical change in the alkaline H_2 saturated dosimeter solution, it can be permanently sealed in an optical cell.

Experimental

Dosimetry. The G value for the production of ferric ion in a standard Fricke solution was taken as 15.6 for ^{60}Co γ-rays and x-rays produced by primary electron beams with energies of 3 and 14 Mev. Ferric ion was estimated spectrophotometrically in a Beckman DU spectrophotometer using an extinction coefficient of 2197 M^{-1} cm.$^{-1}$ at 304 mμ at 25°C.

LiF thermoluminescence was calibrated against Fricke dosimetry with ^{60}Co γ-rays by irradiating a single LiF crystal sealed in a small polyethylene bag held in fixed geometry in a 30 ml. capacity thin-walled borosilicate glass bulb containing Fricke solution. The bulb was immersed in a beaker of water and irradiated $\sim$ 14 cm. from the source. To avoid impurity effects from the polyethylene, Fricke dosimeter readings were taken with the bulb in the same irradiation geometry but without the LiF dosimeter.

Apparatus. The LiF and Fricke dosimeters were separately compared with the hydrated electron absorption using the irradiation assembly shown in Figure 1. This is similar to that previously described (*2*) and makes use of a multiple reflexion cell (64 cm. path length used) for hydrated electron absorption spectroscopy. The absorption detection equipment for these transient species was a conventional oscilloscope photomultiplier combination as described previously (*8*). X-rays were produced by external targets, 7 mm. of tungsten for the 14 Mev. linac electron beam and 3 mm. of lead for the 3 Mev. Van de Graaff beam. Immediately in front of the absorption cell was a 'build up block' to bring the X-radiation into electronic equilibrium throughout the volume of the dosimetry position. The water jacket of the multiple reflexion cell acted in the same way for the irradiation volume. The block consisted of a rectangular container of water 11.3 cm. in depth with respect to the direction of radiation. Electron equilibrium was complete after penetrating 5 cm. of water. Fricke solution was contained in a thin-walled spherical borosilicate glass bulb of 30 ml. capacity immersed in the water can on the beam axis. LiF crystals sealed in polyethylene bags were immersed in Fricke solution in the same bulb for the comparison experiments. Figure 1 shows the LiF crystal holder mounted in the dosimeter bulb.

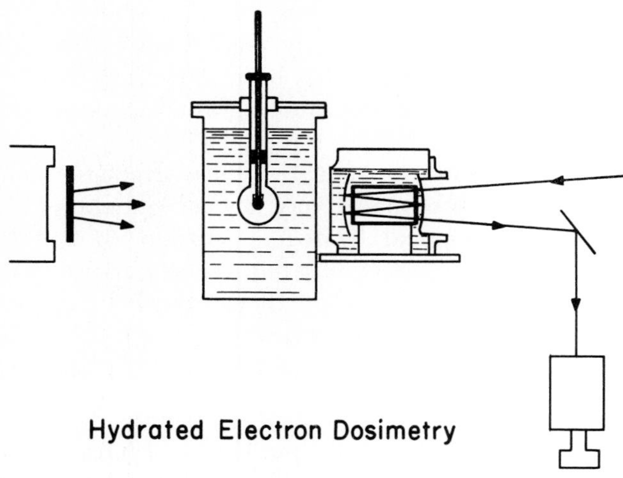

Figure 1. X-irradiation set-up for simultaneous Fricke or LiF and hydrated electron dosimetry. Left to right: Linac, tungsten target, an 11.3 cm. water container with dosimeter bulb on the beam axis and a multiple reflexion cell for transient absorption spectrophotometry. From the multiple reflexion cell the light beam passes into a monochromator-photomultiplier assembly

The dose ratio between the bulb and the absorption cell was obtained by irradiating with Fricke solution in both the bulb and the cell. To calibrate the hydrated electron absorption against the Fricke dosimeter the system was irradiated to a total dose of about 1.5 krad with 300 pulses at 10 per second. The transient absorption following each pulse was recorded on a composite photograph and one three-hundredth of the dose recorded by the Fricke solution was taken to be the dose required to produce the mean absorption recorded on the photograph when corrected for the dose factor between the cell and bulb. The thermoluminescent dosimeter was similarly compared with the hydrated electron absorption by photographing from one to four pulses and relating the mean absorption per pulse to the mean thermoluminescent readout per pulse. Figure 2 shows four oscilloscope traces that were recorded for comparison with simultaneously irradiated thermoluminescent crystals. Thermoluminescent readout was performed immediately after exposure with a standard unit made by Madison Research and Development Laboratories Inc., Model S12L.

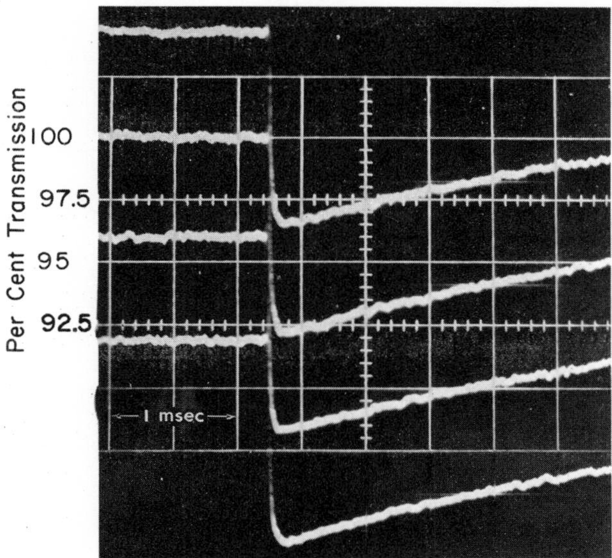

Figure 2. Four consecutive oscilloscope traces taken under identical conditions at pH 12 with doses of 5 rads/pulse. The short horizontal trace represents the 100% light level preceding the radiation pulse (break in curve) followed by the decay of the hydrated electron absorption at 7000 A. The readout of the LiF crystal exposed to those four pulses was 1728 counts

De-aerated, hydrogen-saturated solutions were prepared and handled by the syringe technique which has been described previously (*2*).

Materials. Water was prepared by the standard triple distillation technique. Alkaline solutions were prepared by dissolving 5*N* grade pure sodium in degassed water (*2*). All other materials were of AnalaR grade.

Single crystals of lithium fluoride TLD 100 grade from Harshaw Chemical Co., approximately 4 mm. square and weighing from 17 to 65 mg. were used. The crystals were cleaved from larger units and crystals from different parents had differences in sensitivity of up to a factor of two. Fragments from the same parent crystal generally showed negligible variations in sensitivity. The background was 10 $\pm$ 1 counts compared with a typical readout of 72 counts per rad. At the low doses used the readout process restored the background to its former value and the crystal could be re-used without further annealing. Effects of accidental over-exposure were removed by annealing at 400°C. for one hour.

Results

Figure 3 presents a typical γ-ray calibration of LiF thermoluminescence using a dose rate of 0.90 rads/sec. The γ-ray source was calibrated against the Fricke dosimeter.

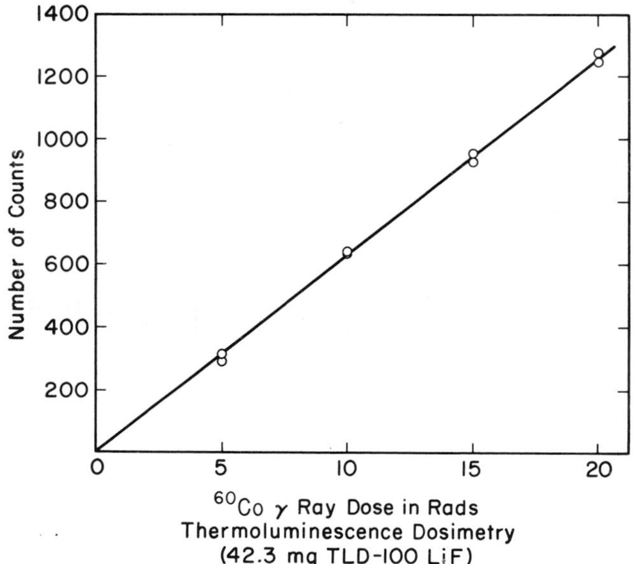

Figure 3. Calibration of a single 42.3 mg. crystal of LiF TLD 100 with ${}^{60}Co$ γ-rays

Comparison of the hydrated electron absorption with the Fricke dosimeter gave the same results as were obtained by Fielden and Hart (*2*) for the product of $G(e^-_{aq})$ and ϵ, the molar extinction coefficient of the hydrated electron at 7000 A.

$$G\epsilon = 12.1 \times 10^4 \pm 3\% \ M^{-1} \text{ cm.}^{-1} \text{ Molecules per 100 e.v.}$$

This value is independent of pH above pH 12 and only applies in solutions where the OH and H atom yield are completely converted into hydrated electrons. pH 12 is optimum as lower pH's do not convert all the H and OH yields (*2*) and higher pH's increase the effects of impurities in the alkali. A hydrogen-saturated solution at pH 12 can be sealed permanently in an optical cell. Such a cell has been used over a period of two years without showing any change in characteristics with an accumulated dose of several megarads. Effects of exposure to high dose rate irradiation (which produces hydrogen peroxide) are removed by exposure to low dose rate radiation which eliminates the hydrogen peroxide by Reaction 5:

$$e^-_{aq} + H_2O_2 \rightarrow OH^- + OH \qquad (5)$$

followed by Reactions 2 and 3.

Comparison between TLD dosimetry and the hydrated electron absorption showed excellent linearity. Figure 4 shows a typical calibration curve; the points on this curve represent data from two LiF crystals with their counts per pulse normalized to the same weight of crystal.

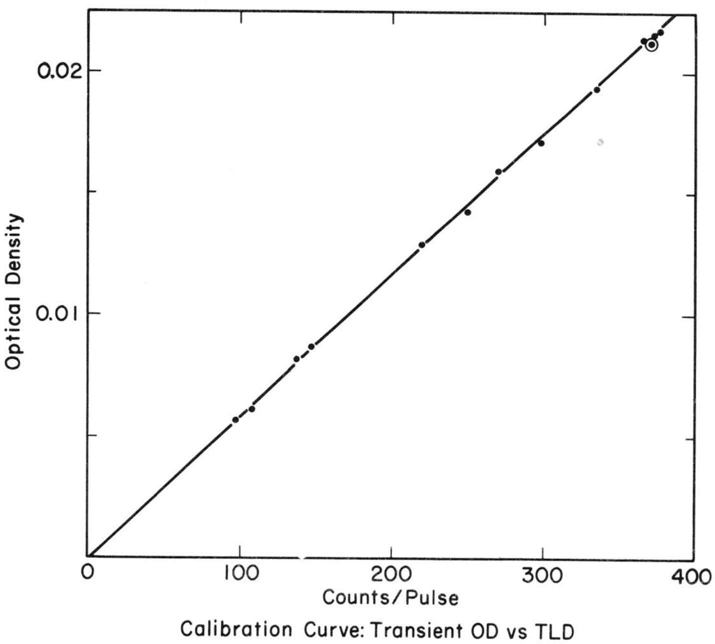

Figure 4. Comparison of LiF thermoluminescence response with the hydrated electron absorption produced by the same x-radiation pulse. The maximum dose per pulse on this curve represents ~5 rads and lowest ~1.3 rads. The points present data obtained from two crystals which differed in weight by 9%. The counts per pulse were normalized to the same weight of crystal to give the single curve

Assuming that the γ-ray calibration of a crystal was valid also for the pulsed conditions, the G_ϵ for the hydrated electron dosimeter was $12.3 \times 10^4 \pm 4\%$ in good agreement with the previous value. The dose rate for this calibration was 10^6 rads/sec. using 5 rad x-ray pulses of 5 μsec. duration from the linear accelerator.

TLD and Fricke dosimetry were also compared for x-ray pulses of 10 to 1000 $\times$ 10^{-9} sec. (nsec.) duration at low doses. The results are given in Table I. They show good agreement with the ^{60}Co calibration and a dose rate independence from 0.90 rad/sec. up to 1.5 $\times$ 10^{6} rad/sec.

Table I. Dosimetry of Linear Accelerator and Van de Graaff X-ray Pulses

Sample Irradiated	*Primary Beam Energy MeV*	*Pulse Length n sec.*	*Number of Pulses*	*Rads per Pulse*	*Counts per Rad*[a]
Fricke	14	1000	10,002	0.106	43.4
LiF (1)	14	1000	1,001	0.106	43.4
Fricke	14	1000	10,000	0.112	
LiF (6)	14	1000	1,007	0.112	42.3
LiF (6)	14	1000	1,004	0.112	42.7
Fricke	3	95	14,270	0.122	
LiF (1)	3	95	476	0.122	46.8
Fricke	3	95	14,451	0.129	
LiF (1)	3	95	473	0.129	42.4
Fricke	3	11	58,057	0.0172	
LiF (1)	3	11	4,808	0.0172	42.7

[a] Calibration of these LiF crystals by ^{60}Co γ-rays gave a sensitivity of 44.0 counts/rad at a dose rate of 0.90 rads/sec. LiF was always used in its linear response region with total doses not exceeding 120 rads.

Discussion

The single crystal LiF dosimeter proved to be convenient, rapid and capable of 2% precision for the measurement of single pulses down to 1 rad/pulse, the limit of this investigation. The long life and convenience of the single crystal method in many cases will outweigh its higher initial cost compared with LiF powder. With the dose rate and energy independence of LiF, the method is very attractive as a dosimeter for pulse radiolysis. As regular calibration is needed, there should be a suitable low dose rate source such as ^{60}Co available for calibration purposes.

The hydrated electron absorption was found to be suitably sensitive for use as a low dose per pulse dosimeter with accuracy mainly limited by the recording oscilloscope. This gives a precision of not better than $\pm 2\%$ down to 1 rad/pulse. Below 1 rad the errors increase because of other instrumental difficulties, mainly in the signal to noise ratio, so that at 0.1 rad/pulse the error is of the order of 50%. With modified apparatus the dose range could probably be lowered by an order of magnitude.

As was discussed earlier, the upper dose limit for this system is 100 to 150 rads/pulse. Above this the OH radical is not completely scavenged and the G value for e^-_{aq} production drops. To cover larger doses the hydrogen should be omitted and the pH lowered to 9 to prevent conversion of the H atom yield to e^-_{aq}. $G\epsilon$ under these conditions has been given (*2*) as 5.0×10^4.

The alkaline e^-_{aq} dosimeter cannot be used with pulses longer than a few μsec. except at very low doses per pulse where the pulse length could be as long as 1 msec. without introducing too much error in measuring a 1 rad pulse. These restrictions arise from the necessity of keeping the pulse length short compared to the half-life of the e^-_{aq} decay so that only a small correction is needed for the amount of e^-_{aq} lost during the irradiation. The restrictions on dose per pulse and pulse length define the minimum dose rates required so that a 100 rad pulse requires a minimum dose rate of 10^7 rads/sec. whereas a 1 rad pulse could be measured at a minimum dose rate of 10^3 rads/sec. The maximum dose rate could not be determined with the present apparatus but it will not be less than 10^8 rads/sec. and may approach 10^{10} rads/sec. The dosimeter should be independent of energy for fast electrons and x-rays over a wide range.

Although the limitations of the method and sophisticated equipment required are likely to restrict the use of the e^-_{aq} dosimeter to places equipped for pulse radiolysis, the system has some advantage in that its low atomic number makes the dosimeter tissue equivalent. LiF, however, is not exactly tissue equivalent for x-rays of energy below about 100 Kev.; its response becomes 20 to 30% too high below 50 Kev. (*3*).

The equipment required to record the electron absorption at these low doses can be much simpler than was used in the present experiments. It is possible to use a 1 cm. absorption cell and a photocell instead of a photomultiplier if the monochromator is replaced by a combination of color or interference filters. This scheme uses a greater spectral band width and thus greatly improves the signal to the noise ratio. As the e^-_{aq} absorption band is very broad, the increased band width will cause only a small change in the apparent e^-_{aq} extinction coefficient, although the e^-_{aq} absorbance would have to be recalibrated for the particular optical system used. With this type of system the major expense is in the oscilloscope and recording camera.

In conclusion, we believe that the e^-_{aq} dosimeter is as precise and reproducible as any method for measuring single pulses of a few μsec. duration in the 1 to 100 rad range. If the dosimetry is to be used for pulse radiolysis experiments performed on the same apparatus, then it has the further advantage of measuring the dose only along the analyzing light path.

Acknowledgments

We gratefully acknowledge the able assistance of R. Clark in these experiments.

Literature Cited

(1) Cameron, J. R., Zimmerman, D., Kenny, G., Bush, R., Bland, R., Grant, R. *Health Phys.* **10,** p. 25 (1964).
(2) Fielden, E. M., Hart, E. J., *Radiation Res.* **32,** 564 (1967).
(3) Fowler, J. F., Attix, F. H., "Radiation Dosimetry," Vol. II, Chap. 13, F. H. Attix, W. C. Roesch, eds., Academic Press, New York, 1966.
(4) Fricke, H., Hart, E. J., "Radiation Dosimetry," Chap. XII, F. H. Attix, W. C. Roesch, eds., Academic Press, New York, 1966.
(5) Goldstein, N., Tochlin, E., *Radiation Res.* **32,** 280 (1967).
(6) Hart, E. J., Boag, J. W., *J. Am. Chem. Soc.* **84,** 4090 (1962).
(7) Hart, E. J., Fielden, E. M., ADVAN. CHEM. SER. **50,** 253 (1965).
(8) Hart, E. J., Gordon, S., Fielden, E. M., *J. Phys. Chem.* **70,** 150 (1966).
(9) Hart, E. J., "Actions Chimiques et Biologiques des Radiations," Vol. 10, Chap. I, M. Haissinsky, ed., Masson & Cie, Paris, 1966.
(10) Karzmark, C. J., White, J. W., Fowler, J. F., *Phys. Med. Biol.* **9,** p. 273 (1964).
(11) Keene, J. P., *Nature* **197,** 47 (1963).
(12) Marrone, M. J., Attix, F. H., *Health Phys.* **10,** 431 (1964).
(13) "Proceeding International Conference on Luminescence Dosimetry," Stanford (1965), *U. S. At. Energy Symp. Ser.* **No. 8.**
(14) Schulman, J. H., Attix, F. H., West, E. J., Ginther, J., *Proc. Symp. Personnel Dosimetry Techn., Madrid,* p. 319, Organisation for Economic Co-operation and Development, Paris (1963).
(15) "Symposium Proceeding Solid State and Chemical Radiation Dosimetry in Medicine and Biology," International Atomic Energy Agency, Vienna, 1967.
(16) Spurny, Z., *At. Energy Rev.* **3,** No. 2, 61 (1965).

RECEIVED December 11, 1967. This work was performed under the auspices of the U. S. Atomic Energy Commission.

Abstracts of Oral Presentations

Plenary Session

Electron Accelerators for Pulsed Radiolysis

W. J. RAMLER, G. MAVROGENES, and K. JOHNSON, Argonne National Laboratory, Argonne, Ill.

With the advent of high intensity electron accelerators, the associated beam characteristics must be carefully considered and understood for the varied uses presented by the field of pulsed radiolysis. Knowledge of the beam characteristics for both the transient and steady state mode of accelerator operation will influence the experimenter in the planning of irradiations and in the planning of transporting the beam to a multiple arrangement of experimental stations. Some of these characteristics can be stated as being: possible range of projectile energies and energy spread; beam pulse shapes (macro and microscopic); spatial distribution of electrons and associated divergence; dark current; space charge effects in both debunching the energy of the beam and increasing spatial size of the beam; and stability of the beam from pulse to pulse as related to spatial position, total charge and projectile energy.

Pulse Methods in Radiation Chemistry and Radiobiology

J. W. BOAG, Department of Physics, Institute of Cancer Research, Royal Cancer Hospital, Clifton Avenue, Belmont, Sutton, Surrey, England

The present scope of pulse methods in radiation chemistry will be discussed and the several limiting parameters of the apparatus considered in detail—the radiation pulse, detection methods, light sources, and recording techniques. Fast pulse methods have begun to be applied also in radiobiology and the rationale of their use in this field will be discussed.

Aqueous Media

Some Considerations on the Primary Processes in the Radiolysis of Water

L. BOTÁR, Central Research Institute for Chemistry of the Hungarian Academy of Sciences, Budapest, Hungary

The yield of radical and molecular products in the radiolysis of water depends on the pH and scavenger concentration. In this work an attempt is made to interpret the experimental results. First of all a quantitative definition is given for the spur, in order to make it possible to differentiate between reactions taking place in the spur and in the volume of the solution. By taking into account the spur-reactions the dependence of radical yield on pH is discussed. A homogeneous kinetical model, including a number of simplifying assumptions is suggested to interpret the dependence of molecular product yield on the scavenger concentration. The simplifying assumptions are controlled by making comparisons between the calculated and measured values.

Electron Paramagnetic Resonance Detection of the Hydrated Electron in Liquid Water

E. C. AVERY, J. R. REMKO, and B. SMALLER, Argonne National Laboratory, Argonne, Ill.

The transient products of pulse radiolysis are usually observed by optical absorption spectroscopy, but, since many of these species are paramagnetic, EPR spectroscopy may be used to supplement the optical work. A number of transient paramagnetic species have been observed using a modified spectrometer which is capable of following signals with lifetimes in the microsecond range. Some results are presented which are attributed to the presence of the hydrated electron in liquid water.

Absorption Spectrum and Rate of Reactions of Hydrated Electrons Under Pressure

U. SCHINDEWOLF, Institut für Kernzersahrenstechnik der Technischen, Hochschule, Karlsruhe, Germany

The pulse radiolytic investigation of the properties of solvated electrons in water at high pressures reveals the following results: (1) absorption spectrum of the electrons under pressure is blue shifted by about 220 A./ 1000 at $\approx 5 \cdot 10^{-5}$ e.v./atm. This blue shift can be interpreted by compression of the solvated electron structure, just as the red shift with increasing temperature is explained by expansion. In ammonia (dissolved sodium) similar values for the relative shift of the electron spectrum ($dE/E \cdot dp$, and $dE/E \cdot dT$) are obtained as in water. (2) The rate of the reaction of electrons in water—*e.g.*, $2e^- \rightarrow H_2$—is within the limit of error not affected by pressure. This is in contrast to reactions in ammonia—*e.g.*, $e^- + NH_3 \rightleftarrows 1/2\ H_2 + NH_2^-$—whose equilibria and consequently reaction rates show high pressure dependencies. This difference supports the assumption that electrons in ammonia occupy a larger volume than in water.

Reactions of the H Atom in γ Irradiated Aqueous Solutions at High Pressures

FARHATAZIZ, DAVID J. MILNER, and ROBERT R. HENTZ, Radiation Laboratory, University of Notre Dame, Notre Dame, Ind.

The competition between Reactions 1 and 2 in aqueous $0.8N$ H_2SO_4

$$H + S \rightarrow \text{no } H_2 \tag{1}$$

$$H + RH \rightarrow H_2 + R \tag{2}$$

solutions was studied over the applied pressure range of 0–6.34 kbar by measurement of $G(H_2)$ from the γ irradiated solutions. With S as O_2, in aerated solutions, relative specific rates k_2/k_1 were determined at atmospheric pressure for methyl alcohol, glucose, glycerol, ethyl alcohol, and isopropyl alcohol as RH. From the pressure dependence of k_2/k_1 and an estimated $\Delta V_1^{2+} = 1.6$ ml. mole^{-1} for S $\equiv$ O_2, values of ΔV_2^{2+} in the range -5.5 to -6.7 ml. mole^{-1} are obtained for the five H donors. The average value $\Delta V_2^{2+} = -6.2$ mole^{-1} is taken as characteristic for Reaction 2. Values of k_2/k_1 at atmospheric pressure also were determined for four deaerated $0.8N$ H_2SO_4 solutions: (1) RH $\equiv$ glucose and S $\equiv$ benzyl alcohol; (2) RH $\equiv$ glucose and S $\equiv$ $BrCH_2COOH$; (3) RH $\equiv$ S $\equiv$ acetone; (4) RH $\equiv$ S $\equiv$ $ClCH_2COOH$. Because little or no pressure dependence of $G(H_2)$, and therefore of k_2/k_1, was observed with these four solutions, $\Delta V_1^{2+} \approx \Delta V_2^{2+} = -6.2$ ml. mole^{-1}. Thus, for a variety of H-atom reactions, which are not diffusion controlled, the value of ΔV^{2+} is approximately constant. From this result a value of $\overline{V}(H)$ in the range 6.2 to 10.6 ml. mole^{-1} is estimated. It also is concluded that abstraction of Br or Cl by H occurs, rather than electron transfer, in Reaction 1 with $BrCH_2COOH$ or $ClCH_2COOH$ as S, respectively. Anomalous results obtained in a deaerated $0.8N$ H_2SO_4 solution of glucose and allyl alcohol are discussed.

The Radiation Laboratory of the University of Notre Dame is operated under contract with the U. S. Atomic Energy Commission. This is AEC Document No. COO-38-594.

On the Oxidizing Radical in the Radiolysis of Aqueous Hydrochloric Acid.

G. HUGHES and H. A. MAKADA, Donnan Laboratories, The University, Liverpool 3, England

It is shown that the chlorine atom (or its counterpart Cl_2^-) produced in the radiolysis of aqueous hydrochloric acid readily reacts with isopropyl alcohol, much less readily with ethyl alcohol, and not at all with methyl alcohol. Scavenger studies clearly indicate that the chlorine atom is produced from two distinct precursors, one of which is the hydroxyl radical which may also be scavenged by alcohols and the other an unidentified precursor, possibly H_2O^+, which does not readily react with alcohols.

Yields of Reducing Species in Binary Mixtures: Water-Ethyl Alcohol

JEAN-CLAUDE ROUX, Laboratoire de Chimie Nucléaire, Faculté des Sciences de l'Université de Bordeaux, Le Haut Vigneau, 33-Gradignan, France and J. SUTTON, Service de Chimie-Physique, C.E.N. Saclay, Boîte Postale No. 2, 91-Gif Sur Yvette, France

Radiolytic yields of hydrogen and nitrite ions from deaerated water-ethyl alcohol mixtures (1, 5, 10, and 15*M* liter^{-1} ethyl alcohol) containing from 10^{-5} to 2–5*M* liter^{-1} nitrate ion are reported. For nitrate concentrations $\lesssim 5 \times 10^{-2}M$ liter^{-1} the increase in $G(NO_2^-)$ is always much greater than the corresponding decrease in $G(H_2)$; for higher nitrate concentrations the corresponding changes are equivalent. It is concluded that the higher concentration region corresponds to the scavenging of electrons which normally recombine with the positive ion $C_2H_5OH_2^+$ while the lower range represents the capture of electrons which react with either (a) ethyl alcohol to give hydrogen or (b) some other species not leading to hydrogen production. The dependence of the free ion yields on the static dielectric constant agrees approximately with the hypothesis of Freeman and Fayadh.

Pulse Radiolysis of Aqueous Solutions of Inorganic Phosphate Ions

E. D. BLACK and E. HAYON, Pioneering Research Laboratory, U. S. Army Natick Laboratories, Natick, Mass. 01760

Aqueous solutions of mono-, di-, tribasic phosphates, and pyrophosphate, have been exposed to an electron beam of average energy 7 Mev. and 1 μsec. duration. The optical absorption spectra of the transients produced in air-free solutions of $H_2PO_4^-$, HPO_4^{2-}, PO_4^{3-}, and $P_2O_7^{4-}$ ions have been determined over the wavelength range from 2400 to 7000 A. The absorption maxima lies between 450–500 mμ in all cases. From a comparison with the transient optical spectra produced in the presence of O_2 and N_2O, it is concluded that the observed intermediates have a common precursor, namely OH radicals. In presence of oxygen, O_2^-

radicals and a relatively long-lived transient absorbing in the far ultraviolet region of the spectrum are formed, in addition to the phosphate radical anions. The mechanism leading to these transients will be discussed. The extinction coefficients and decay constants of the intermediates produced in this study will also be presented.

The Pulse Radiolysis of Liquid Ammonia

B. WARD, "Shell" Research Ltd., Thornton Research Centre, P. O. Box 1, Chester, England

Liquid ammonia has been pulse-radiolyzed at temperatures between −65° and 25°C. and the reactions of the resulting intermediate species followed spectrophotometrically. A broad absorption, similar to that observed in alkali metal-ammonia solutions, is assigned to the solvated electron formed with a *G* value of about 3. The electron disappears in two stages, a fast reaction with the NH_2 radical being followed by a much slower one with the ammonium ion produced during the pulse. The amide ion, formed in the reaction between NH_2 and the electron, absorbs near 3500A. and reacts rapidly with NH_4^+. A weak absorption centered at 6000A. is observed in solutions containing N_2O or O_2 and is tentatively attributed to the NH_2 radical. Rate parameters of the above reactions will be reported.

Oxidation and Reduction of Nitroalkanes in Pulse Irradiated Aqueous Solutions

K.-D. ASMUS and IRWIN A. TAUB, Radiation Research Laboratories, Mellon Institute, Carnegie-Mellon University, Pittsburgh, Pa. 15213

Nitroalkanes exist in aqueous solutions in several forms given by the equilibria

$$\underset{\text{(nitro form)}}{RCH_2NO_2} \rightleftharpoons \underset{\text{(aci anion form)}}{RCH{=}NO_2^- + H^+} \rightleftharpoons \underset{\text{(acidic aci form)}}{RCH{=}NO_2H} \ldots$$

Their reactions with hydrated electrons, H· atoms, OH· and other radicals have been investigated by pulse radiolytic means. The hydrated electron reacts rapidly with the nitro and aci forms. The rate constants $k(e^-_{aq} + CH_3NO_2)$ and $k(e^-_{aq} + CH_2NO_2^-)$ have been determined as $2.1 \times 10^{10}\ M^-{}_1$ sec.$^{-1}$ and $6.6 \times 10^9\ M^{-1}$ sec.$^{-1}$, respectively. Reduced nitroalkanes show broad absorptions in the ultraviolet and exist in the equilibrium

$$RCH_2\dot{N}O_2^- + H^+ \rightleftharpoons RCH_2\dot{N}O_2H.$$

For example, the p*K* of $CH_3\dot{N}O_2H$ is 4.4, as has been determined by both spectral and kinetic means. Both H· atoms and OH· radicals show different behavior towards the nitro and aci forms. Under usual pulse radiolysis conditions no evidence for reaction of H· or OH· with the nitro form has been observed. However, fast addition reactions to the C=N bond occur with the aci form:

$$RCH{=}NO_2^- + OH\cdot \rightarrow \underset{\displaystyle OH}{\underset{|}{RCH}}{-}\dot{N}O_2^-$$

and

$$RCH{=}NO_2^- + H\cdot \rightarrow RCH_2{-}\dot{N}O_2^-$$

$RCHOH\dot{N}O_2^-$ anion radicals have similar spectral properties to the $RCH_2\dot{N}O_2^-$ anion radicals. Reactions of other radicals with nitroalkanes also have been investigated. An alcohol radical, for example, may transfer an electron to both nitro and aci forms or may add to the C=N bond of the aci form. Electron spin resonance data relevant to these reactions are also available.

This work was supported in part by the U. S. Atomic Energy Commission.

Pulse Radiolysis of Monosubstituted Benzene Derivatives in Aqueous Solution.

B. CHUTNY, A. J. SWALLOW and M. EBERT, Nuclear Research Institute of the Czechoslovakian Academy of Sciences, Prague Czechoslovakia

Methods for the study of transient reaction products of OH radicals, H atoms, and hydrated electrons with monosubstituted benzene derivatives are illustrated for benzonitrile. The mechanism and kinetics of formation and decay of cyclohexadienyl radicals (I) and anion-radicals (II) together with a detailed protonation mechanism for (II) are given for this substance. Spectral properties of products of types (I) and (II) have been studied for series of monosubstituted benzene derivatives and are discussed in relation to published data from the point of the mechanism of formation, chemical structure, influence of Hammett σ value of the substituent. Relative bathochromic shifts of primary bands of (I) were compared with those of the original compounds and found to be identical. Simple rules were found for predicting λ_{max} of unknown (I). Results of quantum-mechanical calculations of electronic spectra of (I) and (II) are compared with our measured values and with results of preparation of salts of (II) by another way.

Radiation Chemistry of Aromatic Solutes in Aqueous Solution

D. F. SANGSTER, Australian Atomic Energy Commission Research Establishment, New Illawarra Road, Lucas Heights, N. S. W. Australia

Using competition methods, rate constants for radiolytic hydroxyl radical reactions in aerated aqueous solutions relative to the formation of salicylate in benzoate solution and to the formation of *ortho*-nitrophenol in nitrobenzene solutions have been measured and are compared with published figures in an effort to reconcile the differences that exist in the literature. Some solutions saturated with nitrous oxide have also been investigated. The radiolytic decarboxylation yields of benzoate, salicylate, *m*- and *p*-hydroxybenzoates in aerated aqueous solution can be resolved into prompt and post-irradiation contributions. These are formed by two distinct mechanisms. The electron-benzoate reaction has been studied at high pH as a function of ionic strength.

Biology

Pulse Radiolysis Studies of Aqueous Pyrimidine Base Solutions

L. M. THEARD and F. C. PETERSON, Gulf General Atomic Incorporated, San Diego, Calif. 92112 and L. S. MYERS, JR., Laboratory of Nuclear Medicine and Radiation Biology, University of California, Los Angeles, Calif. 90024

A comparison of transient decay in pulse irradiated deaerated thymine solution with transient decay observed in N_2O saturated thymine solution and deaerated thymine solution containing ethyl alcohol, all at neutral or near-neutral pH, indicates that in deaerated thymine solution, reactions of the e^-_{aq}- and OH-produced transients with each other (possibly to regenerate thymine) is not an exclusive or nearly-exclusive mode of their decay. Similar conclusions are drawn from data on cytosine. Pseudo-first order rate constants determined for reaction of oxygen with the e^-_{aq} + thymine and OH + thymine transients in appropriate oxygen-saturated solutions are 5.6×10^6 and 3.0×10^6 sec.$^{-1}$, respectively.

Dosimetry

Significance of Track Entity Distribution in Radiation Chemistry

J. L. MAGEE and A. MOZUMDER, Department of Chemistry and the Radiation Laboratory, University of Notre Dame, Notre Dame, Ind. 46556

Previous work of the authors indicates that the spectrum of energy losses of a high energy charged particle over all generations of secondary electrons is best described in terms of three categories of entities: (1) spurs ($\sim$ 6–100 .v.), (2) blobs (100–500 e.v.), and (3) short tracks

(500–5000 e.v.). The nature of these entities, their distribution in energy and their various roles in the radiation chemistry of liquid systems will be considered. It is proposed that in low-LET radiation a track is composed of a random sequence of the various entities and that they are so widely-spaced that they do not overlap. The LET effect in these radiations may be traced to variations in the short track fraction. In certain cases, such as ^{3}H, ^{37}Ar, or low energy x-rays, most of the energy appears in the form of short tracks, giving special effects such as increased molecular yields. Indeed, it is plausible that for low-LET radiations most molecular yield in any case originates in sporadic high-LET regions. Remarkable success has been achieved using the track entity distributions for explanation of the yield of separated ion pairs in radiolysis. The facts cannot be explained on the basis of "average spurs." In the case of high-LET radiations also, a track model may be constructed by considering a track as composed of a random sequence of the basic entities closer spaced as required by the overall LET. Here adjacent track entities overlap and form a core of high energy density. Such a model shows lower-LET regions accompanying the high-LET core.

The Radiation Laboratory of the University of Notre Dame is operated under contract with the U. S. Atomic Energy Commission.

A Ferrous-Cupric Dosimeter for Routine Use in the Megarad Range

J. W. HALLIDAY and R. D. JARRETT, U. S. Army Natick Laboratories, Natick, Mass.

A dosimeter suitable for conveniently measuring absorbed doses in the 2–7 megarad range has been developed. This dosimeter, a modification of the "ferrous-cupric dosimeter," possesses the numerous advantages of its predecessor in addition to having an extended dose range. The γ-radiation response of solutions having various ferrous, cupric, and sulfuric acid concentrations was studied. A Fe^{2+}/Cu^{2+} molar ratio of one to ten, or less, was found to be necessary to obtain a linear dose response. A solution of composition 6mM in $FeSO_4$, 60mM in $CuSO_4$, and 10mN in H_2SO_4 was selected for the desired dose range. The effects of the solution temperature during irradiation and the pre-irradiation storage on the γ-radiation response of the solutions were studied. Temperatures in the range 0° to 35°C. throughout the radiation exposure showed little effect, while higher temperatures gave spurious results at higher doses. Freshly prepared dosimeter solutions may be stored without special precaution for several months before use without adverse effect on the γ-radiation response. Post-irradiation changes were studied and found to be several per cent per week. Prepared from shelf reagents, the dosimeter can be made reliable enough to use as a secondary standard. After diluting the sample one to eight, the amount of ferric iron produced is easily measured spectrophotometrically at 3025 A. using a molar extinction coefficient of 2170 (25°C.).

The Microscopic Dose Distribution in Electron Beams Using Poly(vinyl chloride)

R. D. JARRETT and J. W. HALLIDAY, U. S. Army Natick Laboratories, Natick, Mass.

A technique for measuring microscopically the two dimensional dose distribution in electron beams using a modified microdensitometer (Tech Ops Isodentracer) and poly(vinyl chloride) film has been developed. The microdensitometer can measure the dose distribution in any thin film which responds in a systematic manner to the radiation dose received and which absorbs in the visible spectra (> 3200 A.), if used with the proper narrow bandpass filters. To evaluate the usefulness of poly(vinyl chloride) film (Bakelite QCA-5960 pressed polished—10 mils) as a dosimeter we studied the effects of varying the irradiation temperature, annealing time and temperature, storage time before and after annealing, and storage atmosphere on the color development of the film. These studies resulted in the adoption of a standard procedure which involves maintaining the temperature during irradiation between 0° and 35°C., annealing at 64°C. for 15 minutes, and reading at a wavelength of 3950 A.

INDEX

E

I

K

L

P

U

V

W

X

Y

Z